Isco Open Channel Flow Measurement Handbook

D1592456

ISCO

TELEDYNE ISCO
A Teledyne Technologies Company

Isco Open Channel Flow Measurement Handbook

Sixth Edition
Fourth Printing

Edited by Diane K. Walkowiak, M.A.
Teledyne Isco, Inc., Lincoln, Nebraska

Foreword by John A. Replogle, Ph.D., P.E., D.WRE

TELEDYNE ISCO
A Teledyne Technologies Company

ISBN 0-9622757-3-5

Price $50.00
Printed in the United States of America

The material provided in this handbook was obtained from sources that are believed to be reliable. Neither Teledyne Isco, Inc. nor any person acting on its behalf makes any warranty with respect to the accuracy, completeness, or usefulness of the material provided herein. Teledyne Isco, Inc. shall not be held liable for any damages that arise from the use of the information presented herein.

All brand or product names are trademarks or registered trademarks of their respective holders.

FOREWORD

In the current climate of competition for water among agricultural, urban and environmental users, improved management of water resources is imperative. This management depends heavily on reliable water flow measurement and control. This flow-measuring handbook is written with the general philosophy of being a "how-to do, how-to select" book to provide water suppliers and wastewater managers a quick review of hydraulic principles and devices related to water measurement in open channels.

In late 1963 I joined the U.S. Water Conservation Laboratory, Agricultural Research Service-USDA. My assignment was to conduct research that would improve the economics and accuracy of water flow measurement servicing irrigated agriculture. Coming from the University of Illinois in the Midwest where irrigation was not widespread, and was confined mainly to sprinkler systems using pipeline flow meters, I soon was exposed to the difficulties associated with open channel flow measurements. At least those pipes had the decency to not vary in their cross-sectional flow area regardless of flow rate! This made the mathematics appear simple by comparison to the open channel situations.

Flow meters typically have a "primary" element that is in contact, or somehow interacts with, the fluid, and a "secondary" element that presents readouts to the user. I realized that these devices in pipe-flow measurement enjoyed industrial research and development support because of market demands by clients in drinking water and wastewater treatment, as well as industrial-plant operations of all kinds. Primary devices for open-channel flow, however, attracted only limited interest from industry because of the low-budget operations of most irrigation enterprises that used small canals, and the usual practice of building large canal flow measuring structures as contractor-constructed devices on a one-of-a-kind basis. Even secondary devices, used to detect upstream depth in flumes and weirs, were limited because of the complexity of converting these one-of-a-kind depths to flow rates with a rugged, accurate and economical instrument that would still work for the next cropping season. I therefore attempted to level the playing field by concentrating on improving the situation for these "orphaned" canals.

As mentioned above, open channel flows were mathematically difficult to handle. Because of this mathematical difficulty, flume ratings traditionally depended on laboratory calibration. Advances in modern computers eventually allowed this barrier to be breached. Now, the relatively convenient and accurate mathematical rating of flumes is accomplished routinely, as long as their shape produces nearly parallel flow in certain reaches of the flume, as do long-throated flumes. Their primary advantages include minimal head loss, relatively low construction cost compared to earlier flumes, adaptability to a variety of channel shapes, and ability to measure wide ranges of flows with custom-designed structures, with no requirements for laboratory calibrations. Computer-aided design and selection of long-throated flumes are well covered in the "on-line" venues and therefore are given only summary treatment herein.

The engineer in the field, who encounters flumes and weirs from a bygone age with missing calibration information, usually does not have the time and resources to search out the old literature. This handbook places in one volume the needed information on most of these older devices that may be encountered and are still in service.

Other advances in electronics have given birth to a host of technologies that measure flow indirectly by measuring its two basic components - cross-sectional area and average velocity. Different approaches for measuring velocity - acoustic, electromagnetic, even radar - have opened opportunities for water management of systems that previously were difficult to quantify. Users now have a variety of techniques at their disposal, insuring that "somehow, someway" flow rate can be measured in almost any situation. Each technology has its advantages and disadvantages, which must be understood by the user to insure proper application. A synopsis of modern methods is presented here, to provide completeness to this new edition.

Flow measurement methods are being constantly upgraded and new concepts continually exploited, offering the promise of ever-increasing convenience and improved economics for water control and management. These developments are attacking the difficult problems associated with measuring pipe flows near elbows and other fittings that produce irregular flow profile development. The extension of these developments to open channel flows can provide water resource managers vital operational data in locations previously not deemed measurable. The newer flume designs operate with small head loss, but the ultrasonic meters can operate with almost none.

Because of the opportunities and support of the U.S. Water Conservation Laboratory, I have been able to contribute to my original mandate to improve flow measurement for irrigated agriculture and to general water resources applications worldwide. I am honored to contribute this Foreword to a handbook whose intent is to also contribute to these goals.

John A. Replogle, Ph.D., P.E., D.WRE
Research Hydraulic Engineering Collaborator
U.S. Water Conservation Laboratory,
Agricultural Research Service, USDA
4331 E. Broadway Rd., Phoenix, AZ 85040
Web Site: http://www.uswcl.ars.ag.gov/

• • •

Dr. Replogle has spent over forty years with the U.S. Water Conservation Laboratory, Agricultural Research Service, USDA, conducting research on water measurement and water management for irrigated agriculture. He officially retired in 2004, but serves as a Collaborator and Advisor to the Laboratory.

He has degrees in both Civil and Agricultural Engineering, and is considered one of the world's foremost experts in water measurement, particularly in agricultural applications. He is credited with more than 125 technical articles on irrigation, water measurement, and water management. He serves on several technical committees within The American Society of Civil Engineers (ASCE), The American Society of Agricultural and Biological Engineers (ASABE), The United States Committee on Irrigation and Drainage (USCID), and The Irrigation Association (IA), and has served as a consultant and expert for numerous government agencies and water districts. He is the recipient of many awards, including the Hancor Soil and Water Engineering Award (ASABE) in 1992, the Hydraulic Structures Medal (ASCE) in 1995, the Royce J. Tipton Award (ASCE) in 1999, the Merriam Improved Irrigation Award (USCID) in 2002, the Hunter Rouse Hydraulic Engineering Award (ASCE) in 2004, and the 2005 Person of the Year Award (IA).

TABLE OF CONTENTS

List of Illustrations

List of Tables

Chapter 10

Chapter 11

Chapter 12

Chapter 13

Chapter 14

Chapter 15

Chapter 16

Chapter 17

Chapter 18

Chapter 19

CHAPTER

1

Introduction

OVERVIEW

The first chapter of the handbook provides a general introduction to both the handbook itself and the subject of open channel flow measurement. Included are sections briefly dealing with the purpose and organization of the handbook, the early history of flow measurement, and the present need for flow measurement.

Flow measurement applications such as storm water runoff monitoring are critically important for the effective management of water resources.

1 Purpose and organization

This handbook provides assistance to individuals involved in measuring open channel flow. By assembling flow measurement information from various sources into a single comprehensive volume, it is hoped that this handbook will be of practical value to individuals dealing with the realities of difficult open channel flow measurement problems.

The handbook has been divided into 19 chapters:

- Chapter 1 provides a general introduction to the handbook and to the subject.
- Chapter 2 discusses open channel flow measurement in general terms.
- Chapter 3 describes in detail the use of weirs.
- Chapter 4 gives an in-depth look at flumes.
- Chapter 5 contains methods for selecting primary devices.
- Chapter 6 discusses the measurement of gravity flow using the Manning formula.
- Chapter 7 covers the area velocity method of flow measurement, including area velocity flow meters.
- Chapter 8 provides practical information on flow measurement system installations.
- Chapters 9 through 18 provide discharge tables for many commonly used primary measuring devices.
- Chapter 19 presents conversion tables used in flow measurement work.

Early history of flow measurement

The need to quantify the flow of liquids has been recognized since the beginning of civilization. The first efforts were probably directed toward survival during floods and to waterborne transportation. As civilization became more advanced, the demands for water supply, irrigation, navigation, and water power all contributed to the development of techniques to measure liquid level, flow rates, and quantities. It is known that the ancient Egyptians and Babylonians used some form of water accounting as a basis for levies to individual land holders for their usage of water from extensive irrigation systems.

The River Nile of Egypt has probably been studied longer than any other river in the world. The crop yields in the lower Nile Valley are dependent upon the annual flooding of the river, and thus the annual yields are a function of the river's level. Because of this, taxes were based on the maximum level of the river. Mention of the annual rises of the Nile dates back between 3000 and 3500 B.C., and known flood marks extend as far back as 1800 B.C. More than 3000 years ago, the Egyptian Pharaoh Menes developed a flood control system for the Nile River. Part of this system included at least 20 recording stations along the Nile. These stations used a crude form of a staff gauge to measure the level of the river. These levels were recorded daily, and compared with previous years' records to predict the future levels of the river.

One of the earliest and most complete records of an attempt to measure water flow volume is that of Sextus Julius Frontinus, who was the Water Commissioner of Rome in 52 A.D. He attempted to determine the quantity of water delivered to each user in the Roman system by measuring the cross-sectional area of the spouts through which the water was discharged. Since Frontinus ignored the velocity of the flow, his efforts were not entirely successful. However, it presents an interesting record of an early flow measurement system.

The techniques of flow measurement have advanced through the centuries. Much of the theoretical background for the science of hydraulics, which is the basis for modern flow measurement, was developed in the 17th and 18th centuries by researchers such as Torricelli, Pitot, Woltman, and Venturi. Advances in the art and science of liquid flow measurement continued into the 19th and 20th centuries, paralleling the general advancement of technology. However, many methods of open channel flow measurement are simply sophisticated adaptations of the level measurements practiced by the Egyptians on the Nile over 4000 years ago.

Present need for flow measurement

The rapid growth of urban areas throughout the world and advances in technology and industry to meet society's ever increasing demands for more goods, energy, etc. have greatly increased the potential for environmental pollution. They have also contributed to an increasing awareness of and concern for the environment. Population density and advanced technology continue to place increasing demands on society to control the quality and conserve the supply of water.

Increasingly strict legislation and continuing public interest in conservation and environmental matters have emphasized the importance of flow measurement. Uniform and reliable measurement data are needed to identify the resource levels and quality of bodies of water, to determine the results of conservation and quality control efforts, and to enforce water conservation and quality regulatory requirements. The majority of recent interest in flow measurement has centered on water quality regulatory requirements. For example, in the United States, federal law states that "...the purpose of self-monitoring and reporting effluent data is to permit federal and state regulating agencies to follow on a continuing basis, the discharger's effluent quality trends as well as specific variation from established limitations." Local agencies in the U.S. are required by the same legislation to establish a local surcharge on industrial waste to insure that these users pay their "fair share" of the cost of existing and new treatment facilities. Their "fair share" entails the measurement of both the quality and the quantity of industrial discharge. Thus, an economic value has been placed on industrial waste, and it is important for both industrial dischargers and municipalities to be able to measure and record flow data.

There are variations of environmental monitoring regulations throughout the world. There are often layers from national to regional, and a number of local levels for regulatory law as well as enforcement agencies. The purpose of this handbook, however, is not to define the protocols of environmental flow monitoring, but to address the field in general. You should always consult your local regulatory agency regarding the standard practices and requirements for your specific monitoring location.

Of course, flow measurement still is of great importance in more traditional areas such as irrigation, stream measurement, and sewage treatment plants. It also has other applications, for example, in storm and combined sewer flow studies, in sedimentation work, in runoff studies, and inflow and infiltration isolation.

As Kirkpatrick and Shelley [1] state: "Measurements of quantity of flow, usually in conjunction with sampling for flow quality, are essential to nearly all aspects of water pollution control. Research, planning, design, operation and maintenance, and enforcement of pertinent laws—all are activities which rely on flow measurement for their effective conduct."

Thus in the context of modern society, there is an ever increasing need for simple, accurate, and reliable methods of flow measurement. These needs are usually dictated by legislation, but in a larger sense are dictated by society's desire to reverse the trend of increasing environmental pollution, and to ensure a clean, livable planet for this and future generations.

CHAPTER

2

Open Channel
Flow Measurement

OVERVIEW

This chapter provides a general discussion of open channel flow measurement techniques. Included are sections discussing open channel flow, methods of open channel flow measurement, primary and secondary measuring devices, and general units of flow measurement.

Open channels are commonly used in wastewater treatment plants.

Types of flow systems

There are two basic types of flow systems: flow in closed channels and flow in open channels (Figure 2-1). **Closed channel** flow is flow in completely filled pressure conduits (pipes). Pressure conduits are usually used for fresh water lines or for industrial process lines, and flow through them is often measured by some type of device inserted into the line. Common types of closed channel flow measuring devices are venturi meters, ultrasonic meters (both doppler and transit time), flow nozzles, orifice meters, magnetic flow meters, and pitot tube flow meters. A complete discussion of closed channel flow measurement is outside the scope of this handbook; for further information, the reader is directed to references [1] and [2].

Open channel flow is flow in any channel in which the liquid flows with a free surface. Examples are rivers, irrigation ditches, canals, flumes, and other uncovered conduits. Certain closed channels, such as sewers and tunnels when flowing partially full and not under pressure, are also classified as open channels. Open channels are used in most storm and sanitary sewer systems, sewage treatment plants, many industrial waste applications, and some water treatment plants. Most irrigation water is also distributed in open channels.

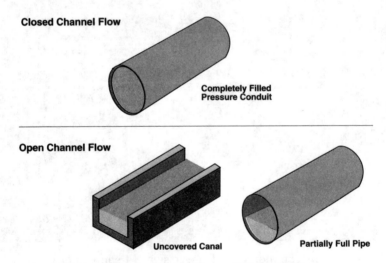

Figure 2-1: Closed Channel and Open Channel Flow

Methods of open channel flow measurement

There are many ways to determine the rate of flow in open channels. Kirkpatrick and Shelley [1] presented a comprehensive review of the various techniques available for measuring flow. Some of the more common methods of open channel flow rate measurement are discussed below, making liberal use of Kirkpatrick and Shelley's comments.

Timed gravimetric

In this method, the entire contents of the flow stream are collected in some type of container over a specific length of time. The weight of the fluid is then determined and the flow rate calculated. If the flow rate was uniform over the period of the collection, the result will be an average flow rate for the period of the collection.

Gravimetric meters include weighers, tilting traps, and weigh dump meters. In its simplest form, a gravimetric meter involves determining the weight of a quantity of fluid in a tank mounted on beam scales, load cells, or some other mass or force measuring device. Weighing the fluid is a primary standard. Since the accuracy of weighing devices is routinely considered to be better than ±0.1%, gravimetric meters are frequently used to calibrate other meters.

In field use, the tipping bucket rain gauge is probably one of the most common meters of this type. Another field application, often used as a calibration method where a scale or some other weighing device is available, is the simple "bucket and stopwatch" technique. This technique requires measurement of the time required to fill a container of a known volume. Practical considerations limit the use of this measurement technique to fairly low flow rates and, because of its nature, it is not suited for continuous measurement.

Dilution

In this method, the flow rate is measured by determining how much the flowing water dilutes an added tracer solution. Although brine tracers have been used, radioactive and fluorescent dye tracers are more commonly used today. The dilution technique produces no pressure loss, requires no drop in hydraulic grade line, offers no obstruction to the flow, and indicates flow rate directly by simple theoretical formulas.

There are two general techniques used in dilution flow measurement: the constant-rate injection method and the total recovery (or slug injection) method. The constant-rate injection method requires the tracer solution to be injected into the flow stream at a constant flow rate for a given period of time. The flow rate is determined by a formula involving the background concentration in the stream (if any), the tracer concentration and injection rate, and the measured plateau of the concentration-time curve at the measuring site. In the total recovery method, a known quantity of the tracer solution is placed in the flow stream, and a continuous sample is removed at a uniform rate during the time needed for the tracer wave to pass, in effect integrating the concentration-time curve. The flow rate is determined from the total quantity of tracer injected and the integral of the concentration-time curve.

Although both of these dilution methods have advantages and limitations, they are basically similar. A fluorometer, Geiger counter, or some other appropriate instrument is required for determining sample concentration, a method of extracting a sample for analysis is needed, and a device to either inject a tracer at a steady, known rate, or withdraw a sample at a steady (but not necessarily known) rate is required. Both methods require complete vertical and lateral mixing at the measurement site. The main disadvantages of dilution techniques are the cost of the instruments required to determine tracer concentrations, the lack of ruggedness of these instruments, and the required training for operator personnel. The reader is directed to references [3], [4], and [5] for more information on the dilution method.

Hydraulic structure

In this method, some type of hydraulic structure (primary device) is introduced into the flow stream. The function of the hydraulic structure is to produce a flow that is characterized by a known relationship (usually nonlinear) between a liquid level measurement (head) at the specified location of that particular device and the flow rate of the stream. This relationship or head-flow rate curve for the particular structure or device is called the rating. The change in liquid level is measured by a secondary device, which may also convert the liquid level to a flow rate automatically.

Slope-hydraulic radius

In this method, measurements of water surface slope, cross-sectional area, and wetted perimeter over a length of uniform section channel are used to determine the flow rate, using a resistance equation such as the Manning formula. The flow channel serves as the primary device. The Manning formula requires a knowledge of the channel cross-section, liquid depth, slope of the water surface, and a roughness factor dependent on the character of the channel.

Area velocity

In this method, the flow rate is calculated by determining the mean flow velocity across a cross-section and multiplying this by the cross-sectional area of flow (wetted area) at that point. In open channels, this will generally require two separate measurements — one to determine the mean velocity and the other to determine the flow depth. The measured depth is then used to calculate the area of the flow based on the size and shape of the channel.

• • •

The timed gravimetric and dilution techniques are generally not suited to provide a continuous record of flow rate. They are more often used for occasional flow rate measurements at a particular time and place, for calibrating some other type of device, or for developing a liquid level-flow rate curve for a particular location. These techniques have a definite role in open channel flow measurement but, because they are not adaptable to continuous flow rate recording, they will not be discussed here. For a complete discussion, see references [1], [3], [4], and [5].

The hydraulic structures technique differs from the other techniques in that, provided a standard type of structure is used and certain installation and application rules are followed, no field calibrations or measurements other than a continuous measurement of liquid level are required to obtain a continuous record of flow rate. Because of this, the hydraulic structures technique is widely used in open channel flow measurement. This technique is briefly discussed in the following two sections and at length in Chapters 3, 4, and 5.

The slope-hydraulic radius technique, using the Manning formula, is applied in a manner similar to the hydraulic structures technique in that only a continuous measurement of liquid level is required to obtain a continuous record of flow rate. Because of uncertainties associated with the Manning formula, the accuracies obtainable are not as good as those achieved with hydraulic structures. The slope-hydraulic radius technique is normally used where great accuracy is not required. But, since this technique does not require the installation of an additional structure in the flow stream, it is often used for temporary measurements such as storm water runoff monitoring. The slope-hydraulic radius method is discussed in Chapter 6.

The area velocity method has an advantage over the other methods in that, in addition to measuring flow under free flow conditions, it can also be used to measure flow under submerged, full pipe, surcharged, and reverse flow conditions. Similar to the Manning formula, area velocity does not require the installation of a weir or flume. Because it incorporates measurements of both liquid depth and velocity, the area velocity method provides greater accuracy than the slope-hydraulic or Manning flow measurement methods. Due to advances in area velocity technology in recent years, it is now considered to be the standard method of flow measurement in the absence of a hydraulic structure. While normally not as accurate as the use of hydraulic structures, area velocity flow measurement accuracy will exceed that of a hydraulic structure's in situations where the flow is subject to downstream restrictions, such as surcharge and submerged flow conditions.

Area velocity flow meters are commonly used in sewer flow monitoring, inflow and infiltration studies, and combined sewer overflow studies. The area velocity method is discussed in greater detail in Chapter 7.

Primary measuring devices: weirs and flumes

2

The most commonly used technique of measuring the rate of flow in an open channel is that of hydraulic structures. This is especially true of permanent locations or applications that require a high degree of accuracy. In this method, flow in an open channel is measured by inserting a hydraulic structure into the channel, which changes the level of liquid in or near the structure. By selecting the shape and dimensions of the hydraulic structure, the rate of flow through or over the restriction will be related to the liquid level at the specified measurement location. Thus, the flow rate through the open channel can be derived from a single measurement of the liquid level.

Figure 2-2: Weir

The hydraulic structures used in measuring flow in open channels are known as primary measuring devices and may be divided into two broad categories: weirs and flumes.

A **weir** (Figure 2-2) is essentially a dam built across an open channel over which the liquid flows, usually through some type of an opening or notch. Weirs are normally classified according to the shape of the notch, the most common types being the rectangular weir, the trapezoidal (or Cipolletti) weir, and the triangular (or V-notch) weir. Each type of weir has an associated equation for determining the flow rate over the weir.

A **flume** (Figure 2-3) is a specially shaped open channel flow section with an area and/or slope that is different from that of the channel. This results in an increased velocity and change in the level of the liquid flowing through the flume. A flume normally consists of a converging section, a throat section, and a diverging section. The flow rate through the flume is a function of the liquid level at some point or points in the flume. The most commonly used types of flumes are Parshall and Palmer-Bowlus flumes, although there are many other types available.

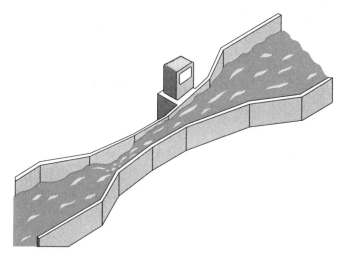

Figure 2-3: Flume

Secondary measuring devices: open channel flow meters

The flow rate or discharge through a weir or flume is usually a function of the liquid level in or near the primary measuring device. A secondary measuring device (or open channel flow meter) is used in conjunction with a primary measuring device to measure the rate of liquid flow in an open channel. The secondary measuring device has two purposes:

1. To measure the liquid level in the primary measuring device.
2. To convert this liquid level into an appropriate flow rate according to the known liquid level-flow rate relationship of the primary measuring device. This flow rate may then be integrated to obtain a totalized volume. Depending on the application, the secondary device can output the flow signal for remote data collection, sampler pacing, or process control functions.

Thus, a combination of a weir or flume (primary measuring device) and an open channel flow meter (secondary measuring device) is necessary to measure flow in an open channel. The flow measurement system requires both a primary and secondary measuring device to be complete. A weir or a flume (primary device) restricts the flow in a controlled manner and generates a liquid level which is related to the flow rate through the device. The open channel flow meter (secondary device) measures this level and converts it into a corresponding flow rate according to the known liquid level-flow rate relationship of the primary device.

The first task of an open channel flow meter is to measure the liquid level at an appropriate point in or near the primary measuring device. The second task is to convert the measured liquid level into a corresponding flow rate according to the level-flow rate relationship for the primary measuring device being used. Following are descriptions of some of the more commonly used methods of achieving these tasks, including some general comments on their application.

Float

A float, in combination with either a cable and pulley or a pivoting arm, converts the liquid level (as measured by the float) into an angular position of a shaft, which is proportional to liquid level. Refer to Figure 2-4 for a view of a float-operated flow meter. Floats may be affected by ambient air temperature changes and are subject to build-up of grease and solids. In addition, floats include moving parts, which are subject to wear and require periodic maintenance and repair, and generally require the use of a stilling well. Technological advances over the years have basically made this method of measurement obsolete.

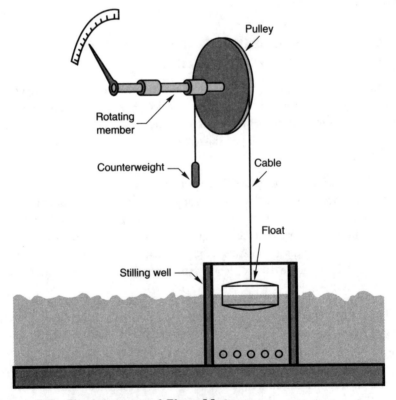

Figure 2-4: Float-operated Flow Meter

Mechanical cam

A mechanical cam, whose profile follows the level-flow rate relationship of the primary measuring device in question, is rotated by the level measuring device. The position of the cam follower is then proportional to flow rate. Refer to Figure 2-5 for a view of a cam used to convert level measurements into flow rate. Like floats, this method of measurement has essentially been rendered obsolete by advances in technology.

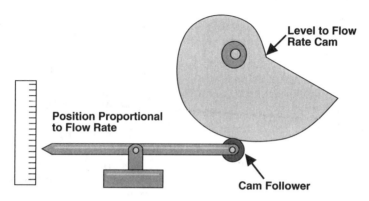

Figure 2-5: Mechanical Cam for Converting Level to Flow Rate

Electrical

This type of level measurement system uses the change in an electrical circuit caused by a changing level to measure the liquid depth. Most designs use a capacitance or admittance probe. The accuracy of electrical systems may be affected by changing liquid characteristics, or coatings of grease or solids. In addition, electrical systems require field calibration at varying flow stream depths, and the probe may be subject to physical damage from debris in the flow stream.

Ultrasonic

A sensor mounted above the flow stream transmits a sound pulse that is reflected by the surface of the liquid. The elapsed time between sending a pulse and receiving an echo determines the level in the channel. Refer to Figure 2-6 for a view of an Isco ultrasonic sensor. Because the speed of sound changes with air temperature, an ultrasonic system must compensate for changes in air temperature, usually with a temperature probe built into the ultrasonic sensor.

An ultrasonic sensor is easy to install and, because it does not contact the liquid, requires minimal maintenance and is not affected by grease, suspended solids, silt, and corrosive chemicals in the flow stream, and liquid temperature fluctuations.

However, ultrasonic systems may be affected by wind, steam, and air temperature gradients, and may provide inaccurate results in channels with turbulence or floating foam or debris. In addition, ultrasonic sensors require space above the flow to mount the sensor, and are usually not suitable for use in very narrow channels.

Because ultrasonic sensors compensate for changes in air temperature, exposure to sunlight can impact performance by artificially heating the sensor and introducing temperature errors to the internal temperature compensation. As a result, it is more suitable to use such devices in applications that are sheltered rather than in an exposed outdoor type of application.

Figure 2-6:
Isco Ultrasonic Sensor

Submerged pressure transducer

A sealed pressure transducer is submerged in the flow stream, and measures the hydrostatic pressure of the liquid, which is proportional to the liquid level. Refer to Figure 2-7 for a view of a submerged pressure transducer. Submerged pressure transducers are not affected by wind, steam, turbulence, and floating foam and debris.

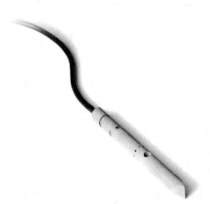

Figure 2-7: Submerged Pressure Transducer

However, because the transducer is located in the flow stream, its accuracy may be affected by changes in the temperature of the flow stream and the transducer is subject to damage by lightning, flowing debris, and corrosive flow stream chemicals. In addition, submerged pressure transducers may be difficult to install in large channels with high flow, and may require periodic maintenance in flow streams with high concentrations of grease, suspended solids, or silt.

Bubbler

A bubbler measures the hydrostatic pressure of the liquid. However, the pressure transducer for a bubbler is located inside the flow meter, and a bubble tube is anchored in the flow stream. Bubbles of pressurized air or other gas are released from the end of the bubble tube at a constant rate, and the transducer measures the pressure required to maintain the bubble rate. This pressure is proportional to the liquid level. Refer to Figure 2-8 to view an Isco 4230 Bubbler Flow Meter.

Figure 2-8: Isco 4230 Bubbler Flow Meter

Similar to submerged pressure transducers, bubblers are not affected by wind, steam, turbulence, and floating foam and debris. In addition, because the pressure transducer is located inside the flow meter, the accuracy of a bubbler is not affected by liquid temperature fluctuations, and the transducer is not subject to damage by lightning, flowing debris, and corrosive flow stream chemicals. Bubblers may require occasional maintenance when used in channels with high concentrations of grease, suspended solids, or silt, although periodic air purges of the bubble tube often minimize this problem. Additional maintenance is also required to regenerate desiccators that prevent moisture from being drawn into the air system of a bubbler.

Electronic memory device

A digital integrated circuit memory device is programmed with the level-flow rate relationship of the primary device. A microprocessor-controlled flow meter accesses the memory device to convert level measurements into flow rate.

Figure 2-9: Isco 2150 Area Velocity Flow Logger

Software

The firmware in a microprocessor-controlled instrument is used to convert the measured liquid level into a flow rate corresponding to that level. See Figure 2-9 for a view of the Isco 2150 Area Velocity Flow Logger that uses internal microprocessor-based firmware for flow conversion.

• • •

The level-to-flow rate conversion methods listed are just some of the more commonly used methods, but others are available. When properly designed and applied, any one of the conversion techniques will give satisfactory results in most situations. In addition, any one of the level measurement technologies may be combined with any one of the level-to-flow rate conversion techniques to result in a complete open channel flow measurement system.

When designing an open channel flow measuring system, the importance of both the primary and secondary measuring devices should be recognized. In a complete open channel flow measurement system, a proper weir or flume installation can be negated through the use of an inaccurate flow meter. Similarly, a very accurate flow meter cannot overcome the inaccuracies of a poorly installed or maintained weir or flume. As with any measurement system, an open channel flow measurement system can be no more accurate than its least accurate component.

Finally, any of the level measurement technologies can also be used with the Manning formula and area velocity methods of open channel flow measurement.

Types of open channel flow meters

There are five types of open channel flow meters, distinguished by the method by which flow data is managed.

Handheld flow meters

Handheld flow meters are used for spot-checking flows and for calibrating other flow meters. They are used for only a short period of time at any one site. While handheld flow meters provide a visual indication of measurements, the data must be manually recorded. The most common example of a handheld flow meter is a current meter, which is used to manually measure the velocity in a flow stream. Current meters are discussed further in Chapter 7.

Flow transmitters

Flow transmitters measure flow and then transmit this information to other recording and/or control instruments. Common outputs on a flow transmitter include analog signals such as a 4 to 20 mA output, relays, and digital outputs such as an RS-232 serial output. Flow transmitters send flow data to equipment such as recorders, computers, automatic samplers, or instruments to control processes such as chlorination and pH neutralization. Flow transmitters typically include a display to view current measurements, and a means such as a keypad to program the instrument. Transmitters are AC powered and permanently installed, with connections often made through conduit. Refer to Figure 2-10 for a view of an Isco 3010 Ultrasonic Flow Transmitter.

Figure 2-10: Isco 3010 Ultrasonic Flow Transmitter

Recording flow meters

Recording flow meters record data on a built-in recording device such as a printer. Recording flow meters are often used in portable applications, with a rechargeable battery providing power for one to two weeks of operation. They may also be used in permanent installations with AC power. Recording flow meters include a keypad and display to program the meter and display measurements. Connections to the flow meter are made with sealed cables and connectors. Meters can also have features such as data logging ability. Refer to Figure 2-11 for a view of an Isco 4210 Ultrasonic Flow Meter.

Figure 2-11: Isco 4210 Ultrasonic Flow Meter

Flow loggers

Flow loggers store data in their internal memory. A flow logger will record a reading at specified intervals. The reading will be carried out as a constant reading until the next scheduled reading interval. Flow loggers are commonly used in flow monitoring projects where flows at multiple sites will be monitored, and a computer will be used to view and analyze the data. Therefore, controls and indicators on a flow logger are minimal. Instead, a computer is used to program the logger, and retrieve and analyze stored data. Data can also be retrieved using data transfer units. Flow loggers are often powered by disposable batteries that can provide power for up to one year. Similar to a recording flow meter, connections to a flow logger are made with sealed cables and connectors. Refer to Figure 2-12 for a view of an Isco 2150 Area Velocity Flow Logger.

Figure 2-12: Retrieving Data from an Isco 2150 Area Velocity Flow Logger Using a Computer

Flow modules

Flow modules plug into an automatic sampler, transforming the sampler into a combination sampler and flow meter. Such a system is designed to meet the needs for portable "spot checking" applications. With a flow module installed, the sampler can measure and totalize flow, activate sampling based on flow measurements, and collect flow proportioned samples.

A keypad and display on the sampler are used to set up the sampler and flow module, and to display current measurements. Flow and sample data are then stored in the sampler's memory for later retrieval and analysis using a computer. Refer to Figure 2-13 for a view of an Isco 710 Ultrasonic Flow Module plugged into a 6712 Sampler.

Figure 2-13: Isco 710 Ultrasonic Flow Module and 6712 Sampler

General units of measurement

2

Two types of units are used in measuring liquids: units of discharge (flow rate) and units of volume.

Discharge, or flow rate, is defined as the volume of liquid that passes a particular reference section in a unit of time. The unit of discharge generally used in irrigation practice in the U.S. is the cubic foot per second (cfs), also known as the second-foot (sec.-ft.). In water supply and waste treatment in the U.S., the units of discharge normally used are million gallons per day (mgd) or, in some cases, gallons per minute (gpm). In metric units, discharge is normally expressed in liters per second (lps or l/s), cubic meters per second (cms or m^3/s), or cubic meters per hour (cmh or m^3/hr).

Total flow, or volume, measurements are usually obtained by integrating flow rate over a period of time, which then represents an accumulated total of liquid. The unit of volume commonly used in irrigation work in the U.S. is the acre-foot (ac.-ft.). An acre-foot is defined as the quantity of water required to cover 1 acre (0.40 ha) of land to a depth of 1 foot (0.30 m), or 43,560 cubic feet (1230 m^3). In water supply and waste treatment the unit of volume normally used is the gallon (gal) or millions of gallons (mg). In metric units, volume is normally expressed in liters (l) or cubic meters (m^3).

Selecting a Measurement Device

Make sure you select the right flow measurement device for your application. Multiple styles of flow monitors are available to meet the specific needs of different applications. There is no one technology or device that will meet every need. When choosing a flow meter, transmitter, or logger, consider what is required for your particular application. Examine your expectations of the equipment you select to see if they are realistic. When you look at different features, determine which are desired and which are necessary.

The following list contains some things you should consider before selecting a flow monitor:

- Why do you need to monitor flow (billing, process control, spotting trends, alarm conditions)?
- What accuracy is required?
- What outputs are required (4-20 mA, contact closure, alarm output, relay output, dialout alarm, digital outputs)?
- What are your communication needs (modem, wireless, Modbus, RS232)?
- Do you need printed reports?
- Do you need a mechanical totalizer?
- What is the duration of the project?

- What are the permit requirements?
- What are the piping requirements?

The characteristics of the application are important to the selection of measurement technology. Determine whether there are corrosive elements, wind, excessive turbulence, debris or other factors present. Table 2-1 is an important aid in determining a suitable technology based upon site conditions.

The ongoing maintenance and operating requirements are also a concern, since staff must know how to operate and maintain the device(s). Regular maintenance programs are recommended for all devices to ensure the ongoing quality of measurements, but the type and frequency of maintenance can vary for different devices.

2

Table 2-1:
Flow Measurement Technology Selection Guide

	Ultrasonic Sensor	Submerged Probe	Bubbler	Area Velocity
Suitability for different applications				
Weirs and flumes	Excellent[1]	Excellent	Excellent	Excellent
Channels less than 6 in. (150 mm)	Not recommended	Excellent	Excellent	Not recommended
Small round pipes, 6 to 8 in. (150 to 200 mm)	Good[2]	Excellent	Excellent	Good
Medium round pipes, 10 to 15 in. (250 to 375 mm)	Good[2]	Excellent	Excellent	Excellent
Large round pipes, 15 to 96 in. (375 to 2500 mm)	Excellent[2]	Good	Excellent	Excellent
Irrigation channels and small streams	Excellent[2]	Good	Excellent	Good
Rivers and large streams	Excellent[2]	Good	Excellent	Good
Chemical Compatibility of Sensor				
Organic solvents	Compatible	Not Recommended	Compatible	Not Recommended
Organic acids	Compatible	Not Recommended	Compatible	Not Recommended
Alcohols	Compatible	Compatible	Compatible	Compatible
Esters	Compatible	Not Recommended	Compatible	Not Recommended
Inorganic acids	Compatible	Not Recommended	Compatible	Not Recommended
Inorganic bases	Compatible	Not Recommended	Compatible	Not Recommended
Inorganic salts	Compatible	Compatible	Compatible	Compatible
Performance under Adverse Conditions				
Strong wind	Not Recommended	Excellent	Excellent	Excellent
Air temperature fluctuations	Very good[3]	Excellent	Very good[3]	Excellent
Steam above liquid	Not Recommended	Excellent	Excellent	Excellent
Foam on liquid	Not Recommended	Excellent	Excellent	Excellent
Flow stream turbulence	Not Recommended	Excellent	Excellent	Excellent
Floating debris	Not Recommended	Excellent	Excellent	Excellent
Floating oil or grease	Not Recommended	Excellent	Excellent	Excellent
Suspended solids	Excellent	Very Good	Good	Very Good
Suspended grease	Excellent	Very Good	Good	Very Good
Silting in	Excellent	Very Good	Good	Very Good
Liquid temperature fluctuations	Very Good[4]	Good[4]	Excellent	Good[4]
Submerged flow	Not Recommended	Not Recommended	Not Recommended	Excellent
Full pipe flow	Not Recommended	Not Recommended	Not Recommended	Excellent
Surcharged flow	Not Recommended	Not Recommended	Not Recommended	Excellent
Reverse flow	Not Recommended	Not Recommended	Not Recommended	Excellent
Maintenance Requirements Caused by Adverse Conditions				
Silting in	None	Occasional	Occasional	Occasional
Suspended solids	None	Occasional	Occasional	Occasional
High grease concentration	None	Occasional	Occasional	Occasional

1. Use with caution in small flumes.
2. There must be adequate space above for mounting sensor.
3. Large air temperature fluctuations will affect accuracy.
4. Large water temperature fluctuations will affect accuracy.

CHAPTER

3

Weirs

OVERVIEW

This chapter provides detailed information concerning the use of various types of weirs.

Please note that the recommendations presented in this chapter are derived from standard references and are intended to be used as general guidelines only. The details of a particular installation may justify a deviation from these recommendations, based on sound engineering judgment.

A weir is a dam built across an open channel over which the liquid flows.

Introduction

Weirs are the simplest, least expensive, and probably the most common type of primary measuring device used to measure flow in open channels. A weir is essentially an obstruction or dam built across an open channel over which the liquid flows, often through a specially shaped opening or notch. Weirs are normally classified according to the shape of the notch. The most common types of weirs, as shown in Figure 3-1, are the rectangular weir, the V-notch (or triangular) weir, and the trapezoidal (or Cipolletti) weir. Each type of weir has an associated equation for determining the flow rate through the weir. The equation is based on the depth of the liquid in the pool formed upstream from the weir.

The edge or surface over which the liquid passes is called the crest of the weir, as shown in Figure 3-2. (Note that the V-notch weir comes to a point at the bottom, so it has no actual crest length; the point may be thought of as the "crest" of a V-notch weir.) Generally, the top edge of the weir is thin or beveled with a sharp upstream corner so that the liquid does not contact any part of the weir structure downstream but, rather, springs past it. Weirs of this type are called sharp-crested weirs, and are discussed in this section. Broad-crested weirs are briefly discussed on page 47.

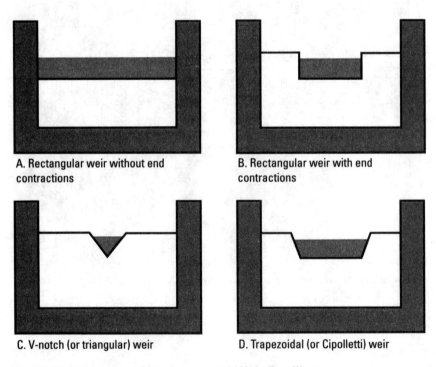

A. Rectangular weir without end contractions

B. Rectangular weir with end contractions

C. V-notch (or triangular) weir

D. Trapezoidal (or Cipolletti) weir

Figure 3-1: Various Sharp-crested Weir Profiles

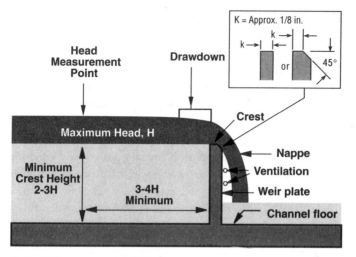

Figure 3-2: Sharp-crested Weir

The stream of water leaving the weir crest is called the **nappe**. When the water surface downstream from the weir is far enough below the weir crest so that air flows freely beneath the nappe, the nappe is aerated and the flow is referred to as **free** or **critical**. When the downstream water level rises to the point where air does not flow freely beneath the nappe, the nappe is not ventilated and the discharge rate may be inaccurate because of the low pressure beneath the nappe. When the downstream water level rises above the crest, the flow is referred to as **submerged** or **subcritical**. This can affect the discharge rate to a measurable degree, so dependable measurements should not be expected in this range. Flow rate under submerged conditions can be determined by measuring both the upstream and downstream levels, and referring to submerged flow tables. Submerged and non-ventilated flows are undesirable for standard conditions and should usually be avoided. In most cases, weirs should be sized and installed to obtain ventilated and free or critical discharge conditions.

The discharge rate of a weir is determined by measuring the vertical distance from the crest of the weir to the liquid surface in the pool upstream from the crest. This liquid depth is called the head. As shown in Figure 3-2, a slight drop in the liquid surface begins upstream from the weir. This drop occurs at a distance of at least twice the head on the crest, and is called the surface contraction or draw-down of the weir. To avoid sensing the effects of drawdown, the head measuring point of the weir should be located upstream of the weir crest a distance of at least three, and preferably four times the maximum head expected over the weir, as shown in Figure 3-2. Once the head is known, the flow rate or discharge can be determined using the known head-flow rate relationship of the weir.

Thus, for a weir of a given size and shape with free-flow, steady-state conditions and proper weir-to-pool relationships, only one depth of liquid can exist in the upstream pool for a given discharge. A weir may be thought of as a device for shaping the flow of the liquid to allow a single depth reading that is uniquely related to a discharge rate.

Although weirs are comparatively easy to construct and convenient to use, they are not always suitable for every application. Accurate flow rate measurements cannot be expected unless the proper conditions and dimensions are maintained. Weirs are not suitable for flat-sloped channel installations where head loss must be considered. Weirs are also not suitable for water carrying excessive solid materials or silt, which will deposit in the approach channel behind the weir. Such buildup will alter the stable hydraulic conditions required for accurate discharge measurement. Some silt, sand, or other solid material will inevitably collect in any open channel flow system. To allow the periodic removal of these deposits, it is suggested that the weir bulkhead be constructed with an opening beneath the notch, through which accumulations can be sluiced as required. A metal plate or plank placed across the upstream side of this opening and securely fixed in place will serve as a cover while the weir is in operation.

To ensure accurate discharge measurement, there are certain general weir design requirements that apply to all types:

1. The weir should consist of a thin plate $^1/_8$ to $^1/_4$ inch (3 to 6 mm) thick with a straight edge or a thicker plate with a downstream chamfered edge. The upstream sharp edge prevents the nappe from adhering to the crest. Knife edges should be avoided because they are difficult to maintain. However, the upstream edge of the weir must be sharp with right angle corners, since rounded edges will decrease the head for a given flow rate.

2. The upstream face of the weir should be smooth and perpendicular to the axis of the channel in both horizontal and vertical directions. The crest of the weir should also be exactly level to insure a uniform depth of flow.

3. The connection of the weir to the channel should be waterproof. Therefore, the joint between the weir plate and channel should be packed with chemically inert cement or asphalt type roofing compound.

4. The length of the weir crest or the notch angle must be accurately determined, because the percentage error in measured flow rate will be proportional to the error in determining these dimensions.

5. The weir should be ventilated, if necessary, to prevent a vacuum from forming on the underside of the nappe.

6. The height of the weir from the bottom of the channel to the crest should be at least 2 times the maximum expected head of liquid above the crest. This is necessary to lower the velocity of approach. The weir height should never be less than 1 foot (0.3 m).

7. The approach section should be straight upstream from the weir for a distance of at least 20 times the maximum expected head of liquid, and should have little or no slope.

8. The crest must be set higher than the maximum downstream elevation of the water surface. Otherwise, a submerged flow condition will occur instead of the free flow condition required for reliable flow measurement.

9. The device for measuring the head (flow meter) should be placed upstream at a distance of at least 3 times the maximum expected head on the weir and should be located in a quiet section of the channel away from all disturbances, preferably in a stilling well. Also, the zero point of the head measuring device must be set exactly level with the weir crest.

10. The crest of the weir must be kept clean. Fibers, stringy materials, and larger particles tend to cling to the crest and should be removed periodically. The upstream side of the weir should also be periodically purged of accumulated silt and solids.

11. The weir size should be selected only after preliminary studies have determined the expected flow rates in the channel in question. The Manning formula, as described in Chapter 6, can sometimes be used to estimate the flow rate in open channels.

12. The cross-sectional area of the approach channel should be at least 8 times that of the nappe at the crest for a distance upstream of 15 to 20 times the head on the crest. This is necessary to minimize the velocity of approach. The approach channel should also permit the liquid to approach the weir in a smooth stream free from turbulence, and the velocity should be uniformly distributed over the channel; this may be accomplished through the use of baffle plates if necessary.

13. If the weir pool is smaller than defined by the above criteria, the velocity of approach may be too high and the head reading too low. Refer to reference [3] for velocity of approach corrections. Weirs should be installed and maintained to make the velocity of approach negligible. Appropriate corrections should be made where this is not possible.

Weirs are classified in accordance with the shape of the notch or opening in the weir. The basic types — V-notch, rectangular, and trapezoidal— are discussed individually in the following pages, along with certain other types of weirs.

V-notch (triangular) weirs

The V-notch or triangular sharp-crested weir (Figures 3-3 and 3-4) consists of an angular notch cut into a bulkhead in the flow channel. The apex of the notch is at the bottom and the sides are set equally on either side of a vertical line from the apex. The angle of the notch ($\propto$) most commonly used is 90°, although V-notch weirs with angles of $22^1/2°$, 30°, 45°, 60° and 120° are also used.

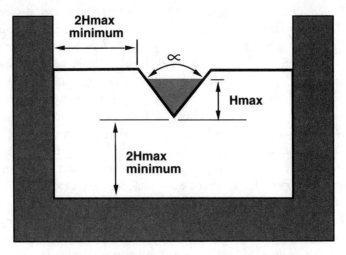

Figure 3-3: V-notch (triangular) Sharp-crested Weir

Some problems exist with narrow-angled V-notch weirs. The small included angle of these weirs makes it difficult to accurately produce the geometry of the weir at the apex. Also, the capillary effect will restrict flow at a surprisingly high head, causing the head/discharge relationship to be unreliable.

When installing a V-notch weir, the minimum distance of the sides of the weir from the channel banks should be at least twice the maximum expected head on the weir. The minimum distance from the crest to the pool bottom should also be at least twice the maximum expected head.

The V-notch weir is an accurate flow measuring device particularly suited for low flows. Because the V-notch weir has no crest length, the head required for a small flow through it is greater than that required with other types of weirs. This is an advantage for small discharges in that the nappe will spring free of the crest, whereas it would cling to the crest of another type of weir and reduce the accuracy of the measurement.

The V-notch weir is the best weir profile for measuring discharges less than 1 cfs (450 gpm – 0.65 mgd – 28 l/s – 100 m³/hr) and has reasonable accuracy for flows up to 10 cfs (4500 gpm – 6.5 mgd – 280 l/s – 1000 m³/hr). It is generally recommended that the minimum head on a V-notch weir be at least 0.2 foot (0.06 m) to prevent the nappe from clinging to the crest. It is also recommended that the maximum head be limited to 2.0 feet (0.6 m), to ensure accuracy of the device head/flow rate relationship. Based on these lower and upper head restrictions, Tables 3-1 and 3-2 present the minimum and maximum recommended flow rates for the most common V-notch weirs.

The discharge (head vs. flow rate) equation of a free flowing V-notch weir takes the form:

$$Q = K\,H^{2.5}$$

where: Q = flow rate

H = head on the weir

K = a constant, dependent on the angle of notch and units of measurement

Tables 3-3 through 3-4 present the discharge equations for the common V-notch weirs. Complete discharge tables for V-notch weirs are found in Chapter 9 of this handbook.

Figure 3-4: A 120° V-notch weir at a municipal wastewater treatment plant.

Table 3-1:
Minimum and Maximum Recommended Flow Rates for V-notch Weirs with Head in Feet

V-notch angle	Min. head, feet	Minimum flow rate			Max. head, feet	Maximum flow rate		
		CFS	GPM	MGD		CFS	GPM	MGD
22.5°	0.2	0.009	3.99	0.006	2.0	2.81	1260	1.82
30°	0.2	0.012	5.43	0.008	2.0	3.82	1720	2.47
45°	0.2	0.019	8.31	0.012	2.0	5.85	2630	3.78
60°	0.2	0.026	11.6	0.017	2.0	8.16	3660	5.28
90°	0.2	0.045	20.1	0.029	2.0	14.1	6350	9.14
120°	0.2	0.077	34.8	0.050	2.0	24.5	11,000	15.80

Table 3-2:
Minimum and Maximum Recommended Flow Rates for V-notch Weirs with Head in Meters

V-notch angle	Min. head, meters	Minimum flow rate		Max. head, meters	Maximum flow rate	
		l/s	m^3/hr		l/s	m^3/hr
22.5°	0.06	0.242	0.871	0.6	76.5	275
30°	0.06	0.329	1.19	0.6	104	375
45°	0.06	0.504	1.81	0.6	159	574
60°	0.06	0.703	2.53	0.6	222	800
90°	0.06	1.22	4.38	0.6	385	1390
120°	0.06	2.11	7.59	0.6	667	2400

Table 3-3:
Discharge Equations for V-notch Weirs with Head in Feet

V-notch angle	CFS	GPM	MGD
22.5°	$Q = 0.4970H^{2.5}$	$Q = 223.1H^{2.5}$	$Q = 0.3212H^{2.5}$
30°	$Q = 0.6760H^{2.5}$	$Q = 303.4H^{2.5}$	$Q = 0.4369H^{2.5}$
45°	$Q = 1.035H^{2.5}$	$Q = 464.5H^{2.5}$	$Q = 0.6689H^{2.5}$
60°	$Q = 1.443H^{2.5}$	$Q = 647.6H^{2.5}$	$Q = 0.9326H^{2.5}$
90°	$Q = 2.500H^{2.5}$	$Q = 1122H^{2.5}$	$Q = 1.616H^{2.5}$
120°	$Q = 4.330H^{2.5}$	$Q = 1943H^{2.5}$	$Q = 2.798H^{2.5}$

Table 3-4:
Discharge Equations for V-notch Weirs with Head in Meters

V-notch angle	l/s	m^3/hr
22.5°	$Q = 274.4H^{2.5}$	$Q = 987.8H^{2.5}$
30°	$Q = 373.2H^{2.5}$	$Q = 1344H^{2.5}$
45°	$Q = 571.4H^{2.5}$	$Q = 2057H^{2.5}$
60°	$Q = 796.7H^{2.5}$	$Q = 2868H^{2.5}$
90°	$Q = 1380H^{2.5}$	$Q = 4969H^{2.5}$
120°	$Q = 2391H^{2.5}$	$Q = 8606H^{2.5}$

Rectangular (contracted and suppressed) weirs

The rectangular sharp-crested weir (Figure 3-5) may be used in one of two configurations. The first configuration (Figure 3-5 A) consists of a rectangular notch cut into a bulkhead in the flow channel, producing a box-like opening. This configuration is called a contracted rectangular weir because a curved flow path or contraction results with the nappe forming a jet narrower than the weir opening. The horizontal distances from the end of the weir crest to the side walls of the channel are called the end contractions. These end contractions reduce the width and accelerate the channel flow as it passes over the weir and provide the needed ventilation. Flow through this type of weir is said to be with end contractions. (Any weir which is narrower than the channel in which it is placed is technically a contracted weir.)

In the second configuration of the rectangular weir (Figure 3-5 B), the end contractions are completely suppressed by extending the weir across the entire width of the channel. Thus, the sides of the channel also act as the sides of the weir and there are no lateral contractions. This type of weir is called a suppressed rectangular weir, and flow through it is said to be without end contractions.

When installing a rectangular weir with end contractions, the distance from the side of the weir notch to the side of the channel should be at least twice the maximum expected head on the weir. This is necessary to allow the liquid in the channel a free, unconstrained lateral approach to the weir crest. Special care must also be taken in the installation of rectangular weirs without end contractions to obtain adequate aeration of the nappe. This is usually accomplished by placing vents on both sides of the weir box under the nappe. For rectangular weirs both with and without end contractions, the minimum distance from the crest to the pool bottom should be at least twice the maximum expected head.

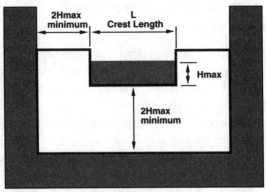

A. Contracted (with end contractions)

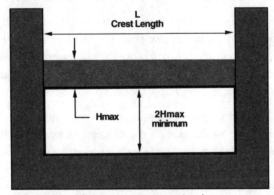

B. Suppressed (without end contractions)

Figure 3-5: Rectangular Sharp-crested Weirs

When constructing a rectangular weir, a crest length of 1 foot (0.3 m) is the minimum that should be considered, since a V-notch weir can more accurately measure the same flow rates as rectangular weirs smaller than 1 foot. In the U.S., it is conventional practice to increase the crest length in increments of 6 inches up to 3 feet, and in 1 foot increments beyond 3 feet, to suit the particular installation. Rectangular weir crest lengths up to 10 feet (3 m) are common and, theoretically, there is no maximum crest length. However, beyond 6 or 8 feet (2 to 2.5 m), a limit is usually set by economic rather than engineering considerations.

This is an example of a rectangular weir without end contractions. Note that the staff gauge and bubble tube are correctly located upstream at a distance of at least three to four times the maximum head.

Vent pipes are located directly above both sides of this rectangular weir without end contractions. This ensures adequate aeration of the nappe.

In general, it is recommended that the minimum head on a rectangular weir be at least 0.2 foot (0.06 m) to prevent the nappe from clinging to the crest. It is generally accepted practice to limit the maximum head to no more than one half the crest length. However, laboratory experiments have shown that the accuracy of measurement is not impaired to a great extent by exceeding this limit, especially for crest lengths of 1 to 4 feet (0.3 to 1.2 m). But, to insure strict conformance to the weir head/flow rate relationship, the maximum head limitation of one half the crest length should usually be adhered to. Based on these lower and upper head restrictions, Tables 3-5 and 3-6 present the minimum and maximum recommended flow rates for common rectangular weirs with end contractions. Tables 3-7 and 3-8 present similar information for rectangular weirs without end contractions.

Table 3-5:
Minimum and Maximum Recommended Flow Rates for
Rectangular Weirs with End Contractions with Head in Feet

Crest length, feet	Min. head, feet	Minimum flow rate			Max. head, feet	Maximum flow rate		
		CFS	GPM	MGD		CFS	GPM	MGD
1	0.2	0.286	128	0.185	0.5	1.06	476	0.685
1.5	0.2	0.435	195	0.281	0.75	2.92	1310	1.89
2	0.2	0.584	262	0.377	1.0	5.99	2690	3.87
2.5	0.2	0.733	329	0.474	1.25	10.5	4700	6.77
3	0.2	0.882	396	0.570	1.5	16.5	7420	10.7
4	0.2	1.18	530	0.762	2.0	33.9	15,200	21.9
5	0.2	1.48	663	0.955	2.5	59.2	26,600	38.3
6	0.2	1.78	797	1.15	3.0	93.4	41,900	60.4
8	0.2	2.37	1060	1.53	4.0	192.0	86,100	124.0
10	0.2	2.97	1330	1.92	5.0	335.0	150,000	217.0

3

Table 3-6:
Minimum and Maximum Recommended Flow Rates for
Rectangular Weirs with End Contractions with Head in Meters

Crest length, meters	Min. head, meters	Minimum flow rate		Max. head, meters	Maximum flow rate	
		l/s	m^3/hr		l/s	m^3/hr
0.3	0.06	7.78	28.0	0.15	28.8	104
0.4	0.06	'10.5	37.7	0.2	59.2	213
0.5	0.06	13.2	47.5	0.25	103	372
0.6	0.06	15.9	57.2	0.3	163	587
0.8	0.06	21.3	76.6	0.4	335	1210
1.0	0.06	26.7	96.1	0.5	585	2110
1.5	0.06	40.2	145.0	0.75	1610	5800
2.0	0.06	53.7	193.0	1.0	3310	11,900
3.0	0.06	80.7	291.0	1.5	9120	32,800

The discharge (head vs flow rate) equation of a free flowing rectangular weir with end contractions takes the form:

$$Q = K (L - 0.2\,H)\,H^{1.5}$$

where: Q = flow rate
H = head on the weir
L = crest length of weir
K = constant dependent upon units

For flow rate in cubic feet per second, gallons per minute, and million gallons per day, and head in feet, the discharge equations for a rectangular weir with end contractions are as follows:

CFS: $Q = 3.330 (L - 0.2\,H)\,H^{1.5}$
GPM: $Q = 1495 (L - 0.2\,H)\,H^{1.5}$
MGD: $Q = 2.152 (L - 0.2\,H)\,H^{1.5}$
where: L = crest length of weir in feet

For flow rate in liters per second and cubic meters per hour, and head in meters, the discharge equation is:

l/s: $Q = 1838 (L - 0.2\,H)\,H^{1.5}$
m³/hr: $Q = 6618 (L - 0.2\,H)\,H^{1.5}$
where: L = crest length of weir in meters

Complete discharge tables for rectangular weirs with end contractions are found in Chapter 10 of this handbook.

Table 3-7:
Minimum and Maximum Recommended Flow Rates for Rectangular Weirs without End Contractions with Head in Feet

Crest length, feet	Min. head, feet	Minimum flow rate			Max. head, feet	Maximum flow rate		
		CFS	GPM	MGD		CFS	GPM	MGD
1	0.2	0.298	134	0.192	0.5	1.18	529	0.761
11/2	0.2	0.447	201	0.289	0.75	3.24	1460	2.10
2	0.2	0.596	267	0.385	1.0	6.66	2990	4.30
21/2	0.2	0.745	334	0.481	1.25	11.6	5220	7.52
3	0.2	0.894	401	0.578	1.5	18.4	8240	11.9
4	0.2	1.19	535	0.770	2.0	37.7	16,900	24.3
5	0.2	1.49	668	0.962	2.5	65.8	29,500	42.5
6	0.2	1.79	802	1.15	3.0	104	46,600	67.1
8	0.2	2.38	1070	1.54	4.0	213	95,700	138
10	0.2	2.98	1340	1.92	5.0	372	167,000	241

Table 3-8:
Minimum and Maximum Recommended Flow Rates for Rectangular Weirs without End Contractions with Head in Meters

Crest length, meters	Min. head, meters	Minimum flow rate		Max. head, meters	Maximum flow rate	
		l/s	m³/hr		l/s	m³/hr
0.3	0.06	8.11	29.2	0.15	32.0	115
0.4	0.06	10.8	38.9	0.2	65.8	237
0.5	0.06	13.5	48.6	0.25	115	414
0.6	0.06	16.2	58.4	0.3	181	653
0.8	0.06	21.6	77.8	0.4	372	1340
1.0	0.06	27.0	97.3	0.5	650	2340
1.5	0.06	40.5	146	0.75	1790	6450
2.0	0.06	54.0	195	1.0	3680	13,200
3.0	0.06	81.1	292	1.5	10,100	36,500

The discharge equation of a free flowing rectangular weir without end contractions takes the form:

$$Q = K L H^{1.5}$$

where: Q = flow rate
H = head on the weir
L = crest length of weir
K = constant dependent upon units

For flow rate in cubic feet per second, gallons per minute, and million gallons per day, and head in feet, the discharge equations for a rectangular weir without end contractions are as follows:

CFS: $Q = 3.330 \text{ L H}^{1.5}$
GPM: $Q = 1495 \text{ L H}^{1.5}$
MGD: $Q = 2.152 \text{ L H}^{1.5}$
where: L = crest length of weir in feet

For flow rate in liters per second and cubic meters per hour, and head in meters, the discharge equation is:

l/s: $Q = 1838 \text{ L H}^{1.5}$
m^3/hr: $Q = 6618 \text{ L H}^{1.5}$
where: L = crest length of weir in meters

Complete discharge tables for rectangular weirs without end contractions are found in Chapter 11.

Trapezoidal (Cipolletti) weirs

The trapezoidal sharp-crested weir (Figure 3-6) is similar to a rectangular weir with end contractions except that the sides incline outwardly, producing a trapezoidal opening. When the end-inclinations of a trapezoidal weir are in the ratio of 4 vertical to 1 horizontal, the weir is known as a Cipolletti weir — named for the Italian experimenter, Cesare Cipolletti, who first proposed its use. Although the Cipolletti weir is a contracted weir, its discharge occurs essentially as though its end contractions were suppressed. Thus, no correction is necessary for the crest width as in a rectangular contracted weir, resulting in a simpler discharge equation.

All of the installation conditions stated for rectangular weirs with end contractions also apply to Cipolletti weirs. The Cipolletti weir offers a slightly wider range than the rectangular weir. However, the measurement accuracy with a Cipolletti weir is inherently less than that obtained with the rectangular or a V-notch weir.

The minimum and maximum recommended heads for a Cipolletti weir are the same as rectangular weirs: minimum head of 0.2 foot (0.06 m) and maximum head of no more than one half the crest length. Based on these lower and upper head restrictions, Tables 3-9 and 3-10 present the minimum and maximum recommended flow rates for common Cipolletti weirs.

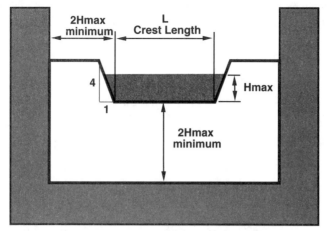

Figure 3-6: Trapezoidal (Cipolletti) Sharp-crested Weir

This Cipolletti weir is used to measure the final effluent from the chlorine contact chamber at a municipal wastewater treatment plant.

The discharge (head vs flow rate) equation of a free flowing Cipolletti weir takes the form:

$$Q = K L H^{1.5}$$

where: Q = flow rate
H = head on the weir
L = crest length of weir
K = constant dependent upon units

For flow rate in cubic feet per second, gallons per minute, and million gallons per day, and head in feet, the discharge equations for a Cipolletti weir are as follows:

CFS: $\quad Q = 3.367\ L\ H^{1.5}$

GPM: $\quad Q = 1511\ L\ H^{1.5}$

MGD: $\quad Q = 2.176\ L\ H^{1.5}$

where: $\quad L$ = crest length of weir in feet

For flow rate in liters per second and cubic meters per hour, and head in meters, the discharge equation is:

l/s: $\quad Q = 1859\ L\ H^{1.5}$

m^3/hr: $\quad Q = 6692\ L\ H^{1.5}$

where: $\quad L$ = crest length of weir in meters

Complete discharge tables for Cipolletti weirs are found in Chapter 12.

Table 3-9:
Minimum and Maximum Recommended Flow Rates for Cipolletti Weirs with Head in Feet

Crest length, feet	Min. head, feet	Minimum flow rate			Max. head, feet	Maximum flow rate		
		CFS	GPM	MGD		CFS	GPM	MGD
1	0.2	0.301	135	0.195	0.5	1.19	534	0.769
1.5	0.2	0.452	203	0.292	0.75	3.28	1470	2.12
2	0.2	0.602	270	0.389	1.0	6.73	3020	4.35
2.5	0.2	0.753	338	0.487	1.25	11.8	5280	7.60
3	0.2	0.903	405	0.584	1.5	18.6	8330	12.0
4	0.2	1.20	541	0.779	2.0	38.1	17,100	24.6
5	0.2	1.51	676	0.973	2.5	66.6	29,900	43.0
6	0.2	1.81	811	1.17	3.0	105	47,100	67.9
8	0.2	2.41	1080	1.56	4.0	216	96,700	139
10	0.2	3.01	1350	1.95	5.0	376	169,000	243

Table 3-10:
Minimum and Maximum Recommended Flow Rates for Cipolletti Weirs with Head in Meters

Crest length, meters	Min. head, meters	Minimum flow rate		Max. head, meters	Maximum flow rate	
		l/s	m^3/hr		l/s	m^3/hr
0.3	0.06	8.20	29.5	0.15	32.4	117
0.4	0.06	10.9	39.3	0.2	66.5	239
0.5	0.06	13.7	49.2	0.25	116	418
0.6	0.06	16.4	59.0	0.3	183	660
0.8	0.06	21.9	78.7	0.4	376	1350
1.0	0.06	27.3	98.4	0.5	657	2370
1.5	0.06	41.0	148	0.75	1810	6520
2.0	0.06	54.6	197	1.0	3720	13,400
3.0	0.06	82.0	295	1.5	10,200	36,900

Other weirs

There are certain other types of primary devices classified as weirs which are in use, but are much less common than the sharp-crested weir profiles discussed above. Among these are special profiles of sharp-crested weirs, compound weirs, Isco Flow Metering Inserts, Thel-Mar Volumetric Weirs, broad-crested weirs, open flow nozzles, and the California Pipe method. These will be briefly discussed in the following sections.

3

Special profiles of sharp-crested weirs

Special sharp-crested weir profiles, as shown in Figure 3-7, have been developed to achieve certain head/discharge relationships or to achieve some benefit peculiar to a particular type of site. The most common of these special devices is the proportional or Sutro weir [6] [7] (Figures 3-7 A and 3-8), designed so that the discharge varies directly with the head on the weir. This weir has the obvious advantage of a simple head/discharge relationship, but its shape is complicated and difficult to fabricate. To overcome this disadvantage, the approximate linear weir (Figure 3-7 B) was developed. This weir consists of a semi-circular plate attached to a rectangular weir with end contractions, making it fairly simple to fabricate. However, its head/discharge relationship is only approximately linear, thus introducing a certain amount of error. Other special purpose sharp-crested weir profiles are shown in Figures 3-7 C and D. None of these special weir profiles have been used or investigated nearly as extensively as the triangular, rectangular, and trapezoidal profiles discussed above, and will not be dealt with here.

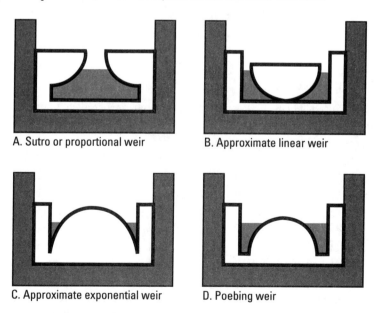

A. Sutro or proportional weir   B. Approximate linear weir

C. Approximate exponential weir   D. Poebing weir

Figure 3-7: Special Sharp-crested Weir Profiles

Figure 3-8: The flow rate through a Sutro weir is proportional to the head.

Compound weirs

For situations where the normal range of discharges at a site might easily be handled by a V-notch weir but occasional larger flows would require, for example, a rectangular weir, the two profiles may be combined to form what is termed a compound weir, as shown in Figure 3-9. Such a weir has a disadvantage, however. While flows may be measured rather accurately when the weir is behaving as a V-notch weir or as a rectangular weir, there will be a transition zone where accurate readings will be difficult to achieve. When the discharge begins to exceed the capacity of the V-notch, thin sheets of liquid will begin to pass over the wide horizontal crests in a less than predictable fashion, causing an ambiguous discontinuity in the discharge curve. The size of the V-notch and the rectangular section should be selected so that the discharge measurements in the transition zone will be of minimum importance. A compound weir may be fabricated from different weir profiles than those mentioned, for example, a combination of a small and large Cipolletti weir.

Quite often, the discharge over a compound weir is calculated by simply applying the standard discharge equation for each segment of the weir to the head on that segment of the weir. The total discharge is then the sum of the discharges of each to the two segments of the weir. Although this technique is commonly used, it apparently has not been fully investigated either in the laboratory or in the field. In fact, it appears as though little research has been performed on compound weirs in general. Thus, to ensure accurate flow rate measurement with a compound weir, the structure should be calibrated either in the laboratory or in place.

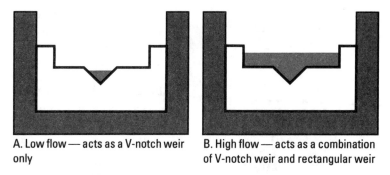

A. Low flow — acts as a V-notch weir only

B. High flow — acts as a combination of V-notch weir and rectangular weir

Figure 3-9: Compound Weir (V-notch Weir with Contracted Rectangular Weir)

This compound weir consists of a V-notch weir at the bottom, with three increasingly wide rectangular weirs with end contractions above it. The flow meter is located in the shelter at the left of the photo, upstream at a distance of at least three to four times the maximum head.

Isco Flow Metering Inserts

The Isco Flow Metering Inserts allow flow rates in small diameter sewer pipes to be measured without the operator entering the manhole. The metering insert is attached to an interlocking pole assembly that allows the insert to be inserted into a sewer pipe from ground level, as shown in Figure 3-10. An inflatable collar secures the insert in the pipe.

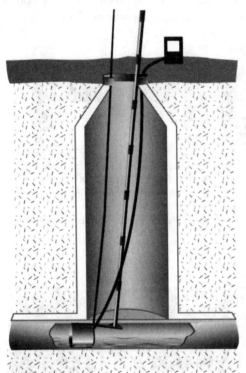

Figure 3-10:
Isco Flow Metering Insert

The Flow Metering Inserts are used for inflow and infiltration studies, for determining the proper size of primary measuring device to install, and for checking the calibration of existing flow meters.

Because the flow metering insert acts as a dam in the flow stream, periodic removal to clean sediment and other deposited solids from the channel is recommended. Failure to address this issue could not only impact accuracy, but also result in restricted or blocked lines. This would be true for any insert-type device!

The insert is held in place by an inflatable collar, which could require periodic re-inflation to maintain the pressure required to hold the insert in its proper position. Avoid flow streams which contain chemicals that could attack the flow metering insert's construction materials.

Isco metering inserts are available for 6, 8, 10, and 12 inch (150, 200, 250, and 300 mm) pipes. The inserts include an integral round orifice, which is 60% of the pipe diameter, for measuring higher flow rates. A 60° V-notch weir plate can be attached for higher accuracy at lower flow rates.

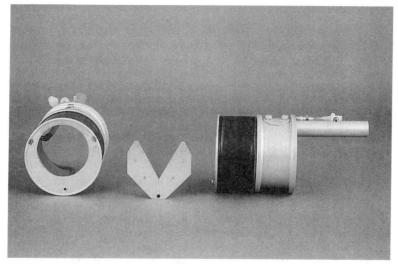

Metering inserts include a round orifice for measuring higher flow rates. An attachable 60° V-notch weir provides higher accuracy at lower flow rates. The inflatable collar secures the insert in place.

A bubbler flow meter can be used to measure the head, providing automatic flow measurement and recording.

The head-flow rate relationships for the metering inserts were determined by St. Anthony Falls Hydraulics Laboratory at the University of Minnesota. The inserts typically provide measurements within 5% of the actual flow rate. Table 3-11 presents the capacity ranges for each insert.

Table 3-11:
Capacity Ranges for Isco Flow Metering Inserts

Metering insert	CFS	GPM	MGD	l/s	m³/hr
6" (150 mm) V-Notch weir	0.002 to 0.201	1 to 90	0.001 to 0.130	0.063 to 5.68	0.227 to 20.4
Round orifice	0.011 to 0.401	5 to 180	0.007 to 0.259	0.315 to 11.4	1.136 to 40.9
8" (200 mm) V-Notch weir	0.002 to 0.357	1 to 160	0.001 to 0.230	0.063 to 10.1	0.227 to 36.3
Round orifice	0.022 to 0.714	10 to 320	0.014 to 0.461	0.630 to 20.2	2.271 to 72.7
10" (250 mm) V-Notch weir	0.002 to 0.513	1 to 230	0.001 to 0.331	0.063 to 14.5	0.227 to 52.2
Round orifice	0.045 to 1.07	20 to 480	0.029 to 0.691	1.262 to 30.3	4.542 to 109
12" (300 mm) V-Notch weir	0.002 to 0.714	1 to 320	0 001 to 0.461	0.063 to 20.2	0.227 to 72.7
Round orifice	0.089 to 1.43	40 to 640	0.058 to 0.922	2.524 to 40.4	9.084 to 145

The attached bubble tube allows a bubbler flow meter to measure the flow through this Thel-Mar Volumetric Weir.

Thel-Mar Volumetric Weir

The Thel-Mar Volumetric Weir is a portable primary measuring device manufactured by the Thel-Mar Company (P.O. Box 1529, Brevard, North Carolina 28712-1529). It is designed to measure flows in manholes and open-ended pipes. Commonly referred to as the "Thel-Mar Weir," it is basically a compound weir, with a V-notch profile on the bottom and a rectangular profile with end contractions on the top. The V-notch section measures flow rates up to 0.0057 cfs (2.57 gpm – 0.0037 mgd – 0.162 l/s – 0.582 m^3/hr), while the rectangular section measures up to 35% of pipe capacity.

The compound weir, which is formed from a clear polycarbonate, is attached to a mounting ring by a neoprene gasket. A thumb-wheel at the top of the mounting ring is used to secure it in place, while the gasket seals the ring to the inside of the pipe.

Flow rates in gallons per day or cubic meters per hour are printed on the weir in 2 mm (0.007 foot) increments, allowing visual measurements to be taken directly. Volumetric Weirs are also available with an attached bubble tube. This allows a bubbler flow meter to be used for automatic measurement and recording.

Volumetric Weirs are available in 6, 8, 10, 12, 14, 15, and 16 inch sizes. Adaptors are available for 18, 21, 24, 27, 30, 36, 42, and 48 inch pipes, and are used in conjunction with the 15 inch weir.

Table 3-12 presents maximum capacities for various sizes of Volumetric Weirs. The depth of the liquid above the apex of the V-notch, not the bottom of the pipe, is the index of discharge.

Table 3-12:
Maximum Capacities for Thel-Mar Volumetric Weirs

Pipe diameter		Maximum head		Maximum flow rate				
inches	mm	feet	meters	CFS	GPM	MGD	l/s	m^3/hr
6	150	0.24	0.072	0.071	31.9	0.046	2.02	7.29
8	200	0.33	0.102	0.192	86.1	0.124	5.44	19.6
10	250	0.43	0.130	0.362	162	0.234	10.3	37.0
12	300	0.48	0.148	0.559	251	0.361	15.9	57.1
14	360	0.48	0.148	0.559	251	0.361	15.9	57.1
15	380	0.61	0.186	0.944	424	0.610	27.2	97.8
16	410	0.61	0.186	0.944	424	0.610	27.2	97.8

The manufacturer claims that, because the discharge calibrations were determined in a hydraulics laboratory where manhole conditions were duplicated, there are no induced errors by insufficient drop of the nappe or by contractions, velocity of approach, submergence or draw-down. Tests at the Fritz Engineering Laboratory at Lehigh University found the discharge calibrations to be within 5% of the actual flow rate.

Broad-crested weirs

If the weir notch is mounted in a wall too thick for the water to spring clear, the weir is called a broad-crested weir. The broad-crested weir can be rectangular, triangular, or trapezoidal in cross-section, and can have either a square or rounded leading edge. Broad-crested weirs have not been used as extensively as sharp-crested weirs. In practice, they are usually pre-existing structures, such as dams, levees, diversion structures, etc. Discharge coefficients and discharge tables are usually obtained by calibrating the weir in place or by model studies. Reference [8] contains discharge equations for square-edged and round-edged broad-crested weirs, along with a fairly extensive discussion of this type of weir.

A broad-crested weir is sometimes used where the sharp-crested weir causes undue maintenance problems. It has a certain structural stability which sharp-crested weirs lack and permits a higher downstream water level without submergence effects. On the other hand, it also possesses the disadvantages of the sharp-crested weirs: trapping of debris, sensitivity of discharge to edge and crest conditions, and susceptibility to leading-edge damage.

Open flow nozzles

The open flow nozzle will be discussed here, although it is actually a combination of a sharp-crested weir and a flume. Flow nozzles are designed to be attached to the end of a conduit flowing partially full and must discharge to a free fall. As with weirs, the design of a flow nozzle is such that a predetermined relationship exists between the depth of the liquid within the nozzle and the rate of flow.

Two designs of flow nozzles are shown in Figure 3-11. In one (the Kennison nozzle), the cross-section is shaped so that this relationship is linear. In the second (the parabolic nozzle), the relationship is a parabola so that each unit increase in the flow produces a smaller incremental increase in head. Open flow nozzles are factory calibrated and offer reasonable accuracy even under rather severe field conditions. Kennison nozzles are available in standard sizes from 6 to 36 inches (150 to 910 mm), with maximum capacities up to 31 cfs (14,000 gpm – 20 mgd – 880 l/s – 3200 m^3/hr). Parabolic nozzles are available in standard sizes from 6 to 24 inches (150 to 610 mm), with maximum capacities up to 16 cfs (7000 gpm – 10 mgd – 440 l/s – 1600 m^3/hr).

Dimensions and approximate capacities for a number of Kennison and parabolic nozzles are listed in Tables 3-13 and 3-14, respectively. Kennison nozzle lengths are twice the pipe diameter, while parabolic nozzle lengths are roughly four times the diameter. Flow nozzles require a length of straight pipe immediately upstream of the nozzle, and the slope of the approach pipe must not exceed certain limits or the calibration will be in error.

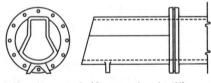

A. Kennison nozzle (Q proportional to H)

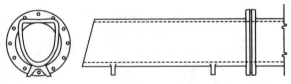

B. Parabolic nozzle (Q proportional to H^2)

Figure 3-11: Open Flow Nozzles

Table 3-13:
Dimensions and Approximate Capacities for Kennison Nozzles

Nozzle diameter		Nozzle length		Approximate maximum capacity				
inches	mm	inches	mm	CFS	GPM	MGD	l/s	m³/hr
6	150	12	300	0.45	200	0.29	13	45
8	200	16	410	0.71	320	0.45	20	73
10	250	20	510	1.2	560	0.80	35	130
12	300	24	610	1.9	850	1.2	54	190
16	410	32	810	4.2	1900	2.7	120	430
20	510	40	1020	6.9	3100	4.5	200	700
24	610	48	1220	12	5200	7.5	330	1200
30	760	60	1520	19	8500	12	540	1900
36	910	72	1830	31	14,000	20	880	3200

Table 3-14:
Dimensions and Approximate Capacities for Parabolic Nozzles

Nozzle diameter		Nozzle length		Approximate maximum capacity				
inches	mm	inches	mm	CFS	GPM	MGD	l/s	m³/hr
6	150	30	760	0.40	180	0.26	11	41
8	200	35	890	0.89	400	0.55	25	91
10	250	40	1020	1.8	800	1.2	50	180
12	300	47	1190	2.5	1100	1.5	69	250
14	360	53	1350	3.6	1600	2.5	100	360
16	410	59	1500	4.7	2100	3.0	130	480
18	460	68	1730	5.8	2600	4.0	160	590
20	510	75	1910	8.3	3700	5.3	230	840
24	610	84	2130	16	7000	10	440	1600

Unlike conventional weirs, flow nozzles can handle suspended solids rather effectively, as a self-scouring action exists, and relatively large solids will pass without clogging. Use of flow nozzles for heavy sludge is not recommended because deposits will alter the contour of the nozzle and, hence, its flow characteristics. The flow nozzle does not have the low head loss characteristics of a flume. The loss of head through the device will be at least one pipe diameter, due to the restriction in the pipe cross-sectional area presented by the nozzle.

California pipe method

The two designs of flow nozzles discussed in the previous section are characterized by a cross sectional profile shaped to give a better depth/flow rate relationship than the ordinary circular pipe cross-section. A circular pipe, however, can be used for measuring flow rate, but high accuracies are not normally achieved. Errors of ±10% or more are typical. The method, developed by Vanleer [9], is commonly referred to as the California pipe method. It is used for determining the flow rate from the open end of a partially filled horizontal pipe discharging freely into the air. The discharge pipe should be level and at least six diameters long. The pipe, which cannot be flowing full, must be located so the liquid falls freely into air. If the pipe is flowing nearly full, there should be an air vent a few diameters back from the outlet to provide for the free circulation of air in the unfilled portion of the discharge pipe. Also, liquid should not enter the discharge pipe with excessive velocity.

The California pipe method is particularly adapted to the measurement of comparatively small flows in pipes. It can also be used to measure flows in small open channels if the liquid can be diverted into a pipe which it does not completely fill and which discharges without any submergence of the outlet.

The empirically-developed rating formula for the California pipe method is as follows (refer to Figure 3-12):

$$Q = K [1 - a / d]^{1.88} d^{2.48}$$

where: Q = flow rate
           a = distance from the top of the inside surface of the pipe to the liquid surface, measured in the plane of the end of the pipe
           d = pipe diameter
           K = constant dependent upon units

For flow rate in cubic feet per second, gallons per minute, and million gallons per day, and distance a and pipe diameter d in feet, the formula is:

CFS: $Q = 8.69 [1 - a / d]^{1.88} d^{2.48}$
GPM: $Q = 3900 [1 - a / d]^{1.88} d^{2.48}$
MGD: $Q = 5.62 [1 - a / d]^{1.88} d^{2.48}$

For flow rate in liters per second and cubic meters per hour, and distance a and pipe diameter d in meters, the formula is:

l/s: $Q = 4680 [1 - a / d]^{1.88} d^{2.48}$
m^3/hr: $Q = 16900 [1 - a / d]^{1.88} d^{2.48}$

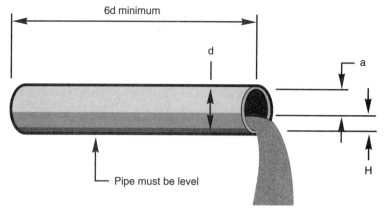

6d minimum

d

a

Pipe must be level

H

Figure 3-12: California Pipe Method

If the California pipe method is to be used with liquid depth measuring instrumentation (for example, an open channel flow meter), the formula may be rewritten as follows:

$$Q = K \left[1 - (d - H) / d \right]^{1.88} d^{2.48}$$
$$= K\, d^{0.60}\, H^{1.88}$$

where: Q = flow rate
H = depth of liquid at the pipe outlet
d = pipe diameter
K = constant dependent upon units

For flow rate in cubic feet per second, gallons per minute, and million gallons per day, and liquid depth H and pipe diameter d in feet, the formula is:

CFS: $Q = 8.69\, d^{0.60}\, H^{1.88}$
GPM: $Q = 3900\, d^{0.60}\, H^{1.88}$
MGD: $Q = 5.62\, d^{0.60}\, H^{1.88}$

For flow rate in liters per second and cubic meters per hour, and liquid depth H and pipe diameter d in meters, the formula is:

l/s: $Q = 4680\, d^{0.60}\, H^{1.88}$
m^3/hr: $Q = 16900\, d^{0.60}\, H^{1.88}$

The above formulas are based on experimental data for pipes 3 to 10 inches (75 to 250 mm) in diameter, and are accurate within these limits. The formulas have also been successfully used on pipes up to 3 feet (900 mm) in diameter.

3

CHAPTER

4   Flumes

OVERVIEW

This chapter provides detailed information concerning the use of various types of flumes.

Please note that the recommendations presented in this chapter are derived from standard references and are intended to be used only as general guidelines. The details of a particular installation may justify a deviation from these recommendations based on sound engineering judgment.

Free flow through a Parshall flume at a municipal wastewater treatment plant, as viewed from downstream.

Introduction

The second major class of commonly used primary measuring devices is the flume. A flume is a specially shaped open channel flow section that restricts the channel area and/or changes the channel slope, resulting in an increased velocity and a change in the level of the liquid flowing through the flume. Normally, a flume (Figure 4-1) consists of a converging section to restrict the flow, a throat section, and a diverging section to assure that the downstream level is less than the level in the converging section. The flume restricts the flow then expands it again in a definite fashion. The flow rate through the flume may be determined by measuring the head on the flume at a single point, usually at some distance downstream from the inlet. The head-flow rate relationship of a flume may be defined by either test data (calibration curves) or by an empirically derived formula.

In general, a flume is used to measure flow in an open channel where the use of a weir is not feasible. A flume can measure a higher flow rate than a comparably sized weir. It can also operate with a much smaller loss of head than a weir, an advantage for many existing open channel flow applications where the available head is limited. Finally, a flume is better suited to the measurement of flows containing sediment or solids because high velocity of flow through the flume tends to make it self-cleaning, reducing deposits of solids. The major disadvantage is that a flume installation is typically more expensive than a weir.

Flumes can be categorized as belonging to one of three general families, depending upon the state of flow induced — subcritical, critical, or supercritical. By definition, the **critical flow** state is that for which the Froude number (the ratio of the inertia force to the force of gravity) is unity; this is the state of flow at which the specific energy is minimum for a given discharge. If the Froude number is less than unity (inertial forces less than gravitational forces), the flow is **subcritical**. In this state, the gravitational forces are predominant, and the flow has a low velocity which is often described as tranquil and streaming. If the Froude number is greater than unity (inertial forces greater than gravitational forces), the flow is **super-critical**. In this state, the inertial forces become dominant and the flow has a high velocity which is usually described as rapid, shooting, and torrential.

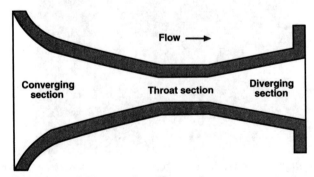

Figure 4-1: General Flume Configuration

For a given discharge through a given channel, the critical depth in the channel is the depth at which critical flow occurs and, similarly, the critical velocity in the channel is the velocity at which critical flow occurs. When the depth of flow is greater than the critical depth, the velocity of flow is less than the critical velocity for the given discharge and, hence, the flow is subcritical. When the depth of flow is less than the critical depth, the velocity of flow is greater than the critical velocity for the given discharge and, hence, the flow is supercritical.

In general, flumes that induce a critical or supercritical state of flow are most commonly used. This is because when critical or supercritical flow occurs in a channel, one head measurement can indicate the discharge rate if it is made far enough upstream so that the flow depth is not affected by the drawdown of the water surface as it achieves or passes through a critical state of flow. For channels in which critical depth is not achieved, it is necessary to measure the head in both the approach section and in the throat in order to determine the discharge rate. For critical or supercritical states of flow, a definitive head-discharge relationship can be established and measured based on a single head reading. Thus, most commonly encountered flumes are designed to pass the flow from subcritical through critical at or near the point of measurement.

In a flume designed to induce critical flow, some means is provided (for example, an increase in the channel slope) to increase the velocity of the flow to a value greater than the critical velocity for the discharge(s) of interest. An increased velocity (due to the increased slope) results in a lower depth of flow, since the same quantity of liquid is being discharged with a higher velocity, and therefore the depth must decrease if the continuity equation is to be satisfied (flow rate = velocity x area). Thus, as a given discharge in a flume passes from sub-critical to supercritical, the depth of flow decreases. Note that critical velocity and critical depth are defined for a given discharge through a particular channel. Critical depth cannot be achieved in a channel by simply decreasing the discharge; this new lower discharge would have a new critical depth, lower than the previous critical depth. Critical depth (and critical flow) can only be achieved in a previously subcritical channel through the introduction of some external means (increased slope, width reduction, etc.) which causes the flow to pass into the critical region.

Kilpatrick and Schneider [10] have identified six approaches used in various flume designs. Of these six, four achieve critical or supercritical flow, and are briefly described, following their discussion:

Type II, critical-flow large width reduction flumes are shown in Figure 4-2. Subcritical flow enters the flume, and the side contractions reduce the width to the extent that critical flow is achieved in the throat. This gives the advantage of requiring measurement at only one location, which may be either in the immediate approach to the flume or in the throat. Measurement in the approach will yield a more sensitive head-discharge relationship because changes in discharge will result in greater changes in depth in subcritical flow than would like changes in discharges in critical flow. Unfortunately, the head-discharge relationship in the approach may be unstable due to approach conditions such as scour and fill. Consequently, the head is usually measured in the throat to alleviate any influences from either upstream or downstream. Approach conditions can have some effect on flow in the throat, but it is generally insignificant. The site at which critical depth is first reached may shift further downstream into the throat as a result of excessive deposition in the approach. For this reason, and to avoid possible flow separations near the entrance, head measurements in the throat should not be too close to the entrance. Flow close to critical is very unstable, constantly attempting to become either subcritical or supercritical. Therefore, this type of flume is seldom encountered in practice.

Type IV, supercritical-flow, width-reduction, steep-slope flumes are shown in Figure 4-3. For flumes that have bed slopes of near zero, critical depth is the minimum depth possible in the flume. Further contraction, either at the side or bottom, will not produce supercritical flow. This can be accomplished only by increasing the available specific energy from the approach into the throat. For Type IV flumes, the bed is placed on a slope sufficient to cause the required increase in specific energy to produce supercritical flow in the throat. It may be thought of as a Type II tilted in the downstream direction. Only a single gauging point is required.

Type V, supercritical flow, width-reduction, drop-in-bed-elevation flumes are shown in Figure 4-4. Here the increase in specific energy required to achieve supercritical flow is provided by a sudden drop in the bed. Measurement of head is made either in the throat or the approach. A discharge rating based upon measurements in the region of supercritical flow, while not as sensitive as compared with measurements in subcritical flow, is the least influenced by disturbances either upstream or downstream, and hence is apt to be the most stable. Similarly, such flumes are the most capable of stable operation up to high submergences.

Type VI, supercritical flow, steep slope flumes are shown in Figure 4-5. Here there is no contraction, the increase in specific energy necessary for achieving supercritical flow being produced simply by the presence of sufficient downstream slope. Although a slope of one degree is usually sufficient to produce critical depth in the vicinity of the upstream edge of the flume, waves and disturbances are apt to be numerous downstream. For this reason, slopes on a flume of this type will more typically range from 2 to 5%.

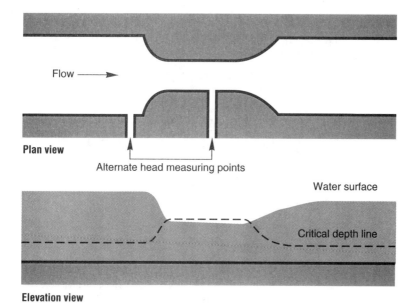

Flow ⟶

Plan view

Alternate head measuring points

Water surface

Critical depth line

Elevation view

Figure 4-2:
Type II Flume-Critical Flow Contraction Obtained by Large Width Reduction, Horizontal Bed

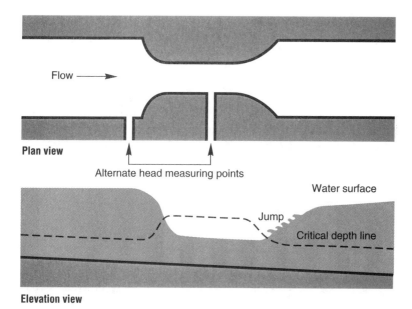

Flow ⟶

Plan view

Alternate head measuring points

Water surface

Jump

Critical depth line

Elevation view

Figure 4-3:
Type IV Flume-Supercritical Flow Contraction Obtained by Width Reduction and Sloping Bed

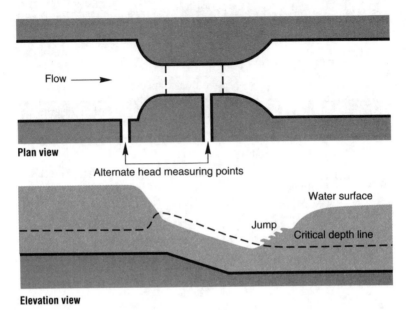

Flow ⟶

Plan view

Alternate head measuring points

Water surface

Jump

Critical depth line

Elevation view

Figure 4-4:
Type V Flume-Supercritical Flow Contraction Obtained by Width Reduction and Drop in Bed Elevation

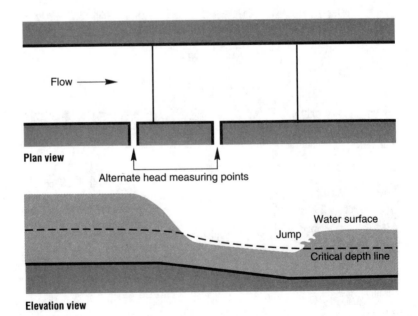

Flow ⟶

Plan view

Alternate head measuring points

Water surface

Jump

Critical depth line

Elevation view

Figure 4-5:
Type VI Flume-Supercritical Flow Contraction Obtained by Steepening Floor

The preceding paragraphs concerning general flume design were included mainly for reference. The majority of flumes currently in use belong to the critical or supercritical families, and are of one of these four designs. Most of the commonly encountered flumes are designed to pass the flow through a critical state for a specified head range, provided the flume is accurately constructed, properly installed and maintained, and operated within the specified head range.

To assure accurate discharge measurement, there are certain general requirements for the installation of flumes that apply to all types and sizes of flumes:

1. The flume must be sized according to the anticipated flow range of the channel or pipe.
2. The flume should be located in a straight section of the open channel, without bends immediately upstream.
3. The approaching flow should be well distributed across the channel, traveling with free flowing velocity, and relatively free of turbulence and waves.
4. Generally, a site with high velocity of approach should not be selected for a flume installation. However, if the water surface just upstream is smooth with no surface boils, waves, or high velocity current concentrations, accuracy may not be greatly affected by velocity of approach.
5. Consideration should be given to the height of upstream banks with regard to their ability to sustain the increased depth caused by the flume installation.
6. Although less head is lost through flumes than over weirs, it should be noted that significant losses may occur with large installations.
7. The possibility of submergence of the flume due to backwater from downstream should also be considered, although the effect of submergence upon the accuracy of most flumes is much less than is the case with weirs. Artificially high velocity (normally due to excessive approach slope or pumped flow) and submergence issues can often be corrected by various modifications. Baffles can be used to slow high flow velocity. Some flumes have methods to detect submerged flow conditions by making a comparison of depth measured at two locations in the flume.

Most flumes in common use today can be traced to one of three early design sources: rectangular English flumes based upon early work in India around 1908-1914 and the writings of F.V.A.E. Engal; the Parshall flume whose forerunner, a venturi flume developed by Cone, was extensively modified and tested by Parshall; and flumes of the type first developed by Palmer and Bowlus. The following sections will discuss in detail some of the more popular flume designs currently in use. Included are discussions of the Parshall flume, the Palmer-Bowlus flume, the Leopold-Lagco® flume, the HS, H, and HL flumes, the trapezoidal flume, the British rectangular flume, Venturi, Khafagi, and certain other types of flumes.

Parshall flumes

The Parshall flume (see Figure 4-6) was developed in the 1920s primarily to measure irrigation water flow, but it is now frequently used in industrial and municipal sewers, and in sewage treatment plants. In 1922, Dr. Ralph L. Parshall of the U.S. Soil Conservation Service made some radical changes to the existing venturi (subcritical) flume design. The essential change introduced by Parshall was a drop in the floor which produced supercritical flow through the throat of the flume (Type V). This perfected device was named the Parshall Measuring Flume by the Irrigation Committee of the American Society of Civil Engineers. The flumes are not patented and the discharge tables are not copyrighted.

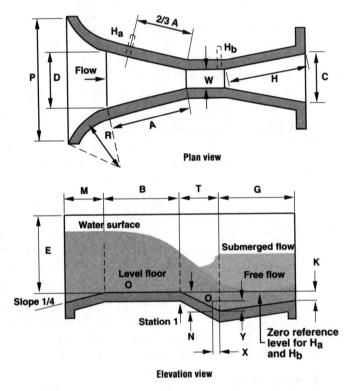

Figure 4-6: Parshall Flume

The constricted throat of the flume produces a head that is related to discharge. The level converging section followed by the downward sloping floor in the throat gives the Parshall flume its ability to withstand relatively high degrees of submergence without affecting the rate of flow. The converging upstream portion of the flume accelerates the entering flow, helping to eliminate deposits of sediment which would otherwise reduce measurement accuracy. The approaching flow should be relatively free of turbulence, eddies, and waves if accurate measurements are expected.

The principal advantages of the Parshall flume are its capabilities for self-cleaning (particularly when compared with sharp-edged weirs), its relatively low head loss, and its ability to function over a wide operating range while requiring only a single head measurement. These characteristics of the Parshall flume make it particularly suitable for flow measurement in irrigation canals, certain natural channels, and sewers.

Parshall flume sizes are designated by the throat width, W, as shown in Figure 4-6. Dimensions are available for flumes with throat widths ranging from 1 inch to 50 feet (0.0254 to 15.2 m). For convenience, Parshall flumes have been somewhat arbitrarily classified into three main groups. The groups are "very small" for 1, 2 and 3 inch (0.0254, 0.0508, and 0.0762 m) flumes, "small" for 6 inch through 8 foot (0.152 through 2.44 m) flumes, and "large" for 10 foot through 50 foot (3.05 through 15.2 m) flumes. The flumes cover a range of discharges from 0.010 to 3000 cfs (4.28 to 1,350,000 gpm – 0.006 to 1940 mgd – 0.263 to 85,000 l/s – 0.948 to 306,000 m^3/hr) and have overlapping capacities to provide wide latitude in selecting sizes.

The configuration and standard nomenclature for Parshall flumes is given in Figure 4-6. For a given throat width (W), all other dimensions are rigidly prescribed. Since the discharge tables for Parshall flumes are based upon extensive research, faithful adherence to all dimensions is necessary to achieve accurate flow measurement.

The flumes must be constructed according to the dimensions listed in Tables 4-1 and 4-2 for each flume, because the flumes are not geometrically similar. For example, it cannot be assumed that a dimension in the 12 foot (3.66 m) flume will be three times the corresponding dimension in the 4 foot (1.22 m) flume. The flumes may be built of wood, concrete, galvanized sheet metal, fiberglass, or other materials. Large flumes are usually constructed on-site, but small flumes may be obtained as prefabricated structures to be installed in one piece. Prefabricated flumes, typically constructed of fiberglass, are available from a number of manufacturers.

Table 4-1:
Parshall Flume Dimensions in Inches and Feet for Various Throat Widths, W

W	A	2/3A	B	C	D	E	T	G	H	K	M	N	P	R	X	Y
1"	1' 2-9/32"	9-17/32"	1'2"	3-21/32"	6-19/32"	6" to 9"	3"	8"	8-1/8"	3/4"		1-1/8"			5/16"	1/2"
2"	1' 4-5/16"	10-7/8"	1' 4"	5-5/16"	8-13/32"	6" to 10"	4-1/2"	10"	10-1/8"	7/8"		1-11/16"			5/8"	1"
3"	1' 6-3/8"	1' 1/4"	1' 6"	7"	10-3/16"	1' to 1' 6"	6"	1'	1' 5/32"	1"		2-1/4"			1"	1-1/2"
6"	2' 7/16"	1' 4-5/16"	2'	1' 3-1/2"	1' 3-5/8"	2'	1'	2'		3"	1'	4-1/2"	2' 11-1/2"	1' 4"	2"	3"
9"	2' 10-5/8"	1' 11-1/8"	2' 10"	1' 3"	1' 10-5/8"	2' 6"	1'	1' 6"		3"	1'	4-1/2"	3' 6-1/2"	1' 4"	2"	3"
1'	4' 6"	3'	4' 4-7/8"	2'	2' 9-1/4"	3'	2'	3'		3"	1' 3"	9"	4' 10-3/4"	1' 8"	2"	3"
1' 6"	4' 9"	3' 2"	4' 7-7/8"	2' 6"	3' 4-3/8"	3'	2'	3'		3"	1' 3"	9"	5' 6"	1' 8"	2"	3"
2'	5'	3' 4"	4' 10-7/8"	3'	3' 11-1/2"	3'	2'	3'		3"	1' 3"	9"	6' 1"	1' 8"	2"	3"
3'	5' 6"	3' 8"	5' 4-3/4"	4'	5' 1-7/8"	3'	2'	3'		3"	1' 3"	9"	7' 3-1/2"	1' 8"	2"	3"
4'	6'	4'	5' 10-5/8"	5'	6' 4-1/4"	3'	2'	3'		3"	1' 6"	9"	8' 10-3/4"	2'	2"	3"
5'	6' 6"	4' 4"	6' 4-1/2"	6'	7' 6-5/8"	3'	2'	3'		3"	1' 6"	9"	10' 1-1/4"	2'	2"	3"
6'	7'	4' 8"	6' 10-3/8"	7'	8' 9"	3'	2'	3'		3"	1' 6"	9"	11' 3-1/2"	2'	2"	3"
7'	7' 6"	5'	7' 4-1/4"	8'	9' 11-3/8"	3'	2'	3'		3"	1' 6"	9"	12' 6"	2'	2"	3"
8'	8'	5' 4"	7' 10-1/8"	9'	11' 1-3/4"	3'	2'	3'		3"	1' 6"	9"	13' 8-1/4"	2'	2"	3"
10'		6'	14'	12'	15' 7-1/4"	4'	3'	6'		6"		1' 1-1/2"			1"	9"
12'		6' 8"	16'	14' 8"	18' 4-3/4"	5'	3'	8'		6"		1' 1-1/2"			1"	9"
15'		7' 8"	25'	18' 4"	25'	6'	4'	10'		9"		1' 6"			1"	9"
20'		9' 4"	25'	24'	30'	7'	6'	12'		1'		2' 3"			1"	9"
25'		11'	25'	29' 4"	35'	7'	6'	13'		1'		2' 3"			1"	9"
30'		12' 8"	26'	34' 8"	40' 4-3/4"	7'	6'	14'		1'		2' 3"			1"	9"
40'		16'	27'	45' 4"	50' 9-1/2"	7'	6'	16'		1'		2' 3"			1"	9"
50'		19' 4"	27'	56' 8"	60' 9-1/2"	7'	6'	20'		1'		2' 3"			1"	9"

4

Table 4-2:
Parshall Flume Dimensions in Meters for Various Throat Widths, W

W (in./ft.)	W (m)	A	2/3A	B	C	D	E	T	G	H	K	M	N	P	R	X	Y
1"	0.0254	0.363	0.242	0.356	0.0929	0.167	0.152 to 0.229	0.0762	0.203	0.206	0.0191		0.0286			0.0079	0.0127
2"	0.0508	0.414	0.276	0.406	0.135	0.214	0.152 to 0.254	0.114	0.254	0.257	0.0222		0.0429			0.0159	0.0254
3"	0.0762	0.467	0.311	0.457	0.178	0.259	0.305 to 0.457	0.152	0.305	0.309	0.0254		0.0572			0.0254	0.0381
6"	0.152	0.621	0.414	0.610	0.394	0.397	0.610	0.305	0.610		0.0762	0.305	0.114	0.902	0.406	0.0508	0.0762
9"	0.229	0.879	0.587	0.864	0.505	0.575	0.762	0.305	0.762		0.0762	0.305	0.114	1.08	0.406	0.0508	0.0762
1'	0.305	1.37	0.914	1.34	0.610	0.845	0.914	0.610	0.914		0.0762	0.381	0.229	1.49	0.508	0.0508	0.0762
1'6"	0.457	1.45	0.965	1.42	0.762	1.03	0.914	0.610	0.914		0.0762	0.381	0.229	1.68	0.508	0.0508	0.0762
2'	0.610	1.52	1.02	1.50	0.914	1.21	0.914	0.610	0.914		0.0762	0.381	0.229	1.85	0.508	0.0508	0.0762
3'	0.914	1.68	1.12	1.64	1.22	1.57	0.914	0.610	0.914		0.0762	0.381	0.229	2.22	0.508	0.0508	0.0762
4'	1.22	1.83	1.22	1.79	1.52	1.94	0.914	0.610	0.914		0.0762	0.457	0.229	2.71	0.610	0.0508	0.0762
5'	1.52	1.98	1.32	1.94	1.83	2.30	0.914	0.610	0.914		0.0762	0.457	0.229	3.08	0.610	0.0508	0.0762
6'	1.83	2.13	1.42	2.09	2.13	2.67	0.914	0.610	0.914		0.0762	0.457	0.229	3.44	0.610	0.0508	0.0762
7'	2.13	2.29	1.52	2.24	2.44	3.03	0.914	0.610	0.914		0.0762	0.457	0.229	3.81	0.610	0.0508	0.0762
8'	2.44	2.44	1.63	2.39	2.74	3.40	0.914	0.610	0.914		0.0762	0.457	0.229	4.17	0.610	0.0508	0.0762
10'	3.05		1.83	4.27	3.66	4.76	1.22	0.914	1.83		0.152		0.343			0.305	0.229
12'	3.66		2.03	4.88	4.47	5.61	1.52	0.914	2.44		0.152		0.343			0.305	0.229
15'	4.57		2.34	7.62	5.59	7.62	1.83	1.22	3.05		0.229		0.457			0.305	0.229
20'	6.10		2.84	7.62	7.32	9.14	2.13	1.83	3.66		0.305		0.686			0.305	0.229
25'	7.62		3.35	7.62	8.94	10.7	2.13	1.83	3.96		0.305		0.686			0.305	0.229
30'	9.14		3.86	7.92	10.6	12.3	2.13	1.83	4.27		0.305		0.686			0.305	0.229
40'	12.2		4.88	8.23	13.8	15.5	2.13	1.83	4.88		0.305		0.686			0.305	0.229
50'	15.2		5.89	8.23	17.3	18.5	2.13	1.83	6.10		0.305		0.686			0.305	0.229

4

Discharge through a Parshall flume can occur for two conditions of flow. The first condition, free flow, occurs when there is insufficient backwater depth to reduce the discharge rate. For free flow, only the head H_a (refer to Figure 4-6) at the upstream gauge location is needed to determine the discharge from a standard table. Under free flow conditions a phenomenon known as the hydraulic jump or "standing wave" occurs downstream from the flume. Formation of this is a certain indication of free flow conditions.

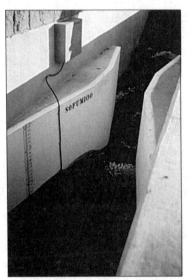 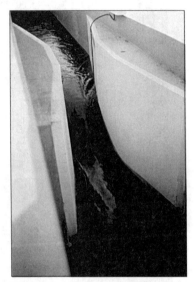

A Parshall flume viewed from upstream. The cable leads to a submerged pressure trans- ducer located across from the staff gauge.

The same Parshall flume viewed from downstream. The flume is in a free flow condi- tion, as evidenced by the hydraulic jump downstream from the flume.

The second condition of flow, submerged flow, occurs when the water surface downstream from the flume is high enough to reduce the discharge. When the dis- charge is increased above a critical value, the resistance to flow in the downstream channel becomes sufficient to reduce the velocity, increase the flow depth, and cause a backwater effect at the flume. In order to determine the discharge, sub- merged flow requires the measurement of both an upstream depth, H_a, and a depth in the throat, H_b (Figure 4-6). The ratio of the downstream depth to the upstream depth, H_b/H_a, expressed as a percentage, is referred to as the submergence ratio. Calibration tests show that the discharge of a Parshall flume is not reduced (that is, the flume is operating under free flow conditions) until the submergence ratio exceeds the following values:

50 percent for flumes 1, 2, and 3 inches (0.0254, 0.0508, and 0.0762 m) wide,

60 percent for flumes 6 and 9 inches (0.152 and 0.229 m) wide,

70 percent for flumes 1 to 8 feet (0.305 to 2.44 m) wide, and

80 percent for flumes 8 to 50 feet (2.44 to 15.2 m) wide.

When the submergence ratio exceeds the values listed above, the flume is operating under submerged conditions, and submerged discharge tables will have to be used to calculate the discharge. See references [3], [11] and [12] for a complete discussion of the calculation of discharge under submerged conditions of flow. In general, selecting and installing a Parshall flume so that conditions of free flow exist is desired since submerged conditions greatly complicate the determination of flow rate.

A backwater effect is apparent in the throat of this Parshall flume, as viewed from downstream.

When selecting and installing a Parshall flume, there are a number of factors to be considered to assure an accurate flow measurement system. The first consideration is the size of flume to be installed. Because of considerable overlap in flume discharges, it is possible to pass a given discharge through any one of several different standard size flumes. The choice of the proper size also requires consideration of other factors in addition to capacity. For example, a different throat width, W, will be required if 20 cfs (8980 gpm – 12.9 mgd – 566 l/s – 2040 m^3/hr) is to be discharged with 2.5 feet (0.76 m) of depth rather than with 1 foot (0.30 m) of depth. In the interests of economy, the smallest practical size should usually be selected.

In selecting a flume size, it is usually necessary to use a "trial-and-error" system on several sizes believed adequate. The final selection is normally made on the basis of the original channel dimensions. Thus, if a 2 foot (0.610 m) flume can accommodate the discharge without overrunning the upstream channel banks or flooding other outlets and facilities, it would be preferred over a 3 or 4 foot (0.914 or 1.22 m) flume. However, when the width of the channel is considered, it may be just as economical to use a 3 or 4 foot flume because longer and more costly wingwalls may be needed to span the channel when using the narrower flume. Reference [3] contains an excellent discussion of the flume size selection process.

When installing a Parshall flume, particularly in the very small sizes, the crest should be used as an index. Careful leveling is necessary in both longitudinal and transverse directions if standard discharge tables are to be used. The flume should be set on a solid foundation to prevent settlement or heaving. Collars should be attached to the upstream and/or downstream flanges of the flume, and should extend well out into the channel banks and invert to prevent flow from bypassing the structure and eroding the foundation.

To assure accurate discharge measurement, the approach flow conditions should be considered. The approaching flow should enter the converging section reasonably well distributed across the entrance width, and flowlines should be essentially parallel to the flume center-line. Surges and waves of any appreciable size should be eliminated. Also, the flow at the flume entrance should be free of "white" water and free from turbulence in the form of visible surface boils. Experience has shown that Parshall flumes should not be placed at right angles to flowing streams unless the flow is effectively straightened and uniformly redistributed before it enters the flume. Although Parshall flumes are usually self-cleaning, large rocks and other debris in the flow may cause problems.

Tables 4-3 and 4-4 present the minimum and maximum recommended flow rates for a number of common sizes of Parshall flumes.

The minimum and maximum recommended flow rates for free flow through Parshall flumes have been experimentally determined. The discharge (head vs. flow rate) equation of free flow through a Parshall flume takes the form:

$$Q = KH^n$$

where: Q = flow rate
             H = head measured at point H_a
             K = constant, dependent upon throat width and units
             n = constant power, dependent upon throat width

Table 4-3:
**Minimum and Maximum Recommended Flow Rates for Free
Flow through Parshall Flumes with Head in Feet**

Throat width, W in./ft.	Min. head, feet	Minimum flow rate			Max. head, feet	Maximum flow rate		
		CFS	GPM	MGD		CFS	GPM	MGD
1 in.	0.10	0.010	4.28	0.006	0.70	0.194	87.3	0.126
2 in.	0.10	0.019	8.55	0.012	0.80	0.478	215	0.309
3 in.	0.10	0.028	12.6	0.018	1.10	1.15	516	0.743
6 in.	0.10	0.054	24.3	0.035	1.50	3.91	1750	2.53
9 in.	0.10	0.091	40.7	0.059	2.00	8.87	3980	5.73
1 ft.	0.10	0.120	54.0	0.078	2.50	16.1	7240	10.4
1.5 ft.	0.10	0.174	78.0	0.112	2.50	24.6	11,000	15.9
2 ft.	0.15	0.423	190	0.273	2.50	33.1	14,900	21.4
3 ft.	0.15	0.615	276	0.398	2.50	50.4	22,600	32.6
4 ft.	0.20	1.26	567	0.816	2.50	67.9	30,500	43.9
5 ft.	0.20	1.56	698	1.01	2.50	85.6	38,400	55.4
6 ft.	0.25	2.63	1180	1.70	2.50	103	46,400	66.9
8 ft.	0.25	3.45	1550	2.23	2.50	140	62,600	90.2
10 ft.	0.30	5.74	2570	3.71	2.75	199	89,200	128
12 ft.	0.33	7.93	3560	5.13	3.50	347	156,000	224

Table 4-4:
**Minimum and Maximum Recommended Flow Rates for Free
Flow through Parshall Flumes with Head in Meters**

Throat width, W		Min. head, meters	Minimum flow rate		Max. head, meters	Maximum flow rate	
in./ft.	meters		l/s	m^3/hr		l/s	m^3/hr
1 in.	0.0254	0.03	0.263	0.948	0.20	4.98	17.9
2 in.	0.0508	0.03	0.526	1.90	0.25	14.1	50.7
3 in.	0.0762	0.03	0.778	2.80	0.35	34.8	125
6 in.	0.152	0.03	1.50	5.39	0.45	108	389
9 in.	0.229	0.03	2.50	9.01	0.60	245	882
1 ft.	0.305	0.03	3.32	12.0	0.75	446	1610
1.5 ft.	0.457	0.03	4.80	17.3	0.75	678	2440
2 ft.	0.610	0.045	11.7	42.0	0.75	915	3290
3 ft.	0.914	0.045	17.0	61.2	0.75	1390	5010
4 ft.	1.22	0.06	34.9	125	0.75	1880	6750
5 ft.	1.52	0.06	42.9	155	0.75	2360	8510
6 ft.	1.83	0.075	72.6	261	0.75	2860	10,300
8 ft.	2.44	0.075	95.2	343	0.75	3850	13,900
10 ft.	3.05	0.09	158	570	0.85	5750	20,700
12 ft.	3.66	0.10	223	801	1.05	9580	34,500

Tables 4-5 and 4-6 present the discharge equations for a number of common Parshall flumes. Complete discharge tables for a number of common Parshall flumes are found in Chapter 13 of this handbook.

Table 4-5:
Discharge Equations for Parshall Flumes with Head in Feet

Throat width, W	CFS	GPM	MGD
1 in.	$Q = 0.3380\ H^{1.550}$	$Q = 151.7\ H^{1.550}$	$Q = 0.2184\ H^{1.550}$
2 in.	$Q = 0.6760\ H^{1.550}$	$Q = 303.4\ H^{1.550}$	$Q = 0.4369\ H^{1.550}$
3 in.	$Q = 0.9920\ H^{1.547}$	$Q = 445.2\ H^{1.547}$	$Q = 0.6411\ H^{1.547}$
6 in.	$Q = 2.060\ H^{1.580}$	$Q = 924.5\ H^{1.580}$	$Q = 1.331\ H^{1.580}$
9 in.	$Q = 3.070\ H^{1.530}$	$Q = 1378\ H^{1.530}$	$Q = 1.984\ H^{1.530}$
1 ft.	$Q = 4.000\ H^{1.522}$	$Q = 1795\ H^{1.522}$	$Q = 2.585\ H^{1.522}$
1.5 ft.	$Q = 6.000\ H^{1.538}$	$Q = 2693\ H^{1.538}$	$Q = 3.878\ H^{1.538}$
2 ft.	$Q = 8.000\ H^{1.550}$	$Q = 3590\ H^{1.550}$	$Q = 5.170\ H^{1.550}$
3 ft.	$Q = 12.00\ H^{1.566}$	$Q = 5386\ H^{1.566}$	$Q = 7.756\ H^{1.566}$
4 ft.	$Q = 16.00\ H^{1.578}$	$Q = 7181\ H^{1.578}$	$Q = 10.34\ H^{1.578}$
5 ft.	$Q = 20.00\ H^{1.587}$	$Q = 8976\ H^{1.587}$	$Q = 12.93\ H^{1.587}$
6 ft.	$Q = 24.00\ H^{1.595}$	$Q = 10770\ H^{1.595}$	$Q = 15.51\ H^{1.595}$
8 ft.	$Q = 32.00\ H^{1.607}$	$Q = 14360\ H^{1.607}$	$Q = 20.68\ H^{1.607}$
10 to 50 ft.	$Q = (3.688\ W + 2.5)\ H^{1.6}$	$Q = (1655\ W + 1122)\ H^{1.6}$	$Q = (2.384\ W + 1.616)\ H^{1.6}$

Table 4-6:
Discharge Equations for Parshall Flumes with Head in Meters

Throat width, W		l/s	m³/hr
in./ft.	meters		
1 in.	0.0254	$Q = 60.36\ H^{1.550}$	$Q = 217.3\ H^{1.550}$
2 in.	0.0508	$Q = 120.7\ H^{1.550}$	$Q = 434.6\ H^{1.550}$
3 in.	0.0762	$Q = 176.5\ H^{1.547}$	$Q = 635.5\ H^{1.547}$
6 in.	0.152	$Q = 381.2\ H^{1.580}$	$Q = 1372\ H^{1.580}$
9 in.	0.229	$Q = 535.4\ H^{1.530}$	$Q = 1927\ H^{1.530}$
1 ft.	0.305	$Q = 690.9\ H^{1.522}$	$Q = 2487\ H^{1.522}$
1.5 ft.	0.457	$Q = 1056\ H^{1.538}$	$Q = 3803\ H^{1.538}$
2 ft.	0.610	$Q = 1429\ H^{1.550}$	$Q = 5143\ H^{1.550}$
3 ft.	0.914	$Q = 2184\ H^{1.566}$	$Q = 7863\ H^{1.566}$
4 ft.	1.22	$Q = 2954\ H^{1.578}$	$Q = 10630\ H^{1.578}$
5 ft.	1.52	$Q = 3732\ H^{1.587}$	$Q = 13440\ H^{1.587}$
6 ft.	1.83	$Q = 4521\ H^{1.595}$	$Q = 16280\ H^{1.595}$
8 ft.	2.44	$Q = 6115\ H^{1.607}$	$Q = 22010\ H^{1.607}$
10 to 50 ft.	3.05 to 15.2	$Q = (2293\ W + 473.8)\ H^{1.6}$	$Q = (8255\ W + 1706)\ H^{1.6}$

Some practitioners have used a simplified version of the Parshall flume, sometimes referred to as the Montana flume [3]. If a Parshall flume is never to be operated above 70 percent submergence, there is no need to construct the portion of the flume downstream from the end of the flat crest section, shown as station 1 in Figure 4-6. This configuration, with only the upstream portion of the flume present, is known as the Montana flume. The crest of a Montana flume should be set above the channel bottom. This will assure that the flow profile over the crest section is not modified by backwater from the downstream channel. As long as the 70 percent submergence limit is not exceeded, the standard discharge equations for Parshall flumes may be applied to similarly sized Montana flumes.

4

Palmer-Bowlus flumes

The Palmer-Bowlus flume was developed in the mid-1930s by Harold V. Palmer and Fred D. Bowlus [13] of the Los Angeles County Sanitation District as a simple and effective wastewater flow measuring device. Palmer-Bowlus flumes are a form of the Type IV flume, being dependent upon an existing conduit slope and channel contractions (provided by the flume) to produce supercritical flow. This type of flume arose out of a desire to have a primary measuring device that could be inserted into an existing conduit, usually round, with minimal site requirements other than suitable slope.

The Palmer-Bowlus flume is essentially a restriction in the channel designed to produce a higher velocity critical flow in the throat. The flume is most often used in manholes or open round or rectangular bottom channels to measure flow rate. It is useful in temporary installations to provide flow data for determining flume size and equipment requirements for permanent installation. Some of the flume's advantages include accuracy of measurement (comparable to Parshall flumes), low energy loss, and minimal restriction to flow. A principal advantage of the Palmer-Bowlus flume is the comparative ease with which it can be installed in existing conduits, since it does not require a drop in the conduit invert as would be required with a Parshall flume. A disadvantage of Palmer-Bowlus flumes is that they have a smaller useful range of flow rates than a Parshall flume, with a range that seldom exceeds twenty to one. Also, the resolution of the Palmer-Bowlus flume is not as good as that of the Parshall flume. For a given change in flow rate, the Parshall flume produces a greater change in head than does the Palmer-Bowlus flume. Thus, more sensitive head measuring instrumentation may be required with the Palmer-Bowlus flume.

The Palmer-Bowlus flume is a type of Venturi flume characterized by a throat of uniform cross section and a length approximately equal to one diameter of the pipe or conduit in which it is to be installed. A number of different cross-sectional shapes have been proposed, tested, and/or used over the years. Typical shapes of Palmer-Bowlus flumes for installation in round and rectangular conduits are shown in Figure 4-7.

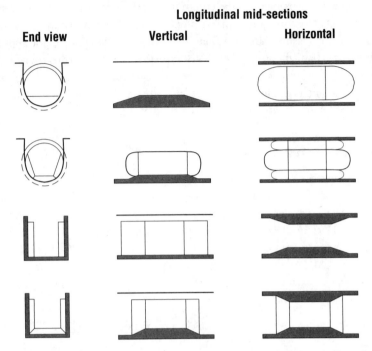

Figure 4-7: Various Cross-sectional Shapes of Palmer-Bowlus Flumes

It is important to note that the term "Palmer-Bowlus flume" technically refers only to the general class of flumes which have a form as discussed previously. Unlike the Parshall flume, the dimensional configuration of a Palmer-Bowlus flume is not rigidly established for each flume size. Much latitude is possible in both the design and construction of Palmer-Bowlus flumes. As shown in Figure 4-7, the cross-sectional configuration of a Palmer-Bowlus flume may assume any of several different shapes: rectangular, trapezoidal (with various slopes and base widths and heights), with or without the bottom slab, etc. Thus, without further qualification, the term "Palmer-Bowlus flume" is not fully definitive of flume configuration and dimensions.

However, there appears to have been a standardization among many commercial manufacturers and users of "Palmer-Bowlus flumes" upon a flume with a trapezoidal throat having the configuration shown in Figure 4-8. This trapezoidal section with a flat bottom is considered to be the preferred design for circular conduits and pipes since this shape has the least constriction through the critical flow area and provides for minimum head loss through the conduit. Most flumes currently being marketed with the description "Palmer-Bowlus flume" are this particular trapezoidal configuration with other dimensions as shown in Figure 4-8. Note that all dimensions are proportional to the conduit diameter, D.

Following what appears to be common practice, the term "Palmer-Bowlus flume" will, in the remainder of this chapter, refer to a flume with the configuration shown in Figure 4-8, and the discussion will be limited to flumes of this type. However, it is advisable to remember that the term "Palmer-Bowlus flume" is not definitive, and may be applied to flumes with any number of different throat cross-sectional configurations.

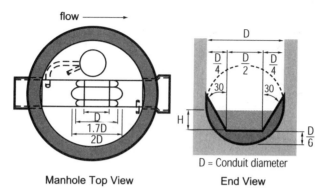

Figure 4-8: Dimensional Configuration of Standardized Palmer-Bowlus Flume-Trapezoidal Throat Cross-section

Palmer-Bowlus flume sizes are designated by the size of the pipe or conduit into which they fit, not by the throat width as is the case with Parshall flumes. Thus, an 8 inch (0.203 m) Palmer-Bowlus flume is designed to be inserted into an 8 inch diameter pipe. Standard Palmer-Bowlus flumes are available from the various manufacturers to fit pipe sizes ranging from 4 inches to 42 inches (0.102 to 1.07 m). Larger sizes are available by special order. The standard sizes appear to be 4, 6, 8, 10, 12, 15, 18, 21, 24, 27, 30, 36, and 42 inches (0.102, 0.152, 0.203, 0.254, 0.305, 0.381, 0.457, 0.533, 0.610, 0.686, 0.762, 0.914, and 1.07 m)

Palmer-Bowlus flumes are usually purchased prefabricated from one of the many flume manufacturers. They are normally made of fiberglass, a reinforced plastic, or stainless steel. Palmer-Bowlus flumes are available in a number of installation configurations, as shown in Figure 4-9. The permanent type flume is intended to be embedded in poured concrete for new construction, and has the same inside radius as the pipe to which it is joined. The permanent type flume is usually available with or without an integral approach section. The approach section is sometimes necessary to assure a smooth approach to reduce the turbulence present in a poorly defined channel. The invert or insert type flume is used for temporary measurements or for permanent installation in an existing pipe. The flume is inserted and seated into the existing half-section of pipe with the outside radius of the flume being the same as the inside radius of the pipe. A final type is the cutback or exit type flume. This special version of the Palmer-Bowlus flume is intended for temporary or permanent installation in the downstream exit pipe of a manhole, allowing space for upstream monitoring and sampling installations.

Permanent Type

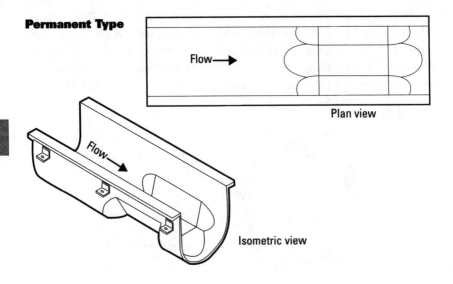

Plan view

Flow →

Isometric view

Invert or Insert Type

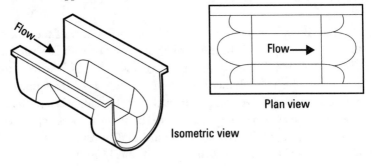

Flow →

Plan view

Isometric view

Cutback or Exit Type

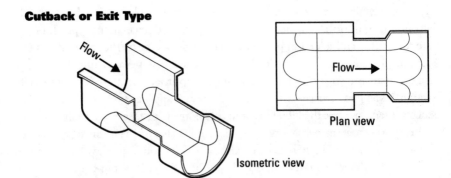

Flow →

Plan view

Isometric view

Figure 4-9: Installation Configurations of Palmer-Bowlus Flumes

When choosing the size of Palmer-Bowlus flume to be installed at a particular location, both the diameter of the conduit or pipe in which the flume is to be installed and the range of expected flow rates should be considered. The expedient sizing technique for flumes (such as Palmer-Bowlus flumes) designed to be inserted into the invert of a pipe is to select a flume whose outside diameter matches the existing diameter of the pipe in which flow is to be measured. However, as with any flume, to achieve maximum accuracy, the size of the flume should be determined by the expected rate of flow rather than strictly by the pipe diameter.

Many large sewer lines have very low flows and therefore require only small size Palmer-Bowlus flumes. In this case, a flume designed for use in a smaller diameter pipe may be used, and the flow channel gently tapered to provide a gradual transition into bulkheads which can be installed to match the smaller flume to the larger pipe inside diameter; typically, flumes with bulkheads are fabricated with an integral approach section (two to four pipe diameters long) to smooth the flow before it reaches the flume section.

The user should be cautioned that there appears to be no research to detail the effects of a tapered transition from a larger diameter pipe to a smaller flume or the use of bulkheads to adapt a smaller flume to a larger pipe. Some users have suggested that the use of either of these techniques can lead to some loss in measurement accuracy, particularly at higher flows. Sometimes, a slightly larger than required flume which will provide adequate accuracy without the difficulty of necking down the pipe or installing bulkheads and with the capacity to accommodate possible future increases in flow rates can be economically justified for use.

The depth of the liquid above the throat of the flume (not the bottom of the pipe or conduit) is the index of discharge. As shown in Figure 4-10, the ideal location for the level measuring point is at a distance one-half D (pipe diameter or channel width) upstream from the entrance of the flume. However, this location is not critical, as long as the point of level measurement is located above the upper transition section (Figure 4-10) in a zone where the depth of flow does not change significantly within a range of one pipe diameter.

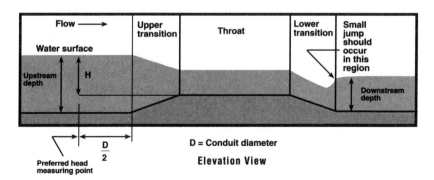

Figure 4-10: Free Flowing Palmer-Bowlus Flume

Tabular data or rating curves are provided by the various manufacturers of Palmer-Bowlus flumes which relate the depth or head of liquid above the flume throat to a corresponding flow rate. Because of the great latitude possible in Palmer-Bowlus flume design mentioned previously, it is important to assure that the rating curve being used is the correct one for the flume in question. The rating curves supplied by two different manufacturers of the same size Palmer-Bowlus flume may have some differences. Therefore, the rating curve used should be the one provided by the manufacturer with the flume.

When installing a Palmer-Bowlus flume it is important to consider the conduit or channel slope. A minimum channel slope (which applies only to the downstream section) is necessary to maintain critical flow through the throat of the flume and prevent the flume from becoming submerged. It has been determined that the required critical flow will occur if the downstream depth of flow is not greater than 85% of the upstream depth (Figure 4-10), that is, if the submergence ratio is less than 85%. This is considered to be the upper limit of submergence allowable for proper flume operation. In new installations, effective operation can be assured by building in a slight drop on the downstream end of the installation. A small jump or rise in the water surface just below the throat of the flume is evidence that the required critical flow is occurring through the flume, as shown in Figure 4-10.

There is also a maximum allowable upstream slope, which is necessary to assure that the upstream flow is subcritical (lower in velocity than the throat of the flume) and is not turbulent. Otherwise, the flow at the point of measurement would be too choppy and rough to make meaningful head determinations. Also, the flow through the flume and at the measuring point above the throat must be straight and parallel. In order to obtain proper head readings, corrective measures must be taken to quiet any turbulence so that the upstream flow is tranquil and the flow is uniformly parallel through the flume. The upper limit of channel conduit slope necessary to maintain subcritical flow in the upstream section is normally on the order of a 2% slope for smaller flume sizes and a lesser slope for larger flume sizes.

When installing a Palmer-Bowlus flume, the downstream outlet pipe slope should be greater than or equal to the upstream pipe slope. The flume itself should be level, although a small slope will not significantly affect the accuracy of the flume. The downstream outlet pipe should be free of obstructions which would contribute to submergence. Upstream turbulence or obstructions to the flow should be avoided. There should be no bends, drop manholes, flow junctions, etc., within 25 pipe diameters (D) upstream of the flume location.

Wells and Gotaas [14] conducted detailed studies on Palmer-Bowlus type flumes. Based on these studies, they summarized the characteristics of a freely discharging (nonsubmerged), properly functioning Palmer-Bowlus flume as follows:

1. Upstream channel: The flow in the upstream channel is smooth and tranquil. There should be no aeration or prominent surface waves, especially at the point of upstream depth measurement.
2. At the flume: The water enters and passes through the flume smoothly and with little turbulence. The surface profile should drop throughout the length of the flume. Streamlines are evident in the flow even after the point of critical depth has been reached.

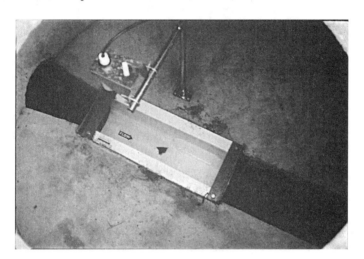

An ultrasonic sensor installed above a Palmer-Bowlus flume in a manhole.

3. Downstream channel: A shooting flow is evident on the downstream side of the flume, indicating that the free discharge necessary for proper functioning of the flume prevails. In no case should the flow merely "neck down," i.e., show a smooth surface depression at the flume. In some instances, a hydraulic jump may form immediately downstream from the flume. Operation will be satisfactory if the upstream edge of the jump remains below the throat of the flume.

Chapter 14 of this handbook presents discharge tables for a number of Palmer-Bowlus flumes manufactured by Plasti-Fab, Inc. (P.O. Box 100, Tualatin, Oregon 97062). Plasti-Fab is a leading manufacturer of corrosion resistant products for the water and wastewater industry, and manufactures a variety of flumes. The discharge tables cover Plasti-Fab Palmer-Bowlus flumes ranging in size from 4 inches to 30 inches (0.102 to 0.762 m). These flumes are of the configuration shown in Figure 4-8. Do not apply these discharge tables to flumes of other manufacture, since discrepancies may exist.

Tables 4-7 and 4-8 present recommended minimum and maximum flow rates through a number of Plasti-Fab Palmer-Bowlus flumes with normal tailwater conditions, based on Plasti-Fab's recommendations.

4

Table 4-7:
Minimum and Maximum Recommended Flow Rates for Free Flow through Plasti-Fab Palmer-Bowlus Flumes with Head in Feet

Flume size, inches	Maximum upstream slope, percent	Min. head, feet	Minimum flow rate			Max. head, feet	Maximum flow rate		
			CFS	GPM	MGD		CFS	GPM	MGD
4	2.2	0.06	0.009	3.87	0.006	0.25	0.121	54.4	0.078
6	2.2	0.07	0.016	7.02	0.010	0.35	0.295	132	0.191
8	2.0	0.09	0.031	13.7	0.020	0.50	0.690	310	0.446
10	1.8	0.11	0.052	23.3	0.034	0.60	1.12	502	0.723
12	1.6	0.12	0.069	31.2	0.045	0.70	1.68	752	1.08
15	1.5	0.14	0.109	48.8	0.070	0.90	3.09	1380	1.99
18	1.4	0.16	0.156	69.9	0.101	1.05	4.61	2070	2.98
21	1.4	0.18	0.222	99.8	0.144	1.25	7.04	3160	4.55
24	1.3	0.20	0.294	132	0.190	1.40	9.47	4250	6.12
27	1.3	0.22	0.377	169	0.244	1.60	13.1	5870	8.46
30	1.3	0.24	0.482	216	0.311	1.75	16.5	7410	10.7

Table 4-8:
Minimum and Maximum Recommended Flow Rates for Free Flow through Plasti-Fab Palmer-Bowlus Flumes with Head in Meters

Flume size		Maximum upstream slope, percent	Min. head, meters	Minimum flow rate		Max. head, meters	Maximum flow rate	
inches	meters			l/s	m³/hr		l/s	m³/hr
4	0.102	2.2	0.020	0.285	1.03	0.075	3.34	12.0
6	0.152	2.2	0.020	0.398	1.43	0.105	8.11	29.2
8	0.203	2.0	0.025	0.742	2.67	0.150	19.0	68.3
10	0.254	1.8	0.035	1.58	5.70	0.180	30.8	111
12	0.305	1.6	0.035	1.83	6.58	0.215	48.1	173
15	0.381	1.5	0.045	3.36	12.1	0.275	87.7	316
18	0.457	1.4	0.050	4.60	16.6	0.320	131	470
21	0.533	1.4	0.055	6.32	22.7	0.380	198	714
24	0.610	1.3	0.060	8.10	29.1	0.425	266	957
27	0.686	1.3	0.065	10.2	36.5	0.490	374	1350
30	0.762	1.3	0.075	14.2	51.3	0.535	470	1690

Leopold-Lagco flumes

The Leopold-Lagco flume (Figure 4-11), originally designed and once manufactured by the F. B. Leopold Company, is actually a "Palmer-Bowlus" type flume with a rectangular cross-section throat, designed to be installed in circular channels. The manufacturer claimed that the flume was "…designed to produce metering heads within 2% of theoretical rating curve for particular physical conditions of installation."

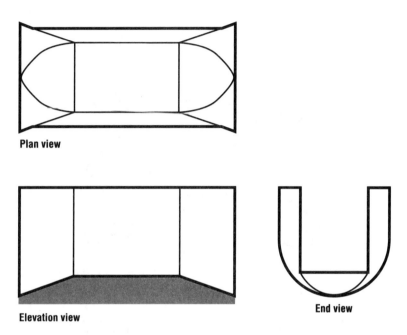

Plan view

Elevation view

End view

Figure 4-11: Leopold-Lagco Flume

The characteristics and installation of the Leopold-Lagco flume are generally similar to those of the trapezoidal-throated conventional Palmer-Bowlus flume. Leopold-Lagco flume sizes were designated by the size of the pipe into which they fit, not by the throat width as is the case with Parshall flumes. Thus, a 12 inch (0.305 m) Leopold-Lagco flume was designed to be inserted into a 12 inch diameter pipe. Leopold-Lagco flumes, when they were manufactured by the F. B. Leopold Company, fit pipe sizes ranging from 4 inches to 72 inches (0.102 to 1.83 m).

Leopold-Lagco flumes were made from Leo-Lite resin reinforced with fiberglass mat. As with Palmer-Bowlus flumes, they were available in three installation configurations. The fixed type was intended for new construction, and had the same inside radius as the pipe to which it was to be joined. The insert type was used for temporary installations or for permanent installation in an existing pipe, and had an outside radius corresponding to the inside radius of the pipe into which it was to be installed. The cutback type was intended for temporary or permanent installation in the downstream exit pipe of a manhole.

When choosing the size of Leopold-Lagco flume to be installed at a particular location, both the diameter of the conduit or pipe in which the flume was to be installed and the range of expected flow rates needed to be considered. For maximum accuracy, the size of the flume was determined by the expected volume of flow, rather than strictly by the pipe diameter.

The manufacturer stated that a Leopold-Lagco flume would give accurate flow measurements on minimum grades or on grades up to 2 percent. They also stated that the flume would result in no more loss in head than a straight pipe of the same size and length.

A Leopold-Lagco flume measures the effluent from a land treatment facility. An ultrasonic sensor measures the depth upstream from the flume.

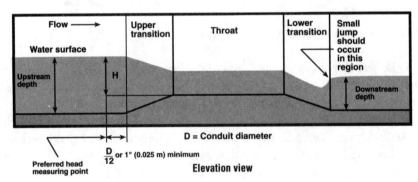

Figure 4-12: Leopold-Lagco Flume Preferred Head Measuring Point

The depth of the liquid above the throat of the flume (not the bottom of the pipe) is the index of discharge. As shown in Figure 4-12, the ideal location for the level measuring point is at a distance $^1/_{12}$ D (pipe diameter), or 1 inch (0.025 m) minimum, upstream from the converging section of the flume.

The manufacturer did not specify minimum recommended flow rates for Leopold-Lagco flumes. However, there are recommendations for maximum flow rates for free flow, as shown in Table 4-9, for a number of common sizes of Leopold-Lagco flumes.

Table 4-9:
Maximum Recommended Flow Rates for Leopold-Lagco Flumes

Flume size		Maximum head		Maximum flow rate				
inches	meters	feet	meters	CFS	GPM	MGD	l/s	m³/hr
4	0.102	0.24	0.075	0.093	41.7	0.060	2.73	9.84
6	0.152	0.35	0.105	0.245	110	0.158	6.77	24.4
8	0.203	0.45	0.135	0.476	213	0.307	13.1	47.3
10	0.254	0.60	0.185	0.918	412	0.593	26.5	95.3
12	0.305	0.70	0.215	1.39	622	0.896	39.7	143
15	0.381	0.90	0.275	2.53	1140	1.64	71.9	259
18	0.457	1.05	0.320	3.82	1710	2.47	108	389
21	0.533	1.25	0.380	5.79	2600	3.75	163	588
24	0.610	1.40	0.425	7.84	3520	5.07	221	794
30	0.762	1.75	0.535	13.7	6150	8.86	390	1400
36	0.914	2.10	0.640	21.6	9700	14.0	612	2200
42	1.07	2.45	0.745	31.8	14,300	20.5	896	3230
48	1.22	2.80	0.855	44.4	19,900	28.7	1260	4540
54	1.37	3.15	0.960	59.5	26,700	38.5	1690	6070
60	1.52	3.50	1.065	77.5	34,800	50.1	2190	7880
66	1.68	3.90	1.190	100	45,000	64.9	2850	10,200
72	1.83	4.10	1.250	118	52,800	76.1	3340	12,000

At one time, the F. B. Leopold Company published copyrighted curves and tabular data detailing the discharge (head vs. flow rate) relationship of Leopold-Lagco flumes. However, it has been determined that the discharge relationship of Leopold-Lagco flumes may also be represented by an equation. The discharge equation for free flow through a Leopold-Lagco flume takes the form:

$$Q = K D^{0.953} H^{1.547}$$

where: Q = flow rate
             H = head
             D = pipe diameter
             K = constant dependent upon units

For flow rate in cubic feet per second, gallons per minute, and million gallons per day, and head and pipe diameter in feet, the discharge equations for a Leopold-Lagco flume are as follows:

    CFS: $Q = 2.407 D^{0.953} H^{1.547}$
    GPM: $Q = 1080 D^{0.953} H^{1.547}$
    MGD: $Q = 1.556 D^{0.953} H^{1.547}$

For flow rate in liters per second and cubic meters per hour, and head and pipe diameter in meters, the discharge equations are:

$$\text{l/s:} \quad Q = 1329 \, D^{0.953} \, H^{1.547}$$
$$\text{m}^3/\text{hr:} \quad Q = 4784 \, D^{0.953} \, H^{1.547}$$

Tables 4-10 and 4-11 present the discharge equations for a number of common Leopold-Lagco flumes. Complete discharge tables for Leopold-Lagco flumes are found in Chapter 15 of this handbook.

Table 4-10:
Discharge Equations for Leopold-Lagco Flumes with Head in Feet

Flume size, inches	CFS	GPM	MGD
4	$0.8448 \, H^{1.547}$	$379.1 \, H^{1.547}$	$0.5462 \, H^{1.547}$
6	$1.243 \, H^{1.547}$	$557.9 \, H^{1.547}$	$0.8038 \, H^{1.547}$
8	$1.636 \, H^{1.547}$	$733.9 \, H^{1.547}$	$1.057 \, H^{1.547}$
10	$2.023 \, H^{1.547}$	$907.7 \, H^{1.547}$	$1.308 \, H^{1.547}$
12	$2.407 \, H^{1.547}$	$1080 \, H^{1.547}$	$1.556 \, H^{1.547}$
15	$2.977 \, H^{1.547}$	$1336 \, H^{1.547}$	$1.925 \, H^{1.547}$
18	$3.542 \, H^{1.547}$	$1589 \, H^{1.547}$	$2.290 \, H^{1.547}$
21	$4.103 \, H^{1.547}$	$1841 \, H^{1.547}$	$2.652 \, H^{1.547}$
24	$4.660 \, H^{1.547}$	$2091 \, H^{1.547}$	$3.012 \, H^{1.547}$
30	$5.764 \, H^{1.547}$	$2586 \, H^{1.547}$	$3.726 \, H^{1.547}$

Table 4-11:
Discharge Equations for Leopold-Lagco Flumes with Head in Meters

Flume size inches	meters	l/s	m³/hr
4	0.102	$150.3 \, H^{1.547}$	$541.2 \, H^{1.547}$
6	0.152	$221.3 \, H^{1.547}$	$796.5 \, H^{1.547}$
8	0.203	$291.1 \, H^{1.547}$	$1048 \, H^{1.547}$
10	0.254	$360.0 \, H^{1.547}$	$1296 \, H^{1.547}$
12	0.305	$428.3 \, H^{1.547}$	$1542 \, H^{1.547}$
15	0.381	$529.8 \, H^{1.547}$	$1907 \, H^{1.547}$
18	0.457	$630.4 \, H^{1.547}$	$2269 \, H^{1.547}$
21	0.533	$730.1 \, H^{1.547}$	$2628 \, H^{1.547}$
24	0.610	$829.2 \, H^{1.547}$	$2985 \, H^{1.547}$
30	0.762	$1026 \, H^{1.547}$	$3692 \, H^{1.547}$

HS, H, and HL flumes

The HS, H and HL flumes were developed in the mid 1930s by the U.S. Department of Agriculture (USDA) Soil Conservation Service to measure runoff from small agricultural watersheds and experimental plots. They have served this purpose adequately. Because of their proven performance, H-type flumes are now used to measure runoff from feedlots, runoff from infiltration areas for wastewater disposal, low flows of streams in pollution abatement work, and flow in sewage systems. The H-type flumes are capable of monitoring flow over a wide range with reasonably good accuracy, and have the advantage of simple construction. The wide span makes this primary device particularly suitable for measuring drainage water and for portable applications where a wide range of flow rates may be encountered. Other applications may be at installations having normal high flows and very low flows during off hours.

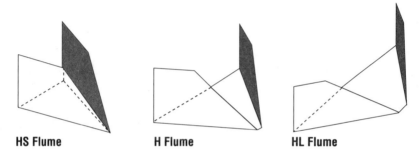

HS Flume   H Flume   HL Flume

Figure 4-13: HS, H, and HL Flumes

The H-type flumes, shown in Figure 4-13, differ from the flumes discussed above because they are more weir than flume. They are more properly termed open channel flow nozzles, but are included here because of historical precedent. Their design attempts to combine the sensitivity and accuracy of the sharp-crested weir with the self-cleaning features of a flume. The result is a compromise in both. The flat, unobstructed bottom allows the passage of silt better than a weir. Like the weir, flow control is achieved by discharging through a sharp-edged opening. However, the flow is contracted gently from the sides only, much like the converging section of ordinary flumes. The plane of the exit tilts backward toward the incoming flow.

The forms of the H-type flumes were dictated by the desire for a simple geometric shape and by the character of the flows from small agricultural watersheds and plots. Because these flows often carry vegetal debris and sediment, the sidewalls of the flumes were made to converge gradually to the control opening, reducing the possibility of debris being caught on the flume and providing an increased velocity through the flume to reduce sediment. Also, these flumes must measure the full range of a flow event, so there was a need to provide both sensitivity for low-flow measurement and maximum capacity, with minimum head loss for the design flow because the available head is usually limited. To meet the requirements for sensitivity and capacity, the tops of the converging vertical sidewalls slope upward from the lip of the outlet. This forms a trapezoidal opening, narrow at the bottom and wide at the top, which acts as the flow-control section. The size of the flow-control opening is a function of the convergence angle and the sidewall top slope. Varying these parameters also varies the sensitivity and maximum capacity of the flume.

HS, H, and HL flumes are designated according to the maximum depth attainable in the flume, which is also the depth of the flume at the entrance. Thus, a 1.0 foot (0.305 m) H flume has a maximum head of 1.0 foot. Dimensional proportions of the H-type flumes are shown in Figures 4-14, 4-15, and 4-16. Note that the dimensions of each type flume are proportional to the maximum depth, D. The HS flumes were designed to measure relatively small flows, with maximum flow rates ranging from 0.085 to 0.821 cfs (38.1 to 368 gpm – 0.055 to 0.531 mgd – 2.32 to 22.4 l/s – 8.36 to 80.8 m³/hr). The H flumes were designed to measure medium flows, with maximum flow rates ranging from 0.347 to 84.5 cfs (156 to 37,900 gpm – 0.224 to 54.6 mgd – 9.47 to 2380 l/s – 34.1 to 8580 m³/hr). The HL flumes were designed to measure larger flows, with maximum flow rates ranging from 20.7 to 117 cfs (9290 to 52,600 gpm – 13.4 to 75.7 mgd – 586 to 3290 l/s – 2110 to 11,800 m³/hr). However, of the HL flumes, only the 4.0 foot (1.22 m) size is recommended because smaller flows are measured more accurately with an H flume. The head measurement section for each of the flumes is shown in Figures 4-14, 4-15, and 4-16.

Depth D	
feet	meters
0.4	0.122
0.6	0.183
0.8	0.244
1.0	0.305

4

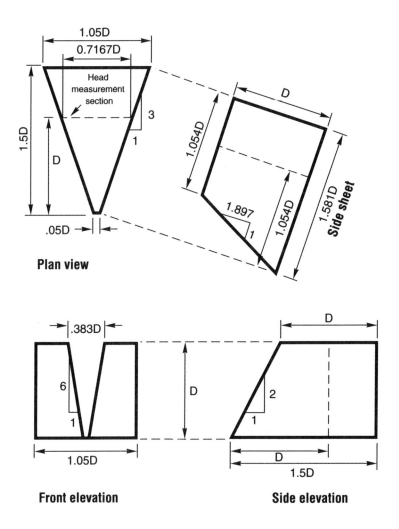

Plan view

Front elevation

Side elevation

Figure 4-14: HS Flume Dimensions

Depth D	
feet	meters
0.5	0.152
0.75	0.229
1.0	0.305
1.5	0.457
2.0	0.610
2.5	0.762
3.0	0.914
4.5	1.37

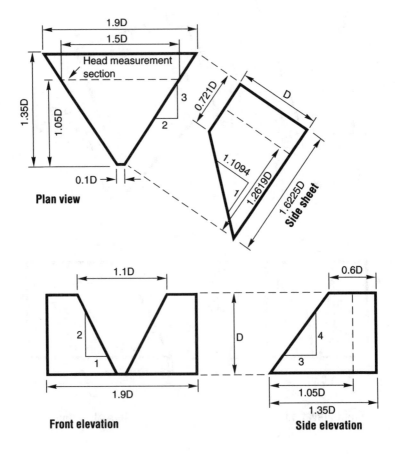

Figure 4-15: H Flume Dimensions

Depth D	
feet	meters
2.0	0.610
2.5	0.762
3.0	0.914
3.5	1.07
4.0	1.22

4

Note: Only the 4.0 foot (1.22 m) HL flume is recommended because smaller flows are measured more accurately with an H Flume.

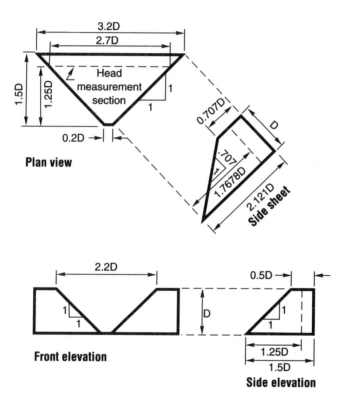

Figure 4-16: HL Flume Dimensions

Figure 4-17: Discharge from H-type Flumes

When installing an H-type flume, the preferred configuration of the approach channel is rectangular, having the same depth and width as the flume and a length 3 to 5 times the depth of the flume. An H-type flume is generally installed with a free spill off the downstream end, as shown in Figure 4-17. Although H-type flumes were not originally intended to be used with a pipe at either the inlet or outlet end, they can often be installed quite satisfactorily in this manner. An H-type flume may be used in conjunction with an outlet pipe, as long as the water is permitted to flow or spill away from the flume in such a way that it does not slow down the flow through the flume notch. The water must spill from the flume or flow unimpeded in a manner comparable to spilling off the end.

An H-type flume must be installed so it is level, with the bottom of the flume at the same elevation as the inlet channel. The velocity of the water entering the flume must be subcritical and not turbulent.

Generally, H-type flumes should be installed so there is free discharge, that is, the flume is not operating in a submerged condition. This may require enlargement and/or regrading of the outfall channel. Submergence of an H-type flume is defined as the ratio, expressed as a percentage, of the downstream water depth to the depth in the head measuring section. Tests have shown that submergence of 30 percent has less than a 1 percent effect on the calibration, and a 50 percent submergence has less than a 3 percent effect.

Since H-type flumes, especially the HS flumes, are designed to measure very small flows relatively accurately, it is necessary to construct the flume according to the dimensions shown in Figures 4-14, 4-15, and 4-16. It is especially important that the slanted opening be bounded by straight edges, have precisely the dimensions shown on the drawings, and that the opening lies in a plane with an inclination of the exact angle shown.

Discharge (head vs. flow rate) equations for free flow through H-type flumes have been developed by Gwinn and Parson. However, these equations are quite complex and are not listed here. For further information, the reader is directed to reference [15].

Tables 4-12 and 4-13 present the minimum and maximum recommended flow rates for free flow through the various sizes of H-type flumes. Complete discharge tables for H-type flumes are found in Chapter 16. These tables are from reference [16] and are derived from tests made by the Soil Conservation Service at the Hydraulic Laboratory of the National Bureau of Standards using H-type flumes with a 1-on-8 sloping false floor. The purpose of the sloping floor in the H-type flume is to concentrate low flows along the sidewall having the stilling well intake. Low flows can scour the sediment from the small channel formed along this wall, thereby permitting water to enter and leave the stilling well. This helps to assure reliable head readings despite heavy sediment loads and the attendant sediment deposition in the flume. The discharges found in Chapter 16 can be used with both flat and sloping floor flumes, since the difference in calibration of a flume with a flat floor and that with a sloping false floor is less than 1 percent. Thus, these tables are commonly applied to both types of H-type flumes.

An H flume with an integral approach channel.

Table 4-12:
MinImum and Maximum Recommended Flow Rates for Free Flow through H-type Flumes with Head in Feet

Type	Flume size, feet	Min. head, feet	Minimum flow rate			Max. head, feet	Maximum flow rate		
			CFS	GPM	MGD		CFS	GPM	MGD
HS	0.4	0.02	0.0002	0.072	0.0001	0.4	0.085	38.1	0.055
HS	0.6	0.02	0.0002	0.103	0.0001	0.6	0.229	103	0.148
HS	0.8	0.02	0.0003	0.135	0.0002	0.8	0.470	211	0.304
HS	1.0	0.02	0.0004	0.166	0.0002	1.0	0.821	368	0.531
H	0.5	0.02	0.0004	0.180	0.0003	0.5	0.347	156	0.224
H	0.75	0.02	0.0006	0.269	0.0004	0.75	0.957	430	0.619
H	1.0	0.02	0.0007	0.314	0.0005	1.0	1.97	884	1.27
H	1.5	0.02	0.001	0.494	0.0007	1.5	5.42	2430	3.50
H	2.0	0.02	0.001	0.628	0.0009	2.0	11.1	4980	7.17
H	2.5	0.02	0.002	0.808	0.001	2.5	19.4	8710	12.5
H	3.0	0.02	0.002	0.942	0.001	3.0	30.7	13,800	19.8
H	4.5	0.02	0.003	1.39	0.002	4.5	84.5	37,900	54.6
HL	4.0	0.02	0.005	2.24	0.003	4.0	117	52,600	75.7

Table 4-13:
Minimum and Maximum Recommended Flow Rates for Free Flow through H-type Flumes with Head in Meters

Type	Flume size		Min. head, meters	Minimum flow rate		Max. head, meters	Maximum flow rate	
	feet	meters		l/s	m^3/hr		l/s	m^3/hr
HS	0.4	0.122	0.005	0.004	0.013	0.12	2.32	8.36
HS	0.6	0.183	0.005	0.005	0.019	0.18	6.27	22.6
HS	0.8	0.244	0.005	0.007	0.025	0.24	12.8	46.2
HS	1.0	0.305	0.005	0.009	0.031	0.3	22.4	80.8
H	0.5	0.152	0.005	0.009	0.033	0.15	9.47	34.1
H	0.75	0.229	0.005	0.014	0.050	0.225	26.1	93.9
H	1.0	0.305	0.005	0.016	0.057	0.3	53.5	193
H	1.5	0.457	0.005	0.025	0.090	0.455	152	546
H	2.0	0.610	0.005	0.033	0.117	0.605	309	1110
H	2.5	0.762	0.005	0.042	0.150	0.76	545	1960
H	3.0	0.914	0.005	0.048	0.174	0.91	857	3080
H	4.5	1.37	0.005	0.072	0.257	1.37	2380	8580
HL	4.0	1.22	0.005	0.116	0.418	1.215	3290	11,800

Trapezoidal flumes

In attempt to obtain wider ranges of discharge than those available with Parshall flumes, several investigators have considered supercritical trapezoidal flumes. These generally operate as Type IV flumes, and a typical configuration is shown in Figure 4-18. The outward sloping of the flume walls provides increased sensitivity to low discharge rates for a given size and, hence, increased range.

The trapezoidal flume was developed primarily to measure flow in irrigation channels and has been used for many years by the Agricultural Research Service, U.S. Department of Agriculture. For agricultural applications it is superior to Parshall-type flumes for a number of reasons, particularly for measuring smaller flows. The trapezoidal shape conforms to the normal shape of ditches, especially those that are lined. This minimizes the amount of transition section needed as compared to that required when changing from a trapezoidal shape to a rectangular one and back to the trapezoidal. The trapezoidal shape is also desirable since the sidewalls expand as the depth increases. This means that a trapezoidal flume can convey a larger range of flow rates since an incremental increase in flow produces a relatively small increase in depth because of the trapezoidal shape. The trapezoidal flume can operate under a higher degree of submergence than the Parshall flume without the need for corrections. Also, the straight through bottom of the flume permits the flume to pass trash quite readily and reduces the problem of silt build-up upstream of the flume.

A trapezoidal flume need not include all of the elements shown in Figure 4-18. In some designs, the throat section is absent. Other designs eliminate the diverging and exit sections where channel erosion is not a problem. In yet another variation, the floor slopes slightly towards the center to form a very shallow "V". There are so many variations that no attempt will be made here to describe them all. Various trapezoidal flumes have been constructed to measure maximum flow rates ranging from 0.010 to 26,000 cfs (4.49 to 11,700,000 gpm – 0.006 to 16,800 mgd – 0.283 to 736,000 l/s – 1.02 to 2,650,000 m^3/hr).

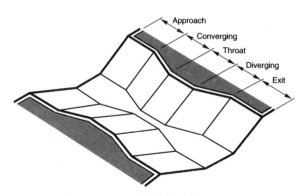

Figure 4-18: Elements of a Trapezoidal Supercritical Flow Flume

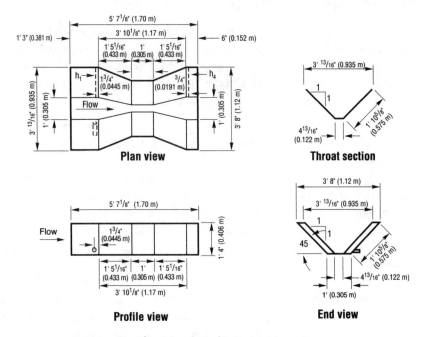

A. Flume No. 1 [for 1 foot (0.3 m) irrigation channel

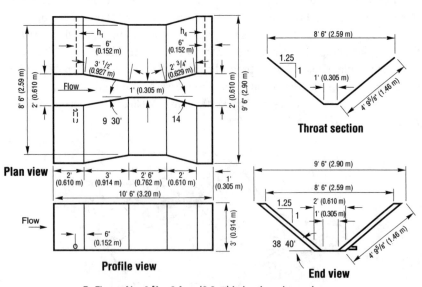

B. Flume No. 2 [for 2 foot (0.6 m) irrigation channel

Figure 4-19: Dimensions of Trapezoidal Flumes No. 1 and 2

Probably the most widely used trapezoidal flumes are those of the various configurations designed and extensively evaluated by Robinson and Chamberlain [17] and [18]. These are similar to the flume shown in Figure 4-18, and feature a flat floor throughout the flume that conforms to the general slope of the channel. Two of these flumes are shown in Figure 4-19. Flume No. 1 was designed for use in a 1 foot (0.3 m) irrigation channel and has a maximum flow rate of approximately 7 cfs (3100 gpm – 4.5 mgd – 200 l/s – 710 m^3/hr). Flume No. 2 was designed for use in a 2 foot (0.6 m) irrigation channel and has a maximum flow rate of approximately 50 cfs (22,000 gpm – 32 mgd –1400 l/s – 5100 m^3/hr).

The discharge (head vs. flow rate) equations for free flow through these two trapezoidal flumes are given by the following equations:

Flume No. 1

CFS:	$Q = 3.23\ H^{2.5} + 0.63\ H^{1.5} + 0.05$ (h$_1$ range 0.20-1.20 ft.)
GPM:	$Q = 1450\ H^{2.5} + 283\ H^{1.5} + 22.4$
MGD:	$Q = 2.09\ H^{2.5} + 0.407\ H^{1.5} + 0.032$
where:	Q = flow rate
	H = head in feet measured at h$_1$
l/s:	$Q = 1780\ H^{2.5} + 106\ H^{1.5} + 1.42$ (h$_1$ range 0.060-0.365 m)
m^3/hr:	$Q = 6410\ H^{2.5} + 382\ H^{1.5} + 5.11$
where:	Q = flow rate
	H = head in meters measured at h$_1$

Flume No. 2

CFS:	$Q = 4.27\ H^{2.5} + 1.67\ H^{1.5} + 0.19$ (h$_1$ range 0.30-2.50 ft.)
GPM:	$Q = 1920\ H^{2.5} + 749\ H^{1.5} + 85.3$
MGD:	$Q = 2.76\ H^{2.5} + 1.08\ H^{1.5} + 0.123$
where:	Q = flow rate
	H = head in feet measured at h$_1$
l/s:	$Q = 2360\ H^{2.5} + 281\ H^{1.5} + 5.38$ (h$_1$ range 0.090-0.760 m)
m^3/hr:	$Q = 8500\ H^{2.5} + 1010\ H^{1.5} + 19.4$
where:	Q = flow rate
	H = head in meters measured at h$_1$

Robinson and Chamberlain also evaluated seven other configurations of trapezoidal flumes, smaller than the two flumes discussed above. These flumes, shown in Figure 4-20, were developed primarily for agricultural and stream flow measurement use. However, the flumes are now being used in wastewater and industrial applications. Discharge curves for these flumes are shown in Figure 4-21. For further discussion, consult reference [18].

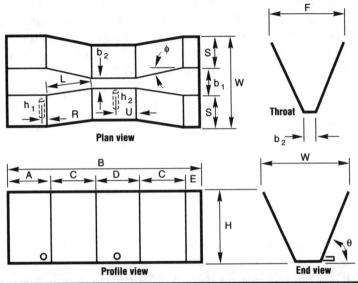

Flume No.	Description	b1	b2	A	L	C
3	Large 60° V	2" (0.051 m)	0	7" (0.178 m)	7" (0.178 m)	6$\frac{15}{16}$" (0.176 m)
4	Small 60° V	2" (0.051 m)	0	5" (0.127 m)	4$\frac{1}{8}$" (0.105 m)	4$\frac{3}{64}$" (0.103 m)
5	2" 60° WSC	4$\frac{7}{8}$" (0.124 m)	2" (0.051 m)	8" (0.203 m)	8$\frac{1}{2}$" (0.216 m)	8$\frac{13}{32}$" (0.214 m)
6	2" 45° WSC	4$\frac{7}{8}$" (0.124 m)	2" (0.051 m)	8" (0.203 m)	8$\frac{1}{2}$" (0.216 m)	8$\frac{3}{8}$" (0.213 m)
7	2" 30° WSC	4$\frac{7}{8}$" (0.124 m)	2" (0.051 m)	8" (0.203 m)	8$\frac{1}{2}$" (0.216 m)	8$\frac{3}{8}$" (0.213 m)
8	4" 60° WSC	8" (0.203 m)	4" (0.102 m)	9" (0.229 m)	10" (0.254 m)	9$\frac{13}{16}$" (0.249 m)
9	2" 30° CSU	10" (0.254 m)	2" (0.051 m)	10" (0.254 m)	10$\frac{3}{4}$" (0.273 m)	10" (0.254 m)

Flume No.	D	E	F	H	B
3	7" (0.178 m)	3" (0.076 m)	8" (0.203 m)	6$\frac{3}{4}$" (0.171 m)	30$\frac{7}{8}$" (0.784 m)
4	5" (0.127 m)	2" (0.051 m)	4$\frac{3}{4}$" (0.121 m)	4" (0.102 m)	20$\frac{3}{32}$" (0.510 m)
5	8$\frac{1}{2}$" (0.216 m)	3" (0.076 m)	14" (0.356 m)	10$\frac{3}{8}$" (0.264 m)	36$\frac{5}{16}$" (0.922 m)
6	8$\frac{1}{2}$" (0.216 m)	3" (0.076 m)	22$\frac{13}{16}$" (0.579 m)	10$\frac{19}{32}$" (0.269 m)	36$\frac{1}{4}$" (0.921 m)
7	8$\frac{1}{2}$" (0.216 m)	3" (0.076 m)	36$\frac{41}{64}$" (0.931 m)	10" (0.254 m)	36$\frac{1}{4}$" (0.921 m)
8	10" (0.254 m)	3" (0.076 m)	20" (0.508 m)	13$\frac{7}{8}$" (0.352 m)	41$\frac{5}{8}$" (1.057 m)
9	10" (0.254 m)	3" (0.076 m)	35$\frac{1}{2}$" (0.902 m)	9$\frac{21}{32}$" (0.245 m)	43" (1.092 m)

Flume No.	R	S	U	W	θ	φ
3	1$\frac{1}{2}$" (0.038 m)	4" (0.102 m)	3$\frac{1}{2}$" (0.089 m)	10" (0.254 m)	60°	8.25°
4	1" (0.025 m)	2$\frac{3}{8}$" (0.060 m)	2$\frac{1}{2}$" (0.064 m)	6$\frac{1}{4}$" (0.159 m)	60°	11.20°
5	1$\frac{1}{2}$" (0.038 m)	6" (0.152 m)	4$\frac{1}{4}$" (0.108 m)	16$\frac{7}{8}$" (0.429 m)	60°	9.22°
6	1$\frac{1}{2}$" (0.038 m)	10$\frac{19}{32}$" (0.269 m)	4$\frac{1}{4}$" (0.108 m)	26$\frac{1}{16}$" (0.662 m)	45°	9.91°
7	1$\frac{1}{2}$" (0.038 m)	17$\frac{5}{16}$" (0.440 m)	4$\frac{1}{4}$" (0.108 m)	39$\frac{33}{64}$" (1.004 m)	30°	9.80°
8	1$\frac{1}{2}$" (0.038 m)	8" (0.203 m)	5" (0.127 m)	24" (0.610 m)	60°	11.20°
9	1$\frac{1}{2}$" (0.038 m)	16$\frac{3}{4}$" (0.425 m)	5" (0.127 m)	43$\frac{1}{2}$" (1.105 m)	30°	21.80°

Figure 4-20: Dimensions of Various Other Trapezoidal Flumes

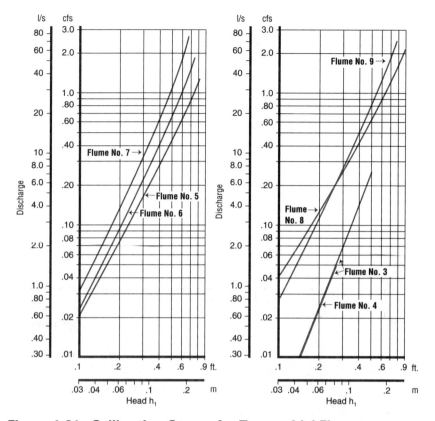

Figure 4-21: Calibration Curves for Trapezoidal Flumes

As with most flumes, it is preferred that these trapezoidal flumes be installed so the flow through them is critical, not submerged. Submergence is defined as the ratio, expressed as a percent, of the downstream depth, h_4 or h_2 (as shown in Figures 4-19 and 4-20) to the upstream depth h_1. Test results have shown that corrections for submerged flow will have to be made for submergence ratios of greater than 80 percent. When operating at free flow, there is a high velocity jet pattern as the water passes through the throat, but as the flow becomes submerged, the velocity in the throat decreases appreciably and the head increases at h_1. By reading the head at both h_1 and h_4 or h_2, the flow rate may be determined under submerged conditions by using the depth at h_1 and making corrections as shown on a submergence flow correction curve or chart. See references [17] and [18] for submerged flow corrections.

Trapezoidal flumes should generally be installed level. Occasionally flumes are installed with a slight slope, which necessitates the adjustment of the head gauges so that the zero level is at the same elevation as the flume throat. If a trapezoidal flume is installed in an earth ditch, the flume bottom should always be placed higher than the ditch bottom. If the flume is installed in a concrete ditch having a flat slope that may cause submergence, then the flume should also be raised above the bottom.

Of the nine trapezoidal flumes discussed above, three have been most widely used. These are Flume No. 1 (12-inch 45° SRCRC), Flume No. 3 (Large 60° V), and Flume No. 6 (2-inch 45° WSC). The 12-inch 45° SRCRC flume has a capacity range of 0.16 to 7.1 cfs (74 to 3200 gpm – 0.11 to 4.6 mgd – 4.5 to 200 l/s – 16 to 730 m³/hr). The Large 60° V flume has a capacity range of 0.0002 to 0.35 cfs (0.082 to 160 gpm – 0.0001 to 0.22 mgd – 0.007 to 9.7 l/s – 0.023 to 35 m³/hr). The 2-inch 45° WSC flume has a capacity range of 0.029 to 2.6 cfs (13 to 1200 gpm – 0.019 to 1.7 mgd – 0.81 to 72 l/s – 2.9 to 260 m³/hr).

Plasti-Fab has also developed an Extra Large 60° V trapezoidal flume with a capacity range of 0.0001 to 1.5 cfs (0.067 to 690 gpm – 0.0001 to 1.0 mgd – 0.005 to 44 l/s – 0.019 to 160 m³/hr).

A trapezoidal flume used to monitor the wastewater discharge from a textile mill. Note the integral bubble tube on the side of the flume opposite the staff gauge.

Complete discharge tables for these four trapezoidal flumes are found in Chapter 17 of this handbook. Tables 4-14 and 4-15 present the minimum and maximum recommended flow rates for free flow through the same four commonly used trapezoidal flumes.

Table 4-14:
Minimum and Maximum Recommended Flow Rates for Plasti-Fab Trapezoidal Flumes with Head in Feet

Flume type	Min. head, feet	Minimum flow rate			Max. head, feet	Maximum flow rate		
		CFS	GPM	MGD		CFS	GPM	MGD
Large 60° V	0.03	0.0002	0.082	0.0001	0.56	0.347	156	0.224
Extra Large 60° V	0.03	0.0001	0.067	0.0001	1.00	1.55	695	1.00
2" 45 WSC	0.10	0.029	13.2	0.019	0.89	2.59	1160	1.67
12" 45 SRCRC	0.20	0.164	73.7	0.106	1.29	7.08	3180	4.58

4

Table 4-15:
Minimum and Maximum Recommended Flow Rates for Plasti-Fab Trapezoidal Flumes with Head in Meters

Flume type	Min. head, meters	Minimum flow rate		Max. head, meters	Maximum flow rate	
		l/s	m³/hr		l/s	m³/hr
Large 60° V	0.010	0.007	0.023	0.170	9.73	35.0
Extra Large 60° V	0.010	0.005	0.019	0.305	43.9	158
2" 45° WSC	0.030	0.815	2.93	0.270	72.4	261
12" 45° SRCRC	0.060	4.55	16.4	0.395	202	729

British Rectangular, Venturi, and Khafagi flumes

The International Organization for Standardization (ISO), based in Geneva, Switzerland, promotes the development of standards in a variety of disciplines. ISO 4359 [19] covers open channel flow measurement using flumes. This standard includes specifications on the construction and installation of rectangular-throated, trapezoidal-throated, and U-throated (round-bottomed) flumes. Methods for calculating the head/flow rate relationship for these flumes are also covered.

The flumes specified in ISO 4359 are commonly used in Europe. The rectangular-throated flume with a flat bottom is by far the most prevalent. ISO 4359 was adopted by the British Standards Institution as British Standard 3680 (BS 3680). As a result, the rectangular-throated flumes are often called British rectangular flumes. They are also often referred to as Venturi flumes. A short throated version of this flume is also available and is referred to as a Khafagi flume.

The British rectangular flume, shown in Figure 4-22, is designed to be installed in an existing rectangular channel. The flume is characterized by a flat bottom with a shaped, restricted throat section. The British rectangular flume is a Type II flume, with the side contractions causing critical flow to be achieved in the throat. British rectangular flumes are easy to construct and can measure a wide range of flow rates. In addition, the flat floor allows them to easily pass debris and sediment.

British rectangular flumes are specified by the approach channel width B, throat width b, and throat length L. No standard flume sizes are specified. Rather, the dimensions of a flume for a particular location are selected based on the characteristics of the site, such as the width of the flow stream and the expected range of flow rates. However, the throat width must be at least 0.33 feet (0.1 m), but must not exceed 70% of the width of the approach channel.

The flow in the approach channel should have a symmetrical velocity distribution, which is achieved using a long straight approach channel of uniform cross-section. The approach channel upstream from the level measurement position should be of uniform cross-section for a distance of at least five times the water-surface width at maximum flow.

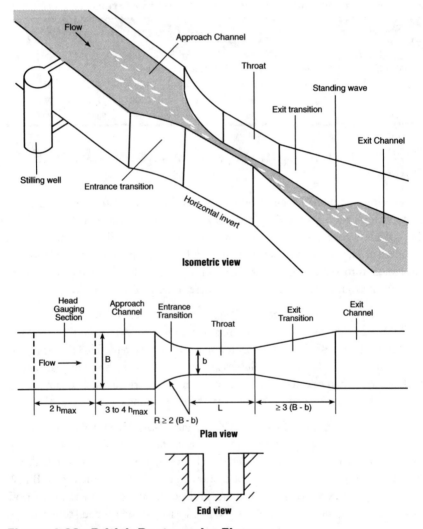

Figure 4-22: British Rectangular Flume

A British rectangular flume should be installed so that the invert of the throat is level throughout its length and width. The sides of the throat should be vertical and parallel, and square with the invert. The axis of the flume should be in line with the direction of flow in the upstream channel, and the center line of the throat should align with the center line of the approach channel. The floor of the approach channel should be level, and not higher than the invert of the throat, for a distance of at least two times the maximum head upstream from the level measurement point.

A British rectangular flume.

Conditions downstream of the flume are important in that they control the tail water level, which may influence the operation of the flume. The flume should be sized and installed so that it does not become submerged under normal operating conditions. This allows the flow rate to be determined by a single level measurement in the approach channel. Typically, free flow will occur if the downstream depth of flow is not greater than 80% of the depth in the approach channel, that is, if the submergence ratio is less than 80%.

The level measurement point on a British rectangular flume is located three to four times the maximum head upstream from the entrance transition. This ensures that the level measurement is not affected by drawdown in the flume, while minimizing energy losses between the measurement point and the throat.

The recommended minimum head is 0.16 feet (0.05 m), or 0.05 times the throat length, whichever is greater. The recommended maximum head is 6.6 feet (2 m). However, the head should not exceed one half of the throat length, or three times the throat width.

The discharge equation for free flow through a British rectangular flume takes the form:

$$Q = K\, C_V\, C_D\, b\, H^{3/2}$$

where: Q = flow rate
H = head
C_V = velocity coefficient
C_D = discharge coefficient
b = throat width
K = constant dependent upon units

The velocity coefficient C_V allows for the effect of approach velocity. With a rectangular approach channel, C_V is determined by solving the following equation:

$$^4/_{27}\, (b/B)^2\, C_V^2 - C_V^{2/3} + 1 = 0$$

Values of C_V for various ratios of b/B are shown in Table 4-16.

Table 4-16:
Values of CV for Various Values of b/B for British Rectangular Flumes with Rectangular Approach Channels

b/B	C_V	b/B	C_V
0.10	1.0022	0.44	1.0476
0.15	1.0051	0.46	1.0526
0.20	1.0091	0.48	1.0579
0.22	1.0110	0.50	1.0635
0.24	1.0132	0.52	1.0695
0.26	1.0155	0.54	1.0760
0.28	1.0181	0.56	1.0829
0.30	1.0209	0.58	1.0901
0.32	1.0240	0.60	1.0980
0.34	1.0272	0.62	1.1065
0.36	1.0308	0.64	1.1154
0.38	1.0346	0.66	1.1253
0.40	1.0386	0.68	1.1354
0.42	1.0430	0.70	1.1469

The discharge coefficient CD accounts for frictional and turbulent losses. It is usually approximated using the following equation:

$$C_D = \left[1 - \frac{0.006L}{b}\right]\left[1 - \frac{0.003L}{b}\right]^{3/2}$$

For flow rate in cubic feet per second, gallons per minute, and million gallons per day, and head in feet, the discharge equations for a British rectangular flume are as follows:

CFS: $\quad Q = 3.088\, C_V\, C_D\, b\, H^{3/2}$
GPM: $\quad Q = 1386\, C_V\, C_D\, b\, H^{3/2}$
MGD: $\quad Q = 1.996\, C_V\, C_D\, b\, H^{3/2}$
where: $\quad$ b = throat width in feet

For flow rate in liters per second, and cubic meters per hour, and head in meters, the discharge equations are:

l/s: $\quad Q = 1705\, C_V\, C_D\, b\, H^{3/2}$
m^3/hr: $\quad Q = 6138\, C_V\, C_D\, b\, H^{3/2}$
where: $\quad$ b = throat width in meters

Venturi and Khafagi flumes

There are variations of the standard British rectangular flume, such as the long throated Venturi and the short throated Khafagi. Simplified formulas for the long throated Venturi and the Khafagi flumes follow:

Venturi flume formula — long throated

$$Q = 6495 \times b \times h_a^{1.5}$$
where: $\quad Q = $ flow m^3/hr
$\quad$ b = width of the throat in the flume (m)
$\quad h_a = $ water depth at the measurement point (m)

The position to locate the level sensing device is determined by the following formula:

$$L = 3 - 4 \times h_{a\,max}$$

Venturi flume formula — Khafagi

$$Q = 6278 \times b \times h_a^{1.5} + 328 \times h_a^{2.5}$$
where: $\quad Q = $ flow m^3/hr
$\quad$ b = width of the throat in the flume (m)
$\quad h_a = $ water depth at the measurement point (m)

The position to locate the level sensing device is determined by the following formula:

$$L = 3 - 4 \times h_{a\,max}$$

Other flumes

A number of other types of flumes have been developed to meet special design criteria or to solve a specific problem. As a general rule, these flumes have not been as widely used or as extensively investigated as the flumes previously discussed. Examples include cutthroat and San Dimas flumes.

4 Cutthroat flumes

The cutthroat flume was developed at the Utah State University Water Research Laboratory in the mid-1960s. It derives its name from the absence of a parallel-wall throat section, as shown in Figure 4-23. The cutthroat flume is a flat-bottomed device whose main advantage is extreme simplicity of form and construction, since fabrication is facilitated by the flat bottom and removal of the throat section. The level flume floor also permits placing the device directly on an existing channel bed, without further excavation.

The cutthroat flume was developed for use in flat gradient channels where a flume which could operate satisfactorily under both free (critical) flow and submerged flow conditions might be desired. Under free flow conditions, the cutthroat flume operates as a Type II flume. The transition from critical (free) to subcritical (submerged) flow occurs for submergence ratios of 79 to 88%, depending upon the size of the flume. The submergence ratio is defined as the ratio of downstream depth to upstream depth (H_b/H_a, as shown in Figure 4-23), expressed as a percentage.

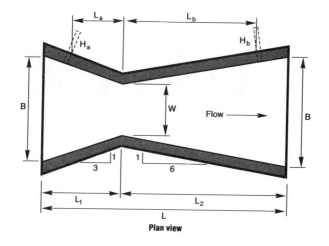

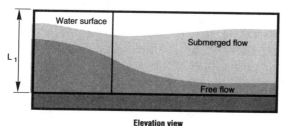

Figure 4-23: Dimensional Configuration of Rectangular Cutthroat Flume

The rectangular cutthroat flume, shown in Figure 4-23, is dimensionally defined by a characteristic length, L, and by the throat width, W. All other flume dimensions can be derived from these two dimensions, as shown. Common sizes of cutthroat flumes are listed in Tables 4-17 and 4-18. For free flow conditions, only the head H_a at the upstream gauge location is needed to determine the discharge. For submerged flow conditions, both the upstream head and the downstream head (H_b) are required to determine the discharge. For this reason, a free flow condition is normally preferred.

The discharge (head vs. flow rate) equation of free flow through a cutthroat flume takes the form:

$$Q = K\,W^{1.025}\,H^{n_1} = C\,H^{n_1}$$

where:
Q = flow rate
H = head measured at point H_a
K = free-flow coefficient
C = free-flow coefficient
W = throat width
n_1 = free-flow exponent

Table 4-17:
Coefficients and Exponents for Free Flow through Cutthroat Flumes with Head in Feet

Length L, feet	Width W, feet	n_1	CFS K	CFS C	GPM K	GPM C	MGD K	MGD C
9.00	1.000	1.560	3.500	3.500	1571	1571	2.262	2.262
9.00	2.000	1.560	3.500	7.122	1571	3197	2.262	4.603
9.00	4.000	1.560	3.500	14.49	1571	6505	2.262	9.367
9.00	6.000	1.560	3.500	21.96	1571	9857	2.262	14.19
4.50	0.250	1.720	3.980	0.9611	1786	431.3	2.572	0.6212
4.50	0.500	1.720	3.980	1.956	1786	877.8	2.572	1.264
4.50	1.000	1.720	3.980	3.980	1786	1786	2.572	2.572
4.50	2.000	1.720	3.980	8.099	1786	3635	2.572	5.234
3.00	0.167	1.840	4.500	0.7171	2020	321.9	2.908	0.4635
3.00	0.333	1.840	4.500	1.459	2020	655.0	2.908	0.9432
3.00	0.667	1.840	4.500	2.970	2020	1333	2.908	1.919
3.00	1.333	1.840	4.500	6.043	2020	2712	2.908	3.906
1.50	0.083	2.000	6.400	0.5012	2872	224.9	4.136	0.3239
1.50	0.167	2.000	6.400	1.020	2872	457.7	4.136	0.6592
1.50	0.333	2.000	6.400	2.076	2872	931.5	4.136	1.341
1.50	0.667	2.000	6.400	4.224	2872	1896	4.136	2.730

Table 4-18:
Coefficients and Exponents for Free Flow through Cutthroat Flumes with Head in Meters

Length, L feet	Length, L meters	Width, W feet	Width, W meters	n_1	l/s K	l/s C	m³/hr K	m³/hr C
9.00	2.74	1.000	0.305	1.560	2138	632.5	7695	2277
9.00	2.74	2.000	0.610	1.560	2138	1287	7695	4633
9.00	2.74	4.000	1.22	1.560	2138	2619	7695	9429
9.00	2.74	6.000	1.83	1.560	2138	3969	7695	14290
4.50	1.37	0.250	0.076	1.720	2940	210.0	10580	756.2
4.50	1.37	0.500	0.152	1.720	2940	427.4	10580	1539
4.50	1.37	1.000	0.305	1.720	2940	869.8	10580	3131
4.50	1.37	2.000	0.610	1.720	2940	1770	10580	6372
3.00	0.914	0.167	0.051	1.840	3833	180.7	13800	650.7
3.00	0.914	0.333	0.102	1.840	3833	367.8	13800	1324
3.00	0.914	0.667	0.203	1.840	3833	748.5	13800	2695
3.00	0.914	1.333	0.406	1.840	3833	1523	13800	5483
1.50	0.457	0.083	0.025	2.000	6593	152.8	23730	550.0
1.50	0.457	0.167	0.051	2.000	6593	310.9	23730	1119
1.50	0.457	0.333	0.102	2.000	6593	632.6	23730	2277
1.50	0.457	0.667	0.203	2.000	6593	1287	23730	4635

4

Tables 4-17 and 4-18 list free flow values for several families of cutthroat flumes. Since K and n_1 depend only upon flume length, interpolations can be made for coefficients of intermediate size flumes which are proportioned according to Figure 4-23. For submerged flow discharge equations, see references [20] and [21].

San Dimas flumes

The San Dimas flume was developed to measure sediment and debris-laden flows in the San Dimas Experimental Forest in 1938. It is a modified Type IV flume in that it uses lateral contraction plus a 3% slope in its floor to create a super-critical flow. In the entry, the floor rises quickly to the crest, after which it falls as indicated in Figure 4-24. Because head measurements are made in supercritical flow in the throat and critical depth occurs upstream, the discharge ratings should be independent of upstream and downstream disturbances. Variation in approach conditions also should have little effect on the ratings. Because of its rectangular cross-section, the San Dimas flume is not sensitive or accurate at low flows.

The dimensional configuration and rating curves for San Dimas flumes ranging in size from 0.5 to 10 feet (0.152 to 3.05 m) are also shown in Figure 4-24.

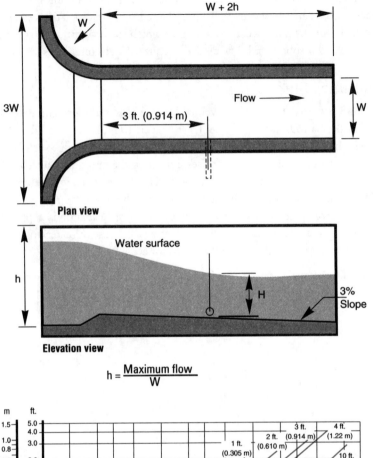

$$h = \frac{\text{Maximum flow}}{W}$$

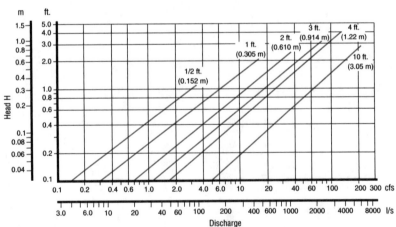

Figure 4-24: Original San Dimas Flume

CHAPTER
5

Selecting a Primary Measuring Device

OVERVIEW

This chapter provides information on methods for selecting primary measuring devices. It also provides information on the advantages and disadvantages of the various types of weirs and flumes.

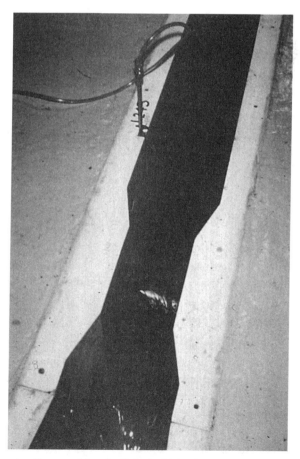

A Palmer-Bowlus flume with a built-in bubble tube.

Selecting a primary measuring device

Preliminary considerations

In the primary device selection process, some important factors for initial consideration are:

- The purpose of the flow measurement
- Required accuracy
- Range and duration of flow
- Possible existence of surcharge or reverse flow conditions
- Budgetary constraints

The purpose for the measurement is possibly the most important factor in the decision process, because it in turn presents other considerations, such as the required accuracy. For example, applications for billing purposes require more accuracy than wet- and dry-weather flow trending or flow proportional sampling.

The duration of the measurement also impacts the decision. Installing a primary device may not be practical if only a few days or weeks of measurement are required. When short term but accurate flow measurement is needed for smaller pipe diameters (6, 8, 10, or 12 inches), options such as Isco's flow metering inserts or Thel-Mar weirs should be considered.

It's important to note whether the monitoring location experiences surcharges or reverse flow conditions. For accurate flow measurement, these conditions require technology that measures the level, direction, and velocity of the flow stream. To achieve this, an area velocity flow device is the most logical and effective method.

The level of accuracy achieved with a primary device, although attractive, might be outweighed by the cost and resources needed to install and maintain a weir or flume. One comes back to determining just how much accuracy is necessary. There are some situations where area velocity or Manning flow measurement is sufficient, e.g. for achieving representative flow proportional sampling.

Final considerations

Once the above issues have been addressed, and it is determined that a primary device is indeed the preferred method of flow measurement, then the process of selecting the appropriate device can begin. First, you need to determine whether to use a weir or a flume. After deciding upon a weir or flume, the specific type of device must be selected. That is, if a weir has been chosen as the general type of device, the specific type such as V-notch, rectangular, Cipolletti, etc., must be decided upon. When the specific type of primary device has been chosen, the third and final decision involves the exact size of the primary device to be installed at the location in question. The factors involved in these three decisions are discussed at length in the following paragraphs.

The first decision involved in the final selection of a primary measuring device is whether to use a weir or a flume. Weirs and flumes each have decided advantages and disadvantages. A weir is the simplest device that can be used to measure flow in open channels. A weir is low in cost, relatively easy to install, and quite accurate when properly used. However, a weir normally operates with a rather significant loss in the head of the flow stream, and its accuracy can be affected by variations in the approach velocity of the liquid in the flow channel. A weir must also be periodically cleaned to prevent deposits of sediment or solids in the upstream side of the weir, which will adversely affect its accuracy.

A flume tends to be self-cleaning since the velocity of flow through it is high and there is no actual "dam" across the channel. It can also operate with a much smaller loss of head than a weir, which can be important for many applications where the available head is limited. A flume is also not affected nearly as much as a weir by varying approach velocities. However, a flume is much more costly than a weir, and the installation is more difficult and time consuming. Flumes are also generally less accurate than weirs.

A very important factor here is the cost involved with the installation and use of the primary device. Weirs are generally much less expensive to fabricate than flumes, due to simpler design and the type of materials required. Weirs are also generally easier and less costly to install than flumes, although the flumes designed to fit inside of a round pipe (such as a Palmer-Bowlus flume) are usually fairly simple to install. Parshall flumes are generally the most difficult and expensive to install.

It should be noted that the initial installation cost is not the only expense that should be considered when choosing a primary device. As mentioned earlier, flumes tend to be self-cleaning, whereas weirs must be periodically cleaned to prevent build-up on the weir. Lower maintenance costs associated with a flume may eventually outweigh the higher initial costs. Therefore, the maintenance and upkeep costs associated with a primary device, along with the acquisition and installation costs, should be kept in mind when choosing the type of primary device to be installed at a particular location.

Another factor to consider in the selection of a primary measuring device is the accuracy required of the flow rate measurement. It has been noted that the majority of water measurement devices can achieve accuracies of ±5% [3]. Mougenot [22] rates the basic error in the head/flow rate relationship of V-notch weirs as ±3 to 6%. It should be noted that primary measuring device head/flow rate errors of much greater magnitudes than those mentioned above can be developed from the improper installation or maintenance of a primary device. A silted weir or an inaccurately constructed flume can have significant errors as high as 10% or more. The exact degree of these errors **cannot** be determined. Primary device accuracy is based upon proper construction, installation, and site conditions!

Once the general type of primary measuring device has been selected (for example, a flume), then the specific type of device within this general type must be chosen (for example, a Parshall flume). This choice is normally based on the existing site configuration, the nature of the flow stream, and the range of expected flow rates. For example, a Palmer-Bowlus flume would normally be chosen over a Parshall flume for use in a round pipe based on its ease of installation in a pipe. Similarly, a rectangular weir would be chosen over a V-notch weir for an application where high flow rates are to be encountered because it is better suited than a V-notch weir to measure high flow rates. The choice between a rectangular weir with or without end contractions for a flow channel of a given width and flow rate range would be limited because the crest length of a rectangular weir without end contractions must correspond to the channel width. If the flow rate range of the rectangular weir without end contractions was not consistent with the range of flow rates in the channel, a rectangular weir with end contractions would be chosen.

The final decision in the selection of a primary measuring device concerns the exact size of the specific type of primary device to be installed at the location in question (for example, a contracted rectangular weir with a crest length of 2 feet (0.6 m). The basic consideration for any primary measuring device is that the minimum and maximum expected flow rates through the open channel in which the device is installed should lie within the useful range of flow rates of the primary device. All types and sizes of primary measuring devices have a minimum flow rate below which their accuracy is questionable, and a maximum flow rate above which their accuracy is again questionable or the device overflows. To select the appropriate size of primary device for a particular application, it is necessary to obtain a reasonable estimate of the minimum and maximum flow rates expected for the location. The primary measuring device chosen to be installed at this location should then have a useful flow rate range which includes the minimum and maximum expected flow rates. Also, the primary device should be sized such that an appreciable change in liquid level occurs for the transition from minimum to maximum flow; a minimum change of 0.5 foot (0.15 m) is recommended.

Chapters 3 and 4 described in detail many of the commonly used types of primary measuring devices. However, as a quick guide in selecting the type and size of primary device to be used for a particular application, Tables 5-1 through 5-5 may be used. Table 5-1 describes the application of many types of weirs. Table 5-2 similarly describes flume applications. Tables 5-3 through 5-5 show the minimum and maximum flow rates for various sizes of some of these primary devices.

Example of device selection process

As an example of the primary measuring device selection process, consider the following hypothetical flow stream: The flow channel is an existing 18 inch (0.457 m) diameter sanitary sewer line. Consequently, the flow contains a relatively high degree of suspended solids and floating materials. Based on rough measurements, the normal minimum flow rate is approximately 0.75 cfs (340 gpm – 0.48 mgd – 21 l/s – 76 m³/hr) and the normal maximum flow rate is approximately 3.0 cfs (1300 gpm – 1.9 mgd – 85 l/s – 310 m³/hr).

Referring to Tables 5-1 and 5-2, it may be seen that flumes are generally more suitable than weirs for a channel of this type which carries a high degree of solid materials, and that their relatively low head loss is an asset in a sewer line where the available head may be limited. Also, because weirs require a minimum crest elevation of 1 foot (0.3 m) from the bottom of the channel, they are generally unsuitable for smaller pipes. Referring to Table 5-2, it may be seen that of the commonly available types of flumes, the Palmer-Bowlus flume is probably most suitable for this type of application, because of its ease of installation in an existing conduit invert. This, of course, assumes that a suitable manhole can be located which has a "U" channel section in which the flume may be installed. Thus, with the aid of Tables 5-1 and 5-2, the general type of primary device was selected, the flume, and then the specific type of device within the general type was chosen, the Palmer-Bowlus flume.

The final decision in the selection process concerns the exact size of primary device to be installed. The logical size of Palmer-Bowlus flume to be installed in an 18 inch (0.457 m) sewer line is, of course, an 18 inch flume. Referring to Table 5-5, it may be seen that the minimum and maximum flow rates of the site in question fall within the useful flow rate range of an 18 inch Palmer-Bowlus flume. Thus, following the three step selection process, an 18 inch (0.457 m) Palmer-Bowlus flume was chosen to be installed in the hypothetical flow stream.

Table 5-1:
Selection of a Primary Device — Weirs

Advantages of Weirs
1. Low cost.
2. Easy to install.
3. Easy to verify.
4. Accuracy generally better than $\pm 10\%$ when properly sized and installed.

Disadvantages of Weirs
1. Fairly high head loss.
2. Must be periodically cleaned-not suitable for channels carrying excessive solids.
3. Accuracy affected by excessive approach velocities.

Type of Weir	Comments
A. V-notch (triangular) weir	An accurate device particularly suited to measuring low flows. It provides the best weir profile for discharges of less than 1 cfs (28 l/s) and may be used for flows up to 10 cfs (280 l/s). Discussed on page 27. For discharge tables see Chapter 9.
B. Rectangular (contracted) weir with end contractions	Able to measure much higher flows than the V-notch weir. Its discharge equation is more complicated than other types of weirs. Widely used for measuring high flow rates in channels suited to weirs. Discussed on page 31. For discharge tables see Chapter 10.
C. Rectangular (suppressed) weir without end contractions	Able to measure the same range of flows as the contracted rectangular weir, but is easier to construct and has a simpler discharge equation. However, the width of the weir crest must correspond to the width of the channel, so its use is restricted. It may have problems obtaining adequate aeration of nappe. Discussed on page 31. For discharge tables see Chapter 11.
D. Trapezoidal (Cipolletti) weir	Similar to the rectangular contracted weir except that its inclined ends result in a simplified discharge equation. It is less accurate than the rectangular or V-notch weir, and therefore is less often used. Discussed on page 38. For discharge tables see Chapter 12.
E. Compound weir	A combination of any two or more types or sizes of above weirs to provide wide range of flows. There is an ambiguous discharge curve in the transition zone between weirs. Discussed on page 42.

Table 5-2:
Selection of a Primary Device — Flumes

Advantages of Flumes

1. Self-cleaning to a certain degree.

2. Relatively low head loss.

3. Easy to verify.

4. Accuracy generally $\pm$ 3-5% when properly sized and installed.

5. Accuracy less affected by approach velocity than weirs.

Disadvantages of Flumes

1. High cost.

2. Difficult to install.

Type of Flume	Comments
A. Parshall flume	The most widely known and used flume for permanent installations. Available in throat widths ranging from 1 inch (0.0254 m) to 50 feet (15.2 m) to cover most flows. Involves a fairly difficult installation requiring a drop in the conduit invert. Discussed on page 60. For discharge tables see Chapter 13.
B. Palmer-Bowlus flume	A flume designed to be easily installed in an existing conduit. Good for portable or temporary installations, as no drop in the conduit invert is required. Widely used in the sanitary field for measuring flows in manholes. Discussed on page 69. For discharge tables see Chapter 14.
C. Leopold-Lagco flume	A flume designed to be easily installed in an existing conduit. Good for portable or temporary installations, as no drop in conduit invert is required. Widely used in the sanitary field for measuring flows in manholes. Discussed on page 77. For discharge tables see Chapter 15.
D. HS, H & HL flumes	Developed to measure agricultural runoff. Its principal advantage is its ability to measure a wide range of flows with reasonable accuracy. Construction is fairly simple and the flume is easily installed. Discussed on page 81. For discharge tables see Chapter 16.
E. Trapezoidal flume	Developed to measure flow in irrigation channels. Its principal advantage is its ability to measure a wide range of flows and to also maintain good accuracy at low flows. Discussed on page 89. For discharge tables see Chapter 17.
F. British Rectangular flume	Developed to be installed in an existing rectangular channel. Commonly used in Europe, and also referred to as a Venturi flume. The most prevalent type is rectangular-throated with a flat bottom. A short throated version of this flume is available and referred to as a Khafagi flume. British rectangular flumes are easy to construct, can measure a wide range of flow rates, and their flat floor lets them easily pass debris and sediment. Discussed on page 95.
G. Cutthroat flume	Similar to Parshall, except that the flat bottom does not require a drop in the conduit invert. It can function well with a high degree of submergence. Its flat bottom passes solids better than Parshall. Discussed on page 100.

Table 5-3:
Useful Flow Rate Range of Various Types of Weirs in Feet

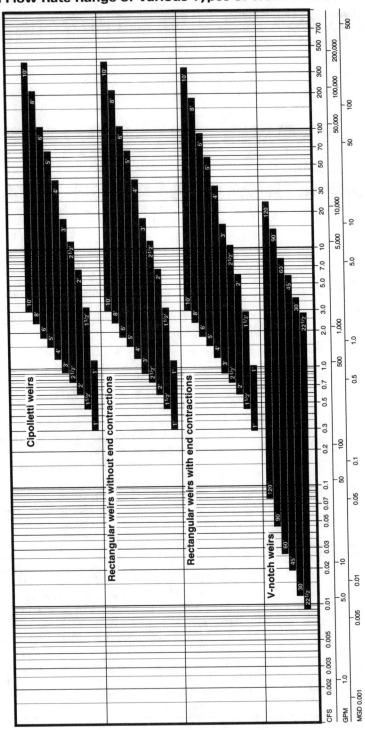

Table 5-4:
Useful Flow Rate Range of Various Types of Weirs in Meters

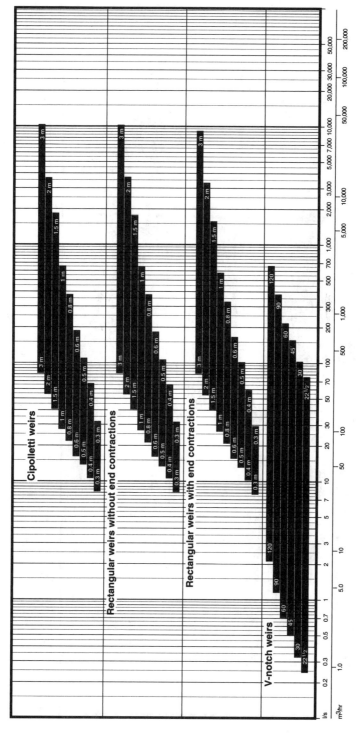

Table 5-5:
Useful Flow Rate Range of Various Types of Flumes

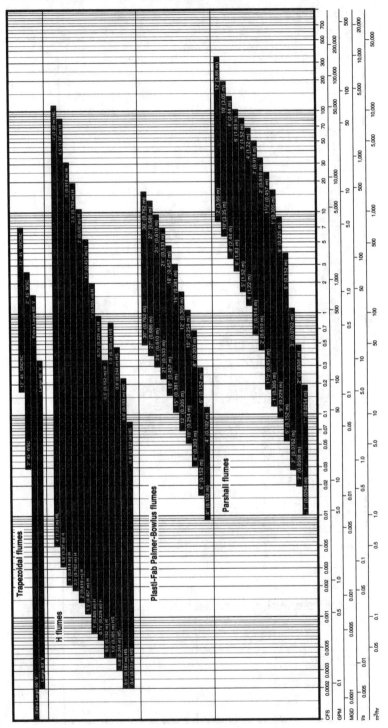

CHAPTER

6

The Manning Formula

OVERVIEW

This chapter provides information on the use of the Manning formula for measuring gravity flow in open channels. Included are sections describing the general use of the formula and its use to estimate flows in circular conduits.

The Manning formula determines flow rate based on the depth of flow, and the size, shape, slope, and roughness of the channel.

Introduction

There is a method by which, under certain circumstances, the rate of flow in an open channel can be determined without the addition of a separate primary measuring device. In this technique the flow conduit itself serves as the primary device. If the cross section of the conduit is uniform, the slope and roughness of the conduit are known, and the flow is moved by the force of gravity only (not under pressure), the rate of flow in the conduit may be calculated using the Manning formula (refer to Figure 6-1):

$$Q = \frac{K A R^{2/3} S^{1/2}}{n}$$

where: Q = flow rate
A = cross sectional area of flow
R = hydraulic radius (cross sectional area divided by the wetted perimeter)
S = slope of the hydraulic gradient
n = Manning coefficient of roughness dependent upon material of conduit
K = constant dependent upon units

For flow rate in cubic feet per second, gallons per minute, and million gallons per day, cross sectional area in square feet, and hydraulic radius in feet, the Manning formula is:

$$CFS = \frac{1.49 \, A \, R^{2/3} \, S^{1/2}}{n}$$

$$GPM = \frac{669 \, A \, R^{2/3} \, S^{1/2}}{n}$$

$$MGD = \frac{0.963 \, A \, R^{2/3} \, S^{1/2}}{n}$$

For flow rate in liters per second and cubic meters per hour, cross sectional area in square meters, and hydraulic radius in meters, the Manning formula is:

$$l/s = \frac{1.00 \, A \, R^{2/3} \, S^{1/2}}{n}$$

$$m^3/hr = \frac{3.60 \, A \, R^{2/3} \, S^{1/2}}{n}$$

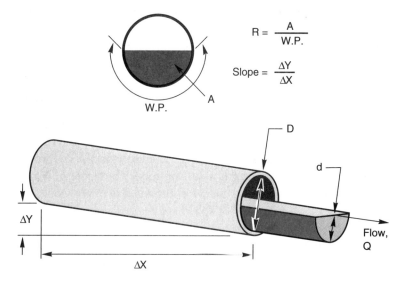

$$R = \frac{A}{W.P.}$$

$$Slope = \frac{\Delta Y}{\Delta X}$$

Figure 6-1: Gravity Flow in Open Channel (Round Pipe)

A version of this formula was presented in 1889 by the Irish engineer Robert Manning at a meeting of the Institute of Civil Engineers of Ireland [23]. The formula was later modified to the form shown above and was recommended for international use in 1936 by the Third World Power Conference. Because of its simple form and generally satisfactory results, the Manning formula became a widely used gravity flow formula for open channel flow computations. Historically, the Manning formula was used as the standard means of flow measurement in applications where it was impractical to install a hydraulic structure such as a flume or weir. Technological advances in flow measurement techniques, such as area velocity measurement, now provide more accurate methods. However, the Manning formula is still a valid comparative method of flow measurement and is very useful as such.

From the formula shown above, it can be seen that the quantities n and S are assumed to be constants for a given conduit, and that the quantities A and R are variables which can be geometrically derived from a single measurement of the depth of the liquid in the conduit. Thus, the flow rate in the conduit can also be calculated from this single depth measurement. The Manning formula can be used in two ways. First, the depth can be measured and the flow rate calculated using the Manning formula; this use is further discussed in the following section. Alternatively, a secondary measuring device can be used to measure the liquid level in the conduit, and automatically convert this level into an appropriate flow rate using the Manning formula.

For best results with the Manning formula, a straight course of channel of at least 200 feet (60 m), and preferably up to 1000 feet (300 m), in length upstream from the point of depth measurement is desired. The conduit channel should be nearly uniform in slope, cross section, and roughness, and free of rapids, abrupt falls (dips), sudden contractions or expansions and tributary inflows. There should also be no downstream backup (reverse flow) or submerged flow (restricted flow).

The normal expected accuracy from the Manning formula under such ideal conditions would be ±10 – 20%. However, in reality, there are likely to be variances in every one of the conditions listed above. Therefore, in the real world, the accuracy achieved may actually be ±25 – 30% or worse. The Manning formula will be consistent though, in free flow conditions, and will deliver very good trending information. If Manning indicates that flows have doubled, they very likely have. It is just that reported values are likely to have inherent error. The Manning variables can be fine tuned if there is another comparative measurement, such as area velocity or a hydraulic structure (weir or flume) to base such adjustments upon.

The Manning formula is often used to measure flow through round pipes in manholes. Poor results will be obtained if any of the following conditions exist in the manhole:

1. The channel in the middle of the manhole does not approximate the shape of a round pipe.
2. There is an abrupt change of the flow in the manhole, such as that caused by the inlet pipe being located at a different height than the exit pipe.
3. There are two or more streams entering the manhole.
4. The flow is not straight, but enters at a different angle than it exits.
5. There are extreme variables in conditions such as roughness or inflows.

Use of the Manning formula requires knowledge of the channel cross section and liquid depth so that the flow cross section and hydraulic radius can be calculated. Note that although the conduit configuration most often encountered is a round pipe, the conduit may be of any cross section: round, rectangular, trapezoidal, semi-circular, etc.

The Manning formula can be used to measure flow in conduits of any cross section, such as this trapezoidal channel that carries storm water runoff from a residential area.

The Manning formula also requires a knowledge of the slope of the water surface or the conduit invert (hydraulic gradient line). This slope is often difficult to measure under actual field operating conditions. In one method, the slope may be determined by dividing the difference in the water surface elevations at the two ends of the course, as determined by secondary devices carefully referenced to a common datum level, by the length of the course. The slope of the conduit invert as shown on design drawings may also be used, although this slope should be verified. The significance of errors in the determination of the water surface slope is diminished by the fact that the slope is a square root function in the formula.

The Manning formula also requires the determination of the Manning roughness coefficient, n, for the conduit in question. This coefficient is basically an index of the frictional resistance to flow offered by the conduit. In applying the Manning formula, the greatest difficulty lies in the determination of the roughness coefficient n, for there is no exact method for selecting the n value. At the present state of knowledge, the selection of a value for n is in reality an estimate of the resistance to flow in a given channel, which is actually a matter of intangibles. For veteran engineers, this means the exercise of sound engineering judgment and experience; for beginners, this can only be a guess, and different individuals will obtain different results.

Values for the Manning roughness coefficient n are usually determined from tabular data. Table 6-1 lists the coefficient n for channels of various configurations and materials. For each kind of channel the minimum, normal, and maximum values of n are shown. The normal values for artificial channels given in the table are recommended only for channels with good maintenance.

The roughness coefficient of this natural channel will vary as the vegetation in the channel grows.

There are numerous factors that affect the value of the roughness coefficient, n. Chow [24] lists ten such factors: surface roughness, vegetation, channel irregularity, channel alignment, silting and scouring, obstruction, size and shape of channel, seasonal change, suspended material and bed load, and stage (depth of flow) and discharge. The latter factor, stage and discharge, is both interesting and distressing. The Manning formula assumes that the roughness coefficient n is a constant. For most channels, however, the value of n is believed to vary with the depth of flow. Figure 6-2 illustrates the variability of the coefficient n for various flow depths in a round pipe, as described by Camp [25]. Maynes [26] has reported a similar (although differently shaped) curve from experiments performed on a 24 inch reinforced concrete sewer pipe. In practice, this means that the n coefficient selected for use in the Manning formula is actually an average value for the channel in question. The actual n value varies with the flow depth, leading to certain inaccuracies in the flow rate determination. It should also be noted that the value of n can change with time, due to erosion, settled solids, corrosion, etc. Thus, the value of the roughness coefficient selected should be periodically re-evaluated if the interior surface condition of the channel is subject to change.

Table 6-1:
Manning Roughness Coefficient "n" for Various Channel
Configurations and Conditions

Description of channel	Min.	Norm.	Max.
I. Closed conduit-partly full			
A. Metal			
1. Steel			
a. Lockbar and welded	0.010	0.012	0.014
b. Riveted and spiral	0.013	0.016	0.017
2. Cast Iron			
a. Coated	0.010	0.013	0.014
b. Uncoated	0.011	0.014	0.016
3. Wrought Iron			
a. Black	0.012	0.014	0.015
b. Galvanized	0.013	0.016	0.017
4. Corrugated			
a. Subdrain	0.017	0.019	0.021
b. Storm drain	0.021	0.024	0.030
B. Nonmetal			
1. Acrylic	0.008	0.009	0.010
2. Glass	0.009	0.010	0.013
3. Wood			
a. Stave	0.010	0.012	0.014
b. Laminated, treated	0.015	0.017	0.020
4. Clay			
a. Common drainage tile	0.011	0.013	0.017
b. Vitrified sewer	0.011	0.014	0.017
c. Vitrified sewer with manholes, inlets, etc.	0.013	0.015	0.017
5. Brick			
a. Glazed	0.011	0.013	0.015
b. Lined with cement	0.012	0.015	0.017
6. Concrete			
a. Culvert, straight and free of debris	0.010	0.011	0.013
b. Culvert with bends, connections, and some debris	0.011	0.013	0.014
c. Sewer with manholes, inlet, etc., straight	0.013	0.015	0.017
d. Unfinished, steel form	0.012	0.013	0.014
e. Unfinished, smooth wood form	0.012	0.014	0.016
f. Unfinished, rough wood form	0.015	0.017	0.020
7. Sanitary sewers coated with sewage slimes	0.012	0.013	0.016
8. Paved invert, sewer, smooth bottom	0.016	0.019	0.020
9. Rubble masonry, cemented	0.018	0.025	0.030

6

Table 6-1:
Manning Roughness Coefficient "n" for Various Channel
Configurations and Conditions (Continued)

	Description of channel	Min.	Norm.	Max.
II.	Lined or built-up channels			
A.	Metal			
1.	Smooth steel surface			
	a. Painted	0.011	0.012	0.014
	b. Unpainted	0.012	0.013	0.017
2.	Corrugated	0.021	0.025	0.030
B.	Nonmetal			
1.	Cement			
	a. Neat surface	0.010	0.011	0.013
	b. Mortar	0.011	0.013	0.015
2.	Concrete			
	a. Trowel finish	0.011	0.013	0.015
	b. Float finish	0.013	0.015	0.016
	c. Finished, with gravel on bottom	0.015	0.017	0.020
	d. Unfinished	0.014	0.017	0.020
3.	Wood			
	a. Planed, untreated	0.010	0.012	0.014
	b. Planed, creosoted	0.011	0.012	0.015
	c. Unplaned	0.011	0.013	0.015
	d. Plank with battens	0.012	0.015	0.018
4.	Brick			
	a. Glazed	0.011	0.013	0.015
	b. In cement mortar	0.012	0.015	0.018
5.	Masonry			
	a. Cemented rubble	0.017	0.025	0.030
	b. Dry rubble	0.023	0.032	0.035
6.	Asphalt			
	a. Smooth	0.013	0.013	-
	b. Rough	0.016	0.016	-
7.	Vegetal lining	0.030	-	0.500
III.	Excavated or dredged			
A.	Earth, straight and uniform	0.016	0.022	0.035
B.	Earth, winding and sluggish	0.023	0.030	0.040
C.	Rock cuts	0.030	0.040	0.050
D.	Unmaintained channels	0.040	0.070	0.140
IV.	Natural channels (Minor streams, top width at flood 100 ft.)			
A.	Fairly regular section	0.030	0.050	0.070
B.	Irregular section with pools	0.040	0.070	0.100

6

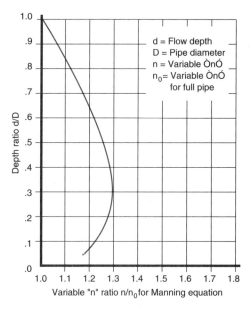

Figure 6-2: Variable "n" Coefficient Ratio for Circular Pipes

Because of the difficulties associated with determining the slope of the hydraulic gradient, and because the selection of a roughness coefficient is at best an estimate (which probably varies with the depth), the flow rate calculated using the Manning formula can only be considered an approximation, and the formula should be used only where accuracy requirements are relatively low. The Manning formula should be applied with caution and with a full knowledge of the uncertainties involved. However, within the limitations imposed by these uncertainties, the formula can produce useful flow data and, at worst, an indexing of the flow can be accomplished. In a field situation, a careful use of the Manning formula can result in the determination of a flow rate which is accurate to within 10 to 20%. Less careful use may result in errors of 20 to 50% or more.

In an attempt to improve upon these accuracies, Lanfear and Coll [27] have suggested the use of a "fitted" Manning formula. In this method, the flow rate through the channel in question is determined (by means other than the Manning formula) for a particular depth. The Manning formula is then "fitted" to this data. This is done by rearranging the Manning formula as follows:

$$Q = C A R^{2/3}$$

where:
Q = flow rate
A = cross sectional area of flow
R = hydraulic radius
$C = \dfrac{K S^{1/2}}{n}$

Thus, the Manning formula constant K (1.49 for flow rate in cubic feet per second), the slope S, and the Manning roughness coefficient n have been combined into a single, new constant C. Knowing a single flow rate Q_1 from a velocity measurement, and the area A_1 and hydraulic radius R_1 from the corresponding depth measurement, C can be calculated as follows:

$$C = \frac{Q_1}{A_1 R_1}$$

This calculated value of C would then be used in the first equation above, resulting in a Manning formula "fitted" to the particular channel. Calculating C in this manner not only avoids the problems associated with determining the Manning roughness coefficient n, but also eliminates the need for slope measurement. Furthermore, if C is measured near the flow rate of most interest (for example, late at night for infiltration, high flows for inflow, etc.), much of the error caused by a variable roughness coefficient can be eliminated. Lanfear and Coll reported very good results using this technique.

The required flow rate measurement can be accomplished by a number of methods. A fast, simple, and accurate method is to take velocity measurements with a current meter. For greatest accuracy, the velocity should be determined at several depths, averaged, and then multiplied by the cross sectional area (as calculated from a depth measurement), resulting in a flow rate. Other methods of flow measurement include dye dilution (adding a known quantity of dye to the flow stream and measuring the concentration downstream), temporary weir or flume installations, or the simple "bucket and stopwatch" approach. Each of these techniques is applicable under certain circumstances. Refer to Chapters 2 and 7 for a general discussion of the above-mentioned methods of open channel flow measurement.

The use of the Lanfear-Coll "fitted" Manning formula has been demonstrated to be a useful technique in the field application of the Manning formula. However, it does not directly address one of the major problems associated with the Manning formula, namely that of the variation of the roughness coefficient, n, with the depth of flow.

In order to compensate for a Manning roughness coefficient, n, which varies with the depth of flow, it is necessary to "calibrate" the flow stream in question. The calibration involves determining the flow rate in the stream for several different depths of flow, usually requiring measurements at several different times of day. The flow rates may be determined as described above and in Chapters 2 and 7. The result is a set of level/flow rate data points.

This empirically derived level/flow rate data for the flow stream may then be used in one of two ways. In the first method, the level/flow rate data is used to calculate a series of roughness coefficients for various zones of level or flow rate. The roughness coefficient appropriate to the level in question is then used in the

Manning formula to calculate the flow rate. Thus, the variation in the roughness coefficient with level is accounted for by using different coefficients for different depths of flow.

In the second method, if sufficient level/flow rate data points have been collected, a graphical or mathematical relationship between the level and the flow rate may be established. This level/flow rate relationship may be established by simply plotting the level/flow rate data points on graph paper, or may be established by mathematically fitting the data to an equation by a technique such as the least squares method [28]. Thus, the variation in the roughness coefficient with level (and in fact, the entire use of the Manning formula) is bypassed by directly establishing a level/flow rate relationship for the flow stream in question.

6

Use of the Manning formula to calculate flow rates in circular conduits

The Manning formula is commonly used to calculate the rate of flow in circular conduits or round sewer pipes. In such cases, the formula is often used to estimate the range of flow rates in order to properly size a primary measuring device to be subsequently installed. The following paragraphs discuss the use of the Manning formula for calculating the rate of flow in round pipes. A similar procedure can be used for a conduit of any cross section; however, because circular conduits are most commonly encountered, only they will be discussed.

Figure 6-3 is a plot of the quantity of flow in a circular pipe calculated using the Manning formula at various depths of flow. The vertical axis of Figure 6-3 represents the ratio of the depth of flow to the full diameter of the pipe, while the horizontal axis represents the ratio of the flow rate for the depth in question to the flow rate at the pipe full condition. Figure 6-3 illustrates the fact that, for a circular pipe, the greatest quantity of flow occurs when the pipe is flowing at about 94% of full depth. The reason for this phenomenon is that as the pipe approaches full flow, the additional frictional resistance caused by the crown of the pipe has a greater affect than the added cross sectional area.

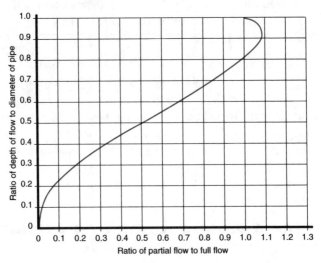

Figure 6-3: Quantity of Flow in a Circular Pipe According to the Manning Formula

To calculate the rate of flow in a circular pipe of a given diameter, the first step is to determine the best values to use for the slope of the hydraulic gradient, S, and the Manning roughness coefficient, n. This can be done (using Table 6-1) as described in the first section of this chapter. After these values have been determined, it is necessary to measure the depth of flow. This can be done with a head meter, ruler, hook gauge, or any other convenient depth measuring procedure. After the depth of flow has been determined, the area of flow, A, and the hydraulic radius, R, for the measured depth of flow need to be calculated.

Table 6-2 lists the area of flow and hydraulic radius for various flow depths. All three quantities are listed as ratios based on the diameter of the pipe in question. Thus, Table 6-2 can be used to determine the area of flow and hydraulic radius for any flow depth in any diameter pipe.

Table 6-2:
Area and Hydraulic Radius for Various Flow Depths

d / D	A / D²	R / D	d / D	A / D²	R / D	d / D	A / D²	R / D
0.01	0.0013	0.0066	0.36	0.2546	0.1978	0.71	0.5964	0.2973
0.02	0.0037	0.0132	0.37	0.2642	0.2020	0.72	0.6054	0.2984
0.03	0.0069	0.0197	0.38	0.2739	0.2061	0.73	0.6143	0.2995
0.04	0.0105	0.0262	0.39	0.2836	0.2102	0.74	0.6231	0.3006
0.05	0.0147	0.0326	0.40	0.2934	0.2142	0.75	0.6318	0.3017
0.06	0.0192	0.0389	0.41	0.3032	0.2181	0.76	0.6404	0.3025
0.07	0.0242	0.0451	0.42	0.3130	0.2220	0.77	0.6489	0.3032
0.08	0.0294	0.0513	0.43	0.3229	0.2257	0.78	0.6573	0.3037
0.09	0.0350	0.0574	0.44	0.3328	0.2294	0.79	0.6655	0.3040
0.10	0.0409	0.0635	0.45	0.3428	0.2331	0.80	0.6736	0.3042
0.11	0.0470	0.0695	0.46	0.3527	0.2366	0.81	0.6815	0.3044
0.12	0.0534	0.0754	0.47	0.3627	0.2400	0.82	0.6893	0.3043
0.13	0.0600	0.0813	0.48	0.3727	0.2434	0.83	0.6969	0.3041
0.14	0.0668	0.0871	0.49	0.3827	0.2467	0.84	0.7043	0.3038
0.15	0.0739	0.0929	0.50	0.3927	0.2500	0.85	0.7115	0.3033
0.16	0.0811	0.0986	0.51	0.4027	0.2531	0.86	0.7186	0.3026
0.17	0.0885	0.1042	0.52	0.4127	0.2561	0.87	0.7254	0.3017
0.18	0.0961	0.1097	0.53	0.4227	0.2591	0.88	0.7320	0.3008
0.19	0.1039	0.1152	0.54	0.4327	0.2620	0.89	0.7384	0.2996
0.20	0.1118	0.1206	0.55	0.4426	0.2649	0.90	0.7445	0.2980
0.21	0.1199	0.1259	0.56	0.4526	0.2676	0.91	0.7504	0.2963
0.22	0.1281	0.1312	0.57	0.4625	0.2703	0.92	0.7560	0.2944
0.23	0.1365	0.1364	0.58	0.4723	0.2728	0.93	0.7612	0.2922
0.24	0.1449	0.1416	0.59	0.4822	0.2753	0.94	0.7662	0.2896
0.25	0.1535	0.1466	0.60	0.4920	0.2776	0.95	0.7707	0.2864
0.26	0.1623	0.1516	0.61	0.5018	0.2797	0.96	0.7749	0.2830
0.27	0.1711	0.1566	0.62	0.5115	0.2818	0.97	0.7785	0.2787
0.28	0.1800	0.1614	0.63	0.5212	0.2839	0.98	0.7816	0.2735
0.29	0.1890	0.1662	0.64	0.5308	0.2860	0.99	0.7841	0.2665
0.30	0.1982	0.1709	0.65	0.5404	0.2881	1.00	0.7854	0.2500
0.31	0.2074	0.1755	0.66	0.5499	0.2899			
0.32	0.2167	0.1801	0.67	0.5594	0.2917			
0.33	0.2260	0.1848	0.68	0.5687	0.2935			
0.34	0.2355	0.1891	0.69	0.5780	0.2950			
0.35	0.2450	0.1935	0.70	0.5872	0.2962			

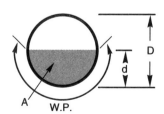

To use Table 6-2, the ratio d/D (the ratio of the actual depth of flow to the pipe diameter) must be calculated. Then, for the calculated d/D ratio, the ratio of the flow area to square of the pipe diameter (A/D^2) and the ratio of the hydraulic radius to the pipe diameter (R/D) can be found in the table. The actual values of these two quantities for the pipe diameter in question can then be calculated by multiplying the tabular values by D^2 and D, respectively. Intermediate values may be determined by interpolation.

After the values of A and R have been determined, the final step is to "plug" the values into the Manning formula and calculate the flow rate for a given depth. Note that the resulting flow rate will be in cubic feet per second if the pipe diameter is in feet, or cubic meters per second if the pipe diameter is in meters. To calculate the flow rate for another depth of flow, appropriate values of A and R will have to be determined from Table 6-2 for the new depth.

Examples:

Suppose water is flowing 1.5 feet deep in a 2 foot diameter concrete pipe. It has been determined that the Manning roughness coefficient of the pipe is 0.013 and the slope of the hydraulic gradient is 0.7 foot per 100 feet. Thus:

$$n = 0.013$$
$$S = 0.7 \text{ ft.} \div 100 \text{ ft.}$$
$$S = 0.007$$

The area of flow, A, and hydraulic radius, R, for a depth of flow of 1.5 feet can be determined using Table 6-2. The first step is to calculate the ratio d/D. In this case:

$$d/D = 1.5 \text{ ft.} \div 2 \text{ ft.}$$
$$d/D = 0.75$$

Then, from Table 6-2, the ratios A/D2 and R/D can be found for a d/D ratio of 0.75, and the actual values of A and R calculated for a 2 foot diameter pipe.

$$A/D^2 = 0.6318$$
$$A = (A/D^2) \times D^2$$
$$= 0.6318 \times (2 \text{ ft.})^2$$
$$A = 2.5272 \text{ ft.}^2$$

$$R/D = 0.3017$$
$$R = (R/D) \times D$$
$$= 0.3017 \times 2 \text{ ft.}$$
$$R/D = 0.6034 \text{ ft.}$$

Finally, substituting these values into the Manning formula, the flow rate in cubic feet per second may be calculated.

$$Q = \frac{1.49\ A\ R^{2/3}\ S^{1/2}}{n}\ \text{cfs}$$

$$= \frac{1.49 \times 2.5272\ \text{ft.}^2 \times (0.6034\ \text{ft.})^{2/3} \times (0.007)^{1/2}}{0.013}\ \text{cfs}$$

$$Q = 17.43\ \text{cfs}$$

This is the flow rate in cubic feet per second calculated using the Manning formula for the conditions stated at a depth of 1.5 feet.

Suppose the depth of flow fell to 0.5 foot. Then the flow rate would be calculated as follows:

$$d/D\ = 0.5\ \text{ft.} \div 2\ \text{ft.}$$
$$d/D\ = 0.25$$

$$A/D^2 = 0.1535$$
$$A = (A/D^2) \times D^2$$
$$= 0.1535 \times (2\ \text{ft.})^2$$
$$A = 0.6140\ \text{ft.}^2$$

$$R/D = 0.1466$$
$$R = (R/D) \times D$$
$$= 0.1466 \times 2\ \text{ft.}$$
$$R = 0.2932\ \text{ft.}$$

$$Q = \frac{1.49 \times 0.6140\ \text{ft.}^2 \times (0.2932\ \text{ft.})^{2/3} \times (0.007)^{1/2}}{0.013}\ \text{cfs}$$

$$Q = 2.60\ \text{cfs}$$

6

6

CHAPTER

7

Area Velocity

OVERVIEW

This chapter provides information on the use of the area velocity method of flow measurement. Included are sections on velocity profiling and area velocity flow meters.

Area velocity flow meters are commonly used in sewer flow monitoring and inflow and infiltration studies.

Introduction

The area velocity method consists of measuring both the cross-sectional area of the flow stream at a certain point (A), and the average velocity of the flow in that cross-section (V). The flow rate is then calculated by multiplying the area of the flow by its average velocity (Figure 7-1). This is often referred to as the continuity equation, **Q=A × V.**

In open channels, the area velocity method requires two separate measurements – one to determine the flow depth and the other to determine the average velocity. The depth measurement is used to calculate the cross-sectional area of the flow based on the size and shape of the channel. Similar to the Manning formula, the channel can be of any shape: round, U-shaped, rectangular, trapezoidal, etc. The area velocity method can also be applied to a channel of nonuniform shape, as long as the relationship between level and area can be determined.

The area velocity method has several advantages when compared to weirs and flumes, and to the Manning formula. The first advantage is that, in addition to measuring flow under free flow conditions, it can also be used to measure flow under submerged, full pipe, surcharged, and reverse flow conditions. The latter conditions can occur due to a variety of circumstances, such as undersized sewers, inflow and infiltration, and tidal effects. As discussed in Chapters 3 and 4, corrections can be made for submerged flow through many weirs and flumes with the addition of a second depth measurement. However, weirs and flumes cannot be used to measure full pipe, surcharged, and reverse flows. Because the Manning formula is based on gravity flow, it is not suitable for measuring submerged, full pipe, surcharged, or reverse flow conditions.

In addition to measuring flow under a wide range of conditions, the area velocity method does not require the installation of a weir or flume. For this reason, area velocity is often used for temporary flow monitoring applications such as inflow and infiltration studies. This also makes the method practical for measuring flows in large channels where it is not reasonable to install a weir or flume.

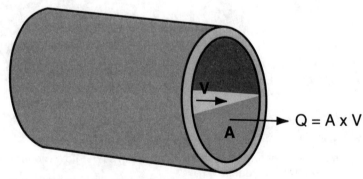

$$Q = A \times V$$

Figure 7-1: Continuity Equation

Finally, because it incorporates measurements of both liquid depth and velocity, the area velocity method provides greater accuracy than the Manning formula, which is based on a measurement of liquid depth, and a calculation of average velocity based on assumptions of the slope and roughness of the channel.

The area velocity technique can be used in two ways. First, the depth and velocity can be measured manually, and used to determine the area of the flow and the flow rate at a particular time. Alternatively, an area velocity flow meter can be used to measure the liquid level and velocity in the channel, and automatically calculate the flow rate. These two alternatives are further discussed in the following sections.

Velocity profiling

Similar to the timed gravimetric and dilution techniques discussed in Chapter 2, the area velocity method is often used to determine the flow rate in a stream at a particular time for calibration purposes. For example, the area velocity method may be used to measure the flow rate through a flume in order to verify the proper operation of the flume.

The area velocity method is also used to determine the level/flow rate relationship for a flow stream. This involves determining the flow rate when the stream is flowing at a series of different depths. This data is then programmed into a level-measuring flow meter, which measures the level and uses the level/flow rate relationship to determine the flow rate.

In such applications, manual measurements of depth and velocity are used to determine the flow rate. Measuring the depth and determining the cross-sectional area is a relatively straightforward procedure. However, because the velocity profile of a flow stream depends on many factors, a series of velocity measurements will frequently be necessary to arrive at the mean velocity across a section. This procedure is often referred to as velocity profiling. The following quotation from reference [3] is given to illustrate some of the problems with determining the mean velocity:

> The following methods are used to determine mean velocities in a vertical line with a current meter:
> 1. Two-point method
> 2. Six-tenths-depth method
> 3. Vertical velocity-curve method
> 4. Subsurface method
> 5. Integration method
> 6. Two-tenths method
> 7. Three-point method
> 8. One-point continuous method

The two-point method consists of measuring the velocity at 0.2 and then at 0.8 of the depth from the water surface, and using the average of the two measurements. The accuracy obtainable with this method is high and its use is recommended. The method should not be used where the depth is less than 2 feet.

The six-tenths-depth method consists of measuring the velocity at 0.6 of the depth from the water surface, and is generally used for shallow flows where the two-point method is not applicable. This method gives fairly satisfactory results.

The vertical velocity-curve method consists of measuring the velocities at equal vertical intervals of 0.5 foot or more and calculating their arithmetical mean, or finding the mean value from a curve obtained by plotting the measurements on cross-section paper. This method is very accurate, but is time consuming and costly.

The subsurface method involves measuring the velocity near the water surface and then multiplying it by a coefficient ranging from 0.85 to 0.95, depending on the depth of water, the velocity, and the nature of the stream or canal bed. The difficulty of determining the exact coefficient limits the usefulness and accuracy of this method.

The integration method is performed by observing the velocity along a vertical line by slowly and uniformly lowering and raising the meter throughout the range of water depth two or more times. This method is not accurate and should be used only for comparisons or quick rough checks.

The two-tenths, three-point, and one-point continuous methods are special procedures based on a relationship previously established for the section between the true discharge and the velocities observed by these methods. These methods are generally reliable for sections which undergo no serious changes because of erosion, sedimentation, or other deformation.

Reference [29] also contains an excellent discussion of velocity profiling.

Devices used to measure velocity in open channels are commonly known as current meters. There are a number of different types of current meters available. Some of the more common types of velocity measuring techniques include floats, tracers, eddy shedding vortex meters, turbine meters, rotating element meters, Doppler ultrasonic meters, and electromagnetic probe meters.

Area velocity flow meters

The area velocity method is used in several types of electronic flow meters. Area velocity flow meters combine depth measurement with velocity measurement. The flow meter uses the depth measurement to calculate the area of the flow based on the programmed size and shape of the channel. The flow meter then calculates the flow rate by multiplying the area of the flow by its calculated value of the average velocity.

Area velocity flow meters are commonly used in sewer flow monitoring, inflow and infiltration studies, combined sewer overflow studies, wastewater treatment plant operations, and regulatory compliance. Reference [30] presents several factors to consider when deciding upon an area velocity flow meter.

Area velocity flow meters use a variety of technologies to measure flow velocity, including several types of acoustic Doppler measurement:

7

- Weighted Average or Continuous Wave Doppler
- Peak Measurement Continuous Wave Doppler
- Pulse Doppler with Range Gating

Other flow velocity measurement technologies include:

- Electromagnetic
- Transit time
- Surface Radar

All of these methods utilize no moving parts, and present minimal obstruction to the flow, creating minimal head loss. In addition, most of these methods provide bi-directional velocity measurement. The following sections discuss each of these technologies, their operating principles, and their advantages and limitations.

Doppler

The Doppler effect, named after Austrian mathematician and physicist Christian Doppler (1803-1853), is the change in frequency observed when the distance between a wave source and the observer is changing in time. By measuring the change in frequency (the Doppler frequency shift), an accurate computation of the velocity of a moving object can be made.

A common example of the Doppler effect occurs when a train passes while sounding its horn. The horn transmits sound of a certain frequency. As the train moves toward the listener, the listener hears a sound of a higher frequency (Figure 7-2). When the train passes and starts moving away, the listener hears a sound of a lower frequency (Figure 7-3). In both cases, the horn has transmitted the same frequency, but the listener hears a higher or lower frequency because of the motion of the train relative to the listener.

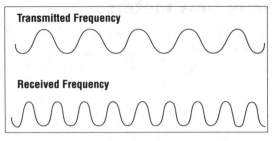

Figure 7-2: Doppler Effect of Positive Velocity — Received Frequency Greater than Transmitted Frequency

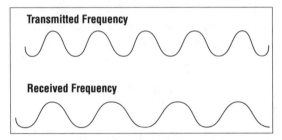

Figure 7-3: Doppler Effect of Negative Velocity — Received Frequency Less than Transmitted Frequency

A Doppler velocity sensor uses the principle of the Doppler effect to measure velocity in a flow stream. In the case of AV flow measurement, the sensor is both the sender and receiver. As shown in Figure 7-4, the stationary sensor transmits high frequency sound waves into the flow. These sound waves are reflected by suspended particles and air bubbles in the flow. The sensor then detects the frequency shifts of the reflected sound waves.

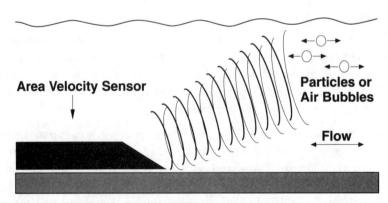

Figure 7-4: Doppler Velocity Measurement

The combination of all the returned echoes is the return signal spectrum. Individual reflected frequencies within this spectrum are related to the velocity of the points in the flow stream at which the reflections occurred. The larger the area of flow that is moving at a particular velocity, the greater the number of reflections of that frequency that will occur. Although different types of Doppler systems process the return spectrum signal differently, the ultimate purpose is to determine the average velocity of the flow stream. For example, the Isco 2150 Area Velocity Flow Module (Figure 7-5) takes a weighted average of the return signal spectrum to determine an average frequency and, therefore, the average velocity of the flow stream. Whether the reflected frequencies are higher or lower than the transmitted frequency indicates the direction of flow.

Because Doppler velocity sensors sense the velocity profile of the flow stream by measuring the return signal spectrum, they can directly detect any changes in the flow profile through changes in the measured spectrum. This can reduce the need for on-site profiling and calibration, and minimizes the time to install the flow meter and sensor. In addition, Doppler velocity sensors are solid state and completely sealed, which prevents the possibility of internal fouling of the sensor.

Large quantities of entrained air in the flow stream will reduce the distance that the sound wave will propagate into the flow. In such instances, a Doppler system will measure velocities relatively close to the sensor. In addition, when the depth of flow is very low, reflections from the surface of the flow stream are much stronger than reflections from within the flow. Under this condition, flow rate is typically estimated based on the level measurement. With low flow depths, the Isco 2150 estimates flow rate based on the level measurement and the "interpolated" velocity derived from readings when flow depths were above one inch.

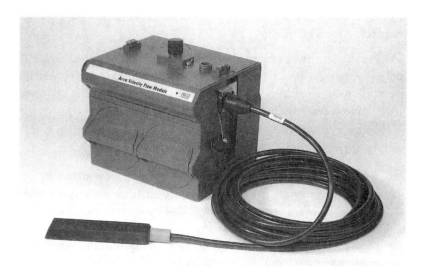

Figure 7-5: Isco 2150 Area Velocity Flow Module

Weighted Average Continuous Wave Doppler

With this type of measurement device, a sensor is placed within the flow stream and a signal of a given frequency is continuously transmitted into the flow. Reflections off of suspended particles and entrained air in the flow are returned to the sensor. These reflections are representative of a sizeable cross-sectional area of flow. This return signal spectrum is then analyzed and weighted proportionally. The result is that the reported velocity is a true average velocity that is based upon cross-sectional measurement of the flow rather than a single point that is then run through a conversion factor. Weighted average Doppler devices have this advantage of providing a measurement based upon the actual profile.

As stated earlier, each measurement technology has its advantages and disadvantages. The disadvantages of this type of measurement device are that:

1. A fairly complex filtering algorithm is required to analyze the reflected signal.
2. There is a limit to the device's range of vision — the device sees only a portion of the full cross-section. This limited vision can be a hindrance in applications with great depth or width.

Another factor to consider is the selected transmission frequency. The frequency used by the measuring velocity meter will determine the distance that the signal is able to travel in the flow stream, as well as its ability to operate under various concentrations of suspended solids.

A lower frequency is capable of traveling farther into a flow stream. It is also better able to function in applications that have a high concentration of solids. However, it is more difficult for a lower frequency Doppler device to see smaller particles in the flow stream, although small particles are not a characteristic of wastewater applications. It will struggle to perform in ultra clean water applications with very few suspended solids.

A higher frequency may not travel as great a distance into the flow stream, thus potentially reducing the overall flow profile seen by the instrument. However, it will be able to see smaller particles in the flow and will perform better in applications that have relatively few reflective particles in the flow stream.

Peak Measurement Continuous Wave Doppler

Peak Doppler devices identify the peak velocity in the flow stream by determining the highest frequency present in the return signal spectrum. Average velocity is determined by performing a simple conversion on the measured peak value. The conversion is typically a fixed value derived from manual calibration measurements of the velocity profile made in the flow stream during installation of the meter. The measured peak velocity is usually multiplied by this conversion factor.

Peak Doppler devices have an advantage in that they do not depend on a particular weighting function. Reasonable accuracy can be obtained by using a crude estimate for the conversion factor. Nevertheless, the accuracy of this measurement remains dependent on the accuracy of the manual calibration measurements. This can provide an additional error source above and beyond normal measurement errors. The additional error arises from both the error within the calibration measurement and the variation of the velocity profile. Velocity profiles in the real world are often in a state of flux, and a truly valid calibration factor must vary as a function of the flow conditions. From a practical perspective, it is difficult to provide calibration data for all flow conditions.

Pulse Doppler with Range Gating

A pulse Doppler with range gating device is capable of measuring velocity in multiple, discrete volumes throughout the water column. These velocity data are used to calculate a flow velocity distribution throughout the flow that is then integrated over the flow's cross-sectional area to determine the discharge.

The sensor assembly is mounted on the invert of a pipe or channel (Figure 7-6). Multiple piezoelectric ceramics emit independent short pulses along narrow acoustic beams pointing in different directions. Echoes of these pulses are back scattered from material suspended in the flow. As this material has motion relative to the transducer, measurement of the returned echo frequency enables the calculation of the flow velocity.

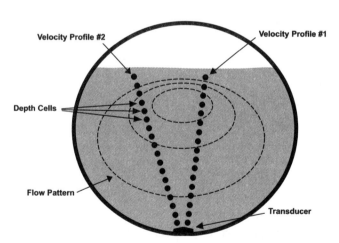

Figure 7-6: Pulse Doppler with Range Gating installation

However, unlike a continuous wave Doppler device, where the receive circuit actively listens for all returned echoes to estimate an average or peak velocity, a range-gating system divides the return signal of each beam into discrete regular intervals that correspond to different depths in the flow along each beam. Velocity is calculated from the frequency shift measured in each interval. The result is a profile, or linear distribution of velocities, along the direction of each beam. The number of intervals in which velocity is measured depends on the depth of flow. An additional ceramic mounted in the center of the transducer assembly, and aimed vertically, is used to measure the depth of flow.

The measured velocity data from the multiple profiles are entered into an algorithm that determines a mathematical description of the flow velocities throughout the entire cross-section of the flow. The algorithm accomplishes this by fitting the basis functions of a parametric model to the actual measured data. This produces a description of flow velocities at all points throughout the flow that is based on measured real-time velocity distribution data. The resulting mathematical description is integrated over the cross-sectional area to determine the discharge.

7 Electromagnetic

Electromagnetic probes measure velocity using the Faraday principle. The Faraday principle states that a conductor moving through a magnetic field produces a voltage that is proportional to the velocity of the conductor. As shown in Figure 7-7, the electromagnetic probe creates a magnetic field. The conductive liquid flowing through the magnetic field produces a voltage. This voltage is measured using electrodes on the surface of the probe that are exposed to the liquid. This voltage is proportional to the velocity of the liquid passing the electrodes. The polarity of the voltage indicates the direction of flow.

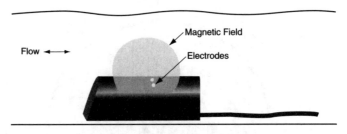

Figure 7-7: Electromagnetic Velocity Measurement

Electromagnetic probes measure the local velocity of the flow at the location of the electrodes which are positioned at the bottom of the channel. Average flow velocity is then estimated based on this local velocity, the measured liquid depth, and the size and shape of the channel. Because this estimate is based on ideal flow conditions, electromagnetic probes require on-site profiling and calibration to obtain the most accurate measurement of flow.

Because the electrodes on the probe are exposed to the flow, they are subject to fouling by oil and grease and require frequent cleaning. In addition, the accuracy of an electromagnetic probe is questionable during the time that its electrodes are fouled.

Transit time

The transit time method is based on the principle that a sound pulse traveling diagonally across a flow stream will be accelerated by the velocity of the liquid when the sound pulse is traveling in a downstream direction, and decelerated when traveling in an upstream direction. As shown in Figure 7-8, transit time flow meters use pairs of transducers mounted at an angle to the direction of flow. The flow meter measures the times for sound pulses to travel between the transducers in the upstream and downstream directions. The flow velocity is then determined based on the travel times of the sound pulses, the distance between the transducers, and the angle between the acoustic path and the flow. Reverse flow is indicated when the travel time in the downstream direction is greater than the upstream travel time.

7

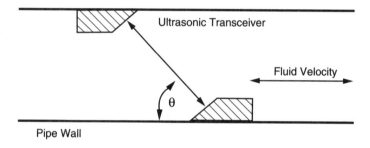

Figure 7-8: Transit Time Velocity Measurement

Transit time flow meters are typically used to measure flow in large pipes and channels. Transit time systems may incorporate one or more pairs of transducers. Multiple acoustic paths are used to increase accuracy when the velocity distribution is not well known, and to allow for changes in liquid level. From two to four pairs of transducers may be used in such instances. Path angles of 30° to 65° are commonly used. A transit time system cannot measure velocity when the liquid level drops below the transducers. Under this condition, flow rate is usually estimated based on the level measurement.

Because their transducers must be precisely located and aligned, transit time systems are more difficult to install than Doppler and electromagnetic systems. In addition, the ability of a transit time flow meter to detect sound pulses will be affected if large quantities of entrained air and/or suspended solids are present in the flow.

Surface Radar

Traditionally, surface velocity measurement involved observing an object floating on the surface and measuring the amount of time it took that object to travel a specific distance. Radar Doppler systems remotely measure a surface velocity using the Doppler principle with electromagnetic radiation as the measurement medium.

A radar Doppler device transmits an electromagnetic signal at a known frequency at a defined angle. Turbulence on the water surface reflects the signal back to the transmitter. This returned signal is analyzed for a Doppler shift in frequency that gives the average velocity of that portion of the surface illuminated by the electromagnetic radiation. This surface velocity measurement is transformed into the average velocity of the flow using a predetermined flow velocity profile.

The main advantage offered by such a remote-sensing device is that it is non-intrusive and can be installed outside of the flow stream.

A disadvantage with such devices is similar to other "point" velocity measurement instruments — a surface velocity measurement device relies on a specific and consistent model of the flow's velocity profile to maintain a degree of accuracy in its "average" velocity conversion from the surface measurement. Installation is also a critical factor with such devices. In addition, the surface velocity method requires a relatively high surface turbulence to obtain a reading. Slow, surcharge, or reverse velocities may result in unreliable readings.

• • •

An area velocity flow meter may combine any of these velocity measurement technologies with any of the level measurement methods discussed in Chapter 2. The most common embodiment utilizes a single sensor that incorporates a Doppler velocity sensor with a built-in pressure transducer.

CHAPTER 8

Flow Measurement System Installations

OVERVIEW

This chapter provides some general recommendations regarding primary and secondary measuring device installation and setup. Included are sections discussing stilling wells, staff gauges, sensor installation, instrument shelters, "zero" adjustment procedures for flow meters, and common errors in open channel flow measurement installations.

A staff gauge mounted on a bridge on the River Seine in Paris.

Stilling well

It is recommended that, where practical, primary measuring device installations include a stilling well. A stilling well is necessary for most types of flow meters using float operated level measuring systems. A stilling well may also be beneficial to the operation of several of the other level measurement methods, such as ultrasonic sensors, submerged pressure transducers, and bubblers. A stilling well (see Figure 8-1) is basically a chamber which is connected to the main flow channel by a small inlet. Waves and surges are often present in a flowing open channel, because of wind, pumps, or high liquid velocities. Since the stilling well is isolated from the main flow stream by the small diameter inlet, the liquid surface in the well will be quiet, but nonetheless will follow all the steady fluctuations of the open channel flow. All the non-flow related oscillations of the open channel will be damped out by the action of the stilling well.

The size of the stilling well depends on the type and configuration of the secondary device to be installed. At a minimum, the inside diameter of the stilling well needs only to be large enough to accommodate the level measuring element, for example, a float. However, it is often advisable to make the stilling well large enough to be easily cleaned, especially if the water carries large amounts of solids. The stilling well must be high enough to accommodate the entire range of expected liquid level, plus enough for proper installation of the flow meter.

The inlet to the stilling well should be located at the appropriate head measuring point in the primary measuring device. The area of liquid inlet from the open channel to the well should be approximately $^1/_{1000}$ the area of the stilling well. If the stilling well is offset from the primary device by some distance, the inlet area may have to be increased. Table 8-1 lists satisfactory port and pipe sizes for stilling well inlets.

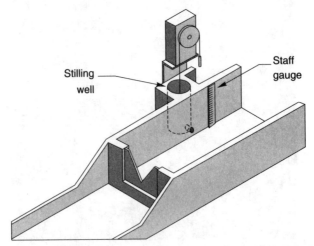

Stilling well

Staff gauge

Figure 8-1: Flow Measurement System with Stilling Well and Staff Gauge

Table 8-1:
Port and Pipe Sizes for Stilling Well Inserts

Diameter of stilling well		Diameter of inlet hole		Diameter of inlet pipe 20 to 30 ft. (6 to 9 m) long	
in./ft.	meters	inches	meters	inches	meters
6 in.	0.152	$3/8$	0.010	$1/2$	0.013
8 in.	0.203	$7/16$	0.011	$1/2$	0.013
10 in.	0.254	$1/2$	0.013	$1/2$	0.013
12 in.	0.305	$1/2$	0.013	$1/2$	0.013
16 in.	0.406	$1/2$	0.013	$3/4$	0.019
20 in.	0.508	$5/8$	0.016	$3/4$	0.019
24 in.	0.610	$3/4$	0.019	1	0.025
30 in.	0.762	1	0.025	$1 1/2$	0.038
36 in.	0.914	$1 1/4$	0.032	2	0.051
3 x 3 ft., square	0.914 x 0.914, square	$1 1/4$	0.032	2	0.051
3 x 4 ft., rectangular	0.914 x 1.22, rectangular	$1 1/2$	0.038	3	0.076
4 x 5 ft., rectangular	1.22 x 1.52, rectangular	$1 1/2$	0.038	4	0.102

8

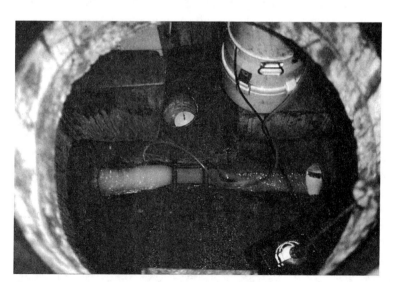

A stilling well is necessary for most float-operated flow meters.

The stilling well may be made of wood, reinforced concrete, metal pipe, sewer pipe, corrugated galvanized iron culvert pipe, or other suitable material. The well must have a bottom, and should be as water tight as possible, except for the inlet.

The inlet on most stilling wells will require occasional cleaning, especially on channels carrying sediment. When the channel is silted, some type of water flushing system may be necessary. This could be manually accomplished using a tank and pump where the tank is filled with a hand pump, and a sudden release of the tank water is used to flush out the well and inlet. Alternatively, fresh water could be continuously fed into the well at a slow rate to provide an automatic flushing action.

To provide for continuous flow monitoring during freezing weather, it is often necessary to take certain measures to keep the stilling well free of ice. This is usually accomplished by one of two methods. In the first method, the liquid in the stilling well is heated, either by means of an electric immersion heater, or by a cluster of lights above the well with a reflector directing the heat onto the liquid surface in the well. In a second method, a layer of oil on the top of the liquid in the well is used to prevent freezing. If this method is used, be sure that the flow meter "zero" level is set with respect to the liquid level in the channel, not in the stilling well, as the oil in the well will stand somewhat higher than the liquid in the channel outside.

Staff gauge

To aid in the zero adjustment of the flow meter, it is strongly recommended that every primary measuring device installation include a staff gauge. A staff gauge (Figure 8-1) is simply a fixed scale, on which the level of liquid in the primary device can be read. Most staff gauges are mounted vertically, but greater accuracy can often be obtained by inclining the staff so the graduations are larger for a given change in liquid level. It is important that the staff gauge be solidly and accurately attached to the primary device. The staff should be placed at the proper head measuring location in the primary device, and the staff gauge zero should be precisely aligned with the primary device zero level. Enameled iron gauges are preferred since they resist rust and will last almost indefinitely.

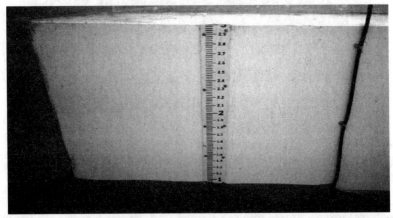

The staff gauge mounted on the wall of this Parshall flume is located at the correct level measurement point. The cable to the right leads to a submerged pressure transducer.

Sensor installation

There are a variety of methods available for installing a flow sensor in an open channel. Ultrasonic level sensors are the easiest to install because they are mounted above the flow stream. Ultrasonic sensors are usually installed using a stainless steel bracket attached to a wall or pipe near the channel. Most ultrasonic sensors also have pipe threads on the end from which the cable exits the sensor. This allows the sensor to be connected directly to conduit. In addition, some ultrasonic sensors can simply be suspended by their cable in portable flow monitoring applications. In this case, a weight is usually added to the sensor to ensure that it maintains its alignment above the flow stream. An ultrasonic level sensor will not work properly if condensation causes water droplets to collect on the transducer surface. If high ambient humidity is a problem, try mounting the ultrasonic level sensor horizontally and aiming it at a 45° angled reflector.

Unless a stilling well is used, submerged pressure transducers and bubble tubes are installed directly in the flow stream. Because they measure the velocity of the flow, area velocity sensors cannot be installed in a stilling well and, therefore, must also be installed directly in the channel. Stainless steel mounting rings are typically used to install these sensors in round pipes and manhole inverts. There are two types of mounting rings — spring rings and scissors rings.

Spring rings are used to install sensors in small pipes ranging in size from approximately 6 to 15 inches (15.2 to 38.1 cm) in diameter. Spring rings are held in place by spring tension against the wall of the pipe. The sensor is first attached to the ring, and plastic ties are used to fasten the sensor cable to the downstream edge of the ring. This minimizes the amount of debris that collects on the cable, which could otherwise affect the hydraulic conditions and the accuracy of the measurement. The ring is then installed by manually collapsing it and placing it in the pipe, upstream of the outfall.

Teledyne Isco has a Street Level Installation tool that provides a way to install various Isco sensors in round pipe sewers without having to enter the manhole. It consists of an insertion tool with a multi-section pole, differently-sized expansion rings, and an adjustable strap for each ring. The device is for use in manholes with a depth of 15 feet or less. The advantage to using this tool is that it eliminates the need for confined space entry. This results in reduced costs and, most importantly, increased safety since no one is at risk in the confined space environment. This device also eliminates the need for entry for sensor removal.

A spring ring is used to install a submerged pressure transducer in a small pipe.

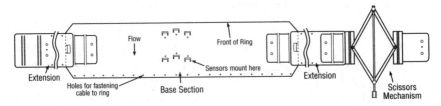

Figure 8-2: Scissors Ring

Scissors rings are used to install sensors in large pipes approximately 18 inches (45.7 cm) in diameter and larger. Scissors rings (Figure 8-2) are a modular mounting system consisting of a base section, a scissors mechanism and, if necessary, one or more pairs of extensions to fit the size of the pipe into which the ring is being installed. The ring is first assembled, the sensor is attached, and the sensor cable is then fastened using plastic ties. The ring is then placed in the pipe, upstream of the outfall, and the scissors mechanism is tightened to secure the ring in the pipe (Figure 8-3). The base section and extensions of a scissors ring can also be installed in a manhole invert (Figure 8-4) using threaded fasteners driven into the wall of the channel, typically with a powder actuated stud gun.

There are other methods for installing sensors in a flow stream. For example, most flumes are available with an integral cavity for a submerged pressure transducer, or a built-in bubble tube for a bubbler. In addition, stainless steel bubble tubes are often attached to the wall or floor of a channel, and a flexible bubble tube is then connected to the inlet of the stainless steel bubble tube.

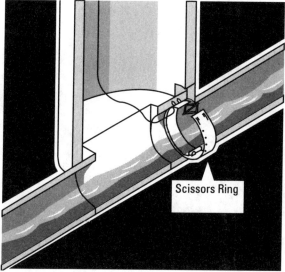

Figure 8-3: Scissors Ring Installed in a Round Pipe

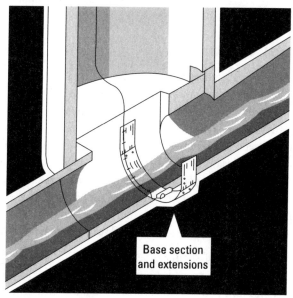

Figure 8-4: Scissors Ring Base Section and Extensions Installed in Manhole Invert

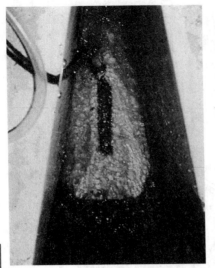

Most flumes can be ordered with a cavity for a submerged pressure transducer.

A built-in bubble tube makes it convenient to connect a bubbler flow meter to this Parshall flume.

Instrument shelters

Under certain circumstances it may be advantageous to provide an instrument shelter as a part of the flow measurement system installation. The instrument shelter houses the flow meter and associated equipment and protects them from the elements and malicious interference. Shelter sizes range from the small "look-in" type, only large enough to house the flow meter, to the large "walk-in" type, big enough to walk about inside. Choosing the type of shelter to be installed depends on a number of factors, including the permanency of the installation, ambient climactic conditions, accessibility of site, degree of protection required, and the availability of funds. There are a number of manufacturers who supply plastic or metal enclosures suitable for providing a shelter for flow measurement instrumentation.

No matter what type of shelter is selected, it should normally be mounted above the maximum liquid level and should be provided with locks to prevent vandalism and unauthorized entrance. The shelter should be well ventilated, especially in humid climates, to prevent excessive build-up of moisture. It may also be advisable to equip the shelter with an electric blower, thermostatically controlled heater, etc. to provide for a controlled environment in the shelter.

This "look-in" shelter has a window through which the display and printer on the flow meter can be viewed.

This fiberglass "walk-in" shelter houses a flow meter and sampler. A rain gauge and solar panel are mounted on top of the shelter.

Flow meter "zero" adjustment

Probably the greatest single controllable source of error associated with an open channel flow measurement system can result from flow meter setup ("zero" errors) [31]. This type of error may originate from improper instrument installation and/or failure to accurately adjust the flow meter's indicated liquid level (or flow rate) with the actual liquid level (or flow rate) in the open channel. It is imperative that the flow meter be properly "zeroed" with the zero reference level in the primary measuring device. It is important to note that a primary device's zero level is **not** always the bottom of the channel! All weirs and many flumes have elevated zero reference points.

If zeroing is not accurately done, a systematic level offset error will be introduced, resulting from the fact that the liquid level indicated by the flow meter will not correspond to the level actually existing in the primary measuring device. Due to the nonlinear level/flow rate relationship of most primary measuring devices, this will result in a flow rate error whose magnitude becomes increasingly large at increased liquid levels (Figure 8-5).

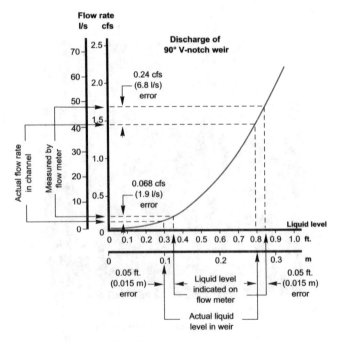

Figure 8-5: Flow Meter "Zero" Errors

A properly constructed flow meter can greatly aid in minimizing setup of "zero" errors. The flow meter should have some type of accurate visual indication of the instrument's liquid level reading, and the resolution of this level should be on the same order as the readability of the level in the primary device. Visual indication of liquid level (as opposed to flow rate) is preferred because the level can be directly observed, while the flow rate is a secondary quantity which must be calculated from the observed level. It is important to note that because of this, flow rate errors are sometimes the result of an incorrectly zeroed level adjustment, improperly programmed flow conversion information, or a site condition that results in poor hydraulics for the selected flow measurement method.

Also, the nonlinear level/flow rate relationship of most primary devices results in a flow rate scale in which a major portion of the level range is compressed into a minor portion of the flow rate range. This causes a consequent decrease in instrument resolution and setability with respect to flow rate at lower liquid level values. The flow meter should have a mechanical or electronic control which easily allows the adjustment of the indicated liquid level. These features are desirable because in most open channel flow measurement situations the flow cannot be stopped and is subject to frequent variation, resulting in a constantly changing, nonzero level setpoint. Thus, any flow meter feature which can ease the task of adjusting the instrument liquid level to match the actual level will aid in decreasing the setup or "zero" errors.

8

Common errors in open channel flow measurement installations

Mort [31] and Thomas [32] discuss sources of errors commonly encountered in open channel flow measurement installations.

They identify two classes of errors: 1) avoidable errors which result from carelessness and can be eliminated through supervision and strict attention to details, and 2) unavoidable errors, which are errors of degree, and although they cannot be completely eliminated, they can, by exercise of extreme care and knowledge of their nature and magnitude, be reduced to such a degree as to ensure satisfactory overall results. The errors identified by Mort and Thomas are briefly summarized on the following pages.

Faulty fabrication or construction of the primary device

There are numerous possibilities for the introduction of errors in flow measurements resulting from faulty construction of the primary measuring device. Most typical of these are errors in the crest length of contracted weirs, errors in the angle of V-notch weirs, deviation from the standard dimensions of Parshall flumes, etc. Any deviation of a primary device from the standard configuration, dimensions, and geometry will result in an error in flow measurement through the device.

Improper gauge or head measuring location

In most types of primary devices, the head/flow rate relationship has been empirically determined with the head being measured at a specific point in relation to the primary device. Errors will occur if the gauge or head measuring instrumentation is not located at the proper location in the primary device. Most typical installation errors of this type occur in weirs where the gauge location is at a point where draw-down over the weir is measured, for example, by mounting a staff gauge on the weir plate instead of at the recommended three to four times the maximum head upstream from the weir. Errors can also occur in flumes if the gauge or head measuring location is not in the specified position.

Incorrect zero setting

These types of errors are basically as discussed on page 152. They may also originate from a lack of knowledge of the proper zero reference level in the primary device. An example of this is the Palmer-Bowlus flume where the zero level is the floor of the flume throat, not the invert of the pipe as might be suspected.

Improper head measurement

Errors in measuring the head in a primary device will result in flow measurement errors of the same type and magnitude as those resulting from an incorrect zero setting. Improper head measurement may result from an incorrect location of the gauge, from carelessness in not obtaining a good head reading, or from a faulty, improperly installed, or poorly maintained head measuring and recording instrument.

Use of primary device outside its proper range

All types and sizes of primary measuring devices have a recommended range of flow rates, outside of which errors in flow measurement will result. The use of a primary device to measure flow rates outside the recommended range of a particular device (for example, a flow rate resulting in a head of less than 0.2 foot (0.06 m) on a weir) will result in inaccurate flow measurement.

Improper installation or maintenance of weirs

There are many possibilities for improper installation or maintenance of weirs which can contribute to errors in flow measurement. Included in these are transverse slope of the weir crest, the weir plate sloping upstream or downstream, roughness of the upstream face of the weir plate, rounding of the sharp edge at the weir crest, improper aeration of the downstream nappe of the weir, submergence of the weir, and excessive velocity of approach.

Turbulence and surges in the approach channel

Turbulence and surges may occur in the approach channel to a primary device, caused by a high velocity of approach, gates, valves, pumps, or a sudden change in section. This results in an erratic head measurement, and it can affect proper velocity measurement when using area velocity measurement, hence inaccurate flow measurement **will** result. Corrective measures to quiet the flow provide the best solution, although this may not be an easy task.

Excessive debris and other solids in flow

Debris, sediment, or other solids can negatively affect the ability to properly measure velocity in a flow stream if they become excessive. They can build up on the sensor and blind it, or build up around the sensor and create erratic vortices that will affect the equipment's ability to accurately measure velocity.

Excessive buildup of solids can also affect the accuracy of a level-only or level-to-flow measurement device. Such buildup can and will artificially raise the water's head, which will be interpreted by the measurement device as meaning increased flow.

8

8

CHAPTER

9

V-notch Weir Discharge Tables

Overview

This chapter contains discharge (head vs. flow rate) tables for V-notch weirs. Note that all of the tabular data is for free flow. If the flow is submerged, corrections will have to be made to determine the discharge, as discussed in Chapter 3.

Discharge tables for V-notch weirs with head in feet

9-1: $22^1/_2°$ V-notch Weir
9-2: 30° V-notch Weir
9-3: 45° V-notch Weir

9-4: 60° V-notch Weir
9-5: 90° V-notch Weir
9-6: 120° V-notch Weir

The discharges of the weirs are listed in three different units of measure:

CFS - cubic feet per second
GPM - gallons per minute
MGD - million gallons per day

Discharge tables for V-notch weirs with head in meters

9-7: $22^1/_2°$ V-notch Weir
9-8: 30° V-notch Weir
9-9: 45° V-notch Weir

9-10: 60° V-notch Weir
9-11: 90° V-notch Weir
9-12: 120° V-notch Weir

The discharges of the weirs are listed in two different units of measure:

l/s - liters per second m^3/hr - cubic meters per hour

The formulas used to develop each table are listed on the table. Values in italics indicate flow below the recommended range of this particular primary device.

Table 9-1:
22$^{1}/_{2}°$ V-Notch Weir Discharge Table with Head in Feet

Formula: CFS = 0.4970 H$^{2.5}$
GPM = 223.1 H$^{2.5}$
MGD = 0.3212 H$^{2.5}$
Where: H = head in feet

Values in italics indicate flow below the recommended range of this particular primary device.

Head (feet)	CFS	GPM	MGD	Head (feet)	CFS	GPM	MGD
0.01	*0*	*0*	*0*	0.51	0.0923	41.44	0.0597
0.02	*0*	*0*	*0*	0.52	0.0969	43.50	0.0626
0.03	*0.0001*	*0.035*	*0.0001*	0.53	0.1016	45.62	0.0657
0.04	*0.0002*	*0.071*	*0.0001*	0.54	0.1065	47.81	0.0688
0.05	*0.0003*	*0.125*	*0.0002*	0.55	0.1115	50.05	0.0721
0.06	*0.0004*	*0.197*	*0.0003*	0.56	0.1166	52.36	0.0754
0.07	*0.0006*	*0.289*	*0.0004*	0.57	0.1219	54.73	0.0788
0.08	*0.0009*	*0.404*	*0.0006*	0.58	0.1273	57.16	0.0823
0.09	*0.0012*	*0.542*	*0.0008*	0.59	0.1329	59.65	0.0859
0.10	*0.0016*	*0.705*	*0.0010*	0.60	0.1386	62.21	0.0896
0.11	*0.0020*	*0.895*	*0.0013*	0.61	0.1444	64.84	0.0933
0.12	*0.0025*	*1.113*	*0.0016*	0.62	0.1504	67.53	0.0972
0.13	*0.0030*	*1.359*	*0.0020*	0.63	0.1566	70.28	0.1012
0.14	*0.0036*	*1.636*	*0.0024*	0.64	0.1629	73.11	0.1053
0.15	*0.0043*	*1.944*	*0.0028*	0.65	0.1693	75.99	0.1094
0.16	*0.0051*	*2.284*	*0.0033*	0.66	0.1759	78.95	0.1137
0.17	*0.0059*	*2.658*	*0.0038*	0.67	0.1826	81.98	0.1180
0.18	*0.0068*	*3.066*	*0.0044*	0.68	0.1895	85.07	0.1225
0.19	*0.0078*	*3.510*	*0.0051*	0.69	0.1966	88.23	0.1270
0.20	0.0089	3.991	0.0057	0.70	0.2038	91.46	0.1317
0.21	0.0100	4.509	0.0065	0.71	0.2111	94.76	0.1364
0.22	0.0113	5.065	0.0073	0.72	0.2186	98.14	0.1413
0.23	0.0126	5.660	0.0081	0.73	0.2263	101.6	0.1462
0.24	0.0140	6.295	0.0091	0.74	0.2341	105.1	0.1513
0.25	0.0155	6.972	0.0100	0.75	0.2421	108.7	0.1565
0.26	0.0171	7.690	0.0111	0.76	0.2503	112.3	0.1617
0.27	0.0188	8.451	0.0122	0.77	0.2586	116.1	0.1671
0.28	0.0206	9.255	0.0133	0.78	0.2671	119.9	0.1726
0.29	0.0225	10.10	0.0145	0.79	0.2757	123.8	0.1782
0.30	0.0245	11.00	0.0158	0.80	0.2845	127.7	0.1839
0.31	0.0266	11.94	0.0172	0.81	0.2935	131.7	0.1897
0.32	0.0288	12.92	0.0186	0.82	0.3026	135.8	0.1956
0.33	0.0311	13.96	0.0201	0.83	0.3119	140.0	0.2016
0.34	0.0335	15.04	0.0217	0.84	0.3214	144.3	0.2077
0.35	0.0360	16.17	0.0233	0.85	0.3311	148.6	0.2140
0.36	0.0386	17.35	0.0250	0.86	0.3409	153.0	0.2203
0.37	0.0414	18.58	0.0267	0.87	0.3509	157.5	0.2268
0.38	0.0442	19.86	0.0286	0.88	0.3610	162.1	0.2333
0.39	0.0472	21.19	0.0305	0.89	0.3714	166.7	0.2400
0.40	0.0503	22.58	0.0325	0.90	0.3819	171.4	0.2468
0.41	0.0535	24.01	0.0346	0.91	0.3926	176.2	0.2537
0.42	0.0568	25.50	0.0367	0.92	0.4035	181.1	0.2608
0.43	0.0603	27.05	0.0389	0.93	0.4145	186.1	0.2679
0.44	0.0638	28.65	0.0412	0.94	0.4258	191.1	0.2752
0.45	0.0675	30.31	0.0436	0.95	0.4372	196.2	0.2825
0.46	0.0713	32.02	0.0461	0.96	0.4488	201.5	0.2900
0.47	0.0753	33.79	0.0486	0.97	0.4606	206.7	0.2976
0.48	0.0793	35.61	0.0513	0.98	0.4725	212.1	0.3054
0.49	0.0835	37.50	0.0540	0.99	0.4847	217.6	0.3132
0.50	0.0879	39.44	0.0568	1.00	0.4970	223.1	0.3212

Table 9-1 (Continued)					Table 9-1 (Continued)			
Head (feet)	CFS	GPM	MGD		Head (feet)	CFS	GPM	MGD
1.01	0.5095	228.7	0.3293		1.51	1.393	625.1	0.8999
1.02	0.5222	234.4	0.3375		1.52	1.416	635.5	0.9149
1.03	0.5351	240.2	0.3458		1.53	1.439	646.0	0.9300
1.04	0.5482	246.1	0.3543		1.54	1.463	656.6	0.9453
1.05	0.5615	252.0	0.3629		1.55	1.487	667.3	0.9607
1.06	0.5749	258.1	0.3716		1.56	1.511	678.1	0.9763
1.07	0.5886	264.2	0.3804		1.57	1.535	689.0	0.9920
1.08	0.6024	270.4	0.3893		1.58	1.560	700.1	1.008
1.09	0.6165	276.7	0.3984		1.59	1.584	711.2	1.024
1.10	0.6307	283.1	0.4076		1.60	1.609	722.4	1.040
1.11	0.6452	289.6	0.4169		1.61	1.635	733.8	1.056
1.12	0.6598	296.2	0.4264		1.62	1.660	745.2	1.073
1.13	0.6746	302.8	0.4360		1.63	1.686	756.8	1.090
1.14	0.6896	309.6	0.4457		1.64	1.712	768.4	1.106
1.15	0.7049	316.4	0.4555		1.65	1.738	780.2	1.123
1.16	0.7203	323.3	0.4655		1.66	1.765	792.1	1.140
1.17	0.7359	330.3	0.4756		1.67	1.791	804.1	1.158
1.18	0.7517	337.4	0.4858		1.68	1.818	816.2	1.175
1.19	0.7678	344.6	0.4962		1.69	1.845	828.4	1.193
1.20	0.7840	351.9	0.5067		1.70	1.873	840.7	1.210
1.21	0.8004	359.3	0.5173		1.71	1.900	853.1	1.228
1.22	0.8171	366.8	0.5281		1.72	1.928	865.6	1.246
1.23	0.8339	374.3	0.5389		1.73	1.956	878.2	1.264
1.24	0.8510	382.0	0.5500		1.74	1.985	891.0	1.283
1.25	0.8682	389.7	0.5611		1.75	2.013	903.8	1.301
1.26	0.8857	397.6	0.5724		1.76	2.042	916.8	1.320
1.27	0.9034	405.5	0.5838		1.77	2.072	929.9	1.339
1.28	0.9213	413.5	0.5954		1.78	2.101	943.1	1.358
1.29	0.9394	421.7	0.6071		1.79	2.131	956.4	1.377
1.30	0.9577	429.9	0.6189		1.80	2.160	969.8	1.396
1.31	0.9762	438.2	0.6309		1.81	2.191	983.3	1.416
1.32	0.9949	446.6	0.6430		1.82	2.221	997.0	1.435
1.33	1.014	455.1	0.6552		1.83	2.252	1011	1.455
1.34	1.033	463.7	0.6676		1.84	2.282	1025	1.475
1.35	1.052	472.4	0.6802		1.85	2.314	1039	1.495
1.36	1.072	481.2	0.6928		1.86	2.345	1053	1.516
1.37	1.092	490.1	0.7056		1.87	2.377	1067	1.536
1.38	1.112	499.1	0.7186		1.88	2.409	1081	1.557
1.39	1.132	508.2	0.7317		1.89	2.441	1096	1.577
1.40	1.153	517.4	0.7449		1.90	2.473	1110	1.598
1.41	1.173	526.7	0.7583		1.91	2.506	1125	1.619
1.42	1.194	536.1	0.7718		1.92	2.539	1140	1.641
1.43	1.215	545.6	0.7854		1.93	2.572	1154	1.662
1.44	1.237	555.1	0.7992		1.94	2.605	1170	1.684
1.45	1.258	564.8	0.8132		1.95	2.639	1185	1.706
1.46	1.280	574.6	0.8273		1.96	2.673	1200	1.727
1.47	1.302	584.5	0.8415		1.97	2.707	1215	1.750
1.48	1.324	594.5	0.8559		1.98	2.742	1231	1.772
1.49	1.347	604.6	0.8704		1.99	2.776	1246	1.794
1.50	1.370	614.8	0.8851		2.00	2.811	1262	1.817

9

V-notch Weir Discharge Tables • 159

Table 9-2:
30° V-notch Weir Discharge Table with Head in Feet

Formula: $CFS = 0.6760\ H^{2.5}$
$GPM = 303.4\ H^{2.5}$
$MGD = 0.4369\ H^{2.5}$

Where: H = head in feet

Values in italics indicate flow below the recommended range of this particular primary device.

Head (feet)	CFS	GPM	MGD	Head (feet)	CFS	GPM	MGD
0.01	*0*	*0*	*0*	0.51	0.1256	56.36	0.0812
0.02	*0*	*0*	*0*	0.52	0.1318	59.16	0.0852
0.03	*0.0001*	*0.047*	*0.0001*	0.53	0.1382	62.04	0.0893
0.04	*0.0002*	*0.097*	*0.0001*	0.54	0.1449	65.01	0.0936
0.05	*0.0004*	*0.170*	*0.0002*	0.55	0.1517	68.06	0.0980
0.06	*0.0006*	*0.268*	*0.0004*	0.56	0.1586	71.20	0.1025
0.07	*0.0009*	*0.393*	*0.0006*	0.57	0.1658	74.42	0.1072
0.08	*0.0012*	*0.549*	*0.0008*	0.58	0.1732	77.73	0.1119
0.09	*0.0016*	*0.737*	*0.0011*	0.59	0.1807	81.12	0.1168
0.10	*0.0021*	*0.960*	*0.0014*	0.60	0.1885	84.60	0.1218
0.11	*0.0027*	*1.218*	*0.0018*	0.61	0.1965	88.17	0.1270
0.12	*0.0034*	*1.514*	*0.0022*	0.62	0.2046	91.83	0.1322
0.13	*0.0041*	*1.849*	*0.0027*	0.63	0.2130	95.58	0.1376
0.14	*0.0050*	*2.225*	*0.0032*	0.64	0.2215	99.42	0.1432
0.15	*0.0059*	*2.644*	*0.0038*	0.65	0.2303	103.3	0.1488
0.16	*0.0069*	*3.107*	*0.0045*	0.66	0.2392	107.4	0.1546
0.17	*0.0081*	*3.615*	*0.0052*	0.67	0.2484	111.5	0.1605
0.18	*0.0093*	*4.171*	*0.0060*	0.68	0.2578	115.7	0.1666
0.19	*0.0106*	*4.774*	*0.0069*	0.69	0.2673	120.0	0.1728
0.20	0.0121	5.427	0.0078	0.70	0.2771	124.4	0.1791
0.21	0.0137	6.131	0.0088	0.71	0.2871	128.9	0.1856
0.22	0.0153	6.888	0.0099	0.72	0.2974	133.5	0.1922
0.23	0.0172	7.697	0.0111	0.73	0.3078	138.1	0.1989
0.24	0.0191	8.561	0.0123	0.74	0.3184	142.9	0.2058
0.25	0.0211	9.481	0.0137	0.75	0.3293	147.8	0.2128
0.26	0.0233	10.46	0.0151	0.76	0.3404	152.8	0.2200
0.27	0.0256	11.49	0.0165	0.77	0.3517	157.8	0.2273
0.28	0.0280	12.59	0.0181	0.78	0.3632	163.0	0.2348
0.29	0.0306	13.74	0.0198	0.79	0.3750	168.3	0.2424
0.30	0.0333	14.96	0.0215	0.80	0.3870	173.7	0.2501
0.31	0.0362	16.23	0.0234	0.81	0.3992	179.2	0.2580
0.32	0.0392	17.57	0.0253	0.82	0.4116	184.7	0.2660
0.33	0.0423	18.98	0.0273	0.83	0.4243	190.4	0.2742
0.34	0.0456	20.45	0.0294	0.84	0.4372	196.2	0.2825
0.35	0.0490	21.99	0.0317	0.85	0.4503	202.1	0.2910
0.36	0.0526	23.59	0.0340	0.86	0.4637	208.1	0.2997
0.37	0.0563	25.27	0.0364	0.87	0.4772	214.2	0.3084
0.38	0.0602	27.01	0.0389	0.88	0.4911	220.4	0.3174
0.39	0.0642	28.82	0.0415	0.89	0.5052	226.7	0.3265
0.40	0.0684	30.70	0.0442	0.90	0.5195	233.1	0.3357
0.41	0.0728	32.66	0.0470	0.91	0.5340	239.7	0.3451
0.42	0.0773	34.68	0.0499	0.92	0.5488	246.3	0.3547
0.43	0.0820	36.79	0.0530	0.93	0.5638	253.1	0.3644
0.44	0.0868	38.96	0.0561	0.94	0.5791	259.9	0.3743
0.45	0.0918	41.21	0.0593	0.95	0.5946	266.9	0.3843
0.46	0.0970	43.54	0.0627	0.96	0.6104	274.0	0.3945
0.47	0.1024	45.95	0.0662	0.97	0.6264	281.2	0.4049
0.48	0.1079	48.43	0.0697	0.98	0.6427	288.5	0.4154
0.49	0.1136	50.99	0.0734	0.99	0.6592	295.9	0.4261
0.50	0.1195	53.63	0.0772	1.00	0.6760	303.4	0.4369

9

Table 9-2 (Continued)					Table 9-2 (Continued)			
Head (feet)	CFS	GPM	MGD		Head (feet)	CFS	GPM	MGD
1.01	0.6930	311.0	0.4479		1.51	1.894	850.1	1.224
1.02	0.7103	318.8	0.4591		1.52	1.926	864.2	1.244
1.03	0.7278	326.7	0.4704		1.53	1.957	878.5	1.265
1.04	0.7456	334.7	0.4819		1.54	1.990	892.9	1.286
1.05	0.7637	342.8	0.4936		1.55	2.022	907.5	1.307
1.06	0.7820	351.0	0.5054		1.56	2.055	922.2	1.328
1.07	0.8006	359.3	0.5174		1.57	2.088	937.1	1.349
1.08	0.8194	367.8	0.5296		1.58	2.121	952.0	1.371
1.09	0.8385	376.3	0.5419		1.59	2.155	967.2	1.393
1.10	0.8579	385.0	0.5545		1.60	2.189	982.5	1.415
1.11	0.8775	393.8	0.5671		1.61	2.223	997.9	1.437
1.12	0.8974	402.8	0.5800		1.62	2.258	1013	1.459
1.13	0.9176	411.8	0.5930		1.63	2.293	1029	1.482
1.14	0.9380	421.0	0.6062		1.64	2.328	1045	1.505
1.15	0.9587	430.3	0.6196		1.65	2.364	1061	1.528
1.16	0.9797	439.7	0.6332		1.66	2.400	1077	1.551
1.17	1.001	449.2	0.6469		1.67	2.436	1093	1.575
1.18	1.022	458.9	0.6608		1.68	2.473	1110	1.598
1.19	1.044	468.7	0.6749		1.69	2.510	1127	1.622
1.20	1.066	478.6	0.6892		1.70	2.547	1143	1.646
1.21	1.089	488.6	0.7036		1.71	2.585	1160	1.671
1.22	1.111	498.8	0.7183		1.72	2.623	1177	1.695
1.23	1.134	509.1	0.7331		1.73	2.661	1194	1.720
1.24	1.157	519.5	0.7481		1.74	2.700	1212	1.745
1.25	1.181	530.0	0.7632		1.75	2.739	1229	1.770
1.26	1.205	540.7	0.7786		1.76	2.778	1247	1.795
1.27	1.229	551.5	0.7941		1.77	2.818	1265	1.821
1.28	1.253	562.4	0.8099		1.78	2.858	1283	1.847
1.29	1.278	573.4	0.8258		1.79	2.898	1301	1.873
1.30	1.303	584.6	0.8419		1.80	2.939	1319	1.899
1.31	1.328	595.9	0.8581		1.81	2.979	1337	1.926
1.32	1.353	607.4	0.8746		1.82	3.021	1356	1.952
1.33	1.379	618.9	0.8913		1.83	3.062	1374	1.979
1.34	1.405	630.6	0.9081		1.84	3.104	1393	2.006
1.35	1.431	642.5	0.9252		1.85	3.147	1412	2.034
1.36	1.458	654.4	0.9424		1.86	3.190	1432	2.061
1.37	1.485	666.5	0.9598		1.87	3.233	1451	2.089
1.38	1.512	678.8	0.9774		1.88	3.276	1470	2.117
1.39	1.540	691.1	0.9952		1.89	3.320	1490	2.146
1.40	1.568	703.6	1.013		1.90	3.364	1510	2.174
1.41	1.596	716.2	1.031		1.91	3.408	1530	2.203
1.42	1.624	729.0	1.050		1.92	3.453	1550	2.232
1.43	1.653	741.9	1.068		1.93	3.498	1570	2.261
1.44	1.682	755.0	1.087		1.94	3.544	1590	2.290
1.45	1.711	768.1	1.106		1.95	3.589	1611	2.320
1.46	1.741	781.4	1.125		1.96	3.636	1632	2.350
1.47	1.771	794.9	1.145		1.97	3.682	1653	2.380
1.48	1.801	808.5	1.164		1.98	3.729	1674	2.410
1.49	1.832	822.2	1.184		1.99	3.776	1695	2.441
1.50	1.863	836.1	1.204		2.00	3.824	1716	2.471

9

Table 9-3:
45° V-notch Weir Discharge Table with Head in Feet

Formula: CFS $= 1.035\ H^{2.5}$
GPM $= 464.5\ H^{2.5}$
MGD $= 0.6689\ H^{2.5}$
Where: H = head in feet

Values in italics indicate flow below the recommended range of this particular primary device.

Table 9-3				Table 9-3 (Continued)			
Head (feet)	CFS	GPM	MGD	Head (feet)	CFS	GPM	MGD
0.01	*0*	*0*	*0*	0.51	0.1922	86.28	0.1242
0.02	*0.0001*	*0.026*	*0.0000*	0.52	0.2018	90.57	0.1304
0.03	*0.0002*	*0.072*	*0.0001*	0.53	0.2117	94.99	0.1368
0.04	*0.0003*	*0.149*	*0.0002*	0.54	0.2218	99.53	0.1433
0.05	*0.0006*	*0.260*	*0.0004*	0.55	0.2322	104.2	0.1501
0.06	*0.0009*	*0.410*	*0.0006*	0.56	0.2429	109.0	0.1570
0.07	*0.0013*	*0.602*	*0.0009*	0.57	0.2539	113.9	0.1641
0.08	*0.0019*	*0.841*	*0.0012*	0.58	0.2652	119.0	0.1714
0.09	*0.0025*	*1.129*	*0.0016*	0.59	0.2767	124.2	0.1789
0.10	*0.0033*	*1.469*	*0.0021*	0.60	0.2886	129.5	0.1865
0.11	*0.0042*	*1.864*	*0.0027*	0.61	0.3008	135.0	0.1944
0.12	*0.0052*	*2.317*	*0.0033*	0.62	0.3133	140.6	0.2025
0.13	*0.0063*	*2.831*	*0.0041*	0.63	0.3261	146.3	0.2107
0.14	*0.0076*	*3.407*	*0.0049*	0.64	0.3391	152.2	0.2192
0.15	*0.0090*	*4.048*	*0.0058*	0.65	0.3526	158.2	0.2278
0.16	*0.0106*	*4.757*	*0.0068*	0.66	0.3663	164.4	0.2367
0.17	*0.0123*	*5.535*	*0.0080*	0.67	0.3803	170.7	0.2458
0.18	*0.0142*	*6.386*	*0.0092*	0.68	0.3947	177.1	0.2551
0.19	*0.0163*	*7.310*	*0.0105*	0.69	0.4093	183.7	0.2645
0.20	0.0185	8.309	0.0120	0.70	0.4243	190.4	0.2742
0.21	0.0209	9.387	0.0135	0.71	0.4396	197.3	0.2841
0.22	0.0235	10.54	0.0152	0.72	0.4553	204.3	0.2942
0.23	0.0263	11.78	0.0170	0.73	0.4712	211.5	0.3046
0.24	0.0292	13.11	0.0189	0.74	0.4876	218.8	0.3151
0.25	0.0323	14.52	0.0209	0.75	0.5042	226.3	0.3258
0.26	0.0357	16.01	0.0231	0.76	0.5212	233.9	0.3368
0.27	0.0392	17.60	0.0253	0.77	0.5385	241.7	0.3480
0.28	0.0429	19.27	0.0277	0.78	0.5561	249.6	0.3594
0.29	0.0469	21.04	0.0303	0.79	0.5741	257.7	0.3710
0.30	0.0510	22.90	0.0330	0.80	0.5925	265.9	0.3829
0.31	0.0554	24.85	0.0358	0.81	0.6112	274.3	0.3950
0.32	0.0600	26.91	0.0387	0.82	0.6302	282.8	0.4073
0.33	0.0647	29.06	0.0418	0.83	0.6496	291.5	0.4198
0.34	0.0698	31.31	0.0451	0.84	0.6693	300.4	0.4326
0.35	0.0750	33.66	0.0485	0.85	0.6894	309.4	0.4456
0.36	0.0805	36.12	0.0520	0.86	0.7099	318.6	0.4588
0.37	0.0862	38.68	0.0557	0.87	0.7307	327.9	0.4722
0.38	0.0921	41.35	0.0595	0.88	0.7519	337.4	0.4859
0.39	0.0983	44.12	0.0635	0.89	0.7734	347.1	0.4998
0.40	0.1047	47.00	0.0677	0.90	0.7953	356.9	0.5140
0.41	0.1114	50.00	0.0720	0.91	0.8176	366.9	0.5284
0.42	0.1183	53.10	0.0765	0.92	0.8403	377.1	0.5430
0.43	0.1255	56.32	0.0811	0.93	0.8633	387.4	0.5579
0.44	0.1329	59.65	0.0859	0.94	0.8867	397.9	0.5730
0.45	0.1406	63.10	0.0909	0.95	0.9104	408.6	0.5884
0.46	0.1485	66.66	0.0960	0.96	0.9346	419.4	0.6040
0.47	0.1567	70.34	0.1013	0.97	0.9591	430.4	0.6199
0.48	0.1652	74.15	0.1068	0.98	0.9840	441.6	0.6360
0.49	0.1740	78.07	0.1124	0.99	1.009	453.0	0.6523
0.50	0.1830	82.11	0.1182	1.00	1.035	464.5	0.6689

Table 9-3 (Continued)				Table 9-3 (Continued)			
Head (feet)	CFS	GPM	MGD	Head (feet)	CFS	GPM	MGD
1.01	1.061	476.2	0.6857	1.51	2.900	1301	1.874
1.02	1.088	488.1	0.7028	1.52	2.948	1323	1.905
1.03	1.114	500.1	0.7202	1.53	2.997	1345	1.937
1.04	1.142	512.4	0.7378	1.54	3.046	1367	1.969
1.05	1.169	524.8	0.7557	1.55	3.096	1389	2.001
1.06	1.197	537.3	0.7738	1.56	3.146	1412	2.033
1.07	1.226	550.1	0.7922	1.57	3.197	1435	2.066
1.08	1.255	563.0	0.8108	1.58	3.248	1458	2.099
1.09	1.284	576.2	0.8297	1.59	3.299	1481	2.132
1.10	1.313	589.5	0.8489	1.60	3.352	1504	2.166
1.11	1.344	603.0	0.8683	1.61	3.404	1528	2.200
1.12	1.374	616.6	0.8880	1.62	3.457	1552	2.234
1.13	1.405	630.5	0.9079	1.63	3.511	1576	2.269
1.14	1.436	644.5	0.9282	1.64	3.565	1600	2.304
1.15	1.468	658.8	0.9486	1.65	3.620	1624	2.339
1.16	1.500	673.2	0.9694	1.66	3.675	1649	2.375
1.17	1.533	687.8	0.9904	1.67	3.730	1674	2.411
1.18	1.565	702.6	1.012	1.68	3.786	1699	2.447
1.19	1.599	717.6	1.033	1.69	3.843	1725	2.484
1.20	1.633	732.7	1.055	1.70	3.900	1750	2.520
1.21	1.667	748.1	1.077	1.71	3.958	1776	2.558
1.22	1.702	763.6	1.100	1.72	4.016	1802	2.595
1.23	1.737	779.4	1.122	1.73	4.074	1829	2.633
1.24	1.772	795.3	1.145	1.74	4.133	1855	2.671
1.25	1.808	811.4	1.169	1.75	4.193	1882	2.710
1.26	1.844	827.8	1.192	1.76	4.253	1909	2.749
1.27	1.881	844.3	1.216	1.77	4.314	1936	2.788
1.28	1.919	861.0	1.240	1.78	4.375	1964	2.828
1.29	1.956	877.9	1.264	1.79	4.437	1991	2.867
1.30	1.994	895.0	1.289	1.80	4.499	2019	2.908
1.31	2.033	912.4	1.314	1.81	4.562	2047	2.948
1.32	2.072	929.9	1.339	1.82	4.625	2076	2.989
1.33	2.111	947.6	1.365	1.83	4.689	2104	3.030
1.34	2.151	965.5	1.390	1.84	4.753	2133	3.072
1.35	2.192	983.6	1.416	1.85	4.818	2162	3.114
1.36	2.232	1002	1.443	1.86	4.883	2192	3.156
1.37	2.274	1020	1.469	1.87	4.949	2221	3.199
1.38	2.315	1039	1.496	1.88	5.016	2251	3.242
1.39	2.358	1058	1.524	1.89	5.083	2281	3.285
1.40	2.400	1077	1.551	1.90	5.150	2311	3.328
1.41	2.443	1097	1.579	1.91	5.218	2342	3.372
1.42	2.487	1116	1.607	1.92	5.287	2373	3.417
1.43	2.531	1136	1.636	1.93	5.356	2404	3.461
1.44	2.575	1156	1.664	1.94	5.426	2435	3.506
1.45	2.620	1176	1.693	1.95	5.496	2466	3.552
1.46	2.666	1196	1.723	1.96	5.566	2498	3.598
1.47	2.712	1217	1.752	1.97	5.638	2530	3.644
1.48	2.758	1238	1.782	1.98	5.710	2562	3.690
1.49	2.805	1259	1.813	1.99	5.782	2595	3.737
1.50	2.852	1280	1.843	2.00	5.855	2628	3.784

9

V-notch Weir Discharge Tables • 163

Table 9-4:
60° V-notch Weir Discharge Table with Head in Feet

Formula: $\text{CFS} = 1.443\ H^{2.5}$
$\text{GPM} = 647.6\ H^{2.5}$
$\text{MGD} = 0.9326\ H^{2.5}$

Where: H = head in feet

Values in italics indicate flow below the recommended range of this particular primary device.

Table 9-4				Table 9-4 (Continued)			
Head (feet)	CFS	GPM	MGD	Head (feet)	CFS	GPM	MGD
0.01	*0*	*0*	*0*	0.51	0.2680	120.3	0.1732
0.02	*0.0001*	*0.04*	*0.0001*	0.52	0.2814	126.3	0.1818
0.03	*0.0002*	*0.10*	*0.0001*	0.53	0.2951	132.4	0.1907
0.04	*0.0005*	*0.21*	*0.0003*	0.54	0.3092	138.8	0.1998
0.05	*0.0008*	*0.36*	*0.0005*	0.55	0.3237	145.3	0.2092
0.06	*0.0013*	*0.57*	*0.0008*	0.56	0.3386	152.0	0.2189
0.07	*0.0019*	*0.84*	*0.0012*	0.57	0.3540	158.9	0.2288
0.08	*0.0026*	*1.17*	*0.0017*	0.58	0.3697	165.9	0.2389
0.09	*0.0035*	*1.57*	*0.0023*	0.59	0.3858	173.2	0.2494
0.10	*0.0046*	*2.04*	*0.0029*	0.60	0.4024	180.6	0.2601
0.11	*0.0058*	*2.59*	*0.0037*	0.61	0.4194	188.2	0.2710
0.12	*0.0072*	*3.22*	*0.0046*	0.62	0.4368	196.0	0.2823
0.13	*0.0088*	*3.94*	*0.0057*	0.63	0.4546	204.0	0.2938
0.14	*0.0106*	*4.74*	*0.0068*	0.64	0.4728	212.2	0.3056
0.15	*0.0125*	*5.63*	*0.0081*	0.65	0.4915	220.6	0.3177
0.16	*0.0147*	*6.62*	*0.0095*	0.66	0.5107	229.2	0.3300
0.17	*0.0172*	*7.70*	*0.0111*	0.67	0.5302	238.0	0.3427
0.18	*0.0198*	*8.88*	*0.0128*	0.68	0.5502	246.9	0.3556
0.19	*0.0227*	*10.17*	*0.0146*	0.69	0.5707	256.1	0.3688
0.20	0.0258	11.58	0.0167	0.70	0.5916	265.5	0.3823
0.21	0.0292	13.09	0.0188	0.71	0.6129	275.1	0.3961
0.22	0.0328	14.70	0.0212	0.72	0.6347	284.9	0.4102
0.23	0.0366	16.43	0.0237	0.73	0.6570	294.9	0.4246
0.24	0.0407	18.27	0.0263	0.74	0.6797	305.1	0.4393
0.25	0.0451	20.24	0.0291	0.75	0.7029	315.5	0.4543
0.26	0.0497	22.32	0.0321	0.76	0.7266	326.1	0.4696
0.27	0.0547	24.53	0.0353	0.77	0.7507	336.9	0.4852
0.28	0.0599	26.87	0.0387	0.78	0.7754	348.0	0.5011
0.29	0.0654	29.33	0.0422	0.79	0.8004	359.2	0.5173
0.30	0.0711	31.92	0.0460	0.80	0.8260	370.7	0.5339
0.31	0.0772	34.65	0.0499	0.81	0.8521	382.4	0.5507
0.32	0.0836	37.51	0.0540	0.82	0.8786	394.3	0.5678
0.33	0.0903	40.51	0.0583	0.83	0.9057	406.4	0.5853
0.34	0.0973	43.65	0.0629	0.84	0.9332	418.8	0.6031
0.35	0.1046	46.93	0.0676	0.85	0.9612	431.4	0.6212
0.36	0.1122	50.36	0.0725	0.86	0.9897	444.2	0.6396
0.37	0.1202	53.93	0.0777	0.87	1.019	457.2	0.6584
0.38	0.1284	57.65	0.0830	0.88	1.048	470.5	0.6775
0.39	0.1371	61.51	0.0886	0.89	1.078	483.9	0.6969
0.40	0.1460	65.53	0.0944	0.90	1.109	497.6	0.7166
0.41	0.1553	69.71	0.1004	0.91	1.140	511.6	0.7367
0.42	0.1650	74.03	0.1066	0.92	1.171	525.7	0.7571
0.43	0.1750	78.52	0.1131	0.93	1.204	540.1	0.7779
0.44	0.1853	83.16	0.1198	0.94	1.236	554.8	0.7989
0.45	0.1960	87.97	0.1267	0.95	1.269	569.7	0.8204
0.46	0.2071	92.94	0.1338	0.96	1.303	584.8	0.8421
0.47	0.2185	98.07	0.1412	0.97	1.337	600.1	0.8642
0.48	0.2303	103.4	0.1489	0.98	1.372	615.7	0.8867
0.49	0.2425	108.8	0.1567	0.99	1.407	631.5	0.9095
0.50	0.2551	114.5	0.1649	1.00	1.443	647.6	0.9326

Table 9-4 (Continued)					Table 9-4 (Continued)			
Head (feet)	CFS	GPM	MGD		Head (feet)	CFS	GPM	MGD
1.01	1.479	663.9	0.9561		1.51	4.043	1814	2.613
1.02	1.516	680.5	0.9799		1.52	4.110	1845	2.656
1.03	1.554	697.3	1.004		1.53	4.178	1875	2.700
1.04	1.592	714.3	1.029		1.54	4.247	1906	2.745
1.05	1.630	731.6	1.054		1.55	4.316	1937	2.789
1.06	1.669	749.2	1.079		1.56	4.386	1968	2.835
1.07	1.709	766.9	1.104		1.57	4.457	2000	2.880
1.08	1.749	785.0	1.130		1.58	4.528	2032	2.926
1.09	1.790	803.3	1.157		1.59	4.600	2064	2.973
1.10	1.831	821.8	1.184		1.60	4.673	2097	3.020
1.11	1.873	840.6	1.211		1.61	4.746	2130	3.067
1.12	1.916	859.7	1.238		1.62	4.820	2163	3.115
1.13	1.959	879.0	1.266		1.63	4.895	2197	3.163
1.14	2.002	898.6	1.294		1.64	4.970	2231	3.212
1.15	2.046	918.4	1.323		1.65	5.046	2265	3.261
1.16	2.091	938.5	1.352		1.66	5.123	2299	3.311
1.17	2.137	958.9	1.381		1.67	5.201	2334	3.361
1.18	2.183	979.5	1.411		1.68	5.279	2369	3.412
1.19	2.229	1000	1.441		1.69	5.358	2404	3.463
1.20	2.276	1022	1.471		1.70	5.437	2440	3.514
1.21	2.324	1043	1.502		1.71	5.518	2476	3.566
1.22	2.372	1065	1.533		1.72	5.599	2513	3.618
1.23	2.421	1087	1.565		1.73	5.680	2549	3.671
1.24	2.471	1109	1.597		1.74	5.763	2586	3.725
1.25	2.521	1131	1.629		1.75	5.846	2624	3.778
1.26	2.572	1154	1.662		1.76	5.930	2661	3.832
1.27	2.623	1177	1.695		1.77	6.014	2699	3.887
1.28	2.675	1200	1.729		1.78	6.100	2738	3.942
1.29	2.727	1224	1.763		1.79	6.186	2776	3.998
1.30	2.781	1248	1.797		1.80	6.273	2815	4.054
1.31	2.834	1272	1.832		1.81	6.360	2854	4.110
1.32	2.889	1296	1.867		1.82	6.448	2894	4.167
1.33	2.944	1321	1.902		1.83	6.537	2934	4.225
1.34	2.999	1346	1.938		1.84	6.627	2974	4.283
1.35	3.056	1371	1.975		1.85	6.717	3015	4.341
1.36	3.113	1397	2.012		1.86	6.808	3056	4.400
1.37	3.170	1423	2.049		1.87	6.900	3097	4.460
1.38	3.228	1449	2.086		1.88	6.993	3138	4.519
1.39	3.287	1475	2.124		1.89	7.086	3180	4.580
1.40	3.346	1502	2.163		1.90	7.180	3222	4.641
1.41	3.407	1529	2.202		1.91	7.275	3265	4.702
1.42	3.467	1556	2.241		1.92	7.371	3308	4.764
1.43	3.529	1584	2.281		1.93	7.467	3351	4.826
1.44	3.591	1611	2.321		1.94	7.564	3395	4.889
1.45	3.653	1640	2.361		1.95	7.662	3439	4.952
1.46	3.717	1668	2.402		1.96	7.761	3483	5.016
1.47	3.781	1697	2.443		1.97	7.860	3528	5.080
1.48	3.845	1726	2.485		1.98	7.960	3572	5.145
1.49	3.910	1755	2.527		1.99	8.061	3618	5.210
1.50	3.976	1785	2.570		2.00	8.163	3663	5.276

9

Table 9-5:
90° V-notch Weir Discharge Table with Head in Feet

Formula: CFS $= 2.500\ H^{2.5}$
GPM $= 1122\ H^{2.5}$
MGD $= 1.616\ H^{2.5}$
Where: H = head in feet

Values in italics indicate flow below the recommended range of this particular primary device.

Table 9-5				Table 9-5 (Continued)			
Head (feet)	CFS	GPM	MGD	Head (feet)	CFS	GPM	MGD
0.01	*0*	*0*	*0*	0.51	0.4644	208.4	0.3002
0.02	*0.0001*	*0.06*	*0.0001*	0.52	0.4875	218.8	0.3151
0.03	*0.0004*	*0.17*	*0.0003*	0.53	0.5112	229.4	0.3305
0.04	*0.0008*	*0.36*	*0.0005*	0.54	0.5357	240.4	0.3463
0.05	*0.0014*	*0.63*	*0.0009*	0.55	0.5609	251.7	0.3625
0.06	*0.0022*	*0.99*	*0.0014*	0.56	0.5867	263.3	0.3792
0.07	*0.0032*	*1.45*	*0.0021*	0.57	0.6132	275.2	0.3964
0.08	*0.0045*	*2.03*	*0.0029*	0.58	0.6405	287.5	0.4140
0.09	*0.0061*	*2.73*	*0.0039*	0.59	0.6685	300.0	0.4321
0.10	*0.0079*	*3.55*	*0.0051*	0.60	0.6971	312.9	0.4506
0.11	*0.0100*	*4.50*	*0.0065*	0.61	0.7265	326.1	0.4696
0.12	*0.0125*	*5.60*	*0.0081*	0.62	0.7567	339.6	0.4891
0.13	*0.0152*	*6.84*	*0.0098*	0.63	0.7876	353.5	0.5091
0.14	*0.0183*	*8.23*	*0.0118*	0.64	0.8192	367.7	0.5295
0.15	*0.0218*	*9.78*	*0.0141*	0.65	0.8516	382.2	0.5505
0.16	*0.0256*	*11.49*	*0.0165*	0.66	0.8847	397.1	0.5719
0.17	*0.0298*	*13.37*	*0.0193*	0.67	0.9186	412.3	0.5938
0.18	*0.0344*	*15.42*	*0.0222*	0.68	0.9533	427.8	0.6162
0.19	*0.0393*	*17.66*	*0.0254*	0.69	0.9887	443.7	0.6391
0.20	0.0447	20.07	0.0289	0.70	1.025	460.0	0.6625
0.21	0.0505	22.67	0.0327	0.71	1.062	476.6	0.6864
0.22	0.0568	25.47	0.0367	0.72	1.100	493.5	0.7108
0.23	0.0634	28.47	0.0410	0.73	1.138	510.9	0.7358
0.24	0.0705	31.66	0.0456	0.74	1.178	528.5	0.7612
0.25	0.0781	35.06	0.0505	0.75	1.218	546.6	0.7872
0.26	0.0862	38.67	0.0557	0.76	1.259	565.0	0.8137
0.27	0.0947	42.50	0.0612	0.77	1.301	583.7	0.8408
0.28	0.1037	46.55	0.0670	0.78	1.343	602.9	0.8683
0.29	0.1132	50.81	0.0732	0.79	1.387	622.4	0.8964
0.30	0.1232	55.31	0.0797	0.80	1.431	642.3	0.9251
0.31	0.1338	60.03	0.0865	0.81	1.476	662.5	0.9542
0.32	0.1448	64.99	0.0936	0.82	1.522	683.2	0.9840
0.33	0.1564	70.19	0.1011	0.83	1.569	704.2	1.014
0.34	0.1685	75.63	0.1089	0.84	1.617	725.6	1.045
0.35	0.1812	81.31	0.1171	0.85	1.665	747.4	1.076
0.36	0.1944	87.25	0.1257	0.86	1.715	769.6	1.108
0.37	0.2082	93.43	0.1346	0.87	1.765	792.1	1.141
0.38	0.2225	99.87	0.1438	0.88	1.816	815.1	1.174
0.39	0.2375	106.6	0.1535	0.89	1.868	838.4	1.208
0.40	0.2530	113.5	0.1635	0.90	1.921	862.2	1.242
0.41	0.2691	120.8	0.1739	0.91	1.975	886.3	1.277
0.42	0.2858	128.3	0.1847	0.92	2.030	910.9	1.312
0.43	0.3031	136.0	0.1959	0.93	2.085	935.8	1.348
0.44	0.3210	144.1	0.2075	0.94	2.142	961.2	1.384
0.45	0.3396	152.4	0.2195	0.95	2.199	987.0	1.422
0.46	0.3588	161.0	0.2319	0.96	2.257	1013	1.459
0.47	0.3786	169.9	0.2447	0.97	2.317	1040	1.498
0.48	0.3991	179.1	0.2580	0.98	2.377	1067	1.536
0.49	0.4202	188.6	0.2716	0.99	2.438	1094	1.576
0.50	0.4419	198.3	0.2857	1.00	2.500	1122	1.616

Table 9-5 (Continued)			
Head (feet)	CFS	GPM	MGD
1.01	2.563	1150	1.657
1.02	2.627	1179	1.698
1.03	2.692	1208	1.740
1.04	2.758	1238	1.782
1.05	2.824	1268	1.826
1.06	2.892	1298	1.869
1.07	2.961	1329	1.914
1.08	3.030	1360	1.959
1.09	3.101	1392	2.005
1.10	3.173	1424	2.051
1.11	3.245	1456	2.098
1.12	3.319	1489	2.145
1.13	3.393	1523	2.193
1.14	3.469	1557	2.242
1.15	3.546	1591	2.292
1.16	3.623	1626	2.342
1.17	3.702	1661	2.393
1.18	3.781	1697	2.444
1.19	3.862	1733	2.496
1.20	3.944	1770	2.549
1.21	4.026	1807	2.603
1.22	4.110	1845	2.657
1.23	4.195	1883	2.711
1.24	4.280	1921	2.767
1.25	4.367	1960	2.823
1.26	4.455	1999	2.880
1.27	4.544	2039	2.937
1.28	4.634	2080	2.995
1.29	4.725	2121	3.054
1.30	4.817	2162	3.114
1.31	4.910	2204	3.174
1.32	5.005	2246	3.235
1.33	5.100	2289	3.297
1.34	5.196	2332	3.359
1.35	5.294	2376	3.422
1.36	5.392	2420	3.486
1.37	5.492	2465	3.550
1.38	5.593	2510	3.615
1.39	5.695	2556	3.681
1.40	5.798	2602	3.748
1.41	5.902	2649	3.815
1.42	6.007	2696	3.883
1.43	6.113	2744	3.952
1.44	6.221	2792	4.021
1.45	6.329	2841	4.091
1.46	6.439	2890	4.162
1.47	6.550	2940	4.234
1.48	6.662	2990	4.306
1.49	6.775	3041	4.379
1.50	6.889	3092	4.453

Table 9-5 (Continued)			
Head (feet)	CFS	GPM	MGD
1.51	7.005	3144	4.528
1.52	7.121	3196	4.603
1.53	7.239	3249	4.679
1.54	7.358	3302	4.756
1.55	7.478	3356	4.834
1.56	7.599	3410	4.912
1.57	7.721	3465	4.991
1.58	7.845	3521	5.071
1.59	7.970	3577	5.152
1.60	8.095	3633	5.233
1.61	8.223	3690	5.315
1.62	8.351	3748	5.398
1.63	8.480	3806	5.482
1.64	8.611	3865	5.566
1.65	8.743	3924	5.651
1.66	8.876	3983	5.737
1.67	9.010	4044	5.824
1.68	9.146	4105	5.912
1.69	9.282	4166	6.000
1.70	9.420	4228	6.089
1.71	9.559	4290	6.179
1.72	9.700	4353	6.270
1.73	9.841	4417	6.361
1.74	9.984	4481	6.454
1.75	10.13	4546	6.547
1.76	10.27	4611	6.641
1.77	10.42	4677	6.736
1.78	10.57	4743	6.831
1.79	10.72	4810	6.927
1.80	10.87	4877	7.025
1.81	11.02	4945	7.123
1.82	11.17	5014	7.221
1.83	11.33	5083	7.321
1.84	11.48	5153	7.421
1.85	11.64	5223	7.523
1.86	11.80	5294	7.625
1.87	11.95	5365	7.728
1.88	12.12	5437	7.831
1.89	12.28	5510	7.936
1.90	12.44	5583	8.041
1.91	12.60	5657	8.148
1.92	12.77	5731	8.255
1.93	12.94	5806	8.362
1.94	13.11	5882	8.471
1.95	13.27	5958	8.581
1.96	13.45	6034	8.691
1.97	13.62	6112	8.803
1.98	13.79	6190	8.915
1.99	13.97	6268	9.028
2.00	14.14	6347	9.141

9

Table 9-6:
120° V-notch Weir Discharge Table with Head in Feet

Formula: CFS $= 4.330\ H^{2.5}$
$\quad\quad\quad$ GPM $= 1943\ H^{2.5}$
$\quad\quad\quad$ MGD $= 2.798\ H^{2.5}$
Where: H = head in feet

Values in italics indicate flow below the recommended range of this particular primary device.

Head (feet)	CFS	GPM	MGD	Head (feet)	CFS	GPM	MGD
0.01	*0*	*0*	*0*	0.51	0.8043	360.9	0.5197
0.02	*0.0002*	*0.11*	*0.0002*	0.52	0.8443	378.9	0.5456
0.03	*0.0007*	*0.30*	*0.0004*	0.53	0.8855	397.3	0.5722
0.04	*0.0014*	*0.62*	*0.0009*	0.54	0.9278	416.3	0.5996
0.05	*0.0024*	*1.09*	*0.0016*	0.55	0.9714	435.9	0.6277
0.06	*0.0038*	*1.71*	*0.0025*	0.56	1.016	456.0	0.6566
0.07	*0.0056*	*2.52*	*0.0036*	0.57	1.062	476.6	0.6863
0.08	*0.0078*	*3.52*	*0.0051*	0.58	1.109	497.8	0.7168
0.09	*0.0105*	*4.72*	*0.0068*	0.59	1.158	519.5	0.7481
0.10	*0.0137*	*6.15*	*0.0088*	0.60	1.207	541.8	0.7802
0.11	*0.0174*	*7.80*	*0.0112*	0.61	1.258	564.7	0.8132
0.12	*0.0216*	*9.69*	*0.0140*	0.62	1.311	588.1	0.8469
0.13	*0.0264*	*11.84*	*0.0171*	0.63	1.364	612.1	0.8815
0.14	*0.0318*	*14.25*	*0.0205*	0.64	1.419	636.7	0.9168
0.15	*0.0377*	*16.94*	*0.0244*	0.65	1.475	661.8	0.9531
0.16	*0.0443*	*19.90*	*0.0287*	0.66	1.532	687.6	0.9902
0.17	*0.0516*	*23.16*	*0.0333*	0.67	1.591	713.9	1.028
0.18	*0.0595*	*26.71*	*0.0385*	0.68	1.651	740.9	1.067
0.19	*0.0681*	*30.58*	*0.0440*	0.69	1.712	768.4	1.107
0.20	0.0775	34.76	0.0501	0.70	1.775	796.6	1.147
0.21	0.0875	39.27	0.0565	0.71	1.839	825.3	1.188
0.22	0.0983	44.11	0.0635	0.72	1.905	854.7	1.231
0.23	0.1099	49.29	0.0710	0.73	1.971	884.7	1.274
0.24	0.1222	54.83	0.0790	0.74	2.040	915.3	1.318
0.25	0.1353	60.72	0.0874	0.75	2.109	946.5	1.363
0.26	0.1493	66.97	0.0964	0.76	2.180	978.4	1.409
0.27	0.1640	73.60	0.1060	0.77	2.253	1011	1.456
0.28	0.1796	80.61	0.1161	0.78	2.327	1044	1.503
0.29	0.1961	88.00	0.1267	0.79	2.402	1078	1.552
0.30	0.2134	95.78	0.1379	0.80	2.479	1112	1.602
0.31	0.2317	104.0	0.1497	0.81	2.557	1147	1.652
0.32	0.2508	112.6	0.1621	0.82	2.636	1183	1.704
0.33	0.2709	121.6	0.1750	0.83	2.718	1219	1.756
0.34	0.2919	131.0	0.1886	0.84	2.800	1257	1.809
0.35	0.3138	140.8	0.2028	0.85	2.884	1294	1.864
0.36	0.3367	151.1	0.2176	0.86	2.970	1333	1.919
0.37	0.3606	161.8	0.2330	0.87	3.057	1372	1.975
0.38	0.3854	173.0	0.2491	0.88	3.146	1411	2.033
0.39	0.4113	184.6	0.2658	0.89	3.236	1452	2.091
0.40	0.4382	196.6	0.2831	0.90	3.327	1493	2.150
0.41	0.4661	209.1	0.3012	0.91	3.421	1535	2.210
0.42	0.4950	222.1	0.3199	0.92	3.515	1577	2.272
0.43	0.5250	235.6	0.3392	0.93	3.612	1621	2.334
0.44	0.5561	249.5	0.3593	0.94	3.709	1665	2.397
0.45	0.5882	263.9	0.3801	0.95	3.809	1709	2.461
0.46	0.6214	278.8	0.4016	0.96	3.910	1754	2.527
0.47	0.6557	294.3	0.4237	0.97	4.013	1801	2.593
0.48	0.6912	310.2	0.4466	0.98	4.117	1847	2.660
0.49	0.7277	326.6	0.4703	0.99	4.223	1895	2.729
0.50	0.7654	343.5	0.4946	1.00	4.330	1943	2.798

9

Table 9-6 (Continued)				Table 9-6 (Continued)			
Head (feet)	CFS	GPM	MGD	Head (feet)	CFS	GPM	MGD
1.01	4.439	1992	2.868	1.51	12.13	5444	7.840
1.02	4.550	2042	2.940	1.52	12.33	5535	7.970
1.03	4.662	2092	3.013	1.53	12.54	5626	8.102
1.04	4.776	2143	3.086	1.54	12.74	5718	8.235
1.05	4.892	2195	3.161	1.55	12.95	5812	8.369
1.06	5.009	2248	3.237	1.56	13.16	5906	8.505
1.07	5.128	2301	3.314	1.57	13.37	6001	8.642
1.08	5.249	2355	3.392	1.58	13.59	6097	8.780
1.09	5.371	2410	3.471	1.59	13.80	6194	8.920
1.10	5.495	2466	3.551	1.60	14.02	6292	9.060
1.11	5.621	2522	3.632	1.61	14.24	6391	9.203
1.12	5.748	2579	3.714	1.62	14.46	6490	9.346
1.13	5.877	2637	3.798	1.63	14.69	6591	9.491
1.14	6.008	2696	3.882	1.64	14.91	6692	9.637
1.15	6.141	2756	3.968	1.65	15.14	6795	9.785
1.16	6.275	2816	4.055	1.66	15.37	6898	9.934
1.17	6.411	2877	4.143	1.67	15.61	7003	10.08
1.18	6.549	2939	4.232	1.68	15.84	7108	10.24
1.19	6.689	3002	4.322	1.69	16.08	7214	10.39
1.20	6.830	3065	4.414	1.70	16.32	7321	10.54
1.21	6.974	3129	4.506	1.71	16.56	7430	10.70
1.22	7.118	3194	4.600	1.72	16.80	7539	10.86
1.23	7.265	3260	4.695	1.73	17.05	7649	11.01
1.24	7.414	3327	4.791	1.74	17.29	7760	11.17
1.25	7.564	3394	4.888	1.75	17.54	7872	11.34
1.26	7.716	3463	4.986	1.76	17.79	7985	11.50
1.27	7.870	3532	5.086	1.77	18.05	8099	11.66
1.28	8.026	3602	5.186	1.78	18.30	8213	11.83
1.29	8.184	3672	5.288	1.79	18.56	8329	11.99
1.30	8.343	3744	5.391	1.80	18.82	8446	12.16
1.31	8.505	3816	5.496	1.81	19.08	8564	12.33
1.32	8.668	3890	5.601	1.82	19.35	8683	12.50
1.33	8.833	3964	5.708	1.83	19.62	8802	12.68
1.34	9.000	4039	5.816	1.84	19.89	8923	12.85
1.35	9.169	4114	5.925	1.85	20.16	9045	13.02
1.36	9.340	4191	6.035	1.86	20.43	9168	13.20
1.37	9.512	4268	6.147	1.87	20.71	9291	13.38
1.38	9.687	4347	6.260	1.88	20.98	9416	13.56
1.39	9.863	4426	6.374	1.89	21.26	9542	13.74
1.40	10.04	4506	6.489	1.90	21.55	9668	13.92
1.41	10.22	4587	6.605	1.91	21.83	9796	14.11
1.42	10.40	4669	6.723	1.92	22.12	9925	14.29
1.43	10.59	4751	6.842	1.93	22.41	10,050	14.48
1.44	10.77	4835	6.962	1.94	22.70	10,190	14.67
1.45	10.96	4919	7.084	1.95	22.99	10,320	14.86
1.46	11.15	5004	7.207	1.96	23.29	10,450	15.05
1.47	11.34	5091	7.331	1.97	23.59	10,580	15.24
1.48	11.54	5178	7.456	1.98	23.89	10,720	15.44
1.49	11.73	5265	7.583	1.99	24.19	10,850	15.63
1.50	11.93	5354	7.710	2.00	24.49	10,990	15.83

9

V-notch Weir Discharge Tables • 169

Table 9-7:

22¹/₂° V-notch Weir Discharge Table with Head in Meters

Formula: $l/s = 274.4\ H^{2.5}$
$m^3/hr = 987.8\ H^{2.5}$

Where: H = head in meters

Values in italics indicate flow below the recommended range of this particular primary device.

Table 9-7			Table 9-7 (Continued)		
Head (meters)	l/s	m³/hr	Head (meters)	l/s	m³/hr
0.005	*0.0005*	*0.0017*	0.255	9.010	32.44
0.010	*0.0027*	*0.0099*	0.260	9.458	34.05
0.015	*0.0076*	*0.0272*	0.265	9.920	35.71
0.020	*0.0155*	*0.0559*	0.270	10.39	37.42
0.025	*0.0271*	*0.0976*	0.275	10.88	39.17
0.030	*0.0428*	*0.1540*	0.280	11.38	40.98
0.035	*0.0629*	*0.2264*	0.285	11.90	42.83
0.040	*0.0878*	*0.3161*	0.290	12.43	44.74
0.045	*0.1179*	*0.4243*	0.295	12.97	46.69
0.050	*0.1534*	*0.5522*	0.300	13.53	48.69
0.055	*0.1947*	*0.7008*	0.305	14.10	50.75
0.060	0.2420	0.8711	0.310	14.68	52.85
0.065	0.2956	1.064	0.315	15.28	55.01
0.070	0.3557	1.281	0.320	15.89	57.22
0.075	0.4227	1.522	0.325	16.52	59.48
0.080	0.4967	1.788	0.330	17.17	61.80
0.085	0.5780	2.081	0.335	17.82	64.16
0.090	0.6668	2.400	0.340	18.50	66.58
0.095	0.7633	2.748	0.345	19.18	69.06
0.100	0.8677	3.124	0.350	19.89	71.59
0.105	0.9803	3.529	0.355	20.60	74.17
0.110	1.101	3.964	0.360	21.34	76.81
0.115	1.231	4.430	0.365	22.09	79.51
0.120	1.369	4.927	0.370	22.85	82.26
0.125	1.516	5.457	0.375	23.63	85.06
0.130	1.672	6.019	0.380	24.43	87.93
0.135	1.837	6.615	0.385	25.24	90.85
0.140	2.012	7.244	0.390	26.06	93.83
0.145	2.197	7.908	0.395	26.91	96.86
0.150	2.391	8.608	0.400	27.77	99.96
0.155	2.595	9.343	0.405	28.64	103.1
0.160	2.810	10.12	0.410	29.54	106.3
0.165	3.035	10.92	0.415	30.44	109.6
0.170	3.270	11.77	0.420	31.37	112.9
0.175	3.515	12.66	0.425	32.31	116.3
0.180	3.772	13.58	0.430	33.27	119.8
0.185	4.039	14.54	0.435	34.25	123.3
0.190	4.318	15.54	0.440	35.24	126.9
0.195	4.608	16.59	0.445	36.25	130.5
0.200	4.909	17.67	0.450	37.27	134.2
0.205	5.221	18.80	0.455	38.32	137.9
0.210	5.545	19.96	0.460	39.38	141.8
0.215	5.881	21.17	0.465	40.46	145.6
0.220	6.229	22.42	0.470	41.56	149.6
0.225	6.589	23.72	0.475	42.67	153.6
0.230	6.962	25.06	0.480	43.80	157.7
0.235	7.346	26.44	0.485	44.95	161.8
0.240	7.743	27.87	0.490	46.12	166.0
0.245	8.153	29.35	0.495	47.30	170.3
0.250	8.575	30.87	0.500	48.51	174.6

9

Table 9-7 (Continued)			Table 9-7 (Continued)		
Head (meters)	l/s	m³/hr	Head (meters)	l/s	m³/hr
0.505	49.73	179.0	0.555	62.97	226.7
0.510	50.97	183.5	0.560	64.40	231.8
0.515	52.23	188.0	0.565	65.84	237.0
0.520	53.50	192.6	0.570	67.31	242.3
0.525	54.80	197.3	0.575	68.79	247.7
0.530	56.11	202.0	0.580	70.30	253.1
0.535	57.45	206.8	0.585	71.82	258.6
0.540	58.80	211.7	0.590	73.37	264.1
0.545	60.17	216.6	0.595	74.93	269.7
0.550	61.56	221.6	0.600	76.52	275.5

9

Table 9-8:
30° V-notch Weir Discharge Table with Head in Meters

Formula: $l/s = 373.2\ H^{2.5}$
$m^3/hr = 1344\ H^{2.5}$
Where: H = head in meters

Values in italics indicate flow below the recommended range of this particular primary device.

Table 9-8			Table 9-8 (Continued)		
Head (meters)	l/s	m³/hr	Head (meters)	l/s	m³/hr
0.005	*0.0007*	*0.002*	0.255	12.25	44.13
0.010	*0.0037*	*0.013*	0.260	12.86	46.33
0.015	*0.0103*	*0.037*	0.265	13.49	48.59
0.020	*0.0211*	*0.076*	0.270	14.14	50.91
0.025	*0.0369*	*0.133*	0.275	14.80	53.30
0.030	*0.0582*	*0.209*	0.280	15.48	55.76
0.035	*0.0855*	*0.308*	0.285	16.18	58.28
0.040	*0.1194*	*0.430*	0.290	16.90	60.87
0.045	*0.1603*	*0.577*	0.295	17.64	63.53
0.050	*0.2086*	*0.751*	0.300	18.40	66.25
0.055	*0.2648*	*0.953*	0.305	19.17	69.05
0.060	0.3291	1.185	0.310	19.97	71.91
0.065	0.4020	1.448	0.315	20.78	74.85
0.070	0.4838	1.742	0.320	21.62	77.85
0.075	0.5749	2.070	0.325	22.47	80.93
0.080	0.6756	2.433	0.330	23.35	84.08
0.085	0.7861	2.831	0.335	24.24	87.30
0.090	0.9069	3.266	0.340	25.16	90.59
0.095	1.038	3.739	0.345	26.09	93.96
0.100	1.180	4.250	0.350	27.05	97.40
0.105	1.333	4.801	0.355	28.02	100.9
0.110	1.498	5.394	0.360	29.02	104.5
0.115	1.674	6.028	0.365	30.04	108.2
0.120	1.862	6.704	0.370	31.08	111.9
0.125	2.062	7.425	0.375	32.14	115.7
0.130	2.274	8.190	0.380	33.22	119.6
0.135	2.499	9.000	0.385	34.32	123.6
0.140	2.737	9.856	0.390	35.45	127.7
0.145	2.988	10.76	0.395	36.60	131.8
0.150	3.252	11.71	0.400	37.77	136.0
0.155	3.530	12.71	0.405	38.96	140.3
0.160	3.822	13.76	0.410	40.17	144.7
0.165	4.127	14.86	0.415	41.41	149.1
0.170	4.447	16.01	0.420	42.66	153.6
0.175	4.781	17.22	0.425	43.95	158.3
0.180	5.130	18.47	0.430	45.25	163.0
0.185	5.494	19.78	0.435	46.58	167.7
0.190	5.873	21.15	0.440	47.93	172.6
0.195	6.267	22.57	0.445	49.30	177.5
0.200	6.676	24.04	0.450	50.70	182.6
0.205	7.101	25.57	0.455	52.12	187.7
0.210	7.542	27.16	0.460	53.56	192.9
0.215	7.999	28.81	0.465	55.03	198.2
0.220	8.472	30.51	0.470	56.52	203.5
0.225	8.962	32.27	0.475	58.03	209.0
0.230	9.468	34.10	0.480	59.57	214.5
0.235	9.991	35.98	0.485	61.14	220.2
0.240	10.53	37.93	0.490	62.72	225.9
0.245	11.09	39.93	0.495	64.34	231.7
0.250	11.66	42.00	0.500	65.97	237.6

Table 9-8 (Continued)		
Head (meters)	l/s	m³/hr
0.505	67.63	243.6
0.510	69.32	249.6
0.515	71.03	255.8
0.520	72.77	262.1
0.525	74.53	268.4
0.530	76.32	274.8
0.535	78.13	281.4
0.540	79.97	288.0
0.545	81.83	294.7
0.550	83.72	301.5

Table 9-8 (Continued)		
Head (meters)	l/s	m³/hr
0.555	85.64	308.4
0.560	87.58	315.4
0.565	89.55	322.5
0.570	91.54	329.7
0.575	93.56	337.0
0.580	95.61	344.3
0.585	97.69	351.8
0.590	99.79	359.4
0.595	101.9	367.0
0.600	104.1	374.8

9

Table 9-9:
45° V-notch Weir Discharge Table with Head in Meters

Formula: $l/s = 571.4\ H^{2.5}$
$m^3/hr = 2057\ H^{2.5}$
Where: H = head in meters

Values in italics indicate flow below the recommended range of this particular primary device.

Head (meters)	l/s	m³/hr	Head (meters)	l/s	m³/hr
	Table 9-9			Table 9-9 (Continued)	
0.005	*0.0010*	*0.004*	0.255	18.76	67.54
0.010	*0.0057*	*0.021*	0.260	19.70	70.90
0.015	*0.0157*	*0.057*	0.265	20.66	74.36
0.020	*0.0323*	*0.116*	0.270	21.64	77.92
0.025	*0.0565*	*0.203*	0.275	22.66	81.58
0.030	*0.0891*	*0.321*	0.280	23.70	85.34
0.035	*0.1310*	*0.471*	0.285	24.78	89.20
0.040	*0.1829*	*0.658*	0.290	25.88	93.16
0.045	*0.2455*	*0.884*	0.295	27.01	97.23
0.050	*0.3194*	*1.150*	0.300	28.17	101.4
0.055	*0.4054*	*1.459*	0.305	29.36	105.7
0.060	0.5039	1.814	0.310	30.57	110.1
0.065	0.6155	2.216	0.315	31.82	114.6
0.070	0.7408	2.667	0.320	33.10	119.2
0.075	0.8802	3.169	0.325	34.41	123.9
0.080	1.034	3.724	0.330	35.75	128.7
0.085	1.204	4.333	0.335	37.12	133.6
0.090	1.389	4.999	0.340	38.52	138.7
0.095	1.589	5.722	0.345	39.95	143.8
0.100	1.807	6.505	0.350	41.41	149.1
0.105	2.041	7.349	0.355	42.91	154.5
0.110	2.293	8.255	0.360	44.43	160.0
0.115	2.563	9.225	0.365	45.99	165.6
0.120	2.850	10.26	0.370	47.58	171.3
0.125	3.157	11.36	0.375	49.21	177.1
0.130	3.482	12.53	0.380	50.86	183.1
0.135	3.826	13.77	0.385	52.55	189.2
0.140	4.190	15.09	0.390	54.28	195.4
0.145	4.575	16.47	0.395	56.03	201.7
0.150	4.979	17.93	0.400	57.82	208.2
0.155	5.405	19.46	0.405	59.65	214.7
0.160	5.851	21.06	0.410	61.50	221.4
0.165	6.319	22.75	0.415	63.40	228.2
0.170	6.809	24.51	0.420	65.32	235.2
0.175	7.320	26.35	0.425	67.28	242.2
0.180	7.855	28.28	0.430	69.28	249.4
0.185	8.411	30.28	0.435	71.31	256.7
0.190	8.991	32.37	0.440	73.38	264.2
0.195	9.595	34.54	0.445	75.48	271.7
0.200	10.22	36.80	0.450	77.62	279.4
0.205	10.87	39.14	0.455	79.79	287.3
0.210	11.55	41.57	0.460	82.00	295.2
0.215	12.25	44.09	0.465	84.25	303.3
0.220	12.97	46.70	0.470	86.53	311.5
0.225	13.72	49.40	0.475	88.85	319.9
0.230	14.50	52.19	0.480	91.21	328.4
0.235	15.30	55.07	0.485	93.60	337.0
0.240	16.12	58.04	0.490	96.04	345.7
0.245	16.98	61.12	0.495	98.50	354.6
0.250	17.86	64.28	0.500	101.0	363.6

Table 9-9 (Continued)		
Head (meters)	l/s	m³/hr
0.505	103.6	372.8
0.510	106.1	382.1
0.515	108.8	391.5
0.520	111.4	401.1
0.525	114.1	410.8
0.530	116.9	420.7
0.535	119.6	430.6
0.540	122.4	440.8
0.545	125.3	451.1
0.550	128.2	461.5

Table 9-9 (Continued)		
Head (meters)	l/s	m³/hr
0.555	131.1	472.0
0.560	134.1	482.7
0.565	137.1	493.6
0.570	140.2	504.6
0.575	143.3	515.7
0.580	146.4	527.0
0.585	149.6	538.4
0.590	152.8	550.0
0.595	156.0	561.7
0.600	159.3	573.6

9

Table 9-10:
60° V-notch Weir Discharge Table with Head in Meters

Formula: $l/s = 796.7\ H^{2.5}$
$m^3/hr = 2868\ H^{2.5}$
Where: H = head in meters

Values in italics indicate flow below the recommended range of this particular primary device.

Table 9-10			Table 9-10 (Continued)		
Head (meters)	l/s	m³/hr	Head (meters)	l/s	m³/hr
0.005	*0.0014*	*0.005*	0.255	26.16	94.17
0.010	*0.0080*	*0.029*	0.260	27.46	98.86
0.015	*0.0219*	*0.079*	0.265	28.80	103.7
0.020	*0.0450*	*0.162*	0.270	30.18	108.6
0.025	*0.0786*	*0.283*	0.275	31.60	113.7
0.030	*0.1239*	*0.446*	0.280	33.05	119.0
0.035	*0.1822*	*0.656*	0.285	34.55	124.4
0.040	*0.2544*	*0.916*	0.290	36.08	129.9
0.045	*0.3415*	*1.229*	0.295	37.66	135.6
0.050	*0.4444*	*1.600*	0.300	39.27	141.4
0.055	*0.5640*	*2.030*	0.305	40.93	147.3
0.060	0.7025	2.529	0.310	42.63	153.5
0.065	0.8582	3.089	0.315	44.37	159.7
0.070	1.033	3.718	0.320	46.15	166.1
0.075	1.227	4.418	0.325	47.97	172.7
0.080	1.442	5.192	0.330	49.84	179.4
0.085	1.678	6.041	0.335	51.75	186.3
0.090	1.936	6.969	0.340	53.70	193.3
0.095	2.216	7.978	0.345	55.70	200.5
0.100	2.519	9.069	0.350	57.74	207.8
0.105	2.846	10.25	0.355	59.82	215.4
0.110	3.197	11.51	0.360	61.95	223.0
0.115	3.573	12.86	0.365	64.12	230.8
0.120	3.974	14.31	0.370	66.34	238.8
0.125	4.401	15.84	0.375	68.61	247.0
0.130	4.855	17.48	0.380	70.92	255.3
0.135	5.335	19.20	0.385	73.27	263.8
0.140	5.843	21.03	0.390	75.68	272.4
0.145	6.378	22.96	0.395	78.12	281.2
0.150	6.943	24.99	0.400	80.62	290.2
0.155	7.536	27.13	0.405	83.16	299.4
0.160	8.158	29.37	0.410	85.75	308.7
0.165	8.811	31.72	0.415	88.39	318.2
0.170	9.493	34.17	0.420	91.08	327.9
0.175	10.21	36.74	0.425	93.81	337.7
0.180	10.95	39.42	0.430	96.60	347.7
0.185	11.73	42.22	0.435	99.43	357.9
0.190	12.54	45.13	0.440	102.3	368.3
0.195	13.38	48.16	0.445	105.2	378.9
0.200	14.25	51.30	0.450	108.2	389.6
0.205	15.16	54.57	0.455	111.3	400.5
0.210	16.10	57.96	0.460	114.3	411.6
0.215	17.08	61.47	0.465	117.5	422.9
0.220	18.09	65.11	0.470	120.7	434.3
0.225	19.13	68.87	0.475	123.9	446.0
0.230	20.21	72.76	0.480	127.2	457.8
0.235	21.33	76.78	0.485	130.5	469.8
0.240	22.48	80.93	0.490	133.9	482.0
0.245	23.67	85.21	0.495	137.3	494.4
0.250	24.90	89.63	0.500	140.8	507.0

9

Table 9-10 (Continued)			Table 9-10 (Continued)		
Head (meters)	l/s	m³/hr	Head (meters)	l/s	m³/hr
0.505	144.4	519.8	0.555	182.8	658.1
0.510	148.0	532.7	0.560	187.0	673.1
0.515	151.6	545.9	0.565	191.2	688.2
0.520	155.3	559.2	0.570	195.4	703.5
0.525	159.1	572.8	0.575	199.7	719.0
0.530	162.9	586.5	0.580	204.1	734.8
0.535	166.8	600.4	0.585	208.5	750.7
0.540	170.7	614.6	0.590	213.0	766.8
0.545	174.7	628.9	0.595	217.6	783.2
0.550	178.7	643.4	0.600	222.2	799.8

9

Table 9-11:
90° V-notch Weir Discharge Table with Head in Meters

Formula: l/s = 1380 H$^{2.5}$
m^3/hr = 4969 H$^{2.5}$
Where: H = head in meters

Values in italics indicate flow below the recommended range of this particular primary device.

Table 9-11			Table 9-11 (Continued)		
Head (meters)	l/s	m^3/hr	Head (meters)	l/s	m^3/hr
0.005	*0.002*	*0.009*	0.255	45.31	163.2
0.010	*0.014*	*0.050*	0.260	47.57	171.3
0.015	*0.038*	*0.137*	0.265	49.89	179.6
0.020	*0.078*	*0.281*	0.270	52.27	188.2
0.025	*0.136*	*0.491*	0.275	54.73	197.1
0.030	*0.215*	*0.775*	0.280	57.25	206.1
0.035	*0.316*	*1.139*	0.285	59.84	215.5
0.040	*0.442*	*1.590*	0.290	62.50	225.0
0.045	*0.593*	*2.134*	0.295	65.23	234.9
0.050	*0.772*	*2.778*	0.300	68.03	244.9
0.055	*0.979*	*3.525*	0.305	70.90	255.3
0.060	1.217	4.382	0.310	73.84	265.9
0.065	1.486	5.352	0.315	76.85	276.7
0.070	1.789	6.442	0.320	79.94	287.8
0.075	2.126	7.655	0.325	83.10	299.2
0.080	2.498	8.995	0.330	86.33	310.9
0.085	2.907	10.47	0.335	89.64	322.8
0.090	3.353	12.07	0.340	93.02	334.9
0.095	3.839	13.82	0.345	96.48	347.4
0.100	4.364	15.71	0.350	100.0	360.1
0.105	4.930	17.75	0.355	103.6	373.1
0.110	5.538	19.94	0.360	107.3	386.4
0.115	6.189	22.29	0.365	111.1	399.9
0.120	6.884	24.79	0.370	114.9	413.8
0.125	7.623	27.45	0.375	118.8	427.9
0.130	8.409	30.28	0.380	122.8	442.3
0.135	9.241	33.27	0.385	126.9	457.0
0.140	10.12	36.44	0.390	131.1	472.0
0.145	11.05	39.78	0.395	135.3	487.3
0.150	12.03	43.30	0.400	139.6	502.8
0.155	13.05	47.00	0.405	144.1	518.7
0.160	14.13	50.88	0.410	148.5	534.8
0.165	15.26	54.95	0.415	153.1	551.3
0.170	16.44	59.21	0.420	157.8	568.1
0.175	17.68	63.66	0.425	162.5	585.1
0.180	18.97	68.30	0.430	167.3	602.5
0.185	20.31	73.15	0.435	172.2	620.1
0.190	21.72	78.19	0.440	177.2	638.1
0.195	23.17	83.44	0.445	182.3	656.4
0.200	24.69	88.89	0.450	187.5	675.0
0.205	26.26	94.55	0.455	192.7	693.9
0.210	27.89	100.4	0.460	198.0	713.1
0.215	29.58	106.5	0.465	203.5	732.7
0.220	31.33	112.8	0.470	209.0	752.5
0.225	33.14	119.3	0.475	214.6	772.7
0.230	35.01	126.1	0.480	220.3	793.2
0.235	36.94	133.0	0.485	226.1	814.0
0.240	38.94	140.2	0.490	231.9	835.1
0.245	41.00	147.6	0.495	237.9	856.6
0.250	43.13	155.3	0.500	244.0	878.4

Table 9-11 (Continued)		
Head (meters)	l/s	m³/hr
0.505	250.1	900.5
0.510	256.3	923.0
0.515	262.7	945.8
0.520	269.1	968.9
0.525	275.6	992.4
0.530	282.2	1016
0.535	288.9	1040
0.540	295.7	1065
0.545	302.6	1090
0.550	309.6	1115

Table 9-11 (Continued)		
Head (meters)	l/s	m³/hr
0.555	316.7	1140
0.560	323.9	1166
0.565	331.1	1192
0.570	338.5	1219
0.575	346.0	1246
0.580	353.5	1273
0.585	361.2	1301
0.590	369.0	1329
0.595	376.9	1357
0.600	384.8	1386

9

Table 9-12:
120° V-notch Weir Discharge Table with Head in Meters

Formula: $l/s = 2391\ H^{2.5}$
$m^3/hr = 8606\ H^{2.5}$

Where: H = head in meters

Values in italics indicate flow below the recommended range of this particular primary device.

Table 9-12			Table 9-12 (Continued)		
Head (meters)	l/s	m³/hr	Head (meters)	l/s	m³/hr
0.005	*0.004*	*0.015*	0.255	78.51	282.6
0.010	*0.024*	*0.086*	0.260	82.42	296.6
0.015	*0.066*	*0.237*	0.265	86.44	311.1
0.020	*0.135*	*0.487*	0.270	90.57	326.0
0.025	*0.236*	*0.850*	0.275	94.82	341.3
0.030	*0.373*	*1.342*	0.280	99.19	357.0
0.035	*0.548*	*1.972*	0.285	103.7	373.2
0.040	*0.765*	*2.754*	0.290	108.3	389.8
0.045	*1.027*	*3.697*	0.295	113.0	406.8
0.050	*1.336*	*4.811*	0.300	117.9	424.2
0.055	*1.696*	*6.105*	0.305	122.8	442.1
0.060	2.108	7.589	0.310	127.9	460.5
0.065	2.576	9.270	0.315	133.2	479.3
0.070	3.100	11.16	0.320	138.5	498.5
0.075	3.683	13.26	0.325	144.0	518.2
0.080	4.328	15.58	0.330	149.6	538.4
0.085	5.036	18.13	0.335	155.3	559.0
0.090	5.810	20.91	0.340	161.2	580.1
0.095	6.651	23.94	0.345	167.2	601.7
0.100	7.561	27.21	0.350	173.3	623.7
0.105	8.542	30.75	0.355	179.5	646.2
0.110	9.595	34.54	0.360	185.9	669.2
0.115	10.72	38.60	0.365	192.4	692.7
0.120	11.93	42.93	0.370	199.1	716.6
0.125	13.21	47.54	0.375	205.9	741.1
0.130	14.57	52.44	0.380	212.8	766.1
0.135	16.01	57.63	0.385	219.9	791.5
0.140	17.53	63.11	0.390	227.1	817.5
0.145	19.14	68.90	0.395	234.5	843.9
0.150	20.84	74.99	0.400	242.0	870.9
0.155	22.62	81.40	0.405	249.6	898.3
0.160	24.48	88.13	0.410	257.4	926.3
0.165	26.44	95.17	0.415	265.3	954.8
0.170	28.49	102.5	0.420	273.3	983.8
0.175	30.63	110.3	0.425	281.5	1013
0.180	32.87	118.3	0.430	289.9	1043
0.185	35.20	126.7	0.435	298.4	1074
0.190	37.62	135.4	0.440	307.1	1105
0.195	40.15	144.5	0.445	315.8	1137
0.200	42.77	153.9	0.450	324.8	1169
0.205	45.50	163.8	0.455	333.9	1202
0.210	48.32	173.9	0.460	343.1	1235
0.215	51.25	184.5	0.465	352.5	1269
0.220	54.28	195.4	0.470	362.1	1303
0.225	57.42	206.7	0.475	371.8	1338
0.230	60.66	218.3	0.480	381.7	1374
0.235	64.01	230.4	0.485	391.7	1410
0.240	67.47	242.8	0.490	401.9	1446
0.245	71.04	255.7	0.495	412.2	1484
0.250	74.72	268.9	0.500	422.7	1521

Table 9-12 (Continued)		
Head (meters)	l/s	m³/hr
0.505	433.3	1560
0.510	444.1	1599
0.515	455.1	1638
0.520	466.2	1678
0.525	477.5	1719
0.530	489.0	1760
0.535	500.6	1802
0.540	512.3	1844
0.545	524.3	1887
0.550	536.4	1931

Table 9-12 (Continued)		
Head (meters)	l/s	m³/hr
0.555	548.7	1975
0.560	561.1	2020
0.565	573.7	2065
0.570	586.5	2111
0.575	599.4	2158
0.580	612.6	2205
0.585	625.8	2253
0.590	639.3	2301
0.595	652.9	2350
0.600	666.7	2400

9

9

CHAPTER

10

Rectangular Weir With End Contractions Discharge Tables

Overview

This chapter contains discharge (head vs. flow rate) tables for rectangular weirs with end contractions. Note that all of the tabular data is for free flow. If the flow is submerged, corrections will have to be made to determine the discharge, as discussed in Chapter 3.

Discharge tables for rectangular weirs with end contractions with head in feet

10-1:	1 ft.	10-6:	4 ft.
10-2:	$1^1/_2$ ft.	10-7:	5 ft.
10-3:	2 ft.	10-8:	6 ft.
10-4:	$2^1/_2$ ft.	10-9:	8 ft.
10-5:	3 ft.	10-10:	10 ft.

The discharges of the weirs are listed in three different units of measure:

CFS - cubic feet per second   GPM - gallons per minute
MGD - million gallons per day

Discharge tables for rectangular weirs with end contractions with head in meters

10-11:	0.3 m	10-16:	1 m
10-12:	0.4 m	10-17:	1.5 m
10-13:	0.5 m	10-18:	2 m
10-14:	0.6 m	10-19:	3 m
10-15:	0.8 m		

The discharges of the weirs are listed in two different units of measure:

l/s - liters per second m^3/hr - cubic meters per hour

The formulas used to develop each table are listed on the table. Values in italics indicate flow below the recommended range of this particular primary device.

Table 10-1:
1 ft. Rectangular Weir with End Contractions Discharge Table
with Head in Feet

Formula: $CFS = 3.33H^{1.5} - 0.666H^{2.5}$
$GPM = 1495H^{1.5} - 299H^{2.5}$
$MGD = 2.152H^{1.5} - 0.430H^{2.5}$
Where: H = head in feet

Values in italics indicate flow below the recommended range of this particular primary device.

Table 10-1				Table 10-1 (Continued)			
Head (feet)	CFS	GPM	MGD	Head (feet)	CFS	GPM	MGD
0.01	*0.0033*	*1.5*	*0.0021*	0.26	0.4185	187.9	0.2705
0.02	*0.0094*	*4.2*	*0.0061*	0.27	0.4420	198.4	0.2856
0.03	*0.0172*	*7.7*	*0.0111*	0.28	0.4658	209.1	0.3010
0.04	*0.0264*	*11.9*	*0.0171*	0.29	0.4899	219.9	0.3166
0.05	*0.0369*	*16.5*	*0.0238*	0.30	0.5143	230.9	0.3324
0.06	*0.0484*	*21.7*	*0.0313*	0.31	0.5391	242.0	0.3484
0.07	*0.0608*	*27.3*	*0.0393*	0.32	0.5642	253.3	0.3646
0.08	*0.0741*	*33.3*	*0.0479*	0.33	0.5896	264.7	0.3810
0.09	*0.0883*	*39.6*	*0.0571*	0.34	0.6153	276.2	0.3976
0.10	*0.1032*	*46.3*	*0.0667*	0.35	0.6413	287.9	0.4144
0.11	*0.1188*	*53.3*	*0.0768*	0.36	0.6675	299.7	0.4314
0.12	*0.1351*	*60.6*	*0.0873*	0.37	0.6940	311.6	0.4485
0.13	*0.1520*	*68.2*	*0.0983*	0.38	0.7208	323.6	0.4658
0.14	*0.1696*	*76.1*	*0.1096*	0.39	0.7478	335.7	0.4832
0.15	*0.1877*	*84.2*	*0.1213*	0.40	0.7750	348.0	0.5009
0.16	*0.2063*	*92.6*	*0.1333*	0.41	0.8025	360.3	0.5186
0.17	*0.2255*	*101.2*	*0.1457*	0.42	0.8303	372.7	0.5366
0.18	*0.2451*	*110.0*	*0.1584*	0.43	0.8582	385.3	0.5546
0.19	*0.2653*	*119.1*	*0.1715*	0.44	0.8864	397.9	0.5728
0.20	0.2859	128.4	0.1848	0.45	0.9148	410.7	0.5912
0.21	0.3070	137.8	0.1984	0.46	0.9433	423.5	0.6096
0.22	0.3285	147.5	0.2123	0.47	0.9721	436.4	0.6282
0.23	0.3504	157.3	0.2265	0.48	1.001	449.4	0.6470
0.24	0.3727	167.3	0.2409	0.49	1.030	462.5	0.6658
0.25	0.3954	177.5	0.2556	0.50	1.060	475.7	0.6848

10

Table 10-2:

1$^1/_2$ ft. Rectangular Weir with End Contractions Discharge Table with Head in Feet

Formula: CFS $= 4.995H^{1.5} - 0.666H^{2.5}$
GPM $= 2242.5H^{1.5} - 299H^{2.5}$
MGD $= 3.228H^{1.5} - 0.430H^{2.5}$
Where: H = head in feet

Values in italics indicate flow below the recommended range of this particular primary device.

Head (feet)	CFS	GPM	MGD	Head (feet)	CFS	GPM	MGD
0.01	*0.0050*	*2.2*	*0.0032*	0.39	1.153	517.8	0.7453
0.02	*0.0141*	*6.3*	*0.0091*	0.40	1.196	537.1	0.7731
0.03	*0.0259*	*11.6*	*00167*	0.41	1.240	556.5	0.8011
0.04	*0.0397*	*17.8*	*0.0257*	0.42	1.283	576.2	0.8294
0.05	*0.0555*	*24.9*	*0.0359*	0.43	1.328	596.1	0.8580
0.06	*0.0728*	*32.7*	*0.0471*	0.44	1.372	616.1	0.8869
0.07	*0.0916*	*41.1*	*0.0592*	0.45	1.417	636.3	0.9160
0.08	*0.1118*	*50.2*	*0.0723*	0.46	1.463	656.7	0.9453
0.09	*0.1332*	*59.8*	*0.0861*	0.47	1.509	677.3	0.9749
0.10	*0.1558*	*70.0*	*0.1007*	0.48	1.555	698.0	1.005
0.11	*0.1796*	*80.6*	*0.1161*	0.49	1.601	718.9	1.035
0.12	*0.2043*	*91.7*	*0.1321*	0.50	1.648	740.0	1.065
0.13	*0.2301*	*103.3*	*0.1487*	0.51	1.696	761.2	1.096
0.14	*0.2568*	*115.2*	*0.1660*	0.52	1.743	782.6	1.127
0.15	*0.2844*	*127.6*	*0.1838*	0.53	1.791	804.1	1.157
0.16	*0.3129*	*140.4*	*0.2022*	0.54	1.839	825.8	1.189
0.17	*0.3422*	*153.6*	*0.2212*	0.55	1.888	847.6	1.220
0.18	*0.3723*	*167.1*	*0.2406*	0.56	1.937	869.6	1.252
0.19	*0.4032*	*181.0*	*0.2606*	0.57	1.986	891.7	1.284
0.20	0.4349	195.2	0.2810	0.58	2.036	913.9	1.316
0.21	0.4672	209.8	0.3019	0.59	2.086	936.3	1.348
0.22	0.5003	224.6	0.3233	0.60	2.136	958.8	1.380
0.23	0.5341	239.8	0.3451	0.61	2.186	981.5	1.413
0.24	0.5685	255.2	0.3674	0.62	2.237	1004	1.446
0.25	0.6036	271.0	0.3901	0.63	2.288	1027	1.479
0.26	0.6393	287.0	0.4131	0.64	2.339	1050	1.512
0.27	0.6756	303.3	0.4366	0.65	2.391	1073	1.545
0.28	0.7124	319.8	0.4604	0.66	2.443	1097	1.578
0.29	0.7499	336.7	0.4846	0.67	2.495	1120	1.612
0.30	0.7879	353.7	0.5092	0.68	2.547	1143	1.646
0.31	0.8265	371.1	0.5341	0.69	2.600	1167	1.680
0.32	0.8656	388.6	0.5594	0.70	2.652	1191	1.714
0.33	0.9052	406.4	0.5850	0.71	2.705	1215	1.748
0.34	0.9454	424.4	0.6109	0.72	2.759	1239	1.783
0.35	0.9860	442.7	0.6372	0.73	2.812	1263	1.817
0.36	1.027	461.1	0.6638	0.74	2.866	1287	1.852
0.37	1.069	479.8	0.6907	0.75	2.920	1311	1.887
0.38	1.111	498.7	0.7178				

10

Table 10-3:
2 ft. Rectangular Weir with End Contractions Discharge Table with Head in Feet

Formula: CFS $= 6.66H^{1.5} - 0.666H^{2.5}$
GPM $= 2990H^{1.5} - 299H^{2.5}$
MGD $= 4.304H^{1.5} - 0.430H^{2.5}$

Where: H = head in feet

Values in italics indicate flow below the recommended range of this particular primary device.

Head (feet)	CFS	GPM	MGD	Head (feet)	CFS	GPM	MGD
0.01	*0.0067*	*3.0*	*0.0043*	0.51	2.302	1033	1.488
0.02	*0.0188*	*8.4*	*0.0122*	0.52	2.367	1063	1.530
0.03	*0.0345*	*15.5*	*0.0223*	0.53	2.434	1093	1.573
0.04	*0.0531*	*23.8*	*0.0343*	0.54	2.500	1122	1.616
0.05	*0.0741*	*33.3*	*0.0479*	0.55	2.567	1153	1.659
0.06	*0.0973*	*43.7*	*0.0629*	0.56	2.635	1183	1.703
0.07	*0.1225*	*55.0*	*0.0792*	0.57	2.703	1213	1.747
0.08	*0.1495*	*67.1*	*0.0966*	0.58	2.771	1244	1.791
0.09	*0.1782*	*80.0*	*0.1152*	0.59	2.840	1275	1.835
0.10	*0.2085*	*93.6*	*0.1348*	0.60	2.910	1306	1.880
0.11	*0.2403*	*107.9*	*0.1553*	0.61	2.979	1338	1.925
0.12	*0.2735*	*122.8*	*0.1768*	0.62	3.050	1369	1.971
0.13	*0.3081*	*138.3*	*0.1991*	0.63	3.121	1401	2.017
0.14	*0.3440*	*154.4*	*0.2223*	0.64	3.192	1433	2.063
0.15	*0.3811*	*171.1*	*0.2463*	0.65	3.263	1465	2.109
0.16	*0.4194*	*188.2*	*0.2711*	0.66	3.335	1497	2.155
0.17	*0.4589*	*206.0*	*0.2966*	0.67	3.408	1530	2.202
0.18	*0.4995*	*224.2*	*0.3228*	0.68	3.481	1563	2.249
0.19	*0.5411*	*242.9*	*0.3497*	0.69	3.554	1595	2.297
0.20	0.5838	262.1	0.3773	0.70	3.627	1629	2.344
0.21	0.6275	281.7	0.4055	0.71	3.701	1662	2.392
0.22	0.6721	301.7	0.4344	0.72	3.776	1695	2.440
0.23	0.7177	322.2	0.4638	0.73	3.851	1729	2.488
0.24	0.7643	343.1	0.4939	0.74	3.926	1763	2.537
0.25	0.8117	364.4	0.5246	0.75	4.001	1796	2.586
0.26	0.8600	386.1	0.5558	0.76	4.077	1830	2.635
0.27	0.9091	408.2	0.5875	0.77	4.153	1865	2.684
0.28	0.9591	430.6	0.6198	0.78	4.230	1899	2.734
0.29	1.010	453.4	0.6527	0.79	4.307	1934	2.783
0.30	1.062	476.6	0.6860	0.80	4.384	1968	2.833
0.31	1.114	500.1	0.7198	0.81	4.462	2003	2.883
0.32	1.167	523.9	0.7542	0.82	4.540	2038	2.934
0.33	1.221	548.1	0.7890	0.83	4.618	2073	2.984
0.34	1.275	572.6	0.8243	0.84	4.697	2109	3.035
0.35	1.331	597.4	0.8600	0.85	4.776	2144	3.086
0.36	1.387	622.6	0.8962	0.86	4.855	2180	3.137
0.37	1.443	648.0	0.9328	0.87	4.934	2215	3.189
0.38	1.501	673.8	0.9699	0.88	5.014	2251	3.240
0.39	1.559	699.8	1.007	0.89	5.094	2287	3.292
0.40	1.617	726.2	1.045	0.90	5.175	2323	3.344
0.41	1.677	752.8	1.084	0.91	5.255	2359	3.396
0.42	1.737	779.7	1.122	0.92	5.336	2396	3.449
0.43	1.797	806.8	1.161	0.93	5.418	2432	3.501
0.44	1.858	834.3	1.201	0.94	5.499	2469	3.554
0.45	1.920	862.0	1.241	0.95	5.581	2506	3.607
0.46	1.982	889.9	1.281	0.96	5.663	2542	3.660
0.47	2.045	918.1	1.322	0.97	5.745	2579	3.713
0.48	2.108	946.6	1.363	0.98	5.828	2616	3.766
0.49	2.172	975.3	1.404	0.99	5.911	2654	3.820
0.50	2.237	1004	1.446	1.00	5.994	2691	3.874

10

Table 10-4:

2¹/₂ ft. Rectangular Weir with End Contractions Discharge Table with Head in Feet

Formula: $CFS = 8.325H^{1.5} - 0.666H^{2.5}$
$GPM = 3737.5H^{1.5} - 299H^{2.5}$
$MGD = 5.38H^{1.5} - 0.430H^{2.5}$

Where: H = head in feet

Values in italics indicate flow below the recommended range of this particular primary device.

Table 10-4				Table 10-4 (Continued)			
Head (feet)	CFS	GPM	MGD	Head (feet)	CFS	GPM	MGD
0.01	*0.0083*	*3.7*	*0.0054*	0.51	2.908	1306	1.880
0.02	*0.0235*	*10.6*	*0.0152*	0.52	2.992	1343	1.933
0.03	*0.0432*	*19.4*	*0.0279*	0.53	3.076	1381	1.988
0.04	*0.0664*	*29.8*	*0.0429*	0.54	3.161	1419	2.043
0.05	*0.0927*	*41.6*	*0.0599*	0.55	3.246	1457	2.098
0.06	*0.1218*	*54.7*	*0.0787*	0.56	3.332	1496	2.154
0.07	*0.1533*	*68.8*	*0.0991*	0.57	3.419	1535	2.210
0.08	*0.1872*	*84.0*	*0.1210*	0.58	3.507	1574	2.266
0.09	*0.2232*	*100.2*	*0.1442*	0.59	3.595	1614	2.323
0.10	*0.2612*	*117.2*	*0.1688*	0.60	3.683	1654	2.380
0.11	*0.3010*	*135.1*	*0.1946*	0.61	3.773	1694	2.438
0.12	*0.3427*	*153.8*	*0.2215*	0.62	3.863	1734	2.496
0.13	*0.3862*	*173.3*	*0.2496*	0.63	3.953	1775	2.555
0.14	*0.4312*	*193.5*	*0.2787*	0.64	4.044	1816	2.614
0.15	*0.4778*	*214.5*	*0.3088*	0.65	4.136	1857	2.673
0.16	*0.5260*	*236.1*	*0.3399*	0.66	4.228	1898	2.732
0.17	*0.5756*	*258.3*	*0.3720*	0.67	4.321	1940	2.792
0.18	*0.6266*	*281.2*	*0.4050*	0.68	4.414	1982	2.853
0.19	*0.6790*	*304.8*	*0.4388*	0.69	4.508	2024	2.913
0.20	0.7327	328.9	0.4735	0.70	4.603	2066	2.974
0.21	0.7877	353.6	0.5090	0.71	4.698	2109	3.036
0.22	0.8439	378.9	0.5454	0.72	4.793	2152	3.098
0.23	0.9014	404.7	0.5825	0.73	4.889	2195	3.160
0.24	0.9600	431.0	0.6204	0.74	4.986	2238	3.222
0.25	1.020	457.8	0.6591	0.75	5.083	2282	3.285
0.26	1.081	485.2	0.6984	0.76	5.180	2326	3.348
0.27	1.143	513.0	0.7385	0.77	5.278	2370	3.411
0.28	1.206	541.4	0.7793	0.78	5.377	2414	3.475
0.29	1.270	570.1	0.8207	0.79	5.476	2458	3.539
0.30	1.335	599.4	0.8628	0.80	5.576	2503	3.603
0.31	1.401	629.1	0.9056	0.81	5.676	2548	3.668
0.32	1.468	659.2	0.9490	0.82	5.776	2593	3.733
0.33	1.537	689.8	0.9930	0.83	5.877	2639	3.798
0.34	1.606	720.8	1.038	0.84	5.978	2684	3.864
0.35	1.676	752.2	1.083	0.85	6.080	2730	3.929
0.36	1.746	784.0	1.129	0.86	6.183	2776	3.996
0.37	1.818	816.3	1.175	0.87	6.285	2822	4.062
0.38	1.891	848.9	1.222	0.88	6.389	2868	4.129
0.39	1.964	881.9	1.269	0.89	6.492	2915	4.196
0.40	2.039	915.3	1.317	0.90	6.596	2961	4.263
0.41	2.114	949.0	1.366	0.91	6.701	3008	4.330
0.42	2.190	983.1	1.415	0.92	6.806	3055	4.398
0.43	2.267	1018	1.465	0.93	6.911	3103	4.466
0.44	2.344	1052	1.515	0.94	7.017	3150	4.534
0.45	2.423	1088	1.566	0.95	7.123	3198	4.603
0.46	2.502	1123	1.617	0.96	7.229	3246	4.672
0.47	2.582	1159	1.668	0.97	7.336	3294	4.741
0.48	2.662	1195	1.720	0.98	7.443	3342	4.810
0.49	2.744	1232	1.773	0.99	7.551	3390	4.880
0.50	2.826	1269	1.826	1.00	7.659	3439	4.950

10

Table 10-4 (Continued)			
Head (feet)	CFS	GPM	MGD
1.01	7.767	3487	5.020
1.02	7.876	3536	5.090
1.03	7.985	3585	5.160
1.04	8.095	3634	5.231
1.05	8.205	3683	5.302
1.06	8.315	3733	5.373
1.07	8.426	3783	5.445
1.08	8.536	3832	5.517
1.09	8.648	3882	5.589
1.10	8.759	3932	5.661
1.11	8.871	3983	5.733
1.12	8.983	4033	5.806
1.13	9.096	4084	5.878

Table 10-4 (Continued)			
Head (feet)	CFS	GPM	MGD
1.14	9.209	4134	5.951
1.15	9.322	4185	6.024
1.16	9.436	4236	6.098
1.17	9.550	4287	6.171
1.18	9.664	4339	6.245
1.19	9.778	4390	6.319
1.20	9.893	4441	6.393
1.21	10.01	4493	6.468
1.22	10.12	4545	6.542
1.23	10.24	4597	6.617
1.24	10.35	4649	6.692
1.25	10.47	4701	6.767

10

Table 10-5:
3 ft. Rectangular Weir with End Contractions Discharge Table
with Head in Feet

Formula: CFS $= 9.99H^{1.5} - 0.666H^{2.5}$
GPM $= 4485H^{1.5} - 299H^{2.5}$
MGD $= 6.456H^{1.5} - 0.430H^{2.5}$
Where: H = head in feet

Values in italics indicate flow below the recommended range of this particular primary device.

Table 10-5				Table 10-5 (Continued)			
Head (feet)	CFS	GPM	MGD	Head (feet)	CFS	GPM	MGD
0.01	*0.0100*	*4.5*	*0.0065*	0.51	3.515	1578	2.271
0.02	*0.0282*	*12.7*	*0.0182*	0.52	3.616	1623	2.337
0.03	*0.0518*	*23.3*	*0.0335*	0.53	3.718	1669	2.403
0.04	*0.0797*	*35.8*	*0.0515*	0.54	3.821	1716	2.470
0.05	*0.1113*	*50.0*	*0.0719*	0.55	3.925	1762	2.537
0.06	*0.1462*	*65.6*	*0.0945*	0.56	4.030	1809	2.604
0.07	*0.1842*	*82.7*	*0.1190*	0.57	4.136	1857	2.673
0.08	*0.2248*	*100.9*	*0.1453*	0.58	4.242	1904	2.741
0.09	*0.2681*	*120.3*	*0.1733*	0.59	4.349	1953	2.811
0.10	*0.3138*	*140.8*	*0.2028*	0.60	4.457	2001	2.880
0.11	*0.3618*	*162.4*	*0.2338*	0.61	4.566	2050	2.951
0.12	*0.4120*	*184.9*	*0.2663*	0.62	4.675	2099	3.021
0.13	*0.4642*	*208.3*	*0.3000*	0.63	4.786	2149	3.093
0.14	*0.5184*	*232.7*	*0.3351*	0.64	4.897	2198	3.164
0.15	*0.5746*	*257.9*	*0.3713*	0.65	5.008	2249	3.237
0.16	*0.6325*	*283.9*	*0.4088*	0.66	5.121	2299	3.309
0.17	*0.6923*	*310.7*	*0.4474*	0.67	5.234	2350	3.382
0.18	*0.7538*	*338.3*	*0.4872*	0.68	5.348	2401	3.456
0.19	*0.8169*	*366.6*	*0.5280*	0.69	5.462	2452	3.530
0.20	0.8816	395.8	0.5697	0.70	5.578	2504	3.605
0.21	0.9479	425.6	0.6126	0.71	5.694	2556	3.680
0.22	1.016	456.0	0.6564	0.72	5.810	2609	3.755
0.23	1.085	487.1	0.7012	0.73	5.928	2661	3.831
0.24	1.156	518.9	0.7469	0.74	6.046	2714	3.907
0.25	1.228	551.3	0.7936	0.75	6.164	2767	3.984
0.26	1.301	584.3	0.8411	0.76	6.284	2821	4.061
0.27	1.376	617.9	0.8894	0.77	6.403	2875	4.138
0.28	1.453	652.1	0.9387	0.78	6.524	2929	4.216
0.29	1.530	686.9	0.9887	0.79	6.645	2983	4.294
0.30	1.609	722.2	1.040	0.80	6.767	3038	4.373
0.31	1.689	758.1	1.091	0.81	6.889	3093	4.452
0.32	1.770	794.6	1.144	0.82	7.012	3148	4.532
0.33	1.852	831.5	1.197	0.83	7.136	3204	4.612
0.34	1.936	869.0	1.251	0.84	7.260	3260	4.692
0.35	2.020	907.0	1.306	0.85	7.385	3316	4.773
0.36	2.106	945.5	1.361	0.86	7.511	3372	4.854
0.37	2.193	984.5	1.417	0.87	7.637	3428	4.935
0.38	2.281	1024	1.474	0.88	7.763	3485	5.017
0.39	2.370	1064	1.532	0.89	7.890	3542	5.099
0.40	2.460	1104	1.590	0.90	8.018	3600	5.181
0.41	2.551	1145	1.649	0.91	8.146	3657	5.264
0.42	2.643	1187	1.708	0.92	8.275	3715	5.348
0.43	2.736	1228	1.768	0.93	8.404	3773	5.431
0.44	2.830	1271	1.829	0.94	8.534	3831	5.515
0.45	2.925	1313	1.890	0.95	8.664	3890	5.599
0.46	3.021	1356	1.952	0.96	8.795	3949	5.684
0.47	3.118	1400	2.015	0.97	8.927	4008	5.769
0.48	3.216	1444	2.078	0.98	9.059	4067	5.854
0.49	3.315	1488	2.142	0.99	9.191	4126	5.940
0.50	3.414	1533	2.206	1.00	9.324	4186	6.026

10

Table 10-5 (Continued)				Table 10-5 (Continued)			
Head (feet)	CFS	GPM	MGD	Head (feet)	CFS	GPM	MGD
1.01	9.457	4246	6.112	1.26	12.94	5811	8.364
1.02	9.591	4306	6.198	1.27	13.09	5876	8.458
1.03	9.726	4366	6.285	1.28	13.23	5941	8.551
1.04	9.861	4427	6.372	1.29	13.38	6006	8.646
1.05	9.996	4488	6.460	1.30	13.52	6072	8.740
1.06	10.13	4549	6.548	1.31	13.67	6137	8.835
1.07	10.27	4610	6.636	1.32	13.82	6203	8.929
1.08	10.41	4671	6.724	1.33	13.96	6269	9.024
1.09	10.54	4733	6.813	1.34	14.11	6335	9.120
1.10	10.68	4795	6.902	1.35	14.26	6402	9.215
1.11	10.82	4857	6.991	1.36	14.41	6468	9.311
1.12	10.96	4919	7.081	1.37	14.56	6535	9.407
1.13	11.10	4982	7.171	1.38	14.71	6602	9.503
1.14	11.24	5044	7.261	1.39	14.85	6669	9.600
1.15	11.38	5107	7.351	1.40	15.00	6736	9.696
1.16	11.52	5170	7.442	1.41	15.15	6803	9.793
1.17	11.66	5233	7.533	1.42	15.30	6871	9.890
1.18	11.80	5297	7.624	1.43	15.45	6938	9.987
1.19	11.94	5360	7.716	1.44	15.61	7006	10.08
1.20	12.08	5424	7.808	1.45	15.76	7074	10.18
1.21	12.22	5488	7.900	1.46	15.91	7142	10.28
1.22	12.37	5552	7.992	1.47	16.06	7210	10.38
1.23	12.51	5616	8.085	1.48	16.21	7278	10.48
1.24	12.65	5681	8.178	1.49	16.36	7347	10.58
1.25	12.80	5746	8.271	1.50	16.52	7416	10.67

10

Table 10-6:
4 ft. Rectangular Weir with End Contractions Discharge Table with Head in Feet

Formula: $CFS = 13.32H^{1.5} - 0.666H^{2.5}$
$GPM = 5980H^{1.5} - 299H^{2.5}$
$MGD = 8.608H^{1.5} - 0.430H^{2.5}$
Where: H = head in feet

Values in italics indicate flow below the recommended range of this particular primary device.

Table 10-6				Table 10-6 (Continued)			
Head (feet)	CFS	GPM	MGD	Head (feet)	CFS	GPM	MGD
0.01	*0.013*	*6.0*	*0.0086*	0.51	4.728	2122	3.055
0.02	*0.038*	*16.9*	*0.0243*	0.52	4.865	2184	3.144
0.03	*0.069*	*31.0*	*0.0447*	0.53	5.003	2246	3.233
0.04	*0.106*	*47.7*	*0.0687*	0.54	5.143	2309	3.324
0.05	*0.149*	*66.7*	*0.0960*	0.55	5.284	2372	3.415
0.06	*0.195*	*87.6*	*0.1261*	0.56	5.426	2436	3.506
0.07	*0.246*	*110.3*	*0.1589*	0.57	5.569	2500	3.599
0.08	*0.300*	*134.7*	*0.1940*	0.58	5.713	2565	3.692
0.09	*0.358*	*160.7*	*0.2314*	0.59	5.858	2630	3.786
0.10	*0.419*	*188.1*	*0.2709*	0.60	6.005	2696	3.881
0.11	*0.483*	*216.9*	*0.3124*	0.61	6.152	2762	3.976
0.12	*0.550*	*247.0*	*0.3557*	0.62	6.301	2829	4.072
0.13	*0.620*	*278.4*	*0.4009*	0.63	6.451	2896	4.169
0.14	*0.693*	*311.0*	*0.4478*	0.64	6.602	2964	4.266
0.15	*0.768*	*344.7*	*0.4964*	0.65	6.753	3032	4.364
0.16	*0.846*	*379.6*	*0.5466*	0.66	6.906	3101	4.463
0.17	*0.926*	*415.5*	*0.5983*	0.67	7.060	3170	4.563
0.18	*1.008*	*452.4*	*0.6515*	0.68	7.215	3239	4.663
0.19	*1.093*	*490.4*	*0.7062*	0.69	7.371	3309	4.764
0.20	1.179	529.5	0.7622	0.70	7.528	3380	4.865
0.21	1.268	569.4	0.8197	0.71	7.686	3451	4.967
0.22	1.359	610.3	0.8785	0.72	7.845	3522	5.070
0.23	1.452	652.0	0.9386	0.73	8.005	3594	5.173
0.24	1.547	694.7	0.9999	0.74	8.165	3666	5.277
0.25	1.644	738.2	1.063	0.75	8.327	3738	5.381
0.26	1.743	782.5	1.126	0.76	8.490	3812	5.487
0.27	1.844	827.6	1.191	0.77	8.653	3885	5.592
0.28	1.946	873.6	1.258	0.78	8.818	3959	5.699
0.29	2.050	920.4	1.325	0.79	8.983	4033	5.806
0.30	2.156	967.9	1.393	0.80	9.150	4108	5.913
0.31	2.263	1016	1.463	0.81	9.317	4183	6.021
0.32	2.373	1065	1.533	0.82	9.485	4258	6.130
0.33	2.483	1115	1.605	0.83	9.654	4334	6.239
0.34	2.596	1165	1.678	0.84	9.824	4410	6.349
0.35	2.710	1217	1.751	0.85	9.995	4487	6.459
0.36	2.825	1268	1.826	0.86	10.17	4564	6.570
0.37	2.942	1321	1.901	0.87	10.34	4642	6.681
0.38	3.061	1374	1.978	0.88	10.51	4719	6.793
0.39	3.181	1428	2.056	0.89	10.69	4798	6.906
0.40	3.302	1483	2.134	0.90	10.86	4876	7.019
0.41	3.425	1538	2.214	0.91	11.04	4955	7.132
0.42	3.549	1594	2.294	0.92	11.21	5034	7.247
0.43	3.675	1650	2.375	0.93	11.39	5114	7.361
0.44	3.802	1707	2.457	0.94	11.57	5194	7.476
0.45	3.930	1765	2.540	0.95	11.75	5274	7.592
0.46	4.060	1823	2.624	0.96	11.93	5355	7.708
0.47	4.191	1882	2.708	0.97	12.11	5436	7.825
0.48	4.323	1941	2.794	0.98	12.29	5517	7.942
0.49	4.457	2001	2.880	0.99	12.47	5599	8.059
0.50	4.592	2061	2.967	1.00	12.65	5681	8.178

10

Table 10-6 (Continued)				Table 10-6 (Continued)			
Head (feet)	CFS	GPM	MGD	Head (feet)	CFS	GPM	MGD
1.01	12.84	5763	8.296	1.51	22.85	10,260	14.77
1.02	13.02	5846	8.415	1.52	23.06	10,350	14.91
1.03	13.21	5929	8.535	1.53	23.28	10,450	15.04
1.04	13.39	6013	8.655	1.54	23.50	10,550	15.18
1.05	13.58	6096	8.775	1.55	23.71	10,650	15.32
1.06	13.77	6180	8.896	1.56	23.93	10,740	15.46
1.07	13.95	6265	9.018	1.57	24.15	10,840	15.60
1.08	14.14	6349	9.140	1.58	24.36	10,940	15.75
1.09	14.33	6434	9.262	1.59	24.58	11,040	15.89
1.10	14.52	6520	9.385	1.60	24.80	11,130	16.03
1.11	14.71	6605	9.508	1.61	25.02	11,230	16.17
1.12	14.90	6691	9.632	1.62	25.24	11,330	16.31
1.13	15.10	6777	9.756	1.63	25.46	11,430	16.45
1.14	15.29	6864	9.880	1.64	25.68	11,530	16.60
1.15	15.48	6951	10.01	1.65	25.90	11,630	16.74
1.16	15.68	7038	10.13	1.66	26.12	11,730	16.88
1.17	15.87	7125	10.26	1.67	26.35	11,830	17.03
1.18	16.07	7213	10.3	1.68	26.57	11,930	17.17
1.19	16.26	7301	10.51	1.69	26.79	12,030	17.31
1.20	16.46	7389	10.64	1.70	27.01	12,130	17.46
1.21	16.66	7478	10.76	1.71	27.24	12,230	17.60
1.22	16.85	7567	10.89	1.72	27.46	12,330	17.75
1.23	17.05	7656	11.02	1.73	27.69	12,430	17.89
1.24	17.25	7745	11.15	1.74	27.91	12,530	18.04
1.25	17.45	7835	11.28	1.75	28.14	12,630	18.18
1.26	17.65	7925	11.41	1.76	28.36	12,730	18.33
1.27	17.85	8015	11.54	1.77	28.59	12,840	18.48
1.28	18.05	8106	11.67	1.78	28.82	12,940	18.62
1.29	18.26	8197	11.80	1.79	29.04	13,040	18.77
1.30	18.46	8288	11.93	1.80	29.27	13,140	18.92
1.31	18.66	8379	12.06	1.81	29.50	13,240	19.06
1.32	18.87	8470	12.19	1.82	29.73	13,350	19.21
1.33	19.07	8562	12.33	1.83	29.96	13,450	19.36
1.34	19.28	8654	12.46	1.84	30.19	13,550	19.51
1.35	19.48	8747	12.59	1.85	30.42	13,660	19.66
1.36	19.69	8839	12.72	1.86	30.65	13,760	19.81
1.37	19.90	8932	12.86	1.87	30.88	13,860	19.95
1.38	20.10	9025	12.99	1.88	31.11	13,970	20.10
1.39	20.31	9119	13.13	1.89	31.34	14,070	20.25
1.40	20.52	9212	13.26	1.90	31.57	14,170	20.40
1.41	20.73	9306	13.40	1.91	31.80	14,280	20.55
1.42	20.94	9400	13.53	1.92	32.03	14,380	20.70
1.43	21.15	9495	13.67	1.93	32.27	14,490	20.85
1.44	21.36	9589	13.80	1.94	32.50	14,590	21.00
1.45	21.57	9684	13.94	1.95	32.73	14,700	21.15
1.46	21.78	9779	14.08	1.96	32.97	14,800	21.31
1.47	22.00	9875	14.21	1.97	33.20	14,910	21.46
1.48	22.21	9970	14.35	1.98	33.44	15,010	21.61
1.49	22.42	10,070	14.49	1.99	33.67	15,120	21.76
1.50	22.64	10,160	14.63	2.00	33.91	15,220	21.91

10

Table 10-7:
5 ft. Rectangular Weir with End Contractions Discharge Table with Head in Feet

Formula:
$$CFS = 16.65H^{1.5} - 0.666H^{2.5}$$
$$GPM = 7475H^{1.5} - 299H^{2.5}$$
$$MGD = 10.76H^{1.5} - 0.430H^{2.5}$$
Where: H = head in feet

Values in italics indicate flow below the recommended range of this particular primary device.

Head (feet)	CFS	GPM	MGD	Head (feet)	CFS	GPM	MGD
0.01	*0.017*	*7.5*	*0.0108*	0.51	5.940	2667	3.839
0.02	*0.047*	*21.1*	*0.0304*	0.52	6.114	2745	3.951
0.03	*0.086*	*38.8*	*0.0558*	0.53	6.288	2823	4.064
0.04	*0.133*	*59.7*	*0.0860*	0.54	6.464	2902	4.178
0.05	*0.186*	*83.4*	*0.1201*	0.55	6.642	2982	4.292
0.06	*0.244*	*109.6*	*0.1578*	0.56	6.821	3062	4.408
0.07	*0.307*	*138.0*	*0.1987*	0.57	7.002	3143	4.525
0.08	*0.376*	*168.6*	*0.2427*	0.58	7.184	3225	4.643
0.09	*0.448*	*201.0*	*0.2895*	0.59	7.367	3308	4.761
0.10	*0.524*	*235.4*	*0.3389*	0.60	7.553	3391	4.881
0.11	*0.605*	*271.4*	*0.3909*	0.61	7.739	3474	5.001
0.12	*0.689*	*309.2*	*0.4452*	0.62	7.927	3559	5.123
0.13	*0.776*	*348.5*	*0.5018*	0.63	8.116	3644	5.245
0.14	*0.867*	*389.3*	*0.5605*	0.64	8.307	3729	5.368
0.15	*0.961*	*431.5*	*0.6214*	0.65	8.499	3815	5.492
0.16	*1.059*	*475.2*	*0.6843*	0.66	8.692	3902	5.617
0.17	*1.159*	*520.2*	*0.7492*	0.67	8.886	3990	5.743
0.18	*1.262*	*566.6*	*0.8159*	0.68	9.082	4078	5.869
0.19	*1.368*	*614.2*	*0.8845*	0.69	9.280	4166	5.997
0.20	1.477	663.2	0.9547	0.70	9.478	4255	6.125
0.21	1.589	713.3	1.027	0.71	9.678	4345	6.254
0.22	1.703	764.6	1.101	0.72	9.879	4435	6.384
0.23	1.820	816.9	1.176	0.73	10.08	4526	6.515
0.24	1.939	870.4	1.253	0.74	10.29	4618	6.647
0.25	2.060	925.0	1.332	0.75	10.49	4710	6.779
0.26	2.184	980.7	1.412	0.76	10.70	4802	6.912
0.27	2.311	1037	1.493	0.77	10.90	4895	7.046
0.28	2.439	1095	1.576	0.78	11.11	4989	7.181
0.29	2.570	1154	1.661	0.79	11.32	5083	7.317
0.30	2.703	1214	1.747	0.80	11.53	5178	7.453
0.31	2.838	1274	1.834	0.81	11.74	5273	7.590
0.32	2.975	1336	1.923	0.82	11.96	5368	7.728
0.33	3.115	1398	2.013	0.83	12.17	5465	7.866
0.34	3.256	1462	2.104	0.84	12.39	5561	8.005
0.35	3.399	1526	2.197	0.85	12.60	5659	8.146
0.36	3.545	1591	2.291	0.86	12.82	5756	8.286
0.37	3.692	1657	2.386	0.87	13.04	5855	8.428
0.38	3.841	1724	2.482	0.88	13.26	5954	8.570
0.39	3.992	1792	2.580	0.89	13.48	6053	8.713
0.40	4.145	1861	2.679	0.90	13.70	6153	8.856
0.41	4.299	1930	2.778	0.91	13.93	6253	9.001
0.42	4.456	2000	2.880	0.92	14.15	6353	9.146
0.43	4.614	2071	2.982	0.93	14.38	6455	9.291
0.44	4.774	2143	3.085	0.94	14.60	6556	9.438
0.45	4.936	2216	3.190	0.95	14.83	6658	9.585
0.46	5.099	2289	3.295	0.96	15.06	6761	9.732
0.47	5.264	2363	3.402	0.97	15.29	6864	9.881
0.48	5.431	2438	3.510	0.98	15.52	6968	10.03
0.49	5.599	2514	3.618	0.99	15.75	7072	10.18
0.50	5.769	2590	3.728	1.00	15.98	7176	10.33

10

Table 10-7 (Continued)				Table 10-7 (Continued)			
Head (feet)	CFS	GPM	MGD	Head (feet)	CFS	GPM	MGD
1.01	16.22	7281	10.48	1.51	29.03	13,030	18.76
1.02	16.45	7386	10.63	1.52	29.30	13,160	18.94
1.03	16.69	7492	10.78	1.53	29.58	13,280	19.12
1.04	16.92	7598	10.94	1.54	29.86	13,410	19.30
1.05	17.16	7705	11.09	1.55	30.14	13,530	19.48
1.06	17.40	7812	11.24	1.56	30.42	13,660	19.66
1.07	17.64	7919	11.40	1.57	30.70	13,780	19.84
1.08	17.88	8027	11.55	1.58	30.98	13,910	20.02
1.09	18.12	8136	11.71	1.59	31.26	14,030	20.20
1.10	18.36	8244	11.87	1.60	31.54	14,160	20.38
1.11	18.61	8354	12.02	1.61	31.82	14,290	20.57
1.12	18.85	8463	12.18	1.62	32.11	14,410	20.75
1.13	19.10	8573	12.34	1.63	32.39	14,540	20.93
1.14	19.34	8684	12.50	1.64	32.67	14,670	21.12
1.15	19.59	8794	12.66	1.65	32.96	14,800	21.30
1.16	19.84	8906	12.82	1.66	33.25	14,930	21.48
1.17	20.09	9017	12.98	1.67	33.53	15,050	21.67
1.18	20.33	9129	13.14	1.68	33.82	15,180	21.86
1.19	20.59	9242	13.30	1.69	34.11	15,310	22.04
1.20	20.84	9354	13.47	1.70	34.40	15,440	22.23
1.21	21.09	9468	13.63	1.71	34.68	15,570	22.41
1.22	21.34	9581	13.79	1.72	34.97	15,700	22.60
1.23	21.60	9695	13.96	1.73	35.26	15,830	22.79
1.24	21.85	9810	14.12	1.74	35.56	15,960	22.98
1.25	22.11	9924	14.29	1.75	35.85	16,090	23.17
1.26	22.36	10,040	14.45	1.76	36.14	16,220	23.35
1.27	22.62	10,150	14.62	1.77	36.43	16,360	23.54
1.28	22.88	10,270	14.78	1.78	36.73	16,490	23.73
1.29	23.14	10,390	14.95	1.79	37.02	16,620	23.92
1.30	23.40	10,500	15.12	1.80	37.31	16,750	24.11
1.31	23.66	10,620	15.29	1.81	37.61	16,880	24.30
1.32	23.92	10,740	15.46	1.82	37.90	17,020	24.50
1.33	24.18	10,860	15.63	1.83	38.20	17,150	24.69
1.34	24.44	10,970	15.80	1.84	38.50	17,280	24.88
1.35	24.71	11,090	15.97	1.85	38.80	17,420	25.07
1.36	24.97	11,210	16.14	1.86	39.09	17,550	25.26
1.37	25.24	11,330	16.31	1.87	39.39	17,690	25.46
1.38	25.50	11,450	16.48	1.88	39.69	17,820	25.65
1.39	25.77	11,570	16.65	1.89	39.99	17,950	25.84
1.40	26.04	11,690	16.83	1.90	40.29	18,090	26.04
1.41	26.30	11,810	17.00	1.91	40.59	18,220	26.23
1.42	26.57	11,930	17.17	1.92	40.89	18,360	26.43
1.43	26.84	12,050	17.35	1.93	41.20	18,500	26.62
1.44	27.11	12,170	17.52	1.94	41.50	18,630	26.82
1.45	27.39	12,290	17.70	1.95	41.80	18,770	27.01
1.46	27.66	12,420	17.87	1.96	42.11	18,900	27.21
1.47	27.93	12,540	18.05	1.97	42.41	19,040	27.41
1.48	28.20	12,660	18.23	1.98	42.71	19,180	27.60
1.49	28.48	12,790	18.40	1.99	43.02	19,310	27.80
1.50	28.75	12,910	18.58	2.00	43.33	19,450	28.00

10

Table 10-7 (Continued)				Table 10-7 (Continued)			
Head (feet)	CFS	GPM	MGD	Head (feet)	CFS	GPM	MGD
2.01	43.63	19,590	28.20	2.26	51.45	23,100	33.25
2.02	43.94	19,730	28.40	2.27	51.77	23,240	33.46
2.03	44.25	19,860	28.59	2.28	52.09	23,390	33.67
2.04	44.55	20,000	28.79	2.29	52.41	23,530	33.87
2.05	44.86	20,140	28.99	2.30	52.73	23,670	34.08
2.06	45.17	20,280	29.19	2.31	53.06	23,820	34.29
2.07	45.48	20,420	29.39	2.32	53.38	23,960	34.49
2.08	45.79	20,560	29.59	2.33	53.70	24,110	34.70
2.09	46.10	20,700	29.79	2.34	54.02	24,250	34.91
2.10	46.41	20,840	29.99	2.35	54.34	24,400	35.12
2.11	46.72	20,980	30.20	2.36	54.67	24,540	35.33
2.12	47.04	21,120	30.40	2.37	54.99	24,690	35.54
2.13	47.35	21,260	30.60	2.38	55.31	24,830	35.75
2.14	47.66	21,400	30.80	2.39	55.64	24,980	35.96
2.15	47.98	21,540	31.00	2.40	55.96	25,120	36.17
2.16	48.29	21,680	31.21	2.41	56.29	25,270	36.38
2.17	48.60	21,820	31.41	2.42	56.61	25,420	36.59
2.18	48.92	21,960	31.61	2.43	56.94	25,560	36.80
2.19	49.23	22,100	31.82	2.44	57.27	25,710	37.01
2.20	49.55	22,250	32.02	2.45	57.59	25,860	37.22
2.21	49.87	22,390	32.23	2.46	57.92	26,000	37.43
2.22	50.18	22,530	32.43	2.47	58.25	26,150	37.64
2.23	50.50	22,670	32.64	2.48	58.58	26,300	37.85
2.24	50.82	22,810	32.84	2.49	58.90	26,450	38.07
2.25	51.14	22,960	33.05	2.50	59.23	26,590	38.28

10

Rectangular Weir With End Contractions Discharge Tables • 195

Table 10-8:
6 ft. Rectangular Weir with End Contractions Discharge Table with Head in Feet

Formula: $CFS = 199.8H^{1.5} - 0.666H^{2.5}$
$GPM = 8970H^{1.5} - 299H^{2.5}$
$MGD = 12.912H^{1.5} - 0.430H^{2.5}$

Where: H = head in feet

Values in italics indicate flow below the recommended range of this particular primary device.

Table 10-8				Table 10-8 (Continued)			
Head (feet)	CFS	GPM	MGD	Head (feet)	CFS	GPM	MGD
0.01	*0.020*	*9.0*	*0.013*	0.51	7.153	3211	4.623
0.02	*0.056*	*25.3*	*0.037*	0.52	7.362	3305	4.758
0.03	*0.104*	*46.6*	*0.067*	0.53	7.573	3400	4.894
0.04	*0.160*	*71.6*	*0.103*	0.54	7.786	3495	5.031
0.05	*0.223*	*100.1*	*0.144*	0.55	8.000	3592	5.170
0.06	*0.293*	*131.5*	*0.189*	0.56	8.217	3689	5.310
0.07	*0.369*	*165.7*	*0.239*	0.57	8.435	3787	5.451
0.08	*0.451*	*202.4*	*0.291*	0.58	8.655	3886	5.593
0.09	*0.538*	*241.4*	*0.348*	0.59	8.877	3985	5.736
0.10	*0.630*	*282.6*	*0.407*	0.60	9.100	4086	5.881
0.11	*0.726*	*326.0*	*0.469*	0.61	9.325	4187	6.027
0.12	*0.827*	*371.3*	*0.535*	0.62	9.552	4289	6.173
0.13	*0.932*	*418.5*	*0.603*	0.63	9.781	4391	6.321
0.14	*1.042*	*467.6*	*0.673*	0.64	10.01	4495	6.470
0.15	*1.155*	*518.4*	*0.747*	0.65	10.24	4599	6.620
0.16	*1.272*	*570.9*	*0.822*	0.66	10.48	4704	6.771
0.17	*1.393*	*625.0*	*0.900*	0.67	10.71	4809	6.923
0.18	*1.517*	*680.7*	*0.980*	0.68	10.95	4916	7.076
0.19	*1.644*	*738.0*	*1.063*	0.69	11.19	5023	7.230
0.20	1.775	797.0	1.147	0.70	11.43	5131	7.386
0.21	1.909	857.2	1.234	0.71	11.67	5239	7.542
0.22	2.047	918.8	1.323	0.72	11.91	5349	7.699
0.23	2.187	981.8	1.413	0.73	12.16	5459	7.857
0.24	2.330	1046	1.506	0.74	12.40	5569	8.017
0.25	2.477	1112	1.601	0.75	12.65	5681	8.177
0.26	2.626	1179	1.697	0.76	12.90	5793	8.338
0.27	2.778	1247	1.795	0.77	13.15	5905	8.500
0.28	2.933	1317	1.895	0.78	13.41	6019	8.664
0.29	3.090	1387	1.997	0.79	13.66	6133	8.828
0.30	3.250	1459	2.100	0.80	13.92	6247	8.993
0.31	3.413	1532	2.206	0.81	14.17	6363	9.159
0.32	3.578	1606	2.312	0.82	14.43	6479	9.326
0.33	3.746	1682	2.421	0.83	14.69	6595	9.493
0.34	3.916	1758	2.531	0.84	14.95	6712	9.662
0.35	4.089	1836	2.642	0.85	15.21	6830	9.832
0.36	4.264	1914	2.756	0.86	15.48	6949	10.00
0.37	4.441	1994	2.870	0.87	15.74	7068	10.17
0.38	4.621	2075	2.986	0.88	16.01	7188	10.35
0.39	4.803	2156	3.104	0.89	16.28	7308	10.52
0.40	4.987	2239	3.223	0.90	16.55	7429	10.69
0.41	5.174	2323	3.343	0.91	16.82	7551	10.87
0.42	5.362	2407	3.465	0.92	17.09	7673	11.04
0.43	5.553	2493	3.589	0.93	17.36	7795	11.22
0.44	5.746	2580	3.713	0.94	17.64	7919	11.40
0.45	5.941	2667	3.839	0.95	17.91	8043	11.58
0.46	6.138	2756	3.967	0.96	18.19	8167	11.76
0.47	6.337	2845	4.095	0.97	18.47	8292	11.94
0.48	6.538	2935	4.225	0.98	18.75	8418	12.12
0.49	6.741	3026	4.356	0.99	19.03	8544	12.30
0.50	6.946	3119	4.489	1.00	19.31	8671	12.48

Table 10-8 (Continued)				Table 10-8 (Continued)			
Head (feet)	CFS	GPM	MGD	Head (feet)	CFS	GPM	MGD
1.01	19.60	8798	12.66	1.51	35.21	15,810	22.75
1.02	19.88	8926	12.85	1.52	35.55	15,960	22.97
1.03	20.17	9055	13.03	1.53	35.88	16,110	23.19
1.04	20.46	9184	13.22	1.54	36.22	16,260	23.41
1.05	20.74	9313	13.41	1.55	36.56	16,420	23.63
1.06	21.03	9443	13.59	1.56	36.91	16,570	23.85
1.07	21.33	9574	13.78	1.57	37.25	16,720	24.07
1.08	21.62	9705	13.97	1.58	37.59	16,880	24.29
1.09	21.91	9837	14.16	1.59	37.94	17,030	24.52
1.10	22.21	9969	14.35	1.60	38.28	17,190	24.74
1.11	22.50	10,100	14.54	1.61	38.63	17,340	24.96
1.12	22.80	10,240	14.73	1.62	38.97	17,500	25.19
1.13	23.10	10,370	14.93	1.63	39.32	17,650	25.41
1.14	23.40	10,500	15.12	1.64	39.67	17,810	25.64
1.15	23.70	10,640	15.31	1.65	40.02	17,970	25.86
1.16	24.00	10,770	15.51	1.66	40.37	18,120	26.09
1.17	24.30	10,910	15.70	1.67	40.72	18,280	26.31
1.18	24.60	11,050	15.90	1.68	41.07	18,440	26.54
1.19	24.91	11,180	16.10	1.69	41.42	18,600	26.77
1.20	25.21	11,320	16.29	1.70	41.78	18,760	27.00
1.21	25.52	11,460	16.49	1.71	42.13	18,910	27.23
1.22	25.83	11,600	16.69	1.72	42.49	19,070	27.46
1.23	26.14	11,730	16.89	1.73	42.84	19,230	27.69
1.24	26.45	11,870	17.09	1.74	43.20	19,390	27.92
1.25	26.76	12,010	17.29	1.75	43.56	19,550	28.15
1.26	27.07	12,150	17.50	1.76	43.91	19,720	28.38
1.27	27.39	12,290	17.70	1.77	44.27	19,880	28.61
1.28	27.70	12,440	17.90	1.78	44.63	20,040	28.84
1.29	28.02	12,580	18.10	1.79	44.99	20,200	29.08
1.30	28.33	12,720	18.31	1.80	45.36	20,360	29.31
1.31	28.65	12,860	18.51	1.81	45.72	20,530	29.55
1.32	28.97	13,010	18.72	1.82	46.08	20,690	29.78
1.33	29.29	13,150	18.93	1.83	46.44	20,850	30.01
1.34	29.61	13,290	19.13	1.84	46.81	21,020	30.25
1.35	29.93	13,440	19.34	1.85	47.17	21,180	30.49
1.36	30.25	13,580	19.55	1.86	47.54	21,340	30.72
1.37	30.58	13,730	19.76	1.87	47.91	21,510	30.96
1.38	30.90	13,870	19.97	1.88	48.28	21,670	31.20
1.39	31.23	14,020	20.18	1.89	48.64	21,840	31.44
1.40	31.55	14,170	20.39	1.90	49.01	22,000	31.67
1.41	31.88	14,310	20.60	1.91	49.38	22,170	31.91
1.42	32.21	14,460	20.81	1.92	49.75	22,340	32.15
1.43	32.54	14,610	21.03	1.93	50.12	22,500	32.39
1.44	32.87	14,760	21.24	1.94	50.50	22,670	32.63
1.45	33.20	14,900	21.46	1.95	50.87	22,840	32.87
1.46	33.53	15,050	21.67	1.96	51.24	23,010	33.12
1.47	33.87	15,200	21.89	1.97	51.62	23,170	33.36
1.48	34.20	15,350	22.10	1.98	51.99	23,340	33.60
1.49	34.53	15,500	22.32	1.99	52.37	23,510	33.84
1.50	34.87	15,650	22.53	2.00	52.74	23,680	34.09

10

Rectangular Weir With End Contractions Discharge Tables • 197

Table 10-8 (Continued)				Table 10-8 (Continued)			
Head (feet)	CFS	GPM	MGD	Head (feet)	CFS	GPM	MGD
2.01	53.12	23,850	34.33	2.51	72.80	32,690	47.05
2.02	53.50	24,020	34.57	2.52	73.21	32,870	47.31
2.03	53.88	24,190	34.82	2.53	73.62	33,050	47.58
2.04	54.26	24,360	35.06	2.54	74.03	33,240	47.84
2.05	54.64	24,530	35.31	2.55	74.44	33,420	48.11
2.06	55.02	24,700	35.55	2.56	74.85	33,610	48.37
2.07	55.40	24,870	35.80	2.57	75.27	33,790	48.64
2.08	55.78	25,040	36.05	2.58	75.68	33,980	48.91
2.09	56.16	25,210	36.30	2.59	76.09	34,160	49.17
2.10	56.55	25,390	36.54	2.60	76.50	34,350	49.44
2.11	56.93	25,560	36.79	2.61	76.92	34,530	49.71
2.12	57.32	25,730	37.04	2.62	77.33	34,720	49.98
2.13	57.70	25,900	37.29	2.63	77.75	34,900	50.24
2.14	58.09	26,080	37.54	2.64	78.16	35,090	50.51
2.15	58.47	26,250	37.79	2.65	78.58	35,280	50.78
2.16	58.86	26,430	38.04	2.66	78.99	35,460	51.05
2.17	59.25	26,600	38.29	2.67	79.41	35,650	51.32
2.18	59.64	26,770	38.54	2.68	79.83	35,840	51.59
2.19	60.03	26,950	38.79	2.69	80.25	36,030	51.86
2.20	60.42	27,120	39.04	2.70	80.66	36,210	52.13
2.21	60.81	27,300	39.30	2.71	81.08	36,400	52.40
2.22	61.20	27,470	39.55	2.72	81.50	36,590	52.67
2.23	61.59	27,650	39.80	2.73	81.92	36,780	52.94
2.24	61.98	27,830	40.06	2.74	82.34	36,970	53.21
2.25	62.38	28,000	40.31	2.75	82.76	37,160	53.49
2.26	62.77	28,180	40.56	2.76	83.18	37,350	53.76
2.27	63.16	28,360	40.82	2.77	83.61	37,540	54.03
2.28	63.56	28,530	41.07	2.78	84.03	37,720	54.30
2.29	63.95	28,710	41.33	2.79	84.45	37,910	54.58
2.30	64.35	28,890	41.59	2.80	84.88	38,100	54.85
2.31	64.75	29,070	41.84	2.81	85.30	38,290	55.12
2.32	65.14	29,250	42.10	2.82	85.72	38,490	55.40
2.33	65.54	29,420	42.36	2.83	86.15	38,680	55.67
2.34	65.94	29,600	42.61	2.84	86.57	38,870	55.95
2.35	66.34	29,780	42.87	2.85	87.00	39,060	56.22
2.36	66.74	29,960	43.13	2.86	87.42	39,250	56.50
2.37	67.14	30,140	43.39	2.87	87.85	39,440	56.77
2.38	67.54	30,320	43.65	2.88	88.28	39,630	57.05
2.39	67.94	30,500	43.91	2.89	88.71	39,820	57.33
2.40	68.34	30,680	44.17	2.90	89.13	40,020	57.60
2.41	68.75	30,860	44.43	2.91	89.56	40,210	57.88
2.42	69.15	31,040	44.69	2.92	89.99	40,400	58.16
2.43	69.55	31,230	44.95	2.93	90.42	40,590	58.43
2.44	69.96	31,410	45.21	2.94	90.85	40,790	58.71
2.45	70.36	31,590	45.47	2.95	91.28	40,980	58.99
2.46	70.77	31,770	45.73	2.96	91.71	41,170	59.27
2.47	71.17	31,950	46.00	2.97	92.14	41,370	59.55
2.48	71.58	32,140	46.26	2.98	92.57	41,560	59.82
2.49	71.99	32,320	46.52	2.99	93.00	41,750	60.10
2.50	72.40	32,500	46.79	3.00	93.44	41,950	60.38

10

Table 10-9:
8 ft. Rectangular Weir with End Contractions Discharge Table with Head in Feet

Formula: $CFS = 26.64H^{1.5} - 0.666H^{2.5}$
$GPM = 11960H^{1.5} - 299H^{2.5}$
$MGD = 17.216H^{1.5} - 0.430H^{2.5}$
Where: H = head in feet

Values in italics indicate flow below the recommended range of this particular primary device.

Table 10-9				Table 10-9 (Continued)			
Head (feet)	CFS	GPM	MGD	Head (feet)	CFS	GPM	MGD
0.01	*0.027*	*12.0*	*0.017*	0.51	9.579	4300	6.190
0.02	*0.075*	*33.8*	*0.049*	0.52	9.860	4426	6.372
0.03	*0.138*	*62.1*	*0.089*	0.53	10.14	4554	6.555
0.04	*0.213*	*95.6*	*0.138*	0.54	10.43	4682	6.739
0.05	*0.297*	*133.5*	*0.192*	0.55	10.72	4811	6.926
0.06	*0.391*	*175.5*	*0.253*	0.56	11.01	4942	7.114
0.07	*0.493*	*221.1*	*0.318*	0.57	11.30	5074	7.303
0.08	*0.602*	*270.0*	*0.389*	0.58	11.60	5206	7.494
0.09	*0.718*	*322.1*	*0.464*	0.59	11.89	5340	7.687
0.10	*0.840*	*377.2*	*0.543*	0.60	12.20	5475	7.881
0.11	*0.969*	*435.0*	*0.626*	0.61	12.50	5611	8.077
0.12	*1.104*	*495.5*	*0.714*	0.62	12.80	5748	8.274
0.13	*1.245*	*558.6*	*0.804*	0.63	13.11	5886	8.473
0.14	*1.391*	*624.1*	*0.899*	0.64	13.42	6026	8.674
0.15	*1.542*	*692.0*	*0.997*	0.65	13.73	6166	8.875
0.16	*1.698*	*762.2*	*1.098*	0.66	14.05	6307	9.079
0.17	*1.859*	*834.5*	*1.202*	0.67	14.37	6449	9.283
0.18	*2.025*	*909.0*	*1.309*	0.68	14.68	6592	9.490
0.19	*2.196*	*985.6*	*1.419*	0.69	15.01	6737	9.697
0.20	2.371	1064	1.532	0.70	15.33	6882	9.906
0.21	2.550	1145	1.648	0.71	15.65	7028	10.12
0.22	2.734	1227	1.767	0.72	15.98	7175	10.33
0.23	2.922	1312	1.888	0.73	16.31	7323	10.54
0.24	3.113	1398	2.012	0.74	16.64	7473	10.76
0.25	3.309	1486	2.139	0.75	16.98	7623	10.97
0.26	3.509	1575	2.268	0.76	17.32	7774	11.19
0.27	3.712	1667	2.399	0.77	17.65	7925	11.41
0.28	3.919	1760	2.533	0.78	17.99	8078	11.63
0.29	4.130	1854	2.669	0.79	18.34	8232	11.85
0.30	4.345	1950	2.808	0.80	18.68	8387	12.07
0.31	4.562	2048	2.948	0.81	19.03	8542	12.30
0.32	4.784	2148	3.091	0.82	19.38	8699	12.52
0.33	5.008	2249	3.237	0.83	19.73	8856	12.75
0.34	5.237	2351	3.384	0.84	20.08	9014	12.98
0.35	5.468	2455	3.534	0.85	20.43	9173	13.20
0.36	5.702	2560	3.685	0.86	20.79	9333	13.44
0.37	5.940	2667	3.839	0.87	21.15	9494	13.67
0.38	6.181	2775	3.994	0.88	21.51	9656	13.90
0.39	6.425	2885	4.152	0.89	21.87	9818	14.13
0.40	6.672	2995	4.312	0.90	22.23	9982	14.37
0.41	6.922	3108	4.473	0.91	22.60	10,150	14.60
0.42	7.175	3221	4.637	0.92	22.97	10,310	14.84
0.43	7.431	3336	4.802	0.93	23.34	10,480	15.08
0.44	7.690	3452	4.969	0.94	23.71	10,640	15.32
0.45	7.951	3570	5.139	0.95	24.08	10,810	15.56
0.46	8.216	3688	5.309	0.96	24.46	10,980	15.80
0.47	8.483	3808	5.482	0.97	24.83	11,150	16.05
0.48	8.753	3930	5.657	0.98	25.21	11,320	16.29
0.49	9.026	4052	5.833	0.99	25.59	11,490	16.54
0.50	9.301	4176	6.011	1.00	25.97	11,660	16.79

10

Table 10-9 (Continued)					Table 10-9 (Continued)			
Head (feet)	CFS	GPM	MGD		Head (feet)	CFS	GPM	MGD
1.01	26.36	11,830	17.03		1.51	47.57	21,350	30.74
1.02	26.74	12,010	17.28		1.52	48.03	21,560	31.04
1.03	27.13	12,180	17.53		1.53	48.49	21,770	31.34
1.04	27.52	12,350	17.78		1.54	48.95	21,980	31.63
1.05	27.91	12,530	18.04		1.55	49.42	22,190	31.93
1.06	28.30	12,710	18.29		1.56	49.88	22,390	32.24
1.07	28.70	12,880	18.55		1.57	50.35	22,600	32.54
1.08	29.09	13,060	18.80		1.58	50.82	22,810	32.84
1.09	29.49	13,240	19.06		1.59	51.29	23,030	33.14
1.10	29.89	13,420	19.32		1.60	51.76	23,240	33.45
1.11	30.29	13,600	19.57		1.61	52.23	23,450	33.75
1.12	30.69	13,780	19.83		1.62	52.70	23,660	34.06
1.13	31.10	13,960	20.10		1.63	53.18	23,880	34.37
1.14	31.50	14,140	20.36		1.64	53.66	24,090	34.68
1.15	31.91	14,330	20.62		1.65	54.13	24,300	34.98
1.16	32.32	14,510	20.89		1.66	54.61	24,520	35.29
1.17	32.73	14,690	21.15		1.67	55.09	24,730	35.60
1.18	33.14	14,880	21.42		1.68	55.57	24,950	35.91
1.19	33.55	15,060	21.68		1.69	56.06	25,170	36.23
1.20	33.97	15,250	21.95		1.70	56.54	25,380	36.54
1.21	34.39	15,440	22.22		1.71	57.02	25,600	36.85
1.22	34.80	15,620	22.49		1.72	57.51	25,820	37.17
1.23	35.22	15,810	22.76		1.73	58.00	26,040	37.48
1.24	35.64	16,000	23.04		1.74	58.48	26,260	37.80
1.25	36.07	16,190	23.31		1.75	58.97	26,480	38.11
1.26	36.49	16,380	23.58		1.76	59.46	26,700	38.43
1.27	36.92	16,570	23.86		1.77	59.96	26,920	38.75
1.28	37.34	16,770	24.13		1.78	60.45	27,140	39.07
1.29	37.77	16,960	24.41		1.79	60.94	27,360	39.38
1.30	38.20	17,150	24.69		1.80	61.44	27,580	39.70
1.31	38.63	17,350	24.97		1.81	61.94	27,810	40.03
1.32	39.07	17,540	25.25		1.82	62.43	28,030	40.35
1.33	39.50	17,730	25.53		1.83	62.93	28,250	40.67
1.34	39.94	17,930	25.81		1.84	63.43	28,480	40.99
1.35	40.38	18,130	26.09		1.85	63.93	28,700	41.32
1.36	40.81	18,320	26.38		1.86	64.44	28,930	41.64
1.37	41.26	18,520	26.66		1.87	64.94	29,150	41.97
1.38	41.70	18,720	26.95		1.88	65.44	29,380	42.29
1.39	42.14	18,920	27.23		1.89	65.95	29,610	42.62
1.40	42.58	19,120	27.52		1.90	66.46	29,840	42.95
1.41	43.03	19,320	27.81		1.91	66.96	30,060	43.27
1.42	43.48	19,520	28.10		1.92	67.47	30,290	43.60
1.43	43.93	19,720	28.39		1.93	67.98	30,520	43.93
1.44	44.38	19,920	28.68		1.94	68.49	30,750	44.26
1.45	44.83	20,130	28.97		1.95	69.01	30,980	44.59
1.46	45.28	20,330	29.26		1.96	69.52	31,210	44.93
1.47	45.74	20,530	29.56		1.97	70.03	31,440	45.26
1.48	46.19	20,740	29.85		1.98	70.55	31,670	45.59
1.49	46.65	20,940	30.15		1.99	71.06	31,900	45.93
1.50	47.11	21,150	30.44		2.00	71.58	32,140	46.26

10

Table 10-9 (Continued)				Table 10-9 (Continued)			
Head (feet)	CFS	GPM	MGD	Head (feet)	CFS	GPM	MGD
2.01	72.10	32,370	46.59	2.51	99.29	44,580	64.17
2.02	72.62	32,600	46.93	2.52	99.86	44,830	64.53
2.03	73.14	32,840	47.27	2.53	100.4	45,090	64.90
2.04	73.66	33,070	47.60	2.54	101.0	45,340	65.27
2.05	74.19	33,310	47.94	2.55	101.6	45,600	65.63
2.06	74.71	33,540	48.28	2.56	102.1	45,850	66.00
2.07	75.23	33,780	48.62	2.57	102.7	46,110	66.37
2.08	75.76	34,010	48.96	2.58	103.3	46,370	66.74
2.09	76.29	34,250	49.30	2.59	103.9	46,620	67.11
2.10	76.81	34,490	49.64	2.60	104.4	46,880	67.48
2.11	77.34	34,720	49.98	2.61	105.0	47,140	67.86
2.12	77.87	34,960	50.33	2.62	105.6	47,400	68.23
2.13	78.40	35,200	50.67	2.63	106.2	47,660	68.60
2.14	78.94	35,440	51.01	2.64	106.7	47,920	68.97
2.15	79.47	35,680	51.36	2.65	107.3	48,180	69.35
2.16	80.00	35,920	51.70	2.66	107.9	48,440	69.72
2.17	80.54	36,160	52.05	2.67	108.5	48,700	70.10
2.18	81.07	36,400	52.39	2.68	109.0	48,960	70.47
2.19	81.61	36,640	52.74	2.69	109.6	49,220	70.85
2.20	82.15	36,880	53.09	2.70	110.2	49,480	71.22
2.21	82.69	37,120	53.44	2.71	110.8	49,740	71.60
2.22	83.23	37,360	53.79	2.72	111.4	50,000	71.98
2.23	83.77	37,610	54.13	2.73	112.0	50,270	72.36
2.24	84.31	37,850	54.48	2.74	112.5	50,530	72.73
2.25	84.85	38,090	54.84	2.75	113.1	50,790	73.11
2.26	85.40	38,340	55.19	2.76	113.7	51,060	73.49
2.27	85.94	38,580	55.54	2.77	114.3	51,320	73.87
2.28	86.49	38,830	55.89	2.78	114.9	51,580	74.25
2.29	87.03	39,070	56.24	2.79	115.5	51,850	74.63
2.30	87.58	39,320	56.60	2.80	116.1	52,110	75.02
2.31	88.13	39,570	56.95	2.81	116.7	52,380	75.40
2.32	88.68	39,810	57.31	2.82	117.3	52,640	75.78
2.33	89.23	40,060	57.66	2.83	117.9	52,910	76.16
2.34	89.78	40,310	58.02	2.84	118.4	53,180	76.55
2.35	90.33	40,550	58.38	2.85	119.0	53,440	76.93
2.36	90.88	40,800	58.73	2.86	119.6	53,710	77.31
2.37	91.44	41,050	59.09	2.87	120.2	53,980	77.70
2.38	91.99	41,300	59.45	2.88	120.8	54,250	78.09
2.39	92.55	41,550	59.81	2.89	121.4	54,510	78.47
2.40	93.11	41,800	60.17	2.90	122.0	54,780	78.86
2.41	93.66	42,050	60.53	2.91	122.6	55,050	79.24
2.42	94.22	42,300	60.89	2.92	123.2	55,320	79.63
2.43	94.78	42,550	61.25	2.93	123.8	55,590	80.02
2.44	95.34	42,800	61.61	2.94	124.4	55,860	80.41
2.45	95.90	43,060	61.98	2.95	125.0	56,130	80.80
2.46	96.47	43,310	62.34	2.96	125.6	56,400	81.19
2.47	97.03	43,560	62.70	2.97	126.2	56,670	81.58
2.48	97.59	43,810	63.07	2.98	126.8	56,940	81.97
2.49	98.16	44,070	63.43	2.99	127.4	57,210	82.36
2.50	98.72	44,320	63.80	3.00	128.0	57,490	82.75

10

Rectangular Weir With End Contractions Discharge Tables • 201

Table 10-9 (Continued)				Table 10-9 (Continued)			
Head (feet)	CFS	GPM	MGD	Head (feet)	CFS	GPM	MGD
3.01	128.6	57,760	83.14	3.51	159.8	71,750	103.3
3.02	129.3	58,030	83.53	3.52	160.5	72,030	103.7
3.03	129.9	58,300	83.92	3.53	161.1	72,320	104.1
3.04	130.5	58,580	84.32	3.54	161.7	72,610	104.5
3.05	131.1	58,850	84.71	3.55	162.4	72,900	104.9
3.06	131.7	59,120	85.10	3.56	163.0	73,190	105.3
3.07	132.3	59,400	85.50	3.57	163.7	73,470	105.8
3.08	132.9	59,670	85.89	3.58	164.3	73,760	106.2
3.09	133.5	59,940	86.29	3.59	164.9	74,050	106.6
3.10	134.1	60,220	86.68	3.60	165.6	74,340	107.0
3.11	134.7	60,500	87.08	3.61	166.2	74,630	107.4
3.12	135.4	60,770	87.48	3.62	166.9	74,920	107.8
3.13	136.0	61,050	87.87	3.63	167.5	75,210	108.3
3.14	136.6	61,320	88.27	3.64	168.2	75,500	108.7
3.15	137.2	61,600	88.67	3.65	168.8	75,790	109.1
3.16	137.8	61,880	89.07	3.66	169.5	76,080	109.5
3.17	138.4	62,150	89.47	3.67	170.1	76,370	109.9
3.18	139.1	62,430	89.87	3.68	170.8	76,660	110.4
3.19	139.7	62,710	90.27	3.69	171.4	76,960	110.8
3.20	140.3	62,990	90.67	3.70	172.1	77,250	111.2
3.21	140.9	63,260	91.07	3.71	172.7	77,540	111.6
3.22	141.5	63,540	91.47	3.72	173.4	77,830	112.0
3.23	142.2	63,820	91.87	3.73	174.0	78,120	112.5
3.24	142.8	64,100	92.27	3.74	174.7	78,420	112.9
3.25	143.4	64,380	92.67	3.75	175.3	78,710	113.3
3.26	144.0	64,660	93.08	3.76	176.0	79,000	113.7
3.27	144.6	64,940	93.48	3.77	176.6	79,300	114.1
3.28	145.3	65,220	93.88	3.78	177.3	79,590	114.6
3.29	145.9	65,500	94.29	3.79	177.9	79,880	115.0
3.30	146.5	65,780	94.69	3.80	178.6	80,180	115.4
3.31	147.2	66,060	95.10	3.81	179.2	80,470	115.8
3.32	147.8	66,340	95.50	3.82	179.9	80,770	116.3
3.33	148.4	66,630	95.91	3.83	180.6	81,060	116.7
3.34	149.0	66,910	96.31	3.84	181.2	81,360	117.1
3.35	149.7	67,190	96.72	3.85	181.9	81,650	117.5
3.36	150.3	67,470	97.13	3.86	182.5	81,950	118.0
3.37	150.9	67,760	97.53	3.87	183.2	82,240	118.4
3.38	151.6	68,040	97.94	3.88	183.9	82,540	118.8
3.39	152.2	68,320	98.35	3.89	184.5	82,840	119.2
3.40	152.8	68,610	98.76	3.90	185.2	83,130	119.7
3.41	153.5	68,890	99.17	3.91	185.8	83,430	120.1
3.42	154.1	69,180	99.58	3.92	186.5	83,730	120.5
3.43	154.7	69,460	99.99	3.93	187.2	84,020	121.0
3.44	155.4	69,750	100.4	3.94	187.8	84,320	121.4
3.45	156.0	70,030	100.8	3.95	188.5	84,620	121.8
3.46	156.6	70,320	101.2	3.96	189.1	84,920	122.2
3.47	157.3	70,600	101.6	3.97	189.8	85,220	122.7
3.48	157.9	70,890	102.0	3.98	190.5	85,510	123.1
3.49	158.5	71,170	102.5	3.99	191.1	85,810	123.5
3.50	159.2	71,460	102.9	4.00	191.8	86,110	124.0

Table 10-10:
10 ft. Rectangular Weir with End Contractions Discharge Table with Head in Feet

Formula: $\text{CFS} = 33.3H^{1.5} - 0.666H^{2.5}$
$\text{GPM} = 14950H^{1.5} - 299H^{2.5}$
$\text{MGD} = 21.52H^{1.5} - 0.430H^{2.5}$
Where: H = head in feet

Values in italics indicate flow below the recommended range of this particular primary device.

Table 10-10				Table 10-10 (Continued)			
Head (feet)	CFS	GPM	MGD	Head (feet)	CFS	GPM	MGD
0.01	*0.033*	*15*	*0.022*	0.51	12.00	5389	7.758
0.02	*0.094*	*42*	*0.061*	0.52	12.36	5548	7.986
0.03	*0.173*	*78*	*0.112*	0.53	12.71	5707	8.215
0.04	*0.266*	*119*	*0.172*	0.54	13.07	5868	8.447
0.05	*0.372*	*167*	*0.240*	0.55	13.43	6031	8.681
0.06	*0.489*	*219*	*0.316*	0.56	13.80	6195	8.917
0.07	*0.616*	*276*	*0.398*	0.57	14.17	6360	9.155
0.08	*0.752*	*338*	*0.486*	0.58	14.54	6527	9.395
0.09	*0.897*	*403*	*0.580*	0.59	14.91	6695	9.638
0.10	*1.051*	*472*	*0.679*	0.60	15.29	6865	9.882
0.11	*1.212*	*544*	*0.783*	0.61	15.67	7036	10.13
0.12	*1.381*	*620*	*0.893*	0.62	16.06	7208	10.38
0.13	*1.557*	*699*	*1.006*	0.63	16.44	7382	10.63
0.14	*1.739*	*781*	*1.124*	0.64	16.83	7556	10.88
0.15	*1.929*	*866*	*1.247*	0.65	17.22	7733	11.13
0.16	*2.124*	*953*	*1.373*	0.66	17.62	7910	11.39
0.17	*2.326*	*1044*	*1.503*	0.67	18.02	8089	11.64
0.18	*2.534*	*1137*	*1.638*	0.68	18.42	8269	11.90
0.19	*2.747*	*1233*	*1.776*	0.69	18.82	8450	12.16
0.20	2.967	1332	1.917	0.70	19.23	8633	12.43
0.21	3.191	1433	2.062	0.71	19.64	8817	12.69
0.22	3.421	1536	2.211	0.72	20.05	9002	12.96
0.23	3.656	1641	2.363	0.73	20.47	9188	13.23
0.24	3.896	1749	2.518	0.74	20.88	9376	13.50
0.25	4.142	1859	2.677	0.75	21.30	9565	13.77
0.26	4.392	1972	2.838	0.76	21.73	9755	14.04
0.27	4.647	2086	3.003	0.77	22.15	9946	14.32
0.28	4.906	2203	3.171	0.78	22.58	10,140	14.59
0.29	5.170	2321	3.341	0.79	23.01	10,330	14.87
0.30	5.439	2442	3.515	0.80	23.45	10,530	15.15
0.31	5.712	2564	3.691	0.81	23.88	10,720	15.43
0.32	5.989	2689	3.871	0.82	24.32	10,920	15.72
0.33	6.271	2815	4.053	0.83	24.76	11,120	16.00
0.34	6.557	2944	4.237	0.84	25.21	11,320	16.29
0.35	6.847	3074	4.425	0.85	25.65	11,520	16.58
0.36	7.141	3206	4.615	0.86	26.10	11,720	16.87
0.37	7.439	3340	4.807	0.87	26.55	11,920	17.16
0.38	7.741	3475	5.003	0.88	27.01	12,120	17.45
0.39	8.047	3613	5.200	0.89	27.46	12,330	17.75
0.40	8.357	3752	5.401	0.90	27.92	12,530	18.04
0.41	8.670	3893	5.603	0.91	28.38	12,740	18.34
0.42	8.988	4035	5.808	0.92	28.84	12,950	18.64
0.43	9.309	4179	6.016	0.93	29.31	13,160	18.94
0.44	9.634	4325	6.226	0.94	29.78	13,370	19.24
0.45	9.962	4472	6.438	0.95	30.25	13,580	19.55
0.46	10.29	4621	6.652	0.96	30.72	13,790	19.85
0.47	10.63	4772	6.869	0.97	31.20	14,010	20.16
0.48	10.97	4924	7.088	0.98	31.67	14,220	20.47
0.49	11.31	5078	7.309	0.99	32.15	14,430	20.78
0.50	11.66	5233	7.532	1.00	32.63	14,650	21.09

10

Table 10-10 (Continued)				Table 10-10 (Continued)			
Head (feet)	CFS	GPM	MGD	Head (feet)	CFS	GPM	MGD
1.01	33.12	14,870	21.40	1.51	59.92	26,900	38.72
1.02	33.60	15,090	21.72	1.52	60.51	27,160	39.10
1.03	34.09	15,310	22.03	1.53	61.09	27,430	39.48
1.04	34.58	15,530	22.35	1.54	61.68	27,690	39.86
1.05	35.08	15,750	22.67	1.55	62.27	27,960	40.24
1.06	35.57	15,970	22.99	1.56	62.86	28,220	40.62
1.07	36.07	16,190	23.31	1.57	63.45	28,490	41.00
1.08	36.57	16,420	23.63	1.58	64.04	28,750	41.39
1.09	37.07	16,640	23.96	1.59	64.64	29,020	41.77
1.10	37.57	16,870	24.28	1.60	65.24	29,290	42.16
1.11	38.08	17,100	24.61	1.61	65.84	29,560	42.55
1.12	38.59	17,320	24.94	1.62	66.44	29,830	42.93
1.13	39.10	17,550	25.27	1.63	67.04	30,100	43.32
1.14	39.61	17,780	25.60	1.64	67.64	30,370	43.71
1.15	40.12	18,010	25.93	1.65	68.25	30,640	44.11
1.16	40.64	18,240	26.26	1.66	68.86	30,910	44.50
1.17	41.16	18,480	26.60	1.67	69.46	31,190	44.89
1.18	41.68	18,710	26.93	1.68	70.08	31,460	45.29
1.19	42.20	18,950	27.27	1.69	70.69	31,730	45.68
1.20	42.72	19,180	27.61	1.70	71.30	32,010	46.08
1.21	43.25	19,420	27.95	1.71	71.92	32,290	46.48
1.22	43.78	19,650	28.29	1.72	72.53	32,560	46.87
1.23	44.31	19,890	28.63	1.73	73.15	32,840	47.27
1.24	44.84	20,130	28.98	1.74	73.77	33,120	47.67
1.25	45.37	20,370	29.32	1.75	74.39	33,400	48.08
1.26	45.91	20,610	29.67	1.76	75.02	33,680	48.48
1.27	46.45	20,850	30.02	1.77	75.64	33,960	48.88
1.28	46.99	21,100	30.37	1.78	76.27	34,240	49.29
1.29	47.53	21,340	30.72	1.79	76.89	34,520	49.69
1.30	48.07	21,580	31.07	1.80	77.52	34,800	50.10
1.31	48.62	21,830	31.42	1.81	78.15	35,090	50.51
1.32	49.17	22,070	31.77	1.82	78.79	35,370	50.92
1.33	49.72	22,320	32.13	1.83	79.42	35,660	51.32
1.34	50.27	22,570	32.49	1.84	80.05	35,940	51.74
1.35	50.82	22,820	32.84	1.85	80.69	36,230	52.15
1.36	51.38	23,070	33.20	1.86	81.33	36,510	52.56
1.37	51.93	23,320	33.56	1.87	81.97	36,800	52.97
1.38	52.49	23,570	33.92	1.88	82.61	37,090	53.39
1.39	53.05	23,820	34.29	1.89	83.25	37,380	53.80
1.40	53.62	24,070	34.65	1.90	83.90	37,670	54.22
1.41	54.18	24,320	35.01	1.91	84.54	37,960	54.64
1.42	54.75	24,580	35.38	1.92	85.19	38,250	55.05
1.43	55.32	24,830	35.75	1.93	85.84	38,540	55.47
1.44	55.89	25,090	36.12	1.94	86.49	38,830	55.89
1.45	56.46	25,350	36.48	1.95	87.14	39,120	56.31
1.46	57.03	25,600	36.86	1.96	87.79	39,410	56.74
1.47	57.61	25,860	37.23	1.97	88.45	39,710	57.16
1.48	58.18	26,120	37.60	1.98	89.10	40,000	57.58
1.49	58.76	26,380	37.97	1.99	89.76	40,300	58.01
1.50	59.34	26,640	38.35	2.00	90.42	40,590	58.43

10

Table 10-10 (Continued)				Table 10-10 (Continued)			
Head (feet)	CFS	GPM	MGD	Head (feet)	CFS	GPM	MGD
2.01	91.08	40,890	58.86	2.51	125.8	56,470	81.28
2.02	91.74	41,190	59.29	2.52	126.5	56,790	81.75
2.03	92.40	41,480	59.72	2.53	127.2	57,120	82.22
2.04	93.07	41,780	60.14	2.54	128.0	57,440	82.69
2.05	93.73	42,080	60.57	2.55	128.7	57,770	83.16
2.06	94.40	42,380	61.01	2.56	129.4	58,100	83.63
2.07	95.07	42,680	61.44	2.57	130.1	58,430	84.11
2.08	95.74	42,980	61.87	2.58	130.9	58,760	84.58
2.09	96.41	43,280	62.30	2.59	131.6	59,090	85.05
2.10	97.08	43,580	62.74	2.60	132.3	59,420	85.53
2.11	97.76	43,890	63.17	2.61	133.1	59,750	86.00
2.12	98.43	44,190	63.61	2.62	133.8	60,080	86.48
2.13	99.11	44,490	64.05	2.63	134.6	60,410	86.96
2.14	99.79	44,800	64.49	2.64	135.3	60,740	87.44
2.15	100.5	45,100	64.92	2.65	136.0	61,070	87.91
2.16	101.1	45,410	65.36	2.66	136.8	61,410	88.39
2.17	101.8	45,720	65.81	2.67	137.5	61,740	88.87
2.18	102.5	46,020	66.25	2.68	138.3	62,080	89.36
2.19	103.2	46,330	66.69	2.69	139.0	62,410	89.84
2.20	103.9	46,640	67.13	2.70	139.8	62,740	90.32
2.21	104.6	46,950	67.58	2.71	140.5	63,080	90.80
2.22	105.3	47,250	68.02	2.72	141.3	63,420	91.29
2.23	105.9	47,560	68.47	2.73	142.0	63,750	91.77
2.24	106.6	47,870	68.91	2.74	142.8	64,090	92.26
2.25	107.3	48,190	69.36	2.75	143.5	64,430	92.74
2.26	108.0	48,500	69.81	2.76	144.3	64,770	93.23
2.27	108.7	48,810	70.26	2.77	145.0	65,100	93.72
2.28	109.4	49,120	70.71	2.78	145.8	65,440	94.20
2.29	110.1	49,430	71.16	2.79	146.5	65,780	94.69
2.30	110.8	49,750	71.61	2.80	147.3	66,120	95.18
2.31	111.5	50,060	72.06	2.81	148.0	66,460	95.67
2.32	112.2	50,380	72.52	2.82	148.8	66,800	96.16
2.33	112.9	50,690	72.97	2.83	149.6	67,150	96.65
2.34	113.6	51,010	73.43	2.84	150.3	67,490	97.15
2.35	114.3	51,330	73.88	2.85	151.1	67,830	97.64
2.36	115.0	51,640	74.34	2.86	151.8	68,170	98.13
2.37	115.7	51,960	74.80	2.87	152.6	68,520	98.63
2.38	116.4	52,280	75.25	2.88	153.4	68,860	99.12
2.39	117.2	52,600	75.71	2.89	154.1	69,200	99.62
2.40	117.9	52,920	76.17	2.90	154.9	69,550	100.1
2.41	118.6	53,240	76.63	2.91	155.7	69,890	100.6
2.42	119.3	53,560	77.09	2.92	156.5	70,240	101.1
2.43	120.0	53,880	77.56	2.93	157.2	70,590	101.6
2.44	120.7	54,200	78.02	2.94	158.0	70,930	102.1
2.45	121.4	54,520	78.48	2.95	158.8	71,280	102.6
2.46	122.2	54,840	78.95	2.96	159.5	71,630	103.1
2.47	122.9	55,170	79.41	2.97	160.3	71,970	103.6
2.48	123.6	55,490	79.88	2.98	161.1	72,320	104.1
2.49	124.3	55,820	80.34	2.99	161.9	72,670	104.6
2.50	125.0	56,140	80.81	3.00	162.6	73,020	105.1

10

Table 10-10 (Continued)				Table 10-10 (Continued)			
Head (feet)	CFS	GPM	MGD	Head (feet)	CFS	GPM	MGD
3.01	163.4	73,370	105.6	3.51	203.6	91,410	131.6
3.02	164.2	73,720	106.1	3.52	204.4	91,780	132.1
3.03	165.0	74,070	106.6	3.53	205.3	92,150	132.6
3.04	165.8	74,420	107.1	3.54	206.1	92,520	133.2
3.05	166.6	74,780	107.6	3.55	206.9	92,900	133.7
3.06	167.3	75,130	108.1	3.56	207.8	93,270	134.3
3.07	168.1	75,480	108.7	3.57	208.6	93,640	134.8
3.08	168.9	75,830	109.2	3.58	209.4	94,020	135.3
3.09	169.7	76,190	109.7	3.59	210.2	94,390	135.9
3.10	170.5	76,540	110.2	3.60	211.1	94,760	136.4
3.11	171.3	76,890	110.7	3.61	211.9	95,140	136.9
3.12	172.1	77,250	111.2	3.62	212.7	95,510	137.5
3.13	172.9	77,600	111.7	3.63	213.6	95,890	138.0
3.14	173.6	77,960	112.2	3.64	214.4	96,260	138.6
3.15	174.4	78,320	112.7	3.65	215.3	96,640	139.1
3.16	175.2	78,670	113.2	3.66	216.1	97,020	139.7
3.17	176.0	79,030	113.8	3.67	216.9	97,390	140.2
3.18	176.8	79,390	114.3	3.68	217.8	97,770	140.7
3.19	177.6	79,740	114.8	3.69	218.6	98,150	141.3
3.20	178.4	80,100	115.3	3.70	219.5	98,530	141.8
3.21	179.2	80,460	115.8	3.71	220.3	98,910	142.4
3.22	180.0	80,820	116.3	3.72	221.1	99,280	142.9
3.23	180.8	81,180	116.9	3.73	222.0	99,660	143.5
3.24	181.6	81,540	117.4	3.74	222.8	100,000	144.0
3.25	182.4	81,900	117.9	3.75	223.7	100,400	144.6
3.26	183.2	82,260	118.4	3.76	224.5	100,800	145.1
3.27	184.0	82,620	118.9	3.77	225.4	101,200	145.6
3.28	184.8	82,980	119.4	3.78	226.2	101,600	146.2
3.29	185.6	83,340	120.0	3.79	227.1	101,900	146.7
3.30	186.4	83,710	120.5	3.80	227.9	102,300	147.3
3.31	187.3	84,070	121.0	3.81	228.8	102,700	147.8
3.32	188.1	84,430	121.5	3.82	229.6	103,100	148.4
3.33	188.9	84,800	122.1	3.83	230.5	103,500	148.9
3.34	189.7	85,160	122.6	3.84	231.3	103,900	149.5
3.35	190.5	85,520	123.1	3.85	232.2	104,200	150.0
3.36	191.3	85,890	123.6	3.86	233.0	104,600	150.6
3.37	192.1	86,250	124.2	3.87	233.9	105,000	151.2
3.38	192.9	86,620	124.7	3.88	234.8	105,400	151.7
3.39	193.8	86,990	125.2	3.89	235.6	105,800	152.3
3.40	194.6	87,350	125.7	3.90	236.5	106,200	152.8
3.41	195.4	87,720	126.3	3.91	237.3	106,500	153.4
3.42	196.2	88,090	126.8	3.92	238.2	106,900	153.9
3.43	197.0	88,450	127.3	3.93	239.0	107,300	154.5
3.44	197.8	88,820	127.9	3.94	239.9	107,700	155.0
3.45	198.7	89,190	128.4	3.95	240.8	108,100	155.6
3.46	199.5	89,560	128.9	3.96	241.6	108,500	156.2
3.47	200.3	89,930	129.4	3.97	242.5	108,900	156.7
3.48	201.1	90,300	130.0	3.98	243.4	109,300	157.3
3.49	202.0	90,670	130.5	3.99	244.2	109,600	157.8
3.50	202.8	91,040	131.0	4.00	245.1	110,000	158.4

Table 10-10 (Continued)					Table 10-10 (Continued)			
Head (feet)	CFS	GPM	MGD		Head (feet)	CFS	GPM	MGD
4.01	246.0	110,400	158.9		4.51	290.2	130,300	187.5
4.02	246.8	110,800	159.5		4.52	291.1	130,700	188.1
4.03	247.7	111,200	160.1		4.53	292.0	131,100	188.7
4.04	248.6	111,600	160.6		4.54	292.9	131,500	189.3
4.05	249.4	112,000	161.2		4.55	293.8	131,900	189.9
4.06	250.3	112,400	161.8		4.56	294.7	132,300	190.4
4.07	251.2	112,800	162.3		4.57	295.6	132,700	191.0
4.08	252.0	113,200	162.9		4.58	296.5	133,100	191.6
4.09	252.9	113,500	163.4		4.59	297.4	133,500	192.2
4.10	253.8	113,900	164.0		4.60	298.3	133,900	192.8
4.11	254.7	114,300	164.6		4.61	299.2	134,300	193.4
4.12	255.5	114,700	165.1		4.62	300.1	134,700	194.0
4.13	256.4	115,100	165.7		4.63	301.0	135,100	194.5
4.14	257.3	115,500	166.3		4.64	301.9	135,600	195.1
4.15	258.2	115,900	166.8		4.65	302.9	136,000	195.7
4.16	259.0	116,300	167.4		4.66	303.8	136,400	196.3
4.17	259.9	116,700	168.0		4.67	304.7	136,800	196.9
4.18	260.8	117,100	168.5		4.68	305.6	137,200	197.5
4.19	261.7	117,500	169.1		4.69	306.5	137,600	198.1
4.20	262.6	117,900	169.7		4.70	307.4	138,000	198.7
4.21	263.4	118,300	170.2		4.71	308.3	138,400	199.3
4.22	264.3	118,700	170.8		4.72	309.2	138,800	199.8
4.23	265.2	119,100	171.4		4.73	310.2	139,200	200.4
4.24	266.1	119,500	172.0		4.74	311.1	139,700	201.0
4.25	267.0	119,900	172.5		4.75	312.0	140,100	201.6
4.26	267.8	120,200	173.1		4.76	312.9	140,500	202.2
4.27	268.7	120,600	173.7		4.77	313.8	140,900	202.8
4.28	269.6	121,000	174.2		4.78	314.7	141,300	203.4
4.29	270.5	121,400	174.8		4.79	315.7	141,700	204.0
4.30	271.4	121,800	175.4		4.80	316.6	142,100	204.6
4.31	272.3	122,200	176.0		4.81	317.5	142,500	205.2
4.32	273.2	122,600	176.5		4.82	318.4	143,000	205.8
4.33	274.1	123,000	177.1		4.83	319.3	143,400	206.4
4.34	274.9	123,400	177.7		4.84	320.3	143,800	207.0
4.35	275.8	123,800	178.3		4.85	321.2	144,200	207.6
4.36	276.7	124,200	178.8		4.86	322.1	144,600	208.2
4.37	277.6	124,600	179.4		4.87	323.0	145,000	208.8
4.38	278.5	125,000	180.0		4.88	323.9	145,400	209.3
4.39	279.4	125,400	180.6		4.89	324.9	145,900	209.9
4.40	280.3	125,800	181.1		4.90	325.8	146,300	210.5
4.41	281.2	126,200	181.7		4.91	326.7	146,700	211.1
4.42	282.1	126,600	182.3		4.92	327.6	147,100	211.7
4.43	283.0	127,000	182.9		4.93	328.6	147,500	212.3
4.44	283.9	127,400	183.5		4.94	329.5	147,900	212.9
4.45	284.8	127,800	184.0		4.95	330.4	148,300	213.5
4.46	285.7	128,300	184.6		4.96	331.4	148,800	214.1
4.47	286.6	128,700	185.2		4.97	332.3	149,200	214.7
4.48	287.5	129,100	185.8		4.98	333.2	149,600	215.3
4.49	288.4	129,500	186.4		4.99	334.1	150,000	215.9
4.50	289.3	129,900	186.9		5.00	335.1	150,400	216.5

10

Rectangular Weir With End Contractions Discharge Tables • 207

Table 10-11:
0.3 m Rectangular Weir with End Contractions Discharge Table with Head in Meters

Formula: $l/s = 551.4H^{1.5} - 367.6H^{2.5}$
$m^3/hr = 1985.4H^{1.5} - 1323.6H^{2.5}$

Where: H = head in meters

Values in italics indicate flow below the recommended range of this particular primary device.

Table 10-11			Table 10-11 (Continued)		
Head (meters)	l/s	m³/hr	Head (meters)	l/s	m³/hr
0.005	*0.194*	*0.70*	0.080	11.81	42.53
0.010	*0.548*	*1.97*	0.085	12.89	46.41
0.015	*1.003*	*3.61*	0.090	13.99	50.39
0.020	*1.539*	*5.54*	0.095	15.12	54.45
0.025	*2.144*	*7.72*	0.100	16.27	58.60
0.030	*2.808*	*10.11*	0.105	17.45	62.82
0.035	*3.527*	*12.70*	0.110	18.64	67.12
0.040	*4.294*	*15.46*	0.115	19.86	71.49
0.045	*5.107*	*18.38*	0.120	21.09	75.93
0.050	*5.960*	*21.46*	0.125	22.34	80.43
0.055	*6.853*	*24.67*	0.130	23.61	84.99
0.060	7.780	28.01	0.135	24.89	89.62
0.065	8.742	31.48	0.140	26.19	94.29
0.070	9.736	35.05	0.145	27.50	99.03
0.075	10.76	38.74	0.150	28.83	103.8

10

Table 10-12:
0.4 m Rectangular Weir with End Contractions Discharge Table with Head in Meters

Formula: $l/s = 735.2H^{1.5} - 367.6H^{2.5}$
$m^3/hr = 2647.2H^{1.5} - 1323.6H^{2.5}$

Where: H = head in meters

Values in italics indicate flow below the recommended range of this particular primary device.

Table 10-12			Table 10-12 (Continued)		
Head (meters)	l/s	m³/hr	Head (meters)	l/s	m³/hr
0.005	*0.26*	*0.93*	0.105	23.70	85.34
0.010	*0.73*	*2.63*	0.110	25.35	91.27
0.015	*1.34*	*4.83*	0.115	27.02	97.30
0.020	*2.06*	*7.41*	0.120	28.73	103.4
0.025	*2.87*	*10.34*	0.125	30.46	109.7
0.030	*3.76*	*13.55*	0.130	32.22	116.0
0.035	*4.73*	*17.03*	0.135	34.01	122.4
0.040	*5.77*	*20.76*	0.140	35.82	129.0
0.045	*6.86*	*24.71*	0.145	37.65	135.6
0.050	*8.02*	*28.86*	0.150	39.51	142.3
0.055	*9.23*	*33.21*	0.155	41.39	149.0
0.060	10.48	37.74	0.160	43.29	155.9
0.065	11.79	42.44	0.165	45.21	162.8
0.070	13.14	47.31	0.170	47.15	169.8
0.075	14.53	52.33	0.175	49.11	176.8
0.080	15.97	57.50	0.180	51.09	184.0
0.085	17.45	62.81	0.185	53.09	191.2
0.090	18.96	68.26	0.190	55.10	198.4
0.095	20.50	73.83	0.195	57.14	205.7
0.100	22.09	79.53	0.200	59.18	213.1

Table 10-13:

0.5 m Rectangular Weir with End Contractions Discharge Table with Head in Meters

Formula: $l/s = 919H^{1.5} - 367.6H^{2.5}$
$m^3/hr = 3309H^{1.5} - 1323.6H^{2.5}$
Where: H = head in meters

Values in italics indicate flow below the recommended range of this particular primary device.

Table 10-13				Table 10-13 (Continued)		
Head (meters)	l/s	m³/hr		Head (meters)	l/s	m³/hr
0.005	*0.32*	*1.17*		0.130	40.84	147.0
0.010	*0.92*	*3.30*		0.135	43.12	155.3
0.015	*1.68*	*6.04*		0.140	45.44	163.6
0.020	*2.58*	*9.29*		0.145	47.80	172.1
0.025	*3.60*	*12.95*		0.150	50.19	180.7
0.030	*4.72*	*16.99*		0.155	52.60	189.4
0.035	*5.94*	*21.37*		0.160	55.05	198.2
0.040	*7.24*	*26.06*		0.165	57.53	207.1
0.045	*8.62*	*31.03*		0.170	60.04	216.2
0.050	*10.07*	*36.27*		0.175	62.57	225.3
0.055	*11.60*	*41.76*		0.180	65.13	234.5
0.060	13.18	47.46		0.185	67.71	243.8
0.065	14.83	53.41		0.190	70.33	253.2
0.070	16.54	59.57		0.195	72.96	262.7
0.075	18.31	65.93		0.200	75.62	272.3
0.080	20.13	72.48		0.205	78.30	281.9
0.085	22.00	79.21		0.210	81.01	291.7
0.090	23.92	86.13		0.215	83.74	301.5
0.095	25.89	93.21		0.220	86.49	311.4
0.100	27.90	100.5		0.225	89.25	321.4
0.105	29.95	107.9		0.230	92.04	331.4
0.110	32.05	115.4		0.235	94.85	341.5
0.115	34.19	123.1		0.240	97.68	351.7
0.120	36.37	131.0		0.245	100.5	362.0
0.125	38.58	138.9		0.250	103.4	372.3

10

Table 10-14:
0.6 m Rectangular Weir with End Contractions Discharge Table
with Head in Meters

Formula: $l/s = 1102.8H^{1.5} - 367.6H^{2.5}$
$m^3/hr = 3970.8H^{1.5} - 1323.6H^{2.5}$
Where: H = head in meters

Values in italics indicate flow below the
recommended range of this particular
primary device.

Table 10-14			Table 10-14 (Continued)		
Head (meters)	l/s	m³/hr	Head (meters)	l/s	m³/hr
0.005	*0.39*	*1.40*	0.155	63.82	229.8
0.010	*1.10*	*3.96*	0.160	66.81	240.6
0.015	*2.02*	*7.26*	0.165	69.85	251.5
0.020	*3.10*	*11.16*	0.170	72.92	262.6
0.025	*4.32*	*15.56*	0.175	76.02	273.7
0.030	*5.67*	*20.43*	0.180	79.17	285.0
0.035	*7.14*	*25.70*	0.185	82.34	296.5
0.040	*8.71*	*31.34*	0.190	85.55	308.0
0.045	*10.37*	*37.34*	0.195	88.79	319.7
0.050	*12.13*	*43.65*	0.200	92.06	331.5
0.055	*13.97*	*50.28*	0.205	95.36	343.4
0.060	15.88	57.19	0.210	98.70	355.4
0.065	17.88	64.38	0.215	102.1	367.5
0.070	19.95	71.82	0.220	105.5	379.7
0.075	22.08	79.52	0.225	108.9	392.0
0.080	24.29	87.45	0.230	112.3	404.4
0.085	26.55	95.61	0.235	115.8	416.9
0.090	28.88	104.0	0.240	119.3	429.5
0.095	31.27	112.6	0.245	122.8	442.2
0.100	33.71	121.4	0.250	126.4	455.0
0.105	36.21	130.4	0.255	129.9	467.9
0.110	38.76	139.6	0.260	133.5	480.8
0.115	41.36	148.9	0.265	137.2	493.8
0.120	44.01	158.5	0.270	140.8	506.9
0.125	46.71	168.2	0.275	144.5	520.1
0.130	49.45	178.1	0.280	148.1	533.4
0.135	52.24	188.1	0.285	151.8	546.8
0.140	55.07	198.3	0.290	155.6	560.2
0.145	57.95	208.6	0.295	159.3	573.7
0.150	60.86	219.1	0.300	163.1	587.2

Table 10-15:
0.8 m Rectangular Weir with End Contractions Discharge Table with Head in Meters

Formula: $l/s = 1470.4H^{1.5} - 367.6H^{2.5}$
$m^3/hr = 5294.4H^{1.5} - 1323.6H^{2.5}$
Where: H = head in meters

Values in italics indicate flow below the recommended range of this particular primary device.

Table 10-15			Table 10-15 (Continued)		
Head (meters)	l/s	m³/hr	Head (meters)	l/s	m³/hr
0.005	*0.52*	*1.87*	0.205	129.5	466.2
0.010	*1.47*	*5.28*	0.210	134.1	482.8
0.015	*2.69*	*9.69*	0.215	138.7	499.4
0.020	*4.14*	*14.90*	0.220	143.4	516.3
0.025	*5.78*	*20.80*	0.225	148.1	533.3
0.030	*7.58*	*27.31*	0.230	152.9	550.4
0.035	*9.55*	*34.37*	0.235	157.7	567.7
0.040	*11.65*	*41.93*	0.240	162.5	585.1
0.045	*13.88*	*49.97*	0.245	167.4	602.7
0.050	*16.24*	*58.46*	0.250	172.3	620.4
0.055	*18.71*	*67.36*	0.255	177.3	638.3
0.060	21.29	76.64	0.260	182.3	656.3
0.065	23.97	86.31	0.265	187.3	674.4
0.070	26.76	96.34	0.270	192.4	692.6
0.075	29.64	106.7	0.275	197.5	711.0
0.080	32.61	117.4	0.280	202.6	729.5
0.085	35.66	128.4	0.285	207.8	748.1
0.090	38.81	139.7	0.290	213.0	766.9
0.095	42.03	151.3	0.295	218.2	785.7
0.100	45.34	163.2	0.300	223.5	804.7
0.105	48.72	175.4	0.305	228.8	823.8
0.110	52.17	187.8	0.310	234.1	843.0
0.115	55.69	200.5	0.315	239.5	862.3
0.120	59.29	213.5	0.320	244.9	881.7
0.125	62.95	226.7	0.325	250.3	901.2
0.130	66.68	240.1	0.330	255.7	920.9
0.135	70.47	253.8	0.335	261.2	940.6
0.140	74.33	267.6	0.340	266.7	960.4
0.145	78.24	281.7	0.345	272.3	980.3
0.150	82.22	296.0	0.350	277.8	1000
0.155	86.25	310.6	0.355	283.4	1020
0.160	90.34	325.3	0.360	289.0	1041
0.165	94.49	340.2	0.365	294.7	1061
0.170	98.68	355.3	0.370	300.3	1081
0.175	102.9	370.6	0.375	306.0	1102
0.180	107.2	386.1	0.380	311.7	1122
0.185	111.6	401.8	0.385	317.4	1143
0.190	116.0	417.6	0.390	323.2	1164
0.195	120.4	433.7	0.395	329.0	1185
0.200	124.9	449.9	0.400	334.8	1205

10

Table 10-16:
1 m Rectangular Weir with End Contractions Discharge Table with Head in Meters

Formula: $l/s = 1838H^{1.5} - 367.6H^{2.5}$
$m^3/hr = 6618H^{1.5} - 1323.6H^{2.5}$

Where: H = head in meters

Values in italics indicate flow below the recommended range of this particular primary device.

Table 10-16			Table 10-16 (Continued)		
Head (meters)	l/s	m³/hr	Head (meters)	l/s	m³/hr
0.005	*0.65*	*2.34*	0.255	224.6	808.7
0.010	*1.83*	*6.61*	0.260	231.0	831.8
0.015	*3.37*	*12.12*	0.265	237.4	855.0
0.020	*5.18*	*18.64*	0.270	243.9	878.3
0.025	*7.23*	*26.03*	0.275	250.5	901.9
0.030	*9.50*	*34.18*	0.280	257.1	925.6
0.035	*11.95*	*43.03*	0.285	263.7	949.5
0.040	*14.59*	*52.52*	0.290	270.4	973.6
0.045	*17.39*	*62.61*	0.295	277.1	997.8
0.050	*20.35*	*73.26*	0.300	283.9	1022
0.055	*23.45*	*84.43*	0.305	290.7	1047
0.060	26.69	96.10	0.310	297.6	1071
0.065	30.06	108.2	0.315	304.5	1096
0.070	33.56	120.9	0.320	311.4	1121
0.075	37.19	133.9	0.325	318.4	1146
0.080	40.92	147.4	0.330	325.4	1172
0.085	44.77	161.2	0.335	332.5	1197
0.090	48.73	175.5	0.340	339.6	1223
0.095	52.80	190.1	0.345	346.8	1249
0.100	56.96	205.1	0.350	353.9	1274
0.105	61.22	220.4	0.355	361.2	1300
0.110	65.58	236.1	0.360	368.4	1327
0.115	70.03	252.2	0.365	375.7	1353
0.120	74.57	268.5	0.370	383.1	1379
0.125	79.20	285.2	0.375	390.4	1406
0.130	83.91	302.1	0.380	397.8	1432
0.135	88.71	319.4	0.385	405.3	1459
0.140	93.58	337.0	0.390	412.7	1486
0.145	98.54	354.8	0.395	420.2	1513
0.150	103.6	372.9	0.400	427.8	1540
0.155	108.7	391.3	0.405	435.4	1568
0.160	113.9	410.0	0.410	443.0	1595
0.165	119.1	428.9	0.415	450.6	1622
0.170	124.5	448.1	0.420	458.3	1650
0.175	129.8	467.5	0.425	466.0	1678
0.180	135.3	487.2	0.430	473.7	1706
0.185	140.8	507.1	0.435	481.4	1734
0.190	146.4	527.3	0.440	489.2	1762
0.195	152.1	547.6	0.445	497.1	1790
0.200	157.8	568.3	0.450	504.9	1818
0.205	163.6	589.1	0.455	512.8	1846
0.210	169.4	610.1	0.460	520.7	1875
0.215	175.4	631.4	0.465	528.6	1903
0.220	181.3	652.9	0.470	536.6	1932
0.225	187.3	674.5	0.475	544.5	1961
0.230	193.4	696.4	0.480	552.6	1990
0.235	199.5	718.5	0.485	560.6	2018
0.240	205.7	740.8	0.490	568.7	2048
0.245	212.0	763.2	0.495	576.7	2077
0.250	218.3	785.9	0.500	584.8	2106

10

Table 10-17:
1.5 m Rectangular Weir with End Contractions Discharge Table with Head in Meters

Formula: $l/s = 2757H^{1.5} - 367.6H^{2.5}$
$m^3/hr = 9927H^{1.5} - 1323.6H^{2.5}$

Where: H = head in meters

Values in italics indicate flow below the recommended range of this particular primary device.

Table 10-17			Table 10-17 (Continued)		
Head (meters)	l/s	m³/hr	Head (meters)	l/s	m³/hr
0.005	*0.97*	*3.5*	0.255	342.9	1235
0.010	*2.75*	*9.9*	0.260	352.8	1270
0.015	*5.06*	*18.2*	0.265	362.8	1306
0.020	*7.78*	*28.0*	0.270	372.9	1343
0.025	*10.86*	*39.1*	0.275	383.0	1379
0.030	*14.27*	*51.4*	0.280	393.2	1416
0.035	*17.97*	*64.7*	0.285	403.5	1453
0.040	*21.94*	*79.0*	0.290	413.9	1490
0.045	*26.17*	*94.2*	0.295	424.4	1528
0.050	*30.63*	*110.3*	0.300	434.9	1566
0.055	*35.31*	*127.1*	0.305	445.5	1604
0.060	40.20	144.7	0.310	456.2	1643
0.065	45.29	163.1	0.315	466.9	1681
0.070	50.58	182.1	0.320	477.8	1720
0.075	56.06	201.9	0.325	488.7	1760
0.080	61.72	222.2	0.330	499.6	1799
0.085	67.55	243.2	0.335	510.7	1839
0.090	73.55	264.8	0.340	521.8	1879
0.095	79.71	287.0	0.345	533.0	1919
0.100	86.02	309.7	0.350	544.2	1960
0.105	92.49	333.0	0.355	555.5	2000
0.110	99.11	356.9	0.360	566.9	2041
0.115	105.9	381.2	0.365	578.4	2083
0.120	112.8	406.1	0.370	589.9	2124
0.125	119.8	431.4	0.375	601.5	2166
0.130	127.0	457.2	0.380	613.1	2208
0.135	134.3	483.5	0.385	624.8	2250
0.140	141.7	510.3	0.390	636.6	2292
0.145	149.3	537.5	0.395	648.4	2335
0.150	157.0	565.2	0.400	660.3	2377
0.155	164.8	593.3	0.405	672.2	2420
0.160	172.7	621.8	0.410	684.2	2464
0.165	180.7	650.7	0.415	696.3	2507
0.170	188.9	680.0	0.420	708.4	2551
0.175	197.1	709.8	0.425	720.6	2595
0.180	205.5	739.9	0.430	732.8	2639
0.185	214.0	770.4	0.435	745.1	2683
0.190	222.5	801.3	0.440	757.5	2727
0.195	231.2	832.6	0.445	769.9	2772
0.200	240.0	864.2	0.450	782.3	2817
0.205	248.9	896.2	0.455	794.8	2862
0.210	257.9	928.6	0.460	807.4	2907
0.215	267.0	961.3	0.465	820.0	2953
0.220	276.1	994.3	0.470	832.7	2998
0.225	285.4	1028	0.475	845.4	3044
0.230	294.8	1061	0.480	858.2	3090
0.235	304.2	1095	0.485	871.0	3136
0.240	313.8	1130	0.490	883.9	3183
0.245	323.4	1165	0.495	896.8	3229
0.250	333.1	1200	0.500	909.8	3276

10

Table 10-17 (Continued)			Table 10-17 (Continued)		
Head (meters)	l/s	m³/hr	Head (meters)	l/s	m³/hr
0.505	922.8	3323	0.630	1263	4547
0.510	935.9	3370	0.635	1277	4598
0.515	949.0	3417	0.640	1291	4649
0.520	962.1	3464	0.645	1305	4700
0.525	975.3	3512	0.650	1320	4751
0.530	988.6	3560	0.655	1334	4803
0.535	1002	3608	0.660	1348	4854
0.540	1015	3656	0.665	1363	4906
0.545	1029	3704	0.670	1377	4958
0.550	1042	3752	0.675	1391	5010
0.555	1056	3801	0.680	1406	5062
0.560	1069	3849	0.685	1420	5114
0.565	1083	3898	0.690	1435	5166
0.570	1096	3947	0.695	1449	5219
0.575	1110	3996	0.700	1464	5271
0.580	1124	4046	0.705	1479	5324
0.585	1137	4095	0.710	1493	5377
0.590	1151	4145	0.715	1508	5430
0.595	1165	4195	0.720	1523	5483
0.600	1179	4245	0.725	1537	5536
0.605	1193	4295	0.730	1552	5589
0.610	1207	4345	0.735	1567	5642
0.615	1221	4395	0.740	1582	5696
0.620	1235	4446	0.745	1597	5749
0.625	1249	4496	0.750	1612	5803

10

Table 10-18:
2 m Rectangular Weir with End Contractions D
with Head in Meters

Formula: $l/s = 3676H^{1.5} - 367.6H^{2.5}$
$m^3/hr = 13236H^{1.5} - 1323.6H^{2.5}$

Where: H = head in meters

Values in i
recomm'
primary

Head (meters)	l/s	m³/hr	Head (meters)	l/s	
0.005	1.30	4.7	0.255	461.3	
0.010	3.67	13.2	0.260	474.7	1709
0.015	6.74	24.3	0.265	488.2	1758
0.020	10.38	37.4	0.270	501.8	1807
0.025	14.50	52.2	0.275	515.5	1856
0.030	19.05	68.6	0.280	529.4	1906
0.035	23.99	86.4	0.285	543.4	1956
0.040	29.30	105.5	0.290	557.4	2007
0.045	34.94	125.8	0.295	571.6	2058
0.050	40.90	147.3	0.300	585.9	2110
0.055	47.17	169.8	0.305	600.3	2161
0.060	53.70	193.4	0.310	614.8	2214
0.065	60.52	217.9	0.315	629.4	2266
0.070	67.60	243.4	0.320	644.1	2319
0.075	74.94	269.8	0.325	658.9	2373
0.080	82.51	297.1	0.330	673.9	2426
0.085	90.32	325.2	0.335	688.9	2480
0.090	98.36	354.2	0.340	704.0	2535
0.095	106.6	383.9	0.345	719.2	2590
0.100	115.1	414.4	0.350	734.5	2645
0.105	123.8	445.6	0.355	749.9	2700
0.110	132.6	477.6	0.360	765.4	2756
0.115	141.7	510.2	0.365	781.0	2812
0.120	151.0	543.6	0.370	796.7	2869
0.125	160.4	577.6	0.375	812.5	2926
0.130	170.1	612.3	0.380	828.4	2983
0.135	179.9	647.7	0.385	844.3	3040
0.140	189.9	683.6	0.390	860.4	3098
0.145	200.0	720.2	0.395	876.5	3156
0.150	210.4	757.4	0.400	892.8	3215
0.155	220.8	795.2	0.405	909.1	3273
0.160	231.5	833.6	0.410	925.5	3332
0.165	242.3	872.5	0.415	942.0	3392
0.170	253.3	912.0	0.420	958.6	3451
0.175	264.4	952.0	0.425	975.2	3511
0.180	275.7	992.6	0.430	992.0	3572
0.185	287.1	1034	0.435	1009	3632
0.190	298.7	1075	0.440	1026	3693
0.195	310.4	1118	0.445	1043	3754
0.200	322.2	1160	0.450	1060	3816
0.205	334.2	1203	0.455	1077	3877
0.210	346.3	1247	0.460	1094	3940
0.215	358.6	1291	0.465	1111	4002
0.220	371.0	1336	0.470	1129	4064
0.225	383.5	1381	0.475	1146	4127
0.230	396.2	1426	0.480	1164	4190
0.235	408.9	1472	0.485	1181	4254
0.240	421.8	1519	0.490	1199	4317
0.245	434.9	1566	0.495	1217	4381
0.250	448.0	1613	0.500	1235	4446

Table 10-18 (Continued)

Head (meters)	l/s	m³/hr	Head (meters)	l/s	m³/hr
0.505	1253	4510	0.755	2229	8028
0.510	1271	4575	0.760	2250	8103
0.515	1289	4640	0.765	2271	8179
0.520	1307	4705	0.770	2293	8255
0.525	1325	4771	0.775	2314	8331
0.530	1343	4836	0.780	2335	8407
0.535	1362	4902	0.785	2356	8483
0.540	1380	4969	0.790	2377	8560
0.545	1398	5035	0.795	2399	8636
0.550	1417	5102	0.800	2420	8713
0.555	1436	5169	0.805	2441	8790
0.560	1454	5236	0.810	2463	8867
0.565	1473	5304	0.815	2484	8945
0.570	1492	5371	0.820	2506	9022
0.575	1511	5439	0.825	2527	9100
0.580	1530	5507	0.830	2549	9178
0.585	1549	5576	0.835	2571	9256
0.590	1568	5644	0.840	2592	9334
0.595	1587	5713	0.845	2614	9412
0.600	1606	5782	0.850	2636	9491
0.605	1625	5852	0.855	2658	9570
0.610	1645	5921	0.860	2680	9648
0.615	1664	5991	0.865	2702	9727
0.620	1683	6061	0.870	2723	9806
0.625	1703	6131	0.875	2745	9886
0.630	1722	6202	0.880	2768	9965
0.635	1742	6272	0.885	2790	10,040
0.640	1762	6343	0.890	2812	10,120
0.645	1781	6414	0.895	2834	10,200
0.650	1801	6485	0.900	2856	10,280
0.655	1821	6557	0.905	2878	10,360
0.660	1841	6629	0.910	2901	10,440
0.665	1861	6700	0.915	2923	10,520
0.670	1881	6773	0.920	2945	10,610
0.675	1901	6845	0.925	2968	10,690
0.680	1921	6917	0.930	2990	10,770
0.685	1941	6990	0.935	3013	10,850
0.690	1962	7063	0.940	3035	10,930
0.695	1982	7136	0.945	3058	11,010
0.700	2002	7209	0.950	3080	11,090
0.705	2023	7283	0.955	3103	11,170
0.710	2043	7356	0.960	3126	11,250
0.715	2064	7430	0.965	3148	11,340
0.720	2084	7504	0.970	3171	11,420
0.725	2105	7578	0.975	3194	11,500
0.730	2125	7653	0.980	3217	11,580
0.735	2146	7727	0.985	3240	11,660
0.740	2167	7802	0.990	3263	11,750
0.745	2188	7877	0.995	3285	11,830
0.750	2209	7952	1.000	3308	11,910

Table 10-19:
3m Rectangular Weir with End Contractions Discharge Table
with Head in Meters

Formula: $l/s = 5514H^{1.5} - 367.6H^{2.5}$
$m^3/hr = 19854H^{1.5} - 1323.6H^{2.5}$
Where: H = head in meters

Values in italics indicate flow below the recommended range of this particular primary device.

Table 10-19			Table 10-19 (Continued)		
Head (meters)	l/s	m³/hr	Head (meters)	l/s	m³/hr
0.005	*1.95*	*7.0*	0.255	698.0	2513
0.010	*5.51*	*19.8*	0.260	718.3	2587
0.015	*10.12*	*36.4*	0.265	738.9	2661
0.020	*15.58*	*56.1*	0.270	759.7	2735
0.025	*21.76*	*78.4*	0.275	780.6	2811
0.030	*28.60*	*103.0*	0.280	801.7	2887
0.035	*36.03*	*129.7*	0.285	823.0	2963
0.040	*44.01*	*158.4*	0.290	844.5	3041
0.045	*52.49*	*189.0*	0.295	866.1	3119
0.050	*61.46*	*221.2*	0.300	887.9	3197
0.055	*70.88*	*255.2*	0.305	909.9	3276
0.060	80.71	290.6	0.310	932.1	3356
0.065	90.98	327.6	0.315	954.4	3436
0.070	101.6	366.0	0.320	976.8	3517
0.075	112.7	405.8	0.325	999.5	3599
0.080	124.1	446.8	0.330	1022	3681
0.085	135.9	489.2	0.335	1045	3764
0.090	148.0	532.8	0.340	1068	3847
0.095	160.4	577.7	0.345	1092	3931
0.100	173.2	623.7	0.350	1115	4015
0.105	186.3	670.8	0.355	1139	4100
0.110	199.7	719.0	0.360	1162	4186
0.115	213.4	768.3	0.365	1186	4272
0.120	227.4	818.7	0.370	1210	4358
0.125	241.7	870.1	0.375	1235	4445
0.130	256.2	922.5	0.380	1259	4533
0.135	271.0	975.9	0.385	1283	4621
0.140	286.1	1030	0.390	1308	4710
0.145	301.5	1086	0.395	1333	4799
0.150	317.1	1142	0.400	1358	4889
0.155	333.0	1199	0.405	1383	4979
0.160	349.1	1257	0.410	1408	5070
0.165	365.5	1316	0.415	1433	5161
0.170	382.1	1376	0.420	1459	5253
0.175	399.0	1437	0.425	1484	5345
0.180	416.0	1498	0.430	1510	5438
0.185	433.3	1560	0.435	1536	5531
0.190	450.9	1623	0.440	1562	5625
0.195	468.6	1687	0.445	1588	5719
0.200	486.6	1752	0.450	1615	5814
0.205	504.8	1818	0.455	1641	5909
0.210	523.2	1884	0.460	1668	6004
0.215	541.8	1951	0.465	1694	6100
0.220	560.6	2019	0.470	1721	6197
0.225	579.7	2087	0.475	1748	6294
0.230	598.9	2156	0.480	1775	6391
0.235	618.3	2226	0.485	1802	6489
0.240	637.9	2297	0.490	1830	6587
0.245	657.8	2368	0.495	1857	6686
0.250	677.8	2440	0.500	1885	6785

10

Table 10-19 (Continued)			Table 10-19 (Continued)		
Head (meters)	l/s	m³/hr	Head (meters)	l/s	m³/hr
0.505	1912	6885	0.755	3435	12,370
0.510	1940	6985	0.760	3468	12,490
0.515	1968	7086	0.765	3501	12,610
0.520	1996	7187	0.770	3534	12,730
0.525	2024	7288	0.775	3568	12,850
0.530	2052	7390	0.780	3601	12,970
0.535	2081	7492	0.785	3634	13,090
0.540	2109	7595	0.790	3668	13,210
0.545	2138	7698	0.795	3701	13,330
0.550	2167	7801	0.800	3735	13,450
0.555	2195	7905	0.805	3769	13,570
0.560	2224	8010	0.810	3803	13,690
0.565	2254	8114	0.815	3837	13,810
0.570	2283	8219	0.820	3871	13,940
0.575	2312	8325	0.825	3905	14,060
0.580	2341	8431	0.830	3939	14,180
0.585	2371	8537	0.835	3973	14,310
0.590	2401	8644	0.840	4007	14,430
0.595	2430	8751	0.845	4042	14,550
0.600	2460	8858	0.850	4076	14,680
0.605	2490	8966	0.855	4111	14,800
0.610	2520	9074	0.860	4145	14,930
0.615	2550	9183	0.865	4180	15,050
0.620	2581	9292	0.870	4215	15,180
0.625	2611	9401	0.875	4250	15,300
0.630	2641	9511	0.880	4285	15,430
0.635	2672	9621	0.885	4320	15,550
0.640	2703	9732	0.890	4355	15,680
0.645	2733	9842	0.895	4390	15,810
0.650	2764	9954	0.900	4425	15,930
0.655	2795	10,070	0.905	4461	16,060
0.660	2826	10,180	0.910	4496	16,190
0.665	2858	10,290	0.915	4532	16,320
0.670	2889	10,400	0.920	4567	16,450
0.675	2920	10,510	0.925	4603	16,570
0.680	2952	10,630	0.930	4639	16,700
0.685	2983	10,740	0.935	4674	16,830
0.690	3015	10,860	0.940	4710	16,960
0.695	3047	10,970	0.945	4746	17,090
0.700	3079	11,090	0.950	4782	17,220
0.705	3111	11,200	0.955	4818	17,350
0.710	3143	11,320	0.960	4855	17,480
0.715	3175	11,430	0.965	4891	17,610
0.720	3207	11,550	0.970	4927	17,740
0.725	3239	11,660	0.975	4963	17,870
0.730	3272	11,780	0.980	5000	18,000
0.735	3304	11,900	0.985	5036	18,130
0.740	3337	12,020	0.990	5073	18,270
0.745	3370	12,130	0.995	5110	18,400
0.750	3402	12,250	1.000	5146	18,530

10

Table 10-19 (Continued)			Table 10-19 (Continued)		
Head (meters)	l/s	m³/hr	Head (meters)	l/s	m³/hr
1.005	5183	18,660	1.255	7104	25,580
1.010	5220	18,800	1.260	7144	25,720
1.015	5257	18,930	1.265	7184	25,870
1.020	5294	19,060	1.270	7224	26,010
1.025	5331	19,200	1.275	7264	26,150
1.030	5368	19,330	1.280	7304	26,300
1.035	5405	19,460	1.285	7344	26,440
1.040	5443	19,600	1.290	7384	26,590
1.045	5480	19,730	1.295	7424	26,730
1.050	5517	19,870	1.300	7465	26,880
1.055	5555	20,000	1.305	7505	27,020
1.060	5592	20,140	1.310	7545	27,170
1.065	5630	20,270	1.315	7586	27,310
1.070	5668	20,410	1.320	7626	27,460
1.075	5705	20,540	1.325	7667	27,610
1.080	5743	20,680	1.330	7708	27,750
1.085	5781	20,820	1.335	7748	27,900
1.090	5819	20,950	1.340	7789	28,050
1.095	5857	21,090	1.345	7830	28,190
1.100	5895	21,230	1.350	7871	28,340
1.105	5933	21,360	1.355	7911	28,490
1.110	5971	21,500	1.360	7952	28,630
1.115	6009	21,640	1.365	7993	28,780
1.120	6048	21,780	1.370	8034	28,930
1.125	6086	21,910	1.375	8075	29,080
1.130	6124	22,050	1.380	8117	29,220
1.135	6163	22,190	1.385	8158	29,370
1.140	6201	22,330	1.390	8199	29,520
1.145	6240	22,470	1.395	8240	29,670
1.150	6279	22,610	1.400	8281	29,820
1.155	6317	22,750	1.405	8323	29,970
1.160	6356	22,890	1.410	8364	30,120
1.165	6395	23,030	1.415	8406	30,270
1.170	6434	23,170	1.420	8447	30,420
1.175	6473	23,310	1.425	8489	30,560
1.180	6512	23,450	1.430	8530	30,710
1.185	6551	23,590	1.435	8572	30,860
1.190	6590	23,730	1.440	8613	31,010
1.195	6629	23,870	1.445	8655	31,160
1.200	6668	24,010	1.450	8697	31,310
1.205	6708	24,150	1.455	8739	31,470
1.210	6747	24,290	1.460	8781	31,620
1.215	6787	24,440	1.465	8822	31,770
1.220	6826	24,580	1.470	8864	31,920
1.225	6865	24,720	1.475	8906	32,070
1.230	6905	24,860	1.480	8948	32,220
1.235	6945	25,010	1.485	8990	32,370
1.240	6984	25,150	1.490	9033	32,520
1.245	7024	25,290	1.495	9075	32,670
1.250	7064	25,430	1.500	9117	32,830

10

10

CHAPTER

11

**Rectangular Weir
Without End Contractions
Discharge Tables**

Overview

This chapter contains discharge (head vs. flow rate) tables for rectangular weirs without end contractions. Note that all of the tabular data is for free flow. If the flow is submerged, corrections will have to be made to determine the discharge, as discussed in Chapter 3.

Discharge tables for rectangular weirs without end contractions with head in feet

11-1:	1 ft.	11-6:	4 ft.
11-2:	$1^1/_2$ ft.	11-7:	5 ft.
11-3:	2 ft.	11-8:	6 ft.
11-4:	$2^1/_2$ ft.	11-9:	8 ft.
11-5:	3 ft.	11-10:	10 ft.

The discharges of the weirs are listed in three different units of measure:

CFS - cubic feet per second   GPM - gallons per minute
MGD - million gallons per day

Discharge tables for rectangular weirs without end contractions with head in meters

11-11:	0.3 m	11-16:	1 m
11-12:	0.4 m	11-17:	1.5 m
11-13:	0.5 m	11-18:	2 m
11-14:	0.6 m	11-19:	3 m
11-15:	0.8 m		

The discharges of the weirs are listed in two different units of measure:

l/s - liters per second m^3/hr - cubic meters per hour

The formulas used to develop each table are listed on the table. Values in italics indicate flow below the recommended range of this particular primary device.

Table 11-1:
1 ft. Rectangular Weir without End Contractions Discharge Table with Head in Feet

Formula: CFS $= 3.330\ H^{1.5}$
  GPM $= 1495\ H^{1.5}$
  MGD $= 2.152\ H^{1.5}$
Where: H = head in feet

Values in italics indicate flow below the recommended range of this particular primary device.

Table 11-1				Table 11-1 (Continued)			
Head (feet)	CFS	GPM	MGD	Head (feet)	CFS	GPM	MGD
0.01	*0.0033*	*1.5*	*0.0022*	0.26	0.4415	198.2	0.2853
0.02	*0.0094*	*4.2*	*0.0061*	0.27	0.4672	209.7	0.3019
0.03	*0.0173*	*7.8*	*0.0112*	0.28	0.4934	221.5	0.3188
0.04	*0.0266*	*12.0*	*0.0172*	0.29	0.5200	233.5	0.3361
0.05	*0.0372*	*16.7*	*0.0241*	0.30	0.5472	245.7	0.3536
0.06	*0.0489*	*22.0*	*0.0316*	0.31	0.5748	258.0	0.3714
0.07	*0.0617*	*27.7*	*0.0399*	0.32	0.6028	270.6	0.3896
0.08	*0.0753*	*33.8*	*0.0487*	0.33	0.6313	283.4	0.4080
0.09	*0.0899*	*40.4*	*0.0581*	0.34	0.6602	296.4	0.4266
0.10	*0.1053*	*47.3*	*0.0681*	0.35	0.6895	309.6	0.4456
0.11	*0.1215*	*54.5*	*0.0785*	0.36	0.7193	322.9	0.4648
0.12	*0.1384*	*62.1*	*0.0895*	0.37	0.7495	336.5	0.4843
0.13	*0.1561*	*70.1*	*0.1009*	0.38	0.7800	350.2	0.5041
0.14	*0.1744*	*78.3*	*0.1127*	0.39	0.8110	364.1	0.5241
0.15	*0.1935*	*86.8*	*0.1250*	0.40	0.8424	378.2	0.5444
0.16	*0.2131*	*95.7*	*0.1377*	0.41	0.8742	392.5	0.5650
0.17	*0.2334*	*104.8*	*0.1509*	0.42	0.9064	406.9	0.5858
0.18	*0.2543*	*114.1*	*0.1644*	0.43	0.9390	421.5	0.6068
0.19	*0.2758*	*123.8*	*0.1782*	0.44	0.9719	436.3	0.6281
0.20	0.2978	133.7	0.1925	0.45	1.005	451.3	0.6496
0.21	0.3205	143.9	0.2071	0.46	1.039	466.4	0.6714
0.22	0.3436	154.3	0.2221	0.47	1.073	481.7	0.6934
0.23	0.3673	164.9	0.2374	0.48	1.107	497.2	0.7157
0.24	0.3915	175.8	0.2530	0.49	1.142	512.8	0.7381
0.25	0.4163	186.9	0.2690	0.50	1.177	528.6	0.7608

11

Table 11-2:

1¹/₂ ft. Rectangular Weir without End Contractions Discharge Table with Head in Feet

Formula: $CFS = 4.995\ H^{1.5}$
$GPM = 2242\ H^{1.5}$
$MGD = 3.228\ H^{1.5}$
Where: H = head in feet

Values in italics indicate flow below the recommended range of this particular primary device.

Table 11-2				Table 11-2 (Continued)			
Head (feet)	CFS	GPM	MGD	Head (feet)	CFS	GPM	MGD
0.01	*0.0050*	*2.2*	*0.0032*	0.39	1.217	546.1	0.7862
0.02	*0.0141*	*6.3*	*0.0091*	0.40	1.264	567.2	0.8166
0.03	*0.0260*	*11.6*	*0.0168*	0.41	1.311	588.6	0.8474
0.04	*0.0400*	*17.9*	*0.0258*	0.42	1.360	610.3	0.8786
0.05	*0.0558*	*25.1*	*0.0361*	0.43	1.408	632.2	0.9102
0.06	*0.0734*	*32.9*	*0.0475*	0.44	1.458	654.4	0.9421
0.07	*0.0925*	*41.5*	*0.0598*	0.45	1.508	676.8	0.9744
0.08	*0.1130*	*50.7*	*0.0731*	0.46	1.558	699.5	1.007
0.09	*0.1349*	*60.5*	*0.0872*	0.47	1.609	722.4	1.040
0.10	*0.1580*	*70.9*	*0.1021*	0.48	1.661	745.6	1.073
0.11	*0.1822*	*81.8*	*0.1178*	0.49	1.713	769.0	1.107
0.12	*0.2076*	*93.2*	*0.1342*	0.50	1.766	792.7	1.141
0.13	*0.2341*	*105.1*	*0.1513*	0.51	1.819	816.6	1.176
0.14	*0.2617*	*117.4*	*0.1691*	0.52	1.873	840.7	1.210
0.15	*0.2902*	*130.2*	*0.1876*	0.53	1.927	865.1	1.246
0.16	*0.3197*	*143.5*	*0.2066*	0.54	1.982	889.7	1.281
0.17	*0.3501*	*157.1*	*0.2263*	0.55	2.037	914.5	1.317
0.18	*0.3815*	*171.2*	*0.2465*	0.56	2.093	939.5	1.353
0.19	*0.4137*	*185.7*	*0.2674*	0.57	2.150	964.8	1.389
0.20	0.4468	200.5	0.2887	0.58	2.206	990.3	1.426
0.21	0.4807	215.8	0.3106	0.59	2.264	1016	1.463
0.22	0.5154	231.4	0.3331	0.60	2.321	1042	1.500
0.23	0.5510	247.3	0.3561	0.61	2.380	1068	1.538
0.24	0.5873	263.6	0.3795	0.62	2.439	1095	1.576
0.25	0.6244	280.3	0.4035	0.63	2.498	1121	1.614
0.26	0.6622	297.2	0.4280	0.64	2.557	1148	1.653
0.27	0.7008	314.5	0.4529	0.65	2.618	1175	1.692
0.28	0.7401	332.2	0.4783	0.66	2.678	1202	1.731
0.29	0.7801	350.1	0.5041	0.67	2.739	1230	1.770
0.30	0.8208	368.4	0.5304	0.68	2.801	1257	1.810
0.31	0.8621	387.0	0.5572	0.69	2.863	1285	1.850
0.32	0.9042	405.8	0.5843	0.70	2.925	1313	1.891
0.33	0.9469	425.0	0.6119	0.71	2.988	1341	1.931
0.34	0.9903	444.5	0.6400	0.72	3.052	1370	1.972
0.35	1.034	464.2	0.6684	0.73	3.115	1398	2.013
0.36	1.079	484.3	0.6972	0.74	3.180	1427	2.055
0.37	1.124	504.6	0.7265	0.75	3.244	1456	2.097
0.38	1.170	525.2	0.7562				

11

Table 11-3:
2 ft. Rectangular Weir without End Contractions Discharge Table with Head in Feet

Formula: $CFS = 6.660\ H^{1.5}$
$GPM = 2989\ H^{1.5}$
$MGD = 4.304\ H^{1.5}$

Where: H = head in feet

Values in italics indicate flow below the recommended range of this particular primary device.

Table 11-3				Table 11-3 (Continued)			
Head (feet)	CFS	GPM	MGD	Head (feet)	CFS	GPM	MGD
0.01	*0.0067*	*3.0*	*0.0043*	0.51	2.426	1089	1.568
0.02	*0.0188*	*8.5*	*0.0122*	0.52	2.497	1121	1.614
0.03	*0.0346*	*15.5*	*0.0224*	0.53	2.570	1153	1.661
0.04	*0.0533*	*23.9*	*0.0344*	0.54	2.643	1186	1.708
0.05	*0.0745*	*33.4*	*0.0481*	0.55	2.717	1219	1.756
0.06	*0.0979*	*43.9*	*0.0633*	0.56	2.791	1253	1.804
0.07	*0.1233*	*55.4*	*0.0797*	0.57	2.866	1286	1.852
0.08	*0.1507*	*67.6*	*0.0974*	0.58	2.942	1320	1.901
0.09	*0.1798*	*80.7*	*0.1162*	0.59	3.018	1355	1.951
0.10	*0.2106*	*94.5*	*0.1361*	0.60	3.095	1389	2.000
0.11	*0.2430*	*109.1*	*0.1570*	0.61	3.173	1424	2.051
0.12	*0.2769*	*124.3*	*0.1789*	0.62	3.251	1459	2.101
0.13	*0.3122*	*140.1*	*0.2018*	0.63	3.330	1495	2.152
0.14	*0.3489*	*156.6*	*0.2255*	0.64	3.410	1530	2.204
0.15	*0.3869*	*173.7*	*0.2501*	0.65	3.490	1566	2.255
0.16	*0.4262*	*191.3*	*0.2755*	0.66	3.571	1603	2.308
0.17	*0.4668*	*209.5*	*0.3017*	0.67	3.652	1639	2.360
0.18	*0.5086*	*228.3*	*0.3287*	0.68	3.735	1676	2.413
0.19	*0.5516*	*247.6*	*0.3565*	0.69	3.817	1713	2.467
0.20	0.5957	267.3	0.3850	0.70	3.901	1751	2.521
0.21	0.6409	287.6	0.4142	0.71	3.984	1788	2.575
0.22	0.6872	308.4	0.4441	0.72	4.069	1826	2.629
0.23	0.7346	329.7	0.4747	0.73	4.154	1864	2.684
0.24	0.7831	351.4	0.5060	0.74	4.240	1903	2.740
0.25	0.8325	373.6	0.5380	0.75	4.326	1941	2.796
0.26	0.8829	396.3	0.5706	0.76	4.413	1980	2.852
0.27	0.9344	419.3	0.6038	0.77	4.500	2020	2.908
0.28	0.9868	442.9	0.6377	0.78	4.588	2059	2.965
0.29	1.040	466.8	0.6722	0.79	4.676	2099	3.022
0.30	1.094	491.1	0.7072	0.80	4.766	2139	3.080
0.31	1.150	515.9	0.7429	0.81	4.855	2179	3.138
0.32	1.206	541.1	0.7791	0.82	4.945	2219	3.196
0.33	1.263	566.6	0.8159	0.83	5.036	2260	3.255
0.34	1.320	592.6	0.8533	0.84	5.127	2301	3.314
0.35	1.379	618.9	0.8912	0.85	5.219	2342	3.373
0.36	1.439	645.6	0.9297	0.86	5.312	2384	3.433
0.37	1.499	672.7	0.9687	0.87	5.404	2426	3.493
0.38	1.560	700.2	1.008	0.88	5.498	2467	3.553
0.39	1.622	728.0	1.048	0.89	5.592	2510	3.614
0.40	1.685	756.2	1.089	0.90	5.686	2552	3.675
0.41	1.748	784.7	1.130	0.91	5.781	2595	3.736
0.42	1.813	813.6	1.172	0.92	5.877	2638	3.798
0.43	1.878	842.8	1.214	0.93	5.973	2681	3.860
0.44	1.944	872.4	1.256	0.94	6.070	2724	3.923
0.45	2.010	902.3	1.299	0.95	6.167	2768	3.985
0.46	2.078	932.5	1.343	0.96	6.264	2811	4.048
0.47	2.146	963.1	1.387	0.97	6.363	2856	4.112
0.48	2.215	994.0	1.431	0.98	6.461	2900	4.176
0.49	2.284	1025	1.476	0.99	6.560	2944	4.240
0.50	2.355	1057	1.522	1.00	6.660	2989	4.304

11

Table 11-4:

2¹/₂ ft. Rectangular Weir without End Contractions Discharge Table with Head in Feet

Formula: CFS = $8.325\ H^{1.5}$
           GPM = $3736\ H^{1.5}$
           MGD = $5.380\ H^{1.5}$
Where: H = head in feet

Values in italics indicate flow below the recommended range of this particular primary device.

Head (feet)	CFS	GPM	MGD	Head (feet)	CFS	GPM	MGD
0.01	*0.0083*	*3.7*	*0.0054*	0.51	3.032	1361	1.959
0.02	*0.0235*	*10.6*	*0.0152*	0.52	3.122	1401	2.017
0.03	*0.0433*	*19.4*	*0.0280*	0.53	3.212	1442	2.076
0.04	*0.0666*	*29.9*	*0.0430*	0.54	3.304	1483	2.135
0.05	*0.0931*	*41.8*	*0.0602*	0.55	3.396	1524	2.194
0.06	*0.1224*	*54.9*	*0.0791*	0.56	3.489	1566	2.255
0.07	*0.1542*	*69.2*	*0.0996*	0.57	3.583	1608	2.315
0.08	*0.1884*	*84.5*	*0.1217*	0.58	3.677	1650	2.376
0.09	*0.2248*	*100.9*	*0.1453*	0.59	3.773	1693	2.438
0.10	*0.2633*	*118.2*	*0.1701*	0.60	3.869	1736	2.500
0.11	*0.3037*	*136.3*	*0.1963*	0.61	3.966	1780	2.563
0.12	*0.3461*	*155.3*	*0.2237*	0.62	4.064	1824	2.626
0.13	*0.3902*	*175.1*	*0.2522*	0.63	4.163	1868	2.690
0.14	*0.4361*	*195.7*	*0.2819*	0.64	4.262	1913	2.755
0.15	*0.4836*	*217.1*	*0.3126*	0.65	4.363	1958	2.819
0.16	*0.5328*	*239.1*	*0.3444*	0.66	4.464	2003	2.885
0.17	*0.5835*	*261.9*	*0.3771*	0.67	4.566	2049	2.950
0.18	*0.6358*	*285.3*	*0.4109*	0.68	4.668	2095	3.017
0.19	*0.6895*	*309.5*	*0.4456*	0.69	4.772	2141	3.084
0.20	0.7446	334.2	0.4812	0.70	4.876	2188	3.151
0.21	0.8011	359.5	0.5177	0.71	4.980	2235	3.219
0.22	0.8590	385.5	0.5552	0.72	5.086	2282	3.287
0.23	0.9183	412.1	0.5934	0.73	5.192	2330	3.356
0.24	0.9788	439.3	0.6326	0.74	5.299	2378	3.425
0.25	1.041	467.0	0.6725	0.75	5.407	2427	3.494
0.26	1.104	495.3	0.7133	0.76	5.516	2475	3.565
0.27	1.168	524.1	0.7548	0.77	5.625	2524	3.635
0.28	1.233	553.5	0.7971	0.78	5.735	2574	3.706
0.29	1.300	583.5	0.8402	0.79	5.846	2623	3.778
0.30	1.368	613.9	0.8840	0.80	5.957	2673	3.850
0.31	1.437	644.8	0.9286	0.81	6.069	2724	3.922
0.32	1.507	676.3	0.9739	0.82	6.182	2774	3.995
0.33	1.578	708.2	1.020	0.83	6.295	2825	4.068
0.34	1.650	740.7	1.067	0.84	6.409	2876	4.142
0.35	1.724	773.6	1.114	0.85	6.524	2928	4.216
0.36	1.798	807.0	1.162	0.86	6.639	2980	4.291
0.37	1.874	840.8	1.211	0.87	6.756	3032	4.366
0.38	1.950	875.1	1.260	0.88	6.872	3084	4.441
0.39	2.028	909.9	1.310	0.89	6.990	3137	4.517
0.40	2.106	945.1	1.361	0.90	7.108	3190	4.594
0.41	2.186	980.8	1.412	0.91	7.227	3243	4.670
0.42	2.266	1017	1.464	0.92	7.346	3297	4.747
0.43	2.347	1053	1.517	0.93	7.466	3351	4.825
0.44	2.430	1090	1.570	0.94	7.587	3405	4.903
0.45	2.513	1128	1.624	0.95	7.708	3459	4.982
0.46	2.597	1166	1.678	0.96	7.831	3514	5.060
0.47	2.682	1204	1.734	0.97	7.953	3569	5.140
0.48	2.769	1242	1.789	0.98	8.077	3624	5.219
0.49	2.855	1281	1.845	0.99	8.200	3680	5.300
0.50	2.943	1321	1.902	1.00	8.325	3736	5.380

Table 11-4 (Continued)				Table 11-4 (Continued)			
Head (feet)	CFS	GPM	MGD	Head (feet)	CFS	GPM	MGD
1.01	8.450	3792	5.461	1.14	10.13	4547	6.548
1.02	8.576	3849	5.542	1.15	10.27	4607	6.635
1.03	8.702	3905	5.624	1.16	10.40	4668	6.722
1.04	8.829	3962	5.706	1.17	10.54	4728	6.809
1.05	8.957	4020	5.789	1.18	10.67	4789	6.896
1.06	9.085	4077	5.871	1.19	10.81	4850	6.984
1.07	9.214	4135	5.955	1.20	10.94	4911	7.072
1.08	9.344	4193	6.038	1.21	11.08	4973	7.161
1.09	9.474	4252	6.122	1.22	11.22	5034	7.250
1.10	9.604	4310	6.207	1.23	11.36	5096	7.339
1.11	9.736	4369	6.292	1.24	11.50	5159	7.429
1.12	9.868	4428	6.377	1.25	11.63	5221	7.519
1.13	10.00	4488	6.462				

11

Table 11-5:
3 ft. Rectangular Weir without End Contractions Discharge Table with Head in Feet

Formula: CFS $= 9.990\ H^{1.5}$
GPM $= 4484\ H^{1.5}$
MGD $= 6.457\ H^{1.5}$
Where: H = head in feet

Values in italics indicate flow below the recommended range of this particular primary device.

Table 11-5				Table 11-5 (Continued)			
Head (feet)	CFS	GPM	MGD	Head (feet)	CFS	GPM	MGD
0.01	*0.0100*	*4.5*	*0.0065*	0.51	3.638	1633	2.352
0.02	*0.0283*	*12.7*	*0.0183*	0.52	3.746	1681	2.421
0.03	*0.0519*	*23.3*	*0.0336*	0.53	3.855	1730	2.491
0.04	*0.0799*	*35.9*	*0.0517*	0.54	3.964	1779	2.562
0.05	*0.1117*	*50.1*	*0.0722*	0.55	4.075	1829	2.634
0.06	*0.1468*	*65.9*	*0.0949*	0.56	4.186	1879	2.706
0.07	*0.1850*	*83.0*	*0.1196*	0.57	4.299	1930	2.779
0.08	*0.2260*	*101.5*	*0.1461*	0.58	4.413	1981	2.852
0.09	*0.2697*	*121.1*	*0.1743*	0.59	4.527	2032	2.926
0.10	*0.3159*	*141.8*	*0.2042*	0.60	4.643	2084	3.001
0.11	*0.3645*	*163.6*	*0.2356*	0.61	4.759	2136	3.076
0.12	*0.4153*	*186.4*	*0.2684*	0.62	4.877	2189	3.152
0.13	*0.4683*	*210.2*	*0.3026*	0.63	4.995	2242	3.229
0.14	*0.5233*	*234.9*	*0.3382*	0.64	5.115	2296	3.306
0.15	*0.5804*	*260.5*	*0.3751*	0.65	5.235	2350	3.384
0.16	*0.6394*	*287.0*	*0.4132*	0.66	5.357	2404	3.462
0.17	*0.7002*	*314.3*	*0.4526*	0.67	5.479	2459	3.541
0.18	*0.7629*	*342.4*	*0.4931*	0.68	5.602	2514	3.621
0.19	*0.8274*	*371.3*	*0.5347*	0.69	5.726	2570	3.701
0.20	0.8935	401.1	0.5775	0.70	5.851	2626	3.782
0.21	0.9614	431.5	0.6214	0.71	5.977	2683	3.863
0.22	1.031	462.7	0.6663	0.72	6.103	2739	3.945
0.23	1.102	494.6	0.7122	0.73	6.231	2797	4.027
0.24	1.175	527.2	0.7592	0.74	6.359	2854	4.110
0.25	1.249	560.5	0.8071	0.75	6.489	2912	4.194
0.26	1.324	594.5	0.8560	0.76	6.619	2971	4.278
0.27	1.402	629.1	0.9059	0.77	6.750	3030	4.363
0.28	1.480	664.4	0.9567	0.78	6.882	3089	4.448
0.29	1.560	700.3	1.008	0.79	7.015	3149	4.534
0.30	1.642	736.8	1.061	0.80	7.148	3208	4.620
0.31	1.724	773.9	1.114	0.81	7.283	3269	4.707
0.32	1.808	811.7	1.169	0.82	7.418	3330	4.795
0.33	1.894	850.0	1.224	0.83	7.554	3391	4.883
0.34	1.981	889.0	1.280	0.84	7.691	3452	4.971
0.35	2.069	928.5	1.337	0.85	7.829	3514	5.060
0.36	2.158	968.5	1.395	0.86	7.967	3576	5.150
0.37	2.248	1009	1.453	0.87	8.107	3639	5.240
0.38	2.340	1050	1.513	0.88	8.247	3702	5.330
0.39	2.433	1092	1.573	0.89	8.388	3765	5.421
0.40	2.527	1134	1.634	0.90	8.530	3829	5.513
0.41	2.623	1177	1.695	0.91	8.672	3892	5.605
0.42	2.719	1221	1.758	0.92	8.816	3957	5.698
0.43	2.817	1264	1.821	0.93	8.960	4022	5.791
0.44	2.916	1309	1.885	0.94	9.105	4087	5.885
0.45	3.016	1354	1.949	0.95	9.250	4152	5.979
0.46	3.117	1399	2.015	0.96	9.397	4218	6.073
0.47	3.219	1445	2.081	0.97	9.544	4284	6.169
0.48	3.322	1491	2.147	0.98	9.692	4350	6.264
0.49	3.427	1538	2.215	0.99	9.841	4417	6.360
0.50	3.532	1585	2.283	1.00	9.990	4484	6.457

11

Table 11-5 (Continued)			
Head (feet)	CFS	GPM	MGD
1.01	10.14	4551	6.554
1.02	10.29	4619	6.652
1.03	10.44	4687	6.750
1.04	10.60	4756	6.848
1.05	10.75	4824	6.947
1.06	10.90	4894	7.047
1.07	11.06	4963	7.147
1.08	11.21	5033	7.247
1.09	11.37	5103	7.348
1.10	11.53	5173	7.449
1.11	11.68	5244	7.551
1.12	11.84	5315	7.653
1.13	12.00	5386	7.756
1.14	12.16	5458	7.859
1.15	12.32	5530	7.963
1.16	12.48	5602	8.067
1.17	12.64	5675	8.172
1.18	12.81	5748	8.277
1.19	12.97	5821	8.382
1.20	13.13	5894	8.488
1.21	13.30	5968	8.594
1.22	13.46	6042	8.701
1.23	13.63	6117	8.808
1.24	13.79	6192	8.916
1.25	13.96	6267	9.024

Table 11-5 (Continued)			
Head (feet)	CFS	GPM	MGD
1.26	14.13	6342	9.132
1.27	14.30	6418	9.241
1.28	14.47	6494	9.351
1.29	14.64	6570	9.461
1.30	14.81	6646	9.571
1.31	14.98	6723	9.681
1.32	15.15	6800	9.792
1.33	15.32	6878	9.904
1.34	15.50	6955	10.02
1.35	15.67	7033	10.13
1.36	15.84	7112	10.24
1.37	16.02	7190	10.35
1.38	16.20	7269	10.47
1.39	16.37	7348	10.58
1.40	16.55	7428	10.70
1.41	16.73	7507	10.81
1.42	16.90	7587	10.93
1.43	17.08	7668	11.04
1.44	17.26	7748	11.16
1.45	17.44	7829	11.27
1.46	17.62	7910	11.39
1.47	17.80	7992	11.51
1.48	17.99	8073	11.63
1.49	18.17	8155	11.74
1.50	18.35	8238	11.86

11

Table 11-6:
4 ft. Rectangular Weir without End Contractions Discharge
Table with Head in Feet

Formula: CFS $= 13.32\ H^{1.5}$
GPM $= 5978\ H^{1.5}$
MGD $= 8.609\ H^{1.5}$
Where: H = head in feet

Values in italics indicate flow below the recommended range of this particular primary device.

Table 11-6				Table 11-6 (Continued)			
Head (feet)	CFS	GPM	MGD	Head (feet)	CFS	GPM	MGD
0.01	*0.013*	*6.0*	*0.0086*	0.51	4.851	2177	3.136
0.02	*0.038*	*16.9*	*0.0243*	0.52	4.995	2242	3.228
0.03	*0.069*	*31.1*	*0.0447*	0.53	5.139	2307	3.322
0.04	*0.107*	*47.8*	*0.0689*	0.54	5.286	2372	3.416
0.05	*0.149*	*66.8*	*0.0963*	0.55	5.433	2438	3.512
0.06	*0.196*	*87.9*	*0.1265*	0.56	5.582	2505	3.608
0.07	*0.247*	*110.7*	*0.1594*	0.57	5.732	2573	3.705
0.08	*0.301*	*135.3*	*0.1948*	0.58	5.884	2641	3.803
0.09	*0.360*	*161.4*	*0.2324*	0.59	6.036	2709	3.901
0.10	*0.421*	*189.1*	*0.2722*	0.60	6.191	2778	4.001
0.11	*0.486*	*218.1*	*0.3141*	0.61	6.346	2848	4.102
0.12	*0.554*	*248.5*	*0.3579*	0.62	6.503	2918	4.203
0.13	*0.624*	*280.2*	*0.4035*	0.63	6.661	2989	4.305
0.14	*0.698*	*313.2*	*0.4510*	0.64	6.820	3061	4.408
0.15	*0.774*	*347.3*	*0.5001*	0.65	6.980	3133	4.512
0.16	*0.853*	*382.6*	*0.5510*	0.66	7.142	3205	4.616
0.17	*0.934*	*419.0*	*0.6034*	0.67	7.305	3278	4.721
0.18	*1.017*	*456.6*	*0.6574*	0.68	7.469	3352	4.827
0.19	*1.103*	*495.1*	*0.7130*	0.69	7.634	3426	4.934
0.20	1.191	534.7	0.7700	0.70	7.801	3501	5.042
0.21	1.282	575.3	0.8285	0.71	7.969	3576	5.150
0.22	1.374	616.9	0.8884	0.72	8.138	3652	5.260
0.23	1.469	659.4	0.9496	0.73	8.308	3729	5.370
0.24	1.566	702.9	1.012	0.74	8.479	3805	5.480
0.25	1.665	747.3	1.076	0.75	8.652	3883	5.592
0.26	1.766	792.5	1.141	0.76	8.825	3961	5.704
0.27	1.869	838.7	1.208	0.77	9.000	4039	5.817
0.28	1.974	885.7	1.276	0.78	9.176	4118	5.931
0.29	2.080	933.6	1.344	0.79	9.353	4198	6.045
0.30	2.189	982.3	1.415	0.80	9.531	4278	6.160
0.31	2.299	1032	1.486	0.81	9.710	4358	6.276
0.32	2.411	1082	1.558	0.82	9.891	4439	6.393
0.33	2.525	1133	1.632	0.83	10.07	4520	6.510
0.34	2.641	1185	1.707	0.84	10.25	4602	6.628
0.35	2.758	1238	1.783	0.85	10.44	4685	6.747
0.36	2.877	1291	1.860	0.86	10.62	4768	6.866
0.37	2.998	1345	1.938	0.87	10.81	4851	6.986
0.38	3.120	1400	2.017	0.88	11.00	4935	7.107
0.39	3.244	1456	2.097	0.89	11.18	5019	7.228
0.40	3.370	1512	2.178	0.90	11.37	5104	7.350
0.41	3.497	1569	2.260	0.91	11.56	5189	7.473
0.42	3.626	1627	2.343	0.92	11.75	5275	7.597
0.43	3.756	1686	2.427	0.93	11.95	5361	7.721
0.44	3.888	1745	2.513	0.94	12.14	5448	7.846
0.45	4.021	1805	2.599	0.95	12.33	5535	7.971
0.46	4.156	1865	2.686	0.96	12.53	5623	8.098
0.47	4.292	1926	2.774	0.97	12.73	5711	8.225
0.48	4.430	1988	2.863	0.98	12.92	5800	8.352
0.49	4.569	2050	2.953	0.99	13.12	5889	8.480
0.50	4.709	2114	3.044	1.00	13.32	5978	8.609

11

	Table 11-6 (Continued)					Table 11-6 (Continued)		
Head (feet)	CFS	GPM	MGD		Head (feet)	CFS	GPM	MGD
1.01	13.52	6068	8.738		1.51	24.72	11,090	15.97
1.02	13.72	6158	8.869		1.52	24.96	11,200	16.13
1.03	13.92	6249	8.999		1.53	25.21	11,310	16.29
1.04	14.13	6340	9.131		1.54	25.46	11,420	16.45
1.05	14.33	6432	9.263		1.55	25.70	11,540	16.61
1.06	14.54	6524	9.395		1.56	25.95	11,650	16.77
1.07	14.74	6617	9.529		1.57	26.20	11,760	16.94
1.08	14.95	6710	9.662		1.58	26.45	11,870	17.10
1.09	15.16	6803	9.797		1.59	26.71	11,990	17.26
1.10	15.37	6897	9.932		1.60	26.96	12,100	17.42
1.11	15.58	6991	10.07		1.61	27.21	12,210	17.59
1.12	15.79	7086	10.20		1.62	27.46	12,330	17.75
1.13	16.00	7181	10.34		1.63	27.72	12,440	17.92
1.14	16.21	7276	10.48		1.64	27.97	12,560	18.08
1.15	16.43	7372	10.62		1.65	28.23	12,670	18.25
1.16	16.64	7469	10.76		1.66	28.49	12,790	18.41
1.17	16.86	7565	10.90		1.67	28.75	12,900	18.58
1.18	17.07	7663	11.04		1.68	29.00	13,020	18.75
1.19	17.29	7760	11.18		1.69	29.26	13,130	18.91
1.20	17.51	7858	11.32		1.70	29.52	13,250	19.08
1.21	17.73	7957	11.46		1.71	29.79	13,370	19.25
1.22	17.95	8056	11.60		1.72	30.05	13,480	19.42
1.23	18.17	8155	11.74		1.73	30.31	13,600	19.59
1.24	18.39	8254	11.89		1.74	30.57	13,720	19.76
1.25	18.62	8355	12.03		1.75	30.84	13,840	19.93
1.26	18.84	8455	12.18		1.76	31.10	13,960	20.10
1.27	19.06	8556	12.32		1.77	31.37	14,080	20.27
1.28	19.29	8657	12.47		1.78	31.63	14,200	20.44
1.29	19.52	8759	12.61		1.79	31.90	14,320	20.62
1.30	19.74	8861	12.76		1.80	32.17	14,440	20.79
1.31	19.97	8963	12.91		1.81	32.44	14,560	20.96
1.32	20.20	9066	13.06		1.82	32.70	14,680	21.14
1.33	20.43	9169	13.20		1.83	32.97	14,800	21.31
1.34	20.66	9273	13.35		1.84	33.25	14,920	21.49
1.35	20.89	9377	13.50		1.85	33.52	15,040	21.66
1.36	21.13	9481	13.65		1.86	33.79	15,160	21.84
1.37	21.36	9586	13.80		1.87	34.06	15,290	22.01
1.38	21.59	9691	13.96		1.88	34.34	15,410	22.19
1.39	21.83	9797	14.11		1.89	34.61	15,530	22.37
1.40	22.06	9903	14.26		1.90	34.88	15,660	22.55
1.41	22.30	10,010	14.41		1.91	35.16	15,780	22.72
1.42	22.54	10,120	14.57		1.92	35.44	15,900	22.90
1.43	22.78	10,220	14.72		1.93	35.71	16,030	23.08
1.44	23.02	10,330	14.88		1.94	35.99	16,150	23.26
1.45	23.26	10,440	15.03		1.95	36.27	16,280	23.44
1.46	23.50	10,550	15.19		1.96	36.55	16,400	23.62
1.47	23.74	10,650	15.34		1.97	36.83	16,530	23.80
1.48	23.98	10,760	15.50		1.98	37.11	16,660	23.99
1.49	24.23	10,870	15.66		1.99	37.39	16,780	24.17
1.50	24.47	10,980	15.82		2.00	37.67	16,910	24.35

11

Table 11-7:
5 ft. Rectangular Weir without End Contractions Discharge Table with Head in Feet

Formula: $CFS = 16.65\ H^{1.5}$
$GPM = 7473\ H^{1.5}$
$MGD = 10.76\ H^{1.5}$
Where: H = head in feet

Values in italics indicate flow below the recommended range of this particular primary device.

Table 11-7				Table 11-7 (Continued)			
Head (feet)	CFS	GPM	MGD	Head (feet)	CFS	GPM	MGD
0.01	*0.017*	*7.5*	*0.0108*	0.51	6.064	2722	3.919
0.02	*0.047*	*21.1*	*0.0304*	0.52	6.243	2802	4.035
0.03	*0.087*	*38.8*	*0.0559*	0.53	6.424	2883	4.152
0.04	*0.133*	*59.8*	*0.0861*	0.54	6.607	2965	4.270
0.05	*0.186*	*83.6*	*0.1203*	0.55	6.791	3048	4.389
0.06	*0.245*	*109.8*	*0.1582*	0.56	6.977	3132	4.509
0.07	*0.308*	*138.4*	*0.1993*	0.57	7.165	3216	4.630
0.08	*0.377*	*169.1*	*0.2435*	0.58	7.355	3301	4.753
0.09	*0.450*	*201.8*	*0.2906*	0.59	7.546	3387	4.876
0.10	*0.527*	*236.3*	*0.3403*	0.60	7.738	3473	5.001
0.11	*0.607*	*272.6*	*0.3926*	0.61	7.932	3560	5.126
0.12	*0.692*	*310.6*	*0.4473*	0.62	8.128	3648	5.253
0.13	*0.780*	*350.3*	*0.5044*	0.63	8.326	3737	5.381
0.14	*0.872*	*391.5*	*0.5637*	0.64	8.525	3826	5.509
0.15	*0.967*	*434.1*	*0.6252*	0.65	8.725	3916	5.639
0.16	*1.066*	*478.3*	*0.6887*	0.66	8.928	4007	5.769
0.17	*1.167*	*523.8*	*0.7543*	0.67	9.131	4098	5.901
0.18	*1.272*	*570.7*	*0.8218*	0.68	9.336	4190	6.034
0.19	*1.379*	*618.9*	*0.8912*	0.69	9.543	4283	6.167
0.20	1.489	668.4	0.9624	0.70	9.751	4377	6.302
0.21	1.602	719.2	1.035	0.71	9.961	4471	6.437
0.22	1.718	771.1	1.110	0.72	10.17	4566	6.574
0.23	1.837	824.3	1.187	0.73	10.38	4661	6.711
0.24	1.958	878.6	1.265	0.74	10.60	4757	6.850
0.25	2.081	934.1	1.345	0.75	10.81	4854	6.989
0.26	2.207	990.7	1.427	0.76	11.03	4951	7.129
0.27	2.336	1048	1.510	0.77	11.25	5049	7.270
0.28	2.467	1107	1.594	0.78	11.47	5148	7.412
0.29	2.600	1167	1.680	0.79	11.69	5247	7.555
0.30	2.736	1228	1.768	0.80	11.91	5347	7.699
0.31	2.874	1290	1.857	0.81	12.14	5448	7.844
0.32	3.014	1353	1.948	0.82	12.36	5549	7.990
0.33	3.156	1417	2.040	0.83	12.59	5651	8.136
0.34	3.301	1482	2.133	0.84	12.82	5753	8.284
0.35	3.448	1547	2.228	0.85	13.05	5856	8.432
0.36	3.596	1614	2.324	0.86	13.28	5960	8.581
0.37	3.747	1682	2.422	0.87	13.51	6064	8.732
0.38	3.900	1751	2.521	0.88	13.74	6169	8.883
0.39	4.055	1820	2.621	0.89	13.98	6275	9.034
0.40	4.212	1891	2.722	0.90	14.22	6381	9.187
0.41	4.371	1962	2.825	0.91	14.45	6487	9.341
0.42	4.532	2034	2.929	0.92	14.69	6594	9.495
0.43	4.695	2107	3.034	0.93	14.93	6702	9.650
0.44	4.860	2181	3.140	0.94	15.17	6811	9.806
0.45	5.026	2256	3.248	0.95	15.42	6920	9.963
0.46	5.195	2331	3.357	0.96	15.66	7029	10.12
0.47	5.365	2408	3.467	0.97	15.91	7139	10.28
0.48	5.537	2485	3.578	0.98	16.15	7250	10.44
0.49	5.711	2563	3.691	0.99	16.40	7361	10.60
0.50	5.887	2642	3.804	1.00	16.65	7473	10.76

11

Table 11-7 (Continued)				Table 11-7 (Continued)			
Head (feet)	CFS	GPM	MGD	Head (feet)	CFS	GPM	MGD
1.01	16.90	7585	10.92	1.51	30.89	13,870	19.97
1.02	17.15	7698	11.08	1.52	31.20	14,000	20.16
1.03	17.40	7812	11.25	1.53	31.51	14,140	20.36
1.04	17.66	7926	11.41	1.54	31.82	14,280	20.56
1.05	17.91	8040	11.58	1.55	32.13	14,420	20.76
1.06	18.17	8156	11.74	1.56	32.44	14,560	20.97
1.07	18.43	8271	11.91	1.57	32.75	14,700	21.17
1.08	18.69	8387	12.08	1.58	33.07	14,840	21.37
1.09	18.95	8504	12.24	1.59	33.38	14,980	21.57
1.10	19.21	8622	12.41	1.60	33.70	15,120	21.78
1.11	19.47	8739	12.58	1.61	34.01	15,270	21.98
1.12	19.74	8858	12.75	1.62	34.33	15,410	22.19
1.13	20.00	8977	12.92	1.63	34.65	15,550	22.39
1.14	20.27	9096	13.10	1.64	34.97	15,690	22.60
1.15	20.53	9216	13.27	1.65	35.29	15,840	22.81
1.16	20.80	9336	13.44	1.66	35.61	15,980	23.01
1.17	21.07	9457	13.62	1.67	35.93	16,130	23.22
1.18	21.34	9579	13.79	1.68	36.26	16,270	23.43
1.19	21.61	9701	13.97	1.69	36.58	16,420	23.64
1.20	21.89	9824	14.14	1.70	36.91	16,560	23.85
1.21	22.16	9947	14.32	1.71	37.23	16,710	24.06
1.22	22.44	10,070	14.50	1.72	37.56	16,860	24.27
1.23	22.71	10,190	14.68	1.73	37.89	17,000	24.48
1.24	22.99	10,320	14.86	1.74	38.22	17,150	24.70
1.25	23.27	10,440	15.04	1.75	38.55	17,300	24.91
1.26	23.55	10,570	15.22	1.76	38.88	17,450	25.12
1.27	23.83	10,700	15.40	1.77	39.21	17,600	25.34
1.28	24.11	10,820	15.58	1.78	39.54	17,750	25.55
1.29	24.39	10,950	15.77	1.79	39.87	17,900	25.77
1.30	24.68	11,080	15.95	1.80	40.21	18,050	25.98
1.31	24.96	11,200	16.13	1.81	40.54	18,200	26.20
1.32	25.25	11,330	16.32	1.82	40.88	18,350	26.42
1.33	25.54	11,460	16.50	1.83	41.22	18,500	26.64
1.34	25.83	11,590	16.69	1.84	41.56	18,650	26.86
1.35	26.12	11,720	16.88	1.85	41.90	18,800	27.08
1.36	26.41	11,850	17.07	1.86	42.24	18,960	27.29
1.37	26.70	11,980	17.25	1.87	42.58	19,110	27.52
1.38	26.99	12,110	17.44	1.88	42.92	19,260	27.74
1.39	27.29	12,250	17.63	1.89	43.26	19,420	27.96
1.40	27.58	12,380	17.82	1.90	43.61	19,570	28.18
1.41	27.88	12,510	18.02	1.91	43.95	19,730	28.40
1.42	28.17	12,650	18.21	1.92	44.30	19,880	28.63
1.43	28.47	12,780	18.40	1.93	44.64	20,040	28.85
1.44	28.77	12,910	18.59	1.94	44.99	20,190	29.07
1.45	29.07	13,050	18.79	1.95	45.34	20,350	29.30
1.46	29.37	13,180	18.98	1.96	45.69	20,510	29.53
1.47	29.67	13,320	19.18	1.97	46.04	20,660	29.75
1.48	29.98	13,460	19.37	1.98	46.39	20,820	29.98
1.49	30.28	13,590	19.57	1.99	46.74	20,980	30.21
1.50	30.59	13,730	19.77	2.00	47.09	21,140	30.43

11

Table 11-7 (Continued)				Table 11-7 (Continued)			
Head (feet)	CFS	GPM	MGD	Head (feet)	CFS	GPM	MGD
2.01	47.45	21,300	30.66	2.26	56.57	25,390	36.56
2.02	47.80	21,450	30.89	2.27	56.94	25,560	36.80
2.03	48.16	21,610	31.12	2.28	57.32	25,730	37.04
2.04	48.51	21,770	31.35	2.29	57.70	25,900	37.29
2.05	48.87	21,930	31.58	2.30	58.08	26,070	37.53
2.06	49.23	22,100	31.81	2.31	58.46	26,240	37.78
2.07	49.59	22,260	32.05	2.32	58.84	26,410	38.02
2.08	49.95	22,420	32.28	2.33	59.22	26,580	38.27
2.09	50.31	22,580	32.51	2.34	59.60	26,750	38.52
2.10	50.67	22,740	32.74	2.35	59.98	26,920	38.76
2.11	51.03	22,900	32.98	2.36	60.36	27,090	39.01
2.12	51.39	23,070	33.21	2.37	60.75	27,270	39.26
2.13	51.76	23,230	33.45	2.38	61.13	27,440	39.51
2.14	52.12	23,390	33.68	2.39	61.52	27,610	39.76
2.15	52.49	23,560	33.92	2.40	61.91	27,790	40.01
2.16	52.86	23,720	34.16	2.41	62.29	27,960	40.26
2.17	53.22	23,890	34.40	2.42	62.68	28,130	40.51
2.18	53.59	24,050	34.63	2.43	63.07	28,310	40.76
2.19	53.96	24,220	34.87	2.44	63.46	28,480	41.01
2.20	54.33	24,390	35.11	2.45	63.85	28,660	41.26
2.21	54.70	24,550	35.35	2.46	64.24	28,830	41.52
2.22	55.07	24,720	35.59	2.47	64.63	29,010	41.77
2.23	55.45	24,890	35.83	2.48	65.03	29,190	42.02
2.24	55.82	25,050	36.07	2.49	65.42	29,360	42.28
2.25	56.19	25,220	36.31	2.50	65.81	29,540	42.53

11

Table 11-8:
6 ft. Rectangular Weir without End Contractions Discharge Table with Head in Feet

Formula: $CFS = 19.98\ H^{1.5}$
$GPM = 8967\ H^{1.5}$
$MGD = 12.91\ H^{1.5}$
Where: H = head in feet

Values in italics indicate flow below the recommended range of this particular primary device.

Table 11-8				Table 11-8 (Continued)			
Head (feet)	CFS	GPM	MGD	Head (feet)	CFS	GPM	MGD
0.01	*0.020*	*9.0*	*0.013*	0.51	7.277	3266	4.702
0.02	*0.057*	*25.4*	*0.037*	0.52	7.492	3362	4.841
0.03	*0.104*	*46.6*	*0.067*	0.53	7.709	3460	4.981
0.04	*0.160*	*71.7*	*0.103*	0.54	7.928	3558	5.123
0.05	*0.223*	*100.3*	*0.144*	0.55	8.150	3658	5.266
0.06	*0.294*	*131.8*	*0.190*	0.56	8.373	3758	5.410
0.07	*0.370*	*166.1*	*0.239*	0.57	8.598	3859	5.556
0.08	*0.452*	*202.9*	*0.292*	0.58	8.825	3961	5.703
0.09	*0.539*	*242.1*	*0.349*	0.59	9.055	4064	5.851
0.10	*0.632*	*283.6*	*0.408*	0.60	9.286	4167	6.000
0.11	*0.729*	*327.2*	*0.471*	0.61	9.519	4272	6.151
0.12	*0.831*	*372.8*	*0.537*	0.62	9.754	4378	6.303
0.13	*0.937*	*420.3*	*0.605*	0.63	9.991	4484	6.456
0.14	*1.047*	*469.8*	*0.676*	0.64	10.23	4591	6.610
0.15	*1.161*	*521.0*	*0.750*	0.65	10.47	4699	6.765
0.16	*1.279*	*573.9*	*0.826*	0.66	10.71	4808	6.922
0.17	*1.400*	*628.6*	*0.905*	0.67	10.96	4918	7.080
0.18	*1.526*	*684.8*	*0.986*	0.68	11.20	5028	7.239
0.19	*1.655*	*742.7*	*1.069*	0.69	11.45	5139	7.399
0.20	1.787	802.0	1.155	0.70	11.70	5252	7.561
0.21	1.923	862.9	1.242	0.71	11.95	5365	7.723
0.22	2.062	925.3	1.332	0.72	12.21	5478	7.887
0.23	2.204	989.1	1.424	0.73	12.46	5593	8.052
0.24	2.349	1054	1.518	0.74	12.72	5708	8.218
0.25	2.498	1121	1.614	0.75	12.98	5824	8.385
0.26	2.649	1189	1.712	0.76	13.24	5941	8.554
0.27	2.803	1258	1.811	0.77	13.50	6059	8.723
0.28	2.960	1329	1.913	0.78	13.76	6177	8.893
0.29	3.120	1400	2.016	0.79	14.03	6296	9.065
0.30	3.283	1473	2.121	0.80	14.30	6416	9.238
0.31	3.449	1548	2.228	0.81	14.57	6537	9.411
0.32	3.617	1623	2.337	0.82	14.84	6658	9.586
0.33	3.788	1700	2.447	0.83	15.11	6781	9.762
0.34	3.961	1778	2.559	0.84	15.38	6903	9.939
0.35	4.137	1857	2.673	0.85	15.66	7027	10.12
0.36	4.316	1937	2.789	0.86	15.93	7151	10.30
0.37	4.497	2018	2.906	0.87	16.21	7277	10.48
0.38	4.680	2100	3.024	0.88	16.49	7402	10.66
0.39	4.866	2184	3.144	0.89	16.78	7529	10.84
0.40	5.055	2268	3.266	0.90	17.06	7656	11.02
0.41	5.245	2354	3.389	0.91	17.34	7784	11.21
0.42	5.438	2441	3.514	0.92	17.63	7913	11.39
0.43	5.634	2528	3.640	0.93	17.92	8042	11.58
0.44	5.831	2617	3.768	0.94	18.21	8172	11.77
0.45	6.031	2707	3.897	0.95	18.50	8303	11.95
0.46	6.234	2798	4.028	0.96	18.79	8434	12.14
0.47	6.438	2889	4.160	0.97	19.09	8567	12.33
0.48	6.644	2982	4.293	0.98	19.38	8699	12.52
0.49	6.853	3076	4.428	0.99	19.68	8833	12.72
0.50	7.064	3170	4.564	1.00	19.98	8967	12.91

11

Table 11-8 (Continued)				Table 11-8 (Continued)			
Head (feet)	CFS	GPM	MGD	Head (feet)	CFS	GPM	MGD
1.01	20.28	9102	13.10	1.51	37.07	16,640	23.95
1.02	20.58	9237	13.30	1.52	37.44	16,800	24.19
1.03	20.89	9374	13.50	1.53	37.81	16,970	24.43
1.04	21.19	9510	13.69	1.54	38.18	17,140	24.67
1.05	21.50	9648	13.89	1.55	38.56	17,300	24.91
1.06	21.80	9786	14.09	1.56	38.93	17,470	25.15
1.07	22.11	9925	14.29	1.57	39.30	17,640	25.40
1.08	22.42	10,060	14.49	1.58	39.68	17,810	25.64
1.09	22.74	10,200	14.69	1.59	40.06	17,980	25.88
1.10	23.05	10,350	14.89	1.60	40.44	18,150	26.13
1.11	23.37	10,490	15.10	1.61	40.82	18,320	26.37
1.12	23.68	10,630	15.30	1.62	41.20	18,490	26.62
1.13	24.00	10,770	15.51	1.63	41.58	18,660	26.87
1.14	24.32	10,910	15.71	1.64	41.96	18,830	27.11
1.15	24.64	11,060	15.92	1.65	42.35	19,010	27.36
1.16	24.96	11,200	16.13	1.66	42.73	19,180	27.61
1.17	25.29	11,350	16.34	1.67	43.12	19,350	27.86
1.18	25.61	11,490	16.55	1.68	43.51	19,530	28.11
1.19	25.94	11,640	16.76	1.69	43.90	19,700	28.36
1.20	26.26	11,790	16.97	1.70	44.29	19,880	28.62
1.21	26.59	11,940	17.18	1.71	44.68	20,050	28.87
1.22	26.92	12,080	17.40	1.72	45.07	20,230	29.12
1.23	27.26	12,230	17.61	1.73	45.46	20,400	29.38
1.24	27.59	12,380	17.83	1.74	45.86	20,580	29.63
1.25	27.92	12,530	18.04	1.75	46.25	20,760	29.89
1.26	28.26	12,680	18.26	1.76	46.65	20,940	30.14
1.27	28.60	12,830	18.48	1.77	47.05	21,120	30.40
1.28	28.93	12,990	18.70	1.78	47.45	21,290	30.66
1.29	29.27	13,140	18.92	1.79	47.85	21,470	30.92
1.30	29.61	13,290	19.14	1.80	48.25	21,650	31.18
1.31	29.96	13,440	19.36	1.81	48.65	21,840	31.44
1.32	30.30	13,600	19.58	1.82	49.06	22,020	31.70
1.33	30.65	13,750	19.80	1.83	49.46	22,200	31.96
1.34	30.99	13,910	20.03	1.84	49.87	22,380	32.22
1.35	31.34	14,070	20.25	1.85	50.28	22,560	32.49
1.36	31.69	14,220	20.48	1.86	50.68	22,750	32.75
1.37	32.04	14,380	20.70	1.87	51.09	22,930	33.01
1.38	32.39	14,540	20.93	1.88	51.50	23,110	33.28
1.39	32.74	14,690	21.16	1.89	51.91	23,300	33.54
1.40	33.10	14,850	21.39	1.90	52.33	23,480	33.81
1.41	33.45	15,010	21.61	1.91	52.74	23,670	34.08
1.42	33.81	15,170	21.85	1.92	53.16	23,860	34.35
1.43	34.17	15,330	22.08	1.93	53.57	24,040	34.61
1.44	34.53	15,490	22.31	1.94	53.99	24,230	34.88
1.45	34.89	15,660	22.54	1.95	54.41	24,420	35.15
1.46	35.25	15,820	22.77	1.96	54.83	24,610	35.43
1.47	35.61	15,980	23.01	1.97	55.25	24,790	35.70
1.48	35.97	16,150	23.24	1.98	55.67	24,980	35.97
1.49	36.34	16,310	23.48	1.99	56.09	25,170	36.24
1.50	36.71	16,470	23.72	2.00	56.51	25,360	36.51

11

Rectangular Weir Without End Contractions Discharge Tables • 235

Table 11-8 (Continued)				Table 11-8 (Continued)			
Head (feet)	CFS	GPM	MGD	Head (feet)	CFS	GPM	MGD
2.01	56.94	25,550	36.79	2.51	79.45	35,660	51.34
2.02	57.36	25,740	37.06	2.52	79.93	35,870	51.64
2.03	57.79	25,940	37.34	2.53	80.40	36,090	51.95
2.04	58.22	26,130	37.62	2.54	80.88	36,300	52.26
2.05	58.64	26,320	37.89	2.55	81.36	36,510	52.57
2.06	59.07	26,510	38.17	2.56	81.84	36,730	52.88
2.07	59.50	26,710	38.45	2.57	82.32	36,940	53.19
2.08	59.94	26,900	38.73	2.58	82.80	37,160	53.50
2.09	60.37	27,090	39.01	2.59	83.28	37,380	53.81
2.10	60.80	27,290	39.29	2.60	83.76	37,590	54.12
2.11	61.24	27,480	39.57	2.61	84.25	37,810	54.44
2.12	61.67	27,680	39.85	2.62	84.73	38,030	54.75
2.13	62.11	27,880	40.13	2.63	85.22	38,250	55.06
2.14	62.55	28,070	40.42	2.64	85.70	38,460	55.38
2.15	62.99	28,270	40.70	2.65	86.19	38,680	55.69
2.16	63.43	28,470	40.98	2.66	86.68	38,900	56.01
2.17	63.87	28,660	41.27	2.67	87.17	39,120	56.32
2.18	64.31	28,860	41.55	2.68	87.66	39,340	56.64
2.19	64.75	29,060	41.84	2.69	88.15	39,560	56.96
2.20	65.20	29,260	42.13	2.70	88.64	39,780	57.28
2.21	65.64	29,460	42.41	2.71	89.14	40,000	57.59
2.22	66.09	29,660	42.70	2.72	89.63	40,230	57.91
2.23	66.54	29,860	42.99	2.73	90.12	40,450	58.23
2.24	66.98	30,060	43.28	2.74	90.62	40,670	58.55
2.25	67.43	30,260	43.57	2.75	91.12	40,890	58.87
2.26	67.88	30,470	43.86	2.76	91.61	41,120	59.20
2.27	68.33	30,670	44.15	2.77	92.11	41,340	59.52
2.28	68.79	30,870	44.45	2.78	92.61	41,560	59.84
2.29	69.24	31,070	44.74	2.79	93.11	41,790	60.16
2.30	69.69	31,280	45.03	2.80	93.61	42,010	60.49
2.31	70.15	31,480	45.33	2.81	94.11	42,240	60.81
2.32	70.60	31,690	45.62	2.82	94.62	42,460	61.14
2.33	71.06	31,890	45.92	2.83	95.12	42,690	61.46
2.34	71.52	32,100	46.21	2.84	95.63	42,920	61.79
2.35	71.98	32,300	46.51	2.85	96.13	43,140	62.11
2.36	72.44	32,510	46.81	2.86	96.64	43,370	62.44
2.37	72.90	32,720	47.10	2.87	97.14	43,600	62.77
2.38	73.36	32,920	47.40	2.88	97.65	43,830	63.10
2.39	73.82	33,130	47.70	2.89	98.16	44,050	63.43
2.40	74.29	33,340	48.00	2.90	98.67	44,280	63.76
2.41	74.75	33,550	48.30	2.91	99.18	44,510	64.09
2.42	75.22	33,760	48.60	2.92	99.69	44,740	64.42
2.43	75.68	33,970	48.90	2.93	100.2	44,970	64.75
2.44	76.15	34,180	49.21	2.94	100.7	45,200	65.08
2.45	76.62	34,390	49.51	2.95	101.2	45,430	65.41
2.46	77.09	34,600	49.81	2.96	101.7	45,670	65.75
2.47	77.56	34,810	50.12	2.97	102.3	45,900	66.08
2.48	78.03	35,020	50.42	2.98	102.8	46,130	66.41
2.49	78.50	35,230	50.73	2.99	103.3	46,360	66.75
2.50	78.98	35,450	51.03	3.00	103.8	46,590	67.08

Table 11-9:
8 ft. Rectangular Weir without End Contractions Discharge Table with Head in Feet

Formula:
$$CFS = 26.64 \, H^{1.5}$$
$$GPM = 11960 \, H^{1.5}$$
$$MGD = 17.22 \, H^{1.5}$$
Where: H = head in feet

Values in italics indicate flow below the recommended range of this particular primary device.

Table 11-9				Table 11-9 (Continued)			
Head (feet)	CFS	GPM	MGD	Head (feet)	CFS	GPM	MGD
0.01	*0.027*	*12*	*0.017*	0.51	9.703	4356	6.272
0.02	*0.075*	*34*	*0.049*	0.52	9.989	4485	6.457
0.03	*0.138*	*62*	*0.089*	0.53	10.28	4615	6.644
0.04	*0.213*	*96*	*0.138*	0.54	10.57	4746	6.833
0.05	*0.298*	*134*	*0.193*	0.55	10.87	4878	7.024
0.06	*0.392*	*176*	*0.253*	0.56	11.16	5012	7.216
0.07	*0.493*	*221*	*0.319*	0.57	11.46	5147	7.410
0.08	*0.603*	*271*	*0.390*	0.58	11.77	5283	7.606
0.09	*0.719*	*323*	*0.465*	0.59	12.07	5420	7.804
0.10	*0.842*	*378*	*0.544*	0.60	12.38	5559	8.003
0.11	*0.972*	*436*	*0.628*	0.61	12.69	5698	8.204
0.12	*1.107*	*497*	*0.716*	0.62	13.01	5839	8.407
0.13	*1.249*	*560*	*0.807*	0.63	13.32	5981	8.611
0.14	*1.395*	*626*	*0.902*	0.64	13.64	6124	8.817
0.15	*1.548*	*695*	*1.000*	0.65	13.96	6268	9.024
0.16	*1.705*	*765*	*1.102*	0.66	14.28	6413	9.233
0.17	*1.867*	*838*	*1.207*	0.67	14.61	6559	9.444
0.18	*2.034*	*913*	*1.315*	0.68	14.94	6706	9.656
0.19	*2.206*	*990*	*1.426*	0.69	15.27	6855	9.870
0.20	2.383	1070	1.540	0.70	15.60	7005	10.09
0.21	2.564	1151	1.657	0.71	15.94	7155	10.30
0.22	2.749	1234	1.777	0.72	16.28	7307	10.52
0.23	2.939	1319	1.899	0.73	16.62	7460	10.74
0.24	3.132	1406	2.025	0.74	16.96	7613	10.96
0.25	3.330	1495	2.153	0.75	17.30	7768	11.18
0.26	3.532	1586	2.283	0.76	17.65	7924	11.41
0.27	3.737	1678	2.416	0.77	18.00	8081	11.64
0.28	3.947	1772	2.551	0.78	18.35	8239	11.86
0.29	4.160	1868	2.689	0.79	18.71	8398	12.09
0.30	4.377	1965	2.830	0.80	19.06	8558	12.32
0.31	4.598	2064	2.972	0.81	19.42	8719	12.55
0.32	4.822	2165	3.117	0.82	19.78	8881	12.79
0.33	5.050	2267	3.264	0.83	20.14	9044	13.02
0.34	5.281	2371	3.414	0.84	20.51	9208	13.26
0.35	5.516	2476	3.566	0.85	20.88	9373	13.49
0.36	5.754	2583	3.720	0.86	21.25	9538	13.73
0.37	5.996	2692	3.876	0.87	21.62	9705	13.97
0.38	6.240	2802	4.034	0.88	21.99	9873	14.22
0.39	6.488	2913	4.194	0.89	22.37	10,040	14.46
0.40	6.739	3026	4.356	0.90	22.75	10,210	14.70
0.41	6.994	3140	4.521	0.91	23.13	10,380	14.95
0.42	7.251	3255	4.687	0.92	23.51	10,550	15.20
0.43	7.512	3372	4.856	0.93	23.89	10,730	15.44
0.44	7.775	3491	5.026	0.94	24.28	10,900	15.69
0.45	8.042	3610	5.198	0.95	24.67	11,070	15.94
0.46	8.311	3731	5.372	0.96	25.06	11,250	16.20
0.47	8.584	3854	5.549	0.97	25.45	11,430	16.45
0.48	8.859	3977	5.727	0.98	25.84	11,600	16.71
0.49	9.138	4102	5.906	0.99	26.24	11,780	16.96
0.50	9.419	4228	6.088	1.00	26.64	11,960	17.22

11

Rectangular Weir Without End Contractions Discharge Tables • 237

Table 11-9 (Continued)				Table 11-9 (Continued)			
Head (feet)	CFS	GPM	MGD	Head (feet)	CFS	GPM	MGD
1.01	27.04	12,140	17.48	1.51	49.43	22,190	31.95
1.02	27.44	12,320	17.74	1.52	49.92	22,410	32.27
1.03	27.85	12,500	18.00	1.53	50.42	22,630	32.59
1.04	28.25	12,680	18.26	1.54	50.91	22,860	32.91
1.05	28.66	12,870	18.53	1.55	51.41	23,080	33.23
1.06	29.07	13,050	18.79	1.56	51.91	23,300	33.55
1.07	29.49	13,240	19.06	1.57	52.41	23,530	33.88
1.08	29.90	13,420	19.33	1.58	52.91	23,750	34.20
1.09	30.32	13,610	19.60	1.59	53.41	23,980	34.52
1.10	30.73	13,800	19.87	1.60	53.92	24,210	34.85
1.11	31.15	13,990	20.14	1.61	54.42	24,430	35.18
1.12	31.58	14,180	20.41	1.62	54.93	24,660	35.51
1.13	32.00	14,370	20.68	1.63	55.44	24,890	35.84
1.14	32.43	14,560	20.96	1.64	55.95	25,120	36.17
1.15	32.85	14,750	21.24	1.65	56.46	25,350	36.50
1.16	33.28	14,940	21.51	1.66	56.98	25,580	36.83
1.17	33.71	15,140	21.79	1.67	57.49	25,810	37.16
1.18	34.15	15,330	22.07	1.68	58.01	26,040	37.50
1.19	34.58	15,530	22.35	1.69	58.53	26,280	37.83
1.20	35.02	15,720	22.64	1.70	59.05	26,510	38.17
1.21	35.46	15,920	22.92	1.71	59.57	26,740	38.51
1.22	35.90	16,120	23.20	1.72	60.09	26,980	38.84
1.23	36.34	16,320	23.49	1.73	60.62	27,210	39.18
1.24	36.78	16,510	23.78	1.74	61.14	27,450	39.52
1.25	37.23	16,710	24.07	1.75	61.67	27,690	39.86
1.26	37.68	16,920	24.36	1.76	62.20	27,930	40.21
1.27	38.13	17,120	24.65	1.77	62.73	28,160	40.55
1.28	38.58	17,320	24.94	1.78	63.27	28,400	40.89
1.29	39.03	17,520	25.23	1.79	63.80	28,640	41.24
1.30	39.49	17,730	25.52	1.80	64.33	28,880	41.59
1.31	39.94	17,930	25.82	1.81	64.87	29,120	41.93
1.32	40.40	18,140	26.12	1.82	65.41	29,370	42.28
1.33	40.86	18,340	26.41	1.83	65.95	29,610	42.63
1.34	41.32	18,550	26.71	1.84	66.49	29,850	42.98
1.35	41.79	18,760	27.01	1.85	67.03	30,090	43.33
1.36	42.25	18,970	27.31	1.86	67.58	30,340	43.68
1.37	42.72	19,180	27.61	1.87	68.12	30,580	44.03
1.38	43.19	19,390	27.92	1.88	68.67	30,830	44.39
1.39	43.66	19,600	28.22	1.89	69.22	31,080	44.74
1.40	44.13	19,810	28.52	1.90	69.77	31,320	45.10
1.41	44.60	20,020	28.83	1.91	70.32	31,570	45.46
1.42	45.08	20,240	29.14	1.92	70.87	31,820	45.81
1.43	45.56	20,450	29.45	1.93	71.43	32,070	46.17
1.44	46.03	20,670	29.76	1.94	71.98	32,320	46.53
1.45	46.51	20,880	30.07	1.95	72.54	32,570	46.89
1.46	47.00	21,100	30.38	1.96	73.10	32,820	47.25
1.47	47.48	21,320	30.69	1.97	73.66	33,070	47.61
1.48	47.97	21,530	31.00	1.98	74.22	33,320	47.98
1.49	48.45	21,750	31.32	1.99	74.78	33,570	48.34
1.50	48.94	21,970	31.64	2.00	75.35	33,830	48.71

Table 11-9 (Continued)				Table 11-9 (Continued)			
Head (feet)	CFS	GPM	MGD	Head (feet)	CFS	GPM	MGD
2.01	75.92	34,080	49.07	2.51	105.9	47,560	68.48
2.02	76.48	34,340	49.44	2.52	106.6	47,840	68.89
2.03	77.05	34,590	49.81	2.53	107.2	48,130	69.30
2.04	77.62	34,850	50.17	2.54	107.8	48,420	69.71
2.05	78.19	35,100	50.54	2.55	108.5	48,700	70.12
2.06	78.77	35,360	50.91	2.56	109.1	48,990	70.53
2.07	79.34	35,620	51.28	2.57	109.8	49,280	70.95
2.08	79.92	35,880	51.66	2.58	110.4	49,560	71.36
2.09	80.49	36,140	52.03	2.59	111.0	49,850	71.78
2.10	81.07	36,400	52.40	2.60	111.7	50,140	72.19
2.11	81.65	36,660	52.78	2.61	112.3	50,430	72.61
2.12	82.23	36,920	53.15	2.62	113.0	50,720	73.03
2.13	82.81	37,180	53.53	2.63	113.6	51,010	73.45
2.14	83.40	37,440	53.91	2.64	114.3	51,300	73.87
2.15	83.98	37,700	54.29	2.65	114.9	51,590	74.29
2.16	84.57	37,970	54.67	2.66	115.6	51,890	74.71
2.17	85.16	38,230	55.05	2.67	116.2	52,180	75.13
2.18	85.75	38,500	55.43	2.68	116.9	52,470	75.55
2.19	86.34	38,760	55.81	2.69	117.5	52,770	75.97
2.20	86.93	39,030	56.19	2.70	118.2	53,060	76.40
2.21	87.52	39,290	56.57	2.71	118.8	53,360	76.82
2.22	88.12	39,560	56.96	2.72	119.5	53,650	77.25
2.23	88.71	39,830	57.34	2.73	120.2	53,950	77.67
2.24	89.31	40,100	57.73	2.74	120.8	54,240	78.10
2.25	89.91	40,360	58.12	2.75	121.5	54,540	78.53
2.26	90.51	40,630	58.51	2.76	122.2	54,840	78.96
2.27	91.11	40,900	58.89	2.77	122.8	55,140	79.39
2.28	91.71	41,170	59.28	2.78	123.5	55,440	79.82
2.29	92.32	41,450	59.67	2.79	124.1	55,740	80.25
2.30	92.92	41,720	60.07	2.80	124.8	56,040	80.68
2.31	93.53	41,990	60.46	2.81	125.5	56,340	81.11
2.32	94.14	42,260	60.85	2.82	126.2	56,640	81.55
2.33	94.75	42,540	61.24	2.83	126.8	56,940	81.98
2.34	95.36	42,810	61.64	2.84	127.5	57,240	82.42
2.35	95.97	43,090	62.03	2.85	128.2	57,540	82.85
2.36	96.58	43,360	62.43	2.86	128.8	57,850	83.29
2.37	97.20	43,640	62.83	2.87	129.5	58,150	83.73
2.38	97.81	43,910	63.23	2.88	130.2	58,450	84.16
2.39	98.43	44,190	63.63	2.89	130.9	58,760	84.60
2.40	99.05	44,470	64.03	2.90	131.6	59,060	85.04
2.41	99.67	44,750	64.43	2.91	132.2	59,370	85.48
2.42	100.3	45,030	64.83	2.92	132.9	59,680	85.92
2.43	100.9	45,300	65.23	2.93	133.6	59,980	86.36
2.44	101.5	45,580	65.63	2.94	134.3	60,290	86.81
2.45	102.2	45,860	66.04	2.95	135.0	60,600	87.25
2.46	102.8	46,150	66.44	2.96	135.7	60,910	87.69
2.47	103.4	46,430	66.85	2.97	136.4	61,220	88.14
2.48	104.0	46,710	67.25	2.98	137.0	61,530	88.58
2.49	104.7	46,990	67.66	2.99	137.7	61,840	89.03
2.50	105.3	47,280	68.07	3.00	138.4	62,150	89.48

11

Table 11-9 (Continued)				Table 11-9 (Continued)			
Head (feet)	CFS	GPM	MGD	Head (feet)	CFS	GPM	MGD
3.01	139.1	62,460	89.93	3.51	175.2	78,650	113.2
3.02	139.8	62,770	90.37	3.52	175.9	78,990	113.7
3.03	140.5	63,080	90.82	3.53	176.7	79,320	114.2
3.04	141.2	63,390	91.27	3.54	177.4	79,660	114.7
3.05	141.9	63,710	91.72	3.55	178.2	80,000	115.2
3.06	142.6	64,020	92.18	3.56	178.9	80,340	115.7
3.07	143.3	64,330	92.63	3.57	179.7	80,670	116.2
3.08	144.0	64,650	93.08	3.58	180.5	81,010	116.6
3.09	144.7	64,960	93.53	3.59	181.2	81,350	117.1
3.10	145.4	65,280	93.99	3.60	182.0	81,690	117.6
3.11	146.1	65,600	94.44	3.61	182.7	82,030	118.1
3.12	146.8	65,910	94.90	3.62	183.5	82,370	118.6
3.13	147.5	66,230	95.36	3.63	184.2	82,720	119.1
3.14	148.2	66,550	95.81	3.64	185.0	83,060	119.6
3.15	148.9	66,860	96.27	3.65	185.8	83,400	120.1
3.16	149.6	67,180	96.73	3.66	186.5	83,740	120.6
3.17	150.4	67,500	97.19	3.67	187.3	84,090	121.1
3.18	151.1	67,820	97.65	3.68	188.1	84,430	121.6
3.19	151.8	68,140	98.11	3.69	188.8	84,780	122.1
3.20	152.5	68,460	98.57	3.70	189.6	85,120	122.6
3.21	153.2	68,780	99.04	3.71	190.4	85,470	123.1
3.22	153.9	69,110	99.50	3.72	191.1	85,810	123.6
3.23	154.6	69,430	99.96	3.73	191.9	86,160	124.0
3.24	155.4	69,750	100.4	3.74	192.7	86,500	124.5
3.25	156.1	70,070	100.9	3.75	193.5	86,850	125.0
3.26	156.8	70,400	101.4	3.76	194.2	87,200	125.5
3.27	157.5	70,720	101.8	3.77	195.0	87,550	126.1
3.28	158.3	71,050	102.3	3.78	195.8	87,900	126.6
3.29	159.0	71,370	102.8	3.79	196.6	88,240	127.1
3.30	159.7	71,700	103.2	3.80	197.3	88,590	127.6
3.31	160.4	72,020	103.7	3.81	198.1	88,940	128.1
3.32	161.2	72,350	104.2	3.82	198.9	89,290	128.6
3.33	161.9	72,680	104.6	3.83	199.7	89,650	129.1
3.34	162.6	73,000	105.1	3.84	200.5	90,000	129.6
3.35	163.3	73,330	105.6	3.85	201.2	90,350	130.1
3.36	164.1	73,660	106.1	3.86	202.0	90,700	130.6
3.37	164.8	73,990	106.5	3.87	202.8	91,050	131.1
3.38	165.5	74,320	107.0	3.88	203.6	91,410	131.6
3.39	166.3	74,650	107.5	3.89	204.4	91,760	132.1
3.40	167.0	74,980	108.0	3.90	205.2	92,110	132.6
3.41	167.8	75,310	108.4	3.91	206.0	92,470	133.1
3.42	168.5	75,640	108.9	3.92	206.8	92,820	133.6
3.43	169.2	75,980	109.4	3.93	207.6	93,180	134.2
3.44	170.0	76,310	109.9	3.94	208.3	93,540	134.7
3.45	170.7	76,640	110.3	3.95	209.1	93,890	135.2
3.46	171.5	76,970	110.8	3.96	209.9	94,250	135.7
3.47	172.2	77,310	111.3	3.97	210.7	94,610	136.2
3.48	172.9	77,640	111.8	3.98	211.5	94,960	136.7
3.49	173.7	77,980	112.3	3.99	212.3	95,320	137.2
3.50	174.4	78,310	112.8	4.00	213.1	95,680	137.8

11

Table 11-10:
10 ft. Rectangular Weir without End Contractions Discharge
Table with Head in Feet

Formula: CFS $= 33.30\ H^{1.5}$
GPM $= 14950\ H^{1.5}$
MGD $= 21.52\ H^{1.5}$
Where: H = head in feet

Values in italics indicate flow below the recommended range of this particular primary device.

Table 11-10				Table 11-10 (Continued)			
Head (feet)	CFS	GPM	MGD	Head (feet)	CFS	GPM	MGD
0.01	*0.027*	*12*	*0.017*	0.51	12.13	5445	7.838
0.02	*0.075*	*34*	*0.049*	0.52	12.49	5606	8.070
0.03	*0.138*	*62*	*0.089*	0.53	12.85	5768	8.303
0.04	*0.213*	*96*	*0.138*	0.54	13.21	5932	8.540
0.05	*0.298*	*134*	*0.193*	0.55	13.58	6098	8.778
0.06	*0.392*	*176*	*0.253*	0.56	13.95	6265	9.018
0.07	*0.493*	*221*	*0.319*	0.57	14.33	6434	9.261
0.08	*0.603*	*271*	*0.390*	0.58	14.71	6604	9.506
0.09	*0.719*	*323*	*0.465*	0.59	15.09	6775	9.753
0.10	*0.842*	*378*	*0.544*	0.60	15.48	6948	10.00
0.11	*0.972*	*436*	*0.628*	0.61	15.86	7123	10.25
0.12	*1.107*	*497*	*0.716*	0.62	16.26	7298	10.51
0.13	*1.249*	*560*	*0.807*	0.63	16.65	7476	10.76
0.14	*1.395*	*626*	*0.902*	0.64	17.05	7654	11.02
0.15	*1.548*	*695*	*1.000*	0.65	17.45	7834	11.28
0.16	*1.705*	*765*	*1.102*	0.66	17.86	8016	11.54
0.17	*1.867*	*838*	*1.207*	0.67	18.26	8199	11.80
0.18	*2.034*	*913*	*1.315*	0.68	18.67	8383	12.07
0.19	*2.206*	*990*	*1.426*	0.69	19.09	8569	12.33
0.20	2.978	1337	1.925	0.70	19.50	8756	12.60
0.21	3.205	1439	2.071	0.71	19.92	8944	12.87
0.22	3.436	1543	2.221	0.72	20.34	9134	13.15
0.23	3.673	1649	2.374	0.73	20.77	9324	13.42
0.24	3.915	1758	2.530	0.74	21.20	9517	13.70
0.25	4.163	1869	2.690	0.75	21.63	9710	13.98
0.26	4.415	1982	2.853	0.76	22.06	9905	14.26
0.27	4.672	2097	3.019	0.77	22.50	10,100	14.54
0.28	4.934	2215	3.188	0.78	22.94	10,300	14.82
0.29	5.200	2335	3.361	0.79	23.38	10,500	15.11
0.30	5.472	2457	3.536	0.80	23.83	10,700	15.40
0.31	5.748	2580	3.714	0.81	24.28	10,900	15.69
0.32	6.028	2706	3.896	0.82	24.73	11,100	15.98
0.33	6.313	2834	4.080	0.83	25.18	11,300	16.27
0.34	6.602	2964	4.266	0.84	25.64	11,510	16.57
0.35	6.895	3096	4.456	0.85	26.10	11,720	16.86
0.36	7.193	3229	4.648	0.86	26.56	11,920	17.16
0.37	7.495	3365	4.843	0.87	27.02	12,130	17.46
0.38	7.800	3502	5.041	0.88	27.49	12,340	17.77
0.39	8.110	3641	5.241	0.89	27.96	12,550	18.07
0.40	8.424	3782	5.444	0.90	28.43	12,760	18.37
0.41	8.742	3925	5.650	0.91	28.91	12,980	18.68
0.42	9.064	4069	5.858	0.92	29.39	13,190	18.99
0.43	9.390	4215	6.068	0.93	29.87	13,410	19.30
0.44	9.719	4363	6.281	0.94	30.35	13,620	19.61
0.45	10.05	4513	6.496	0.95	30.83	13,840	19.93
0.46	10.39	4664	6.714	0.96	31.32	14,060	20.24
0.47	10.73	4817	6.934	0.97	31.81	14,280	20.56
0.48	11.07	4972	7.157	0.98	32.31	14,500	20.88
0.49	11.42	5128	7.381	0.99	32.80	14,730	21.20
0.50	11.77	5286	7.608	1.00	33.30	14,950	21.52

11

Table 11-10 (Continued)				Table 11-10 (Continued)			
Head (feet)	CFS	GPM	MGD	Head (feet)	CFS	GPM	MGD
1.01	33.80	15,170	21.84	1.51	61.79	27,740	39.93
1.02	34.30	15,400	22.17	1.52	62.40	28,020	40.33
1.03	34.81	15,630	22.50	1.53	63.02	28,290	40.73
1.04	35.32	15,860	22.82	1.54	63.64	28,570	41.13
1.05	35.83	16,090	23.15	1.55	64.26	28,850	41.53
1.06	36.34	16,320	23.49	1.56	64.88	29,130	41.93
1.07	36.86	16,550	23.82	1.57	65.51	29,410	42.33
1.08	37.37	16,780	24.15	1.58	66.13	29,690	42.74
1.09	37.90	17,010	24.49	1.59	66.76	29,970	43.15
1.10	38.42	17,250	24.83	1.60	67.39	30,260	43.55
1.11	38.94	17,480	25.17	1.61	68.03	30,540	43.96
1.12	39.47	17,720	25.51	1.62	68.66	30,830	44.37
1.13	40.00	17,960	25.85	1.63	69.30	31,110	44.78
1.14	40.53	18,200	26.19	1.64	69.94	31,400	45.20
1.15	41.07	18,440	26.54	1.65	70.58	31,690	45.61
1.16	41.60	18,680	26.89	1.66	71.22	31,970	46.03
1.17	42.14	18,920	27.23	1.67	71.87	32,260	46.44
1.18	42.68	19,160	27.58	1.68	72.51	32,550	46.86
1.19	43.23	19,410	27.94	1.69	73.16	32,850	47.28
1.20	43.77	19,650	28.29	1.70	73.81	33,140	47.70
1.21	44.32	19,900	28.64	1.71	74.46	33,430	48.12
1.22	44.87	20,150	29.00	1.72	75.12	33,720	48.54
1.23	45.43	20,390	29.36	1.73	75.77	34,020	48.97
1.24	45.98	20,640	29.71	1.74	76.43	34,310	49.39
1.25	46.54	20,890	30.08	1.75	77.09	34,610	49.82
1.26	47.10	21,140	30.44	1.76	77.75	34,910	50.25
1.27	47.66	21,400	30.80	1.77	78.42	35,200	50.68
1.28	48.22	21,650	31.16	1.78	79.08	35,500	51.11
1.29	48.79	21,900	31.53	1.79	79.75	35,800	51.54
1.30	49.36	22,160	31.90	1.80	80.42	36,100	51.97
1.31	49.93	22,420	32.27	1.81	81.09	36,400	52.40
1.32	50.50	22,670	32.64	1.82	81.76	36,710	52.84
1.33	51.08	22,930	33.01	1.83	82.44	37,010	53.27
1.34	51.65	23,190	33.38	1.84	83.11	37,310	53.71
1.35	52.23	23,450	33.76	1.85	83.79	37,620	54.15
1.36	52.81	23,710	34.13	1.86	84.47	37,920	54.59
1.37	53.40	23,970	34.51	1.87	85.15	38,230	55.03
1.38	53.98	24,240	34.89	1.88	85.84	38,540	55.47
1.39	54.57	24,500	35.27	1.89	86.52	38,840	55.92
1.40	55.16	24,760	35.65	1.90	87.21	39,150	56.36
1.41	55.75	25,030	36.03	1.91	87.90	39,460	56.81
1.42	56.35	25,300	36.41	1.92	88.59	39,770	57.25
1.43	56.94	25,560	36.80	1.93	89.29	40,080	57.70
1.44	57.54	25,830	37.19	1.94	89.98	40,400	58.15
1.45	58.14	26,100	37.57	1.95	90.68	40,710	58.60
1.46	58.75	26,370	37.96	1.96	91.38	41,020	59.05
1.47	59.35	26,650	38.35	1.97	92.08	41,340	59.50
1.48	59.96	26,920	38.75	1.98	92.78	41,650	59.96
1.49	60.57	27,190	39.14	1.99	93.48	41,970	60.41
1.50	61.18	27,460	39.53	2.00	94.19	42,280	60.87

11

Table 11-10 (Continued)

Head (feet)	CFS	GPM	MGD
2.01	94.89	42,600	61.32
2.02	95.60	42,920	61.78
2.03	96.31	43,240	62.24
2.04	97.03	43,560	62.70
2.05	97.74	43,880	63.16
2.06	98.46	44,200	63.63
2.07	99.17	44,520	64.09
2.08	99.89	44,850	64.56
2.09	100.6	45,170	65.02
2.10	101.3	45,500	65.49
2.11	102.1	45,820	65.96
2.12	102.8	46,150	66.43
2.13	103.5	46,470	66.90
2.14	104.2	46,800	67.37
2.15	105.0	47,130	67.84
2.16	105.7	47,460	68.32
2.17	106.4	47,790	68.79
2.18	107.2	48,120	69.27
2.19	107.9	48,450	69.74
2.20	108.7	48,780	70.22
2.21	109.4	49,120	70.70
2.22	110.1	49,450	71.18
2.23	110.9	49,780	71.66
2.24	111.6	50,120	72.15
2.25	112.4	50,460	72.63
2.26	113.1	50,790	73.11
2.27	113.9	51,130	73.60
2.28	114.6	51,470	74.09
2.29	115.4	51,810	74.58
2.30	116.2	52,150	75.06
2.31	116.9	52,490	75.55
2.32	117.7	52,830	76.05
2.33	118.4	53,170	76.54
2.34	119.2	53,510	77.03
2.35	120.0	53,860	77.53
2.36	120.7	54,200	78.02
2.37	121.5	54,550	78.52
2.38	122.3	54,890	79.01
2.39	123.0	55,240	79.51
2.40	123.8	55,590	80.01
2.41	124.6	55,930	80.51
2.42	125.4	56,280	81.01
2.43	126.1	56,630	81.52
2.44	126.9	56,980	82.02
2.45	127.7	57,330	82.53
2.46	128.5	57,680	83.03
2.47	129.3	58,030	83.54
2.48	130.1	58,390	84.05
2.49	130.8	58,740	84.56
2.50	131.6	59,100	85.07

Table 11-10 (Continued)

Head (feet)	CFS	GPM	MGD
2.51	132.4	59,450	85.58
2.52	133.2	59,810	86.09
2.53	134.0	60,160	86.60
2.54	134.8	60,520	87.11
2.55	135.6	60,880	87.63
2.56	136.4	61,240	88.15
2.57	137.2	61,590	88.66
2.58	138.0	61,950	89.18
2.59	138.8	62,310	89.70
2.60	139.6	62,680	90.22
2.61	140.4	63,040	90.74
2.62	141.2	63,400	91.26
2.63	142.0	63,760	91.79
2.64	142.8	64,130	92.31
2.65	143.7	64,490	92.83
2.66	144.5	64,860	93.36
2.67	145.3	65,220	93.89
2.68	146.1	65,590	94.42
2.69	146.9	65,960	94.94
2.70	147.7	66,330	95.47
2.71	148.6	66,700	96.01
2.72	149.4	67,060	96.54
2.73	150.2	67,430	97.07
2.74	151.0	67,810	97.60
2.75	151.9	68,180	98.14
2.76	152.7	68,550	98.67
2.77	153.5	68,920	99.21
2.78	154.4	69,300	99.75
2.79	155.2	69,670	100.3
2.80	156.0	70,050	100.8
2.81	156.9	70,420	101.4
2.82	157.7	70,800	101.9
2.83	158.5	71,170	102.5
2.84	159.4	71,550	103.0
2.85	160.2	71,930	103.5
2.86	161.1	72,310	104.1
2.87	161.9	72,690	104.6
2.88	162.8	73,070	105.2
2.89	163.6	73,450	105.7
2.90	164.5	73,830	106.3
2.91	165.3	74,210	106.8
2.92	166.2	74,600	107.4
2.93	167.0	74,980	107.9
2.94	167.9	75,360	108.5
2.95	168.7	75,750	109.0
2.96	169.6	76,130	109.6
2.97	170.4	76,520	110.1
2.98	171.3	76,910	110.7
2.99	172.2	77,290	111.3
3.00	173.0	77,680	111.8

11

Table 11-10 (Continued)				Table 11-10 (Continued)			
Head (feet)	CFS	GPM	MGD	Head (feet)	CFS	GPM	MGD
3.01	173.9	78,070	112.4	3.51	219.0	98,310	141.5
3.02	174.8	78,460	112.9	3.52	219.9	98,730	142.1
3.03	175.6	78,850	113.5	3.53	220.9	99,150	142.7
3.04	176.5	79,240	114.1	3.54	221.8	99,570	143.3
3.05	177.4	79,630	114.6	3.55	222.7	100,000	143.9
3.06	178.2	80,020	115.2	3.56	223.7	100,400	144.5
3.07	179.1	80,420	115.8	3.57	224.6	100,800	145.2
3.08	180.0	80,810	116.3	3.58	225.6	101,300	145.8
3.09	180.9	81,200	116.9	3.59	226.5	101,700	146.4
3.10	181.8	81,600	117.5	3.60	227.5	102,100	147.0
3.11	182.6	81,990	118.0	3.61	228.4	102,500	147.6
3.12	183.5	82,390	118.6	3.62	229.4	103,000	148.2
3.13	184.4	82,790	119.2	3.63	230.3	103,400	148.8
3.14	185.3	83,180	119.7	3.64	231.3	103,800	149.4
3.15	186.2	83,580	120.3	3.65	232.2	104,300	150.1
3.16	187.1	83,980	120.9	3.66	233.2	104,700	150.7
3.17	187.9	84,380	121.5	3.67	234.1	105,100	151.3
3.18	188.8	84,780	122.0	3.68	235.1	105,500	151.9
3.19	189.7	85,180	122.6	3.69	236.0	106,000	152.5
3.20	190.6	85,580	123.2	3.70	237.0	106,400	153.2
3.21	191.5	85,980	123.8	3.71	238.0	106,800	153.8
3.22	192.4	86,380	124.3	3.72	238.9	107,300	154.4
3.23	193.3	86,790	124.9	3.73	239.9	107,700	155.0
3.24	194.2	87,190	125.5	3.74	240.9	108,100	155.7
3.25	195.1	87,590	126.1	3.75	241.8	108,600	156.3
3.26	196.0	88,000	126.7	3.76	242.8	109,000	156.9
3.27	196.9	88,400	127.3	3.77	243.8	109,400	157.5
3.28	197.8	88,810	127.8	3.78	244.7	109,900	158.2
3.29	198.7	89,210	128.4	3.79	245.7	110,300	158.8
3.30	199.6	89,620	129.0	3.80	246.7	110,700	159.4
3.31	200.5	90,030	129.6	3.81	247.6	111,200	160.0
3.32	201.4	90,440	130.2	3.82	248.6	111,600	160.7
3.33	202.4	90,850	130.8	3.83	249.6	112,100	161.3
3.34	203.3	91,260	131.4	3.84	250.6	112,500	161.9
3.35	204.2	91,670	132.0	3.85	251.6	112,900	162.6
3.36	205.1	92,080	132.5	3.86	252.5	113,400	163.2
3.37	206.0	92,490	133.1	3.87	253.5	113,800	163.8
3.38	206.9	92,900	133.7	3.88	254.5	114,300	164.5
3.39	207.8	93,310	134.3	3.89	255.5	114,700	165.1
3.40	208.8	93,730	134.9	3.90	256.5	115,100	165.7
3.41	209.7	94,140	135.5	3.91	257.5	115,600	166.4
3.42	210.6	94,550	136.1	3.92	258.4	116,000	167.0
3.43	211.5	94,970	136.7	3.93	259.4	116,500	167.7
3.44	212.5	95,380	137.3	3.94	260.4	116,900	168.3
3.45	213.4	95,800	137.9	3.95	261.4	117,400	168.9
3.46	214.3	96,220	138.5	3.96	262.4	117,800	169.6
3.47	215.2	96,640	139.1	3.97	263.4	118,300	170.2
3.48	216.2	97,050	139.7	3.98	264.4	118,700	170.9
3.49	217.1	97,470	140.3	3.99	265.4	119,200	171.5
3.50	218.0	97,890	140.9	4.00	266.4	119,600	172.2

11

Table 11-10 (Continued)					Table 11-10 (Continued)			
Head (feet)	CFS	GPM	MGD		Head (feet)	CFS	GPM	MGD
4.01	267.4	120,000	172.8		4.51	318.9	143,200	206.1
4.02	268.4	120,500	173.5		4.52	320.0	143,700	206.8
4.03	269.4	120,900	174.1		4.53	321.1	144,100	207.5
4.04	270.4	121,400	174.7		4.54	322.1	144,600	208.2
4.05	271.4	121,800	175.4		4.55	323.2	145,100	208.9
4.06	272.4	122,300	176.0		4.56	324.3	145,600	209.6
4.07	273.4	122,800	176.7		4.57	325.3	146,100	210.2
4.08	274.4	123,200	177.4		4.58	326.4	146,500	210.9
4.09	275.4	123,700	178.0		4.59	327.5	147,000	211.6
4.10	276.5	124,100	178.7		4.60	328.5	147,500	212.3
4.11	277.5	124,600	179.3		4.61	329.6	148,000	213.0
4.12	278.5	125,000	180.0		4.62	330.7	148,500	213.7
4.13	279.5	125,500	180.6		4.63	331.8	148,900	214.4
4.14	280.5	125,900	181.3		4.64	332.8	149,400	215.1
4.15	281.5	126,400	181.9		4.65	333.9	149,900	215.8
4.16	282.5	126,800	182.6		4.66	335.0	150,400	216.5
4.17	283.6	127,300	183.3		4.67	336.1	150,900	217.2
4.18	284.6	127,800	183.9		4.68	337.1	151,400	217.9
4.19	285.6	128,200	184.6		4.69	338.2	151,800	218.6
4.20	286.6	128,700	185.2		4.70	339.3	152,300	219.3
4.21	287.7	129,100	185.9		4.71	340.4	152,800	220.0
4.22	288.7	129,600	186.6		4.72	341.5	153,300	220.7
4.23	289.7	130,100	187.2		4.73	342.6	153,800	221.4
4.24	290.7	130,500	187.9		4.74	343.6	154,300	222.1
4.25	291.8	131,000	188.5		4.75	344.7	154,800	222.8
4.26	292.8	131,400	189.2		4.76	345.8	155,300	223.5
4.27	293.8	131,900	189.9		4.77	346.9	155,700	224.2
4.28	294.9	132,400	190.5		4.78	348.0	156,200	224.9
4.29	295.9	132,800	191.2		4.79	349.1	156,700	225.6
4.30	296.9	133,300	191.9		4.80	350.2	157,200	226.3
4.31	298.0	133,800	192.6		4.81	351.3	157,700	227.0
4.32	299.0	134,200	193.2		4.82	352.4	158,200	227.7
4.33	300.0	134,700	193.9		4.83	353.5	158,700	228.4
4.34	301.1	135,200	194.6		4.84	354.6	159,200	229.1
4.35	302.1	135,600	195.2		4.85	355.7	159,700	229.9
4.36	303.2	136,100	195.9		4.86	356.8	160,200	230.6
4.37	304.2	136,600	196.6		4.87	357.9	160,700	231.3
4.38	305.2	137,000	197.3		4.88	359.0	161,200	232.0
4.39	306.3	137,500	197.9		4.89	360.1	161,700	232.7
4.40	307.3	138,000	198.6		4.90	361.2	162,200	233.4
4.41	308.4	138,500	199.3		4.91	362.3	162,700	234.1
4.42	309.4	138,900	200.0		4.92	363.4	163,200	234.8
4.43	310.5	139,400	200.7		4.93	364.5	163,600	235.6
4.44	311.5	139,900	201.3		4.94	365.6	164,100	236.3
4.45	312.6	140,300	202.0		4.95	366.7	164,600	237.0
4.46	313.7	140,800	202.7		4.96	367.8	165,100	237.7
4.47	314.7	141,300	203.4		4.97	369.0	165,600	238.4
4.48	315.8	141,800	204.1		4.98	370.1	166,100	239.2
4.49	316.8	142,200	204.7		4.99	371.2	166,600	239.9
4.50	317.9	142,700	205.4		5.00	372.3	167,100	240.6

11

Rectangular Weir Without End Contractions Discharge Tables • 245

Table 11-11:
0.3 m Rectangular Weir without End Contractions Discharge Table with Head in Meters

Formula: l/s $= 551.5\ H^{1.5}$
$m^3/hr = 1986\ H^{1.5}$
Where: H = head in meters

Values in italics indicate flow below the recommended range of this particular primary device.

Table 11-11			Table 11-11 (Continued)		
Head (meters)	l/s	m³/hr	Head (meters)	l/s	m³/hr
0.005	*0.195*	*0.70*	0.080	12.48	44.94
0.010	*0.552*	*1.99*	0.085	13.67	49.22
0.015	*1.013*	*3.65*	0.090	14.89	53.62
0.020	*1.560*	*5.62*	0.095	16.15	58.15
0.025	*2.180*	*7.85*	0.100	17.44	62.80
0.030	*2.866*	*10.32*	0.105	18.76	67.57
0.035	*3.611*	*13.00*	0.110	20.12	72.45
0.040	*4.412*	*15.88*	0.115	21.51	77.45
0.045	*5.265*	*18.95*	0.120	22.93	82.56
0.050	*6.166*	*22.20*	0.125	24.37	87.77
0.055	*7.114*	*25.61*	0.130	25.85	93.09
0.060	8.105	29.19	0.135	27.36	98.51
0.065	9.139	32.91	0.140	28.89	104.0
0.070	10.21	36.78	0.145	30.45	109.7
0.075	11.33	40.79	0.150	32.04	115.4

Table 11-12:
0.4 m Rectangular Weir without End Contractions Discharge Table with Head in Meters

Formula: l/s $= 735.4\ H^{1.5}$
$m^3/hr = 2647\ H^{1.5}$
Where: H = head in meters

Values in italics indicate flow below the recommended range of this particular primary device.

Table 11-12			Table 11-12 (Continued)		
Head (meters)	l/s	m³/hr	Head (meters)	l/s	m³/hr
0.005	*0.26*	*0.94*	0.105	25.02	90.06
0.010	*0.74*	*2.65*	0.110	26.83	96.57
0.015	*1.35*	*4.86*	0.115	28.68	103.2
0.020	*2.08*	*7.49*	0.120	30.57	110.0
0.025	*2.91*	*10.46*	0.125	32.50	117.0
0.030	*3.82*	*13.76*	0.130	34.47	124.1
0.035	*4.82*	*17.33*	0.135	36.48	131.3
0.040	*5.88*	*21.18*	0.140	38.52	138.7
0.045	*7.02*	*25.27*	0.145	40.60	146.2
0.050	*8.22*	*29.60*	0.150	42.72	153.8
0.055	*9.49*	*34.15*	0.155	44.88	161.5
0.060	10.81	38.90	0.160	47.07	169.4
0.065	12.19	43.87	0.165	49.29	177.4
0.070	13.62	49.02	0.170	51.55	185.5
0.075	15.10	54.37	0.175	53.84	193.8
0.080	16.64	59.89	0.180	56.16	202.1
0.085	18.22	65.60	0.185	58.52	210.6
0.090	19.86	71.47	0.190	60.91	219.2
0.095	21.53	77.51	0.195	63.33	227.9
0.100	23.26	83.71	0.200	65.78	236.8

Table 11-13:
0.5 m Rectangular Weir without End Contractions Discharge
Table with Head in Meters

Formula: l/s $= 919.2\ H^{1.5}$
          $m^3/hr = 3309\ H^{1.5}$
Where: H = head in meters

Values in italics indicate flow below the recommended range of this particular primary device.

Table 11-13			Table 11-13 (Continued)		
Head (meters)	l/s	m³/hr	Head (meters)	l/s	m³/hr
0.005	*0.32*	*1.17*	0.130	43.08	155.1
0.010	*0.92*	*3.31*	0.135	45.59	164.1
0.015	*1.69*	*6.08*	0.140	48.15	173.3
0.020	*2.60*	*9.36*	0.145	50.75	182.7
0.025	*3.63*	*13.08*	0.150	53.40	192.2
0.030	*4.78*	*17.20*	0.155	56.09	201.9
0.035	*6.02*	*21.67*	0.160	58.83	211.8
0.040	*7.35*	*26.47*	0.165	61.61	221.8
0.045	*8.77*	*31.59*	0.170	64.43	231.9
0.050	*10.28*	*37.00*	0.175	67.29	242.2
0.055	*11.86*	*42.68*	0.180	70.20	252.7
0.060	13.51	48.63	0.185	73.14	263.3
0.065	15.23	54.84	0.190	76.13	274.0
0.070	17.02	61.28	0.195	79.15	284.9
0.075	18.88	67.97	0.200	82.22	296.0
0.080	20.80	74.87	0.205	85.32	307.1
0.085	22.78	82.00	0.210	88.46	318.4
0.090	24.82	89.34	0.215	91.64	329.9
0.095	26.92	96.89	0.220	94.85	341.5
0.100	29.07	104.6	0.225	98.10	353.2
0.105	31.27	112.6	0.230	101.4	365.0
0.110	33.54	120.7	0.235	104.7	377.0
0.115	35.85	129.0	0.240	108.1	389.1
0.120	38.21	137.6	0.245	111.5	401.3
0.125	40.62	146.2	0.250	114.9	413.6

11

Table 11-14:
0.6 m Rectangular Weir without End Contractions Discharge Table with Head in Meters

Formula: l/s $= 1103\,H^{1.5}$
$m^3/hr = 3971\,H^{1.5}$

Where: H = head in meters

Values in italics indicate flow below the recommended range of this particular primary device.

Head (meters)	l/s	m³/hr	Head (meters)	l/s	m³/hr
0.005	*0.39*	*1.40*	0.155	67.31	242.3
0.010	*1.10*	*3.97*	0.160	70.59	254.1
0.015	*2.03*	*7.30*	0.165	73.93	266.1
0.020	*3.12*	*11.23*	0.170	77.31	278.3
0.025	*4.36*	*15.70*	0.175	80.75	290.7
0.030	*5.73*	*20.63*	0.180	84.23	303.3
0.035	*7.22*	*26.00*	0.185	87.77	316.0
0.040	*8.82*	*31.77*	0.190	91.35	328.9
0.045	*10.53*	*37.91*	0.195	94.98	341.9
0.050	*12.33*	*44.40*	0.200	98.66	355.2
0.055	*14.23*	*51.22*	0.205	102.4	368.6
0.060	16.21	58.36	0.210	106.1	382.1
0.065	18.28	65.81	0.215	110.0	395.9
0.070	20.43	73.54	0.220	113.8	409.8
0.075	22.66	81.56	0.225	117.7	423.8
0.080	24.96	89.85	0.230	121.7	438.0
0.085	27.33	98.41	0.235	125.7	452.4
0.090	29.78	107.2	0.240	129.7	466.9
0.095	32.30	116.3	0.245	133.8	481.6
0.100	34.88	125.6	0.250	137.9	496.4
0.105	37.53	135.1	0.255	142.0	511.3
0.110	40.24	144.9	0.260	146.2	526.5
0.115	43.02	154.9	0.265	150.5	541.7
0.120	45.85	165.1	0.270	154.7	557.1
0.125	48.75	175.5	0.275	159.1	572.7
0.130	51.70	186.1	0.280	163.4	588.4
0.135	54.71	197.0	0.285	167.8	604.2
0.140	57.78	208.0	0.290	172.3	620.2
0.145	60.90	219.3	0.295	176.7	636.3
0.150	64.08	230.7	0.300	181.2	652.5

Table 11-15:
0.8 m Rectangular Weir without End Contractions Discharge Table with Head in Meters

Formula: $l/s = 1471\,H^{1.5}$
$m^3/hr = 5295\,H^{1.5}$
Where: H = head in meters

Values in italics indicate flow below the recommended range of this particular primary device.

Table 11-15			Table 11-15 (Continued)		
Head (meters)	l/s	m³/hr	Head (meters)	l/s	m³/hr
0.005	*0.52*	*1.87*	0.205	136.5	491.5
0.010	*1.47*	*5.29*	0.210	141.6	509.6
0.015	*2.70*	*9.73*	0.215	146.6	527.9
0.020	*4.16*	*14.98*	0.220	151.8	546.4
0.025	*5.81*	*20.93*	0.225	157.0	565.1
0.030	*7.64*	*27.51*	0.230	162.3	584.1
0.035	*9.63*	*34.67*	0.235	167.6	603.2
0.040	*11.77*	*42.36*	0.240	173.0	622.6
0.045	*14.04*	*50.54*	0.245	178 4	642.1
0.050	*16.44*	*59.20*	0.250	183.9	661.9
0.055	*18.97*	*68.29*	0.255	189.4	681.8
0.060	21.62	77.82	0.260	195.0	702.0
0.065	24.38	87.75	0.265	200.7	722.3
0.070	27.24	98.06	0.270	206.4	742.9
0.075	30.21	108.8	0.275	212.1	763.6
0.080	33.28	119.8	0.280	217.9	784.5
0.085	36.45	131.2	0.285	223.8	805.6
0.090	39.72	143.0	0.290	229.7	826.9
0.095	43.07	155.0	0.295	235.7	848.4
0.100	46.52	167.4	0.300	241.7	870.1
0.105	50.05	180.2	0.305	247.8	891.9
0.110	53.67	193.2	0.310	253.9	913.9
0.115	57.37	206.5	0.315	260.1	936.1
0.120	61.15	220.1	0.320	266.3	958.5
0.125	65.01	234.0	0.325	272.5	981.0
0.130	68.95	248.2	0.330	278.9	1004
0.135	72.96	262.6	0.335	285.2	1027
0.140	77.06	277.4	0.340	291.6	1050
0.145	81.22	292.4	0.345	298.1	1073
0.150	85.46	307.6	0.350	304.6	1096
0.155	89.77	323.1	0.355	311.1	1120
0.160	94.14	338.9	0.360	317.7	1144
0.165	98.59	354.9	0.365	324.4	1168
0.170	103.1	371.1	0.370	331.1	1192
0.175	107.7	387.6	0.375	337.8	1216
0.180	112.3	404.4	0.380	344.6	1240
0.185	117.0	421.3	0.385	351.4	1265
0.190	121.8	438.5	0.390	358.3	1290
0.195	126.7	456.0	0.395	365.2	1315
0.200	131.6	473.6	0.400	372.1	1340

11

Table 11-16:
1 m Rectangular Weir without End Contractions Discharge Table with Head in Meters

Formula: $l/s = 1838 H^{1.5}$
$m^3/hr = 6618 H^{1.5}$
Where: H = head in meters

Values in italics indicate flow below the recommended range of this particular primary device.

Table 11-16			Table 11-16 (Continued)		
Head (meters)	l/s	m³/hr	Head (meters)	l/s	m³/hr
0.005	*0.65*	*2.34*	0.255	236.7	852.2
0.010	*1.84*	*6.62*	0.260	243.7	877.4
0.015	*3.38*	*12.16*	0.265	250.7	902.8
0.020	*5.20*	*18.72*	0.270	257.9	928.5
0.025	*7.27*	*26.16*	0.275	265.1	954.4
0.030	*9.55*	*34.39*	0.280	272.3	980.5
0.035	*12.04*	*43.34*	0.285	279.6	1007
0.040	*14.71*	*52.95*	0.290	287.0	1034
0.045	*17.55*	*63.18*	0.295	294.5	1060
0.050	*20.55*	*74.00*	0.300	302.0	1087
0.055	*23.71*	*85.37*	0.305	309.6	1115
0.060	27.01	97.26	0.310	317.2	1142
0.065	30.46	109.7	0.315	324.9	1170
0.070	34.04	122.6	0.320	332.7	1198
0.075	37.75	135.9	0.325	340.5	1226
0.080	41.59	149.7	0.330	348.4	1255
0.085	45.55	164.0	0.335	356.4	1283
0.090	49.63	178.7	0.340	364.4	1312
0.095	53.82	193.8	0.345	372.5	1341
0.100	58.12	209.3	0.350	380.6	1370
0.105	62.54	225.2	0.355	388.8	1400
0.110	67.06	241.4	0.360	397.0	1429
0.115	71.68	258.1	0.365	405.3	1459
0.120	76.40	275.1	0.370	413.7	1489
0.125	81.23	292.5	0.375	422.1	1520
0.130	86.15	310.2	0.380	430.5	1550
0.135	91.17	328.3	0.385	439.1	1581
0.140	96.28	346.7	0.390	447.7	1612
0.145	101.5	365.4	0.395	456.3	1643
0.150	106.8	384.5	0.400	465.0	1674
0.155	112.2	403.9	0.405	473.7	1706
0.160	117.6	423.6	0.410	482.5	1737
0.165	123.2	443.6	0.415	491.4	1769
0.170	128.8	463.9	0.420	500.3	1801
0.175	134.6	484.5	0.425	509.2	1834
0.180	140.4	505.4	0.430	518.3	1866
0.185	146.3	526.6	0.435	527.3	1899
0.190	152.2	548.1	0.440	536.4	1932
0.195	158.3	569.9	0.445	545.6	1965
0.200	164.4	591.9	0.450	554.8	1998
0.205	170.6	614.3	0.455	564.1	2031
0.210	176.9	636.9	0.460	573.4	2065
0.215	183.2	659.8	0.465	582.8	2098
0.220	189.7	682.9	0.470	592.2	2132
0.225	196.2	706.3	0.475	601.7	2167
0.230	202.7	730.0	0.480	611.2	2201
0.235	209.4	753.9	0.485	620.8	2235
0.240	216.1	778.1	0.490	630.4	2270
0.245	222.9	802.6	0.495	640.1	2305
0.250	229.8	827.3	0.500	649.8	2340

11

Table 11-17:
1.5 m Rectangular Weir without End Contractions Discharge Table with Head in Meters

Formula: $l/s = 2758 H^{1.5}$
$m^3/hr = 9928 H^{1.5}$

Where: H = head in meters

Values in italics indicate flow below the recommended range of this particular primary device.

Head (meters)	l/s	m³/hr	Head (meters)	l/s	m³/hr
0.005	*0.97*	*3.51*	0.255	355.1	1278
0.010	*2.76*	*9.93*	0.260	365.6	1316
0.015	*5.07*	*18.24*	0.265	376.2	1354
0.020	*7.80*	*28.08*	0.270	386.9	1393
0.025	*10.90*	*39.24*	0.275	397.7	1432
0.030	*14.33*	*51.59*	0.280	408.6	1471
0.035	*18.06*	*65.01*	0.285	419.6	1511
0.040	*22.06*	*79.42*	0.290	430.7	1550
0.045	*26.32*	*94.77*	0.295	441.9	1591
0.050	*30.83*	*110.99*	0.300	453.2	1631
0.055	*35.57*	*128.05*	0.305	464.6	1672
0.060	40.53	145.9	0.310	476.0	1714
0.065	45.71	164.5	0.315	487.6	1755
0.070	51.08	183.9	0.320	499.3	1797
0.075	56.65	203.9	0.325	511.0	1839
0.080	62.41	224.6	0.330	522.8	1882
0.085	68.35	246.0	0.335	534.8	1925
0.090	74.47	268.1	0.340	546.8	1968
0.095	80.76	290.7	0.345	558.9	2012
0.100	87.22	314.0	0.350	571.1	2056
0.105	93.84	337.8	0.355	583.4	2100
0.110	100.6	362.2	0.360	595.7	2144
0.115	107.6	387.2	0.365	608.2	2189
0.120	114.6	412.7	0.370	620.7	2234
0.125	121.9	438.8	0.375	633.3	2280
0.130	129.3	465.3	0.380	646.1	2326
0.135	136.8	492.5	0.385	658.8	2372
0.140	144.5	520.1	0.390	671.7	2418
0.145	152.3	548.2	0.395	684.7	2465
0.150	160.2	576.8	0.400	697.7	2512
0.155	168.3	605.8	0.405	710.8	2559
0.160	176.5	635.4	0.410	724.1	2606
0.165	184.9	665.4	0.415	737.3	2654
0.170	193.3	695.9	0.420	750.7	2702
0.175	201.9	726.8	0.425	764.1	2751
0.180	210.6	758.2	0.430	777.7	2799
0.185	219.5	790.0	0.435	791.3	2848
0.190	228.4	822.2	0.440	805.0	2898
0.195	237.5	854.9	0.445	818.7	2947
0.200	246.7	888.0	0.450	832.6	2997
0.205	256.0	921.5	0.455	846.5	3047
0.210	265.4	955.4	0.460	860.5	3097
0.215	274.9	989.7	0.465	874.5	3148
0.220	284.6	1024	0.470	888.7	3199
0.225	294.4	1060	0.475	902.9	3250
0.230	304.2	1095	0.480	917.2	3302
0.235	314.2	1131	0.485	931.6	3353
0.240	324.3	1167	0.490	946.0	3405
0.245	334.5	1204	0.495	960.5	3458
0.250	344.8	1241	0.500	975.1	3510

11

Table 11-17 (Continued)				Table 11-17 (Continued)		
Head (meters)	l/s	m³/hr		Head (meters)	l/s	m³/hr
0.505	989.8	3563		0.630	1379	4964
0.510	1004	3616		0.635	1396	5024
0.515	1019	3669		0.640	1412	5083
0.520	1034	3723		0.645	1429	5143
0.525	1049	3777		0.650	1445	5203
0.530	1064	3831		0.655	1462	5263
0.535	1079	3885		0.660	1479	5323
0.540	1094	3940		0.665	1496	5384
0.545	1110	3994		0.670	1513	5445
0.550	1125	4050		0.675	1530	5506
0.555	1140	4105		0.680	1547	5567
0.560	1156	4160		0.685	1564	5629
0.565	1171	4216		0.690	1581	5690
0.570	1187	4272		0.695	1598	5752
0.575	1203	4329		0.700	1615	5814
0.580	1218	4385		0.705	1633	5877
0.585	1234	4442		0.710	1650	5939
0.590	1250	4499		0.715	1667	6002
0.595	1266	4557		0.720	1685	6065
0.600	1282	4614		0.725	1703	6129
0.605	1298	4672		0.730	1720	6192
0.610	1314	4730		0.735	1738	6256
0.615	1330	4788		0.740	1756	6320
0.620	1346	4847		0.745	1773	6384
0.625	1363	4905		0.750	1791	6448

11

Table 11-18:
2 m Rectangular Weir without End Contractions Discharge Table with Head in Meters

Formula: l/s = $3677\ H^{1.5}$
$m^3/hr = 13240\ H^{1.5}$
Where: H = head in meters

Values in italics indicate flow below the recommended range of this particular primary device.

Table 11-18			Table 11-18 (Continued)		
Head (meters)	l/s	m³/hr	Head (meters)	l/s	m³/hr
0.005	*1.30*	*4.7*	0.255	473.5	1705
0.010	*3.68*	*13.2*	0.260	487.5	1755
0.015	*6.75*	*24.3*	0.265	501.6	1806
0.020	*10.40*	*37.4*	0.270	515.9	1858
0.025	*14.53*	*52.3*	0.275	530.3	1909
0.030	*19.11*	*68.8*	0.280	544.8	1962
0.035	*24.08*	*86.7*	0.285	559.4	2014
0.040	*29.42*	*105.9*	0.290	574.2	2068
0.045	*35.10*	*126.4*	0.295	589.2	2121
0.050	*41.11*	*148.0*	0.300	604.2	2176
0.055	*47.43*	*170.7*	0.305	619.4	2230
0.060	54.04	194.6	0.310	634.7	2285
0.065	60.93	219.4	0.315	650.1	2341
0.070	68.10	245.2	0.320	665.6	2397
0.075	75.52	271.9	0.325	681.3	2453
0.080	83.20	299.6	0.330	697.1	2510
0.085	91.12	328.1	0.335	713.0	2567
0.090	99.28	357.5	0.340	729.0	2625
0.095	107.7	387.7	0.345	745.1	2683
0.100	116.3	418.7	0.350	761.4	2742
0.105	125.1	450.5	0.355	777.7	2800
0.110	134.1	483.0	0.360	794.2	2860
0.115	143.4	516.3	0.365	810.8	2920
0.120	152.9	550.4	0.370	827.6	2980
0.125	162.5	585.1	0.375	844.4	3040
0.130	172.3	620.6	0.380	861.3	3101
0.135	182.4	656.7	0.385	878.4	3163
0.140	192.6	693.6	0.390	895.6	3225
0.145	203.0	731.0	0.395	912.8	3287
0.150	213.6	769.2	0.400	930.2	3349
0.155	224.4	808.0	0.405	947.7	3412
0.160	235.3	847.4	0.410	965.3	3476
0.165	246.4	887.4	0.415	983.0	3540
0.170	257.7	928.0	0.420	1001	3604
0.175	269.2	969.3	0.425	1019	3668
0.180	280.8	1011	0.430	1037	3733
0.185	292.6	1054	0.435	1055	3799
0.190	304.5	1097	0.440	1073	3864
0.195	316.6	1140	0.445	1092	3930
0.200	328.9	1184	0.450	1110	3997
0.205	341.3	1229	0.455	1129	4064
0.210	353.9	1274	0.460	1147	4131
0.215	366.6	1320	0.465	1166	4198
0.220	379.4	1366	0.470	1185	4266
0.225	392.4	1413	0.475	1204	4334
0.230	405.6	1460	0.480	1223	4403
0.235	418.9	1508	0.485	1242	4472
0.240	432.3	1557	0.490	1261	4541
0.245	445.9	1606	0.495	1281	4611
0.250	459.6	1655	0.500	1300	4681

11

Table 11-18 (Continued)		
Head (meters)	l/s	m³/hr
0.505	1320	4751
0.510	1339	4822
0.515	1359	4893
0.520	1379	4965
0.525	1399	5036
0.530	1419	5109
0.535	1439	5181
0.540	1459	5254
0.545	1479	5327
0.550	1500	5400
0.555	1520	5474
0.560	1541	5548
0.565	1562	5623
0.570	1582	5698
0.575	1603	5773
0.580	1624	5848
0.585	1645	5924
0.590	1666	6000
0.595	1688	6077
0.600	1709	6153
0.605	1730	6230
0.610	1752	6308
0.615	1773	6386
0.620	1795	6464
0.625	1817	6542
0.630	1839	6621
0.635	1861	6700
0.640	1883	6779
0.645	1905	6858
0.650	1927	6938
0.655	1949	7019
0.660	1972	7099
0.665	1994	7180
0.670	2017	7261
0.675	2039	7342
0.680	2062	7424
0.685	2085	7506
0.690	2107	7589
0.695	2130	7671
0.700	2153	7754
0.705	2177	7837
0.710	2200	7921
0.715	2223	8005
0.720	2246	8089
0.725	2270	8173
0.730	2293	8258
0.735	2317	8343
0.740	2341	8428
0.745	2364	8514
0.750	2388	8600

Table 11-18 (Continued)		
Head (meters)	l/s	m³/hr
0.755	2412	8686
0.760	2436	8772
0.765	2460	8859
0.770	2484	8946
0.775	2509	9033
0.780	2533	9121
0.785	2557	9209
0.790	2582	9297
0.795	2606	9385
0.800	2631	9474
0.805	2656	9563
0.810	2681	9652
0.815	2705	9741
0.820	2730	9831
0.825	2755	9921
0.830	2780	10,010
0.835	2806	10,100
0.840	2831	10,190
0.845	2856	10,280
0.850	2882	10,380
0.855	2907	10,470
0.860	2933	10,560
0.865	2958	10,650
0.870	2984	10,740
0.875	3010	10,840
0.880	3035	10,930
0.885	3061	11,020
0.890	3087	11,120
0.895	3113	11,210
0.900	3139	11,300
0.905	3166	11,400
0.910	3192	11,490
0.915	3218	11,590
0.920	3245	11,680
0.925	3271	11,780
0.930	3298	11,870
0.935	3324	11,970
0.940	3351	12,070
0.945	3378	12,160
0.950	3405	12,260
0.955	3432	12,360
0.960	3459	12,450
0.965	3486	12,550
0.970	3513	12,650
0.975	3540	12,750
0.980	3567	12,840
0.985	3595	12,940
0.990	3622	13,040
0.995	3649	13,140
1.000	3677	13,240

11

Table 11-19:
3m Rectangular Weir without End Contractions Discharge Table
with Head in Meters

Formula: $l/s = 5515\,H^{1.5}$
$m^3/hr = 19860\,H^{1.5}$
Where: H = head in meters

Values in italics indicate flow below the recommended range of this particular primary device.

Table 11-19			Table 11-19 (Continued)		
Head (meters)	l/s	m³/hr	Head (meters)	l/s	m³/hr
0.005	*1.95*	*7.0*	0.255	710.2	2557
0.010	*5.52*	*19.9*	0.260	731.1	2633
0.015	*10.13*	*36.5*	0.265	752.3	2709
0.020	*15.60*	*56.2*	0.270	773.7	2786
0.025	*21.80*	*78.5*	0.275	795.3	2864
0.030	*28.66*	*103.2*	0.280	817.1	2942
0.035	*36.11*	*130.0*	0.285	839.1	3022
0.040	*44.12*	*158.8*	0.290	861.3	3102
0.045	*52.65*	*189.5*	0.295	883.6	3182
0.050	*61.66*	*222.0*	0.300	906.2	3263
0.055	*71.14*	*256.1*	0.305	929.0	3345
0.060	81.05	291.9	0.310	951.9	3428
0.065	91.39	329.1	0.315	975.0	3511
0.070	102.1	367.8	0.320	998.3	3595
0.075	113.3	407.9	0.325	1022	3680
0.080	124.8	449.4	0.330	1045	3765
0.085	136.7	492.2	0.335	1069	3851
0.090	148.9	536.2	0.340	1093	3937
0.095	161.5	581.5	0.345	1118	4024
0.100	174.4	628.0	0.350	1142	4112
0.105	187.6	675.7	0.355	1167	4201
0.110	201.2	724.5	0.360	1191	4290
0.115	215.1	774.5	0.365	1216	4379
0.120	229.3	825.6	0.370	1241	4470
0.125	243.7	877.7	0.375	1266	4561
0.130	258.5	930.9	0.380	1292	4652
0.135	273.6	985.1	0.385	1317	4744
0.140	288.9	1040	0.390	1343	4837
0.145	304.5	1097	0.395	1369	4930
0.150	320.4	1154	0.400	1395	5024
0.155	336.5	1212	0.405	1421	5119
0.160	353.0	1271	0.410	1448	5214
0.165	369.6	1331	0.415	1474	5309
0.170	386.6	1392	0.420	1501	5406
0.175	403.7	1454	0.425	1528	5503
0.180	421.2	1517	0.430	1555	5600
0.185	438.8	1580	0.435	1582	5698
0.190	456.7	1645	0.440	1610	5796
0.195	474.9	1710	0.445	1637	5895
0.200	493.3	1776	0.450	1665	5995
0.205	511.9	1843	0.455	1693	6095
0.210	530.7	1911	0.460	1721	6196
0.215	549.8	1980	0.465	1749	6297
0.220	569.1	2049	0.470	1777	6399
0.225	588.6	2120	0.475	1805	6502
0.230	608.3	2191	0.480	1834	6605
0.235	628.3	2262	0.485	1863	6708
0.240	648.4	2335	0.490	1892	6812
0.245	668.8	2408	0.495	1921	6917
0.250	689.4	2483	0.500	1950	7022

11

Table 11-19 (Continued)			Table 11-19 (Continued)		
Head (meters)	l/s	m³/hr	Head (meters)	l/s	m³/hr
0.505	1979	7127	0.755	3618	13,030
0.510	2009	7233	0.760	3654	13,160
0.515	2038	7340	0.765	3690	13,290
0.520	2068	7447	0.770	3726	13,420
0.525	2098	7555	0.775	3763	13,550
0.530	2128	7663	0.780	3799	13,680
0.535	2158	7772	0.785	3836	13,810
0.540	2188	7881	0.790	3872	13,950
0.545	2219	7991	0.795	3909	14,080
0.550	2250	8101	0.800	3946	14,210
0.555	2280	8211	0.805	3983	14,340
0.560	2311	8323	0.810	4020	14,480
0.565	2342	8434	0.815	4058	14,610
0.570	2373	8547	0.820	4095	14,750
0.575	2405	8659	0.825	4133	14,880
0.580	2436	8772	0.830	4170	15,020
0.585	2468	8886	0.835	4208	15,150
0.590	2499	9000	0.840	4246	15,290
0.595	2531	9115	0.845	4284	15,430
0.600	2563	9230	0.850	4322	15,560
0.605	2595	9346	0.855	4360	15,700
0.610	2627	9462	0.860	4398	15,840
0.615	2660	9578	0.865	4437	15,980
0.620	2692	9695	0.870	4475	16,120
0.625	2725	9813	0.875	4514	16,260
0.630	2758	9931	0.880	4553	16,390
0.635	2791	10,050	0.885	4592	16,530
0.640	2824	10,170	0.890	4631	16,670
0.645	2857	10,290	0.895	4670	16,820
0.650	2890	10,410	0.900	4709	16,960
0.655	2924	10,530	0.905	4748	17,100
0.660	2957	10,650	0.910	4787	17,240
0.665	2991	10,770	0.915	4827	17,380
0.670	3025	10,890	0.920	4867	17,530
0.675	3058	11,010	0.925	4906	17,670
0.680	3092	11,140	0.930	4946	17,810
0.685	3127	11,260	0.935	4986	17,960
0.690	3161	11,380	0.940	5026	18,100
0.695	3195	11,510	0.945	5066	18,240
0.700	3230	11,630	0.950	5107	18,390
0.705	3265	11,760	0.955	5147	18,530
0.710	3299	11,880	0.960	5187	18,680
0.715	3334	12,010	0.965	5228	18,830
0.720	3369	12,130	0.970	5269	18,970
0.725	3404	12,260	0.975	5309	19,120
0.730	3440	12,390	0.980	5350	19,270
0.735	3475	12,510	0.985	5391	19,410
0.740	3511	12,640	0.990	5432	19,560
0.745	3546	12,770	0.995	5474	19,710
0.750	3582	12,900	1.000	5515	19,860

11

Table 11-19 (Continued)				Table 11-19 (Continued)		
Head (meters)	l/s	m³/hr		Head (meters)	l/s	m³/hr
1.005	5556	20,010		1.255	7754	27,920
1.010	5598	20,160		1.260	7800	28,090
1.015	5640	20,310		1.265	7847	28,260
1.020	5681	20,460		1.270	7893	28,420
1.025	5723	20,610		1.275	7940	28,590
1.030	5765	20,760		1.280	7987	28,760
1.035	5807	20,910		1.285	8033	28,930
1.040	5849	21,060		1.290	8080	29,100
1.045	5891	21,220		1.295	8127	29,270
1.050	5934	21,370		1.300	8174	29,440
1.055	5976	21,520		1.305	8222	29,610
1.060	6019	21,670		1.310	8269	29,780
1.065	6061	21,830		1.315	8316	29,950
1.070	6104	21,980		1.320	8364	30,120
1.075	6147	22,140		1.325	8411	30,290
1.080	6190	22,290		1.330	8459	30,460
1.085	6233	22,450		1.335	8507	30,630
1.090	6276	22,600		1.340	8555	30,810
1.095	6319	22,760		1.345	8603	30,980
1.100	6363	22,910		1.350	8651	31,150
1.105	6406	23,070		1.355	8699	31,320
1.110	6450	23,230		1.360	8747	31,500
1.115	6493	23,380		1.365	8795	31,670
1.120	6537	23,540		1.370	8844	31,850
1.125	6581	23,700		1.375	8892	32,020
1.130	6625	23,860		1.380	8941	32,200
1.135	6669	24,010		1.385	8989	32,370
1.140	6713	24,170		1.390	9038	32,550
1.145	6757	24,330		1.395	9087	32,720
1.150	6801	24,490		1.400	9136	32,900
1.155	6846	24,650		1.405	9185	33,070
1.160	6890	24,810		1.410	9234	33,250
1.165	6935	24,970		1.415	9283	33,430
1.170	6979	25,130		1.420	9332	33610
1.175	7024	25,300		1.425	9381	33,780
1.180	7069	25,460		1.430	9431	33,960
1.185	7114	25,620		1.435	9480	34,140
1.190	7159	25,780		1.440	9530	34,320
1.195	7204	25,940		1.445	9580	34,500
1.200	7250	26,110		1.450	9629	34,680
1.205	7295	26,270		1.455	9679	34,860
1.210	7340	26,430		1.460	9729	35,040
1.215	7386	26,600		1.465	9779	35,220
1.220	7432	26,760		1.470	9829	35,400
1.225	7477	26,930		1.475	9879	35,580
1.230	7523	27,090		1.480	9930	35,760
1.235	7569	27,260		1.485	9980	35,940
1.240	7615	27,420		1.490	10,030	36,120
1.245	7661	27,590		1.495	10,080	36,300
1.250	7707	27,760		1.500	10,130	36,490

11

Rectangular Weir Without End Contractions Discharge Tables • 257

11

Overview

This chapter contains discharge (head vs. flow rate) tables for Cipolletti weirs. Note that all of the tabular data is for free flow. If the flow is submerged, corrections will have to be made to determine the discharge, as discussed in Chapter 3.

Discharge tables for Cipolletti weirs with head in feet

12-1:	1 ft.	12-6:	4 ft.
12-2:	$1^1/_2$ ft.	12-7:	5 ft.
12-3:	2 ft.	12-8:	6 ft.
12-4:	$2^1/_2$ ft.	12-9:	8 ft.
12-5:	3 ft.	12-10:	10 ft.

The discharges of the weirs are listed in three different units of measure:

CFS - cubic feet per second   GPM - gallons per minute
MGD - million gallons per day

Discharge tables for Cipolletti weirs with head in meters

12-11:	0.3 m	12-16:	1 m
12-12:	0.4 m	12-17:	1.5 m
12-13:	0.5 m	12-18:	2 m
12-14:	0.6 m	12-19:	3 m
12-15:	0.8 m		

The discharges of the weirs are listed in two different units of measure:

l/s - liters per second m^3/hr - cubic meters per hour

The formulas used to develop each table are listed on the table. Values in italics indicate flow below the recommended range of this particular primary device.

Table 12-1:
1 ft. Cipolletti Weir Discharge Table with Head in Feet

Formula: CFS $= 3.367\ H^{1.5}$
GPM $= 1511\ H^{1.5}$
MGD $= 2.176\ H^{1.5}$
Where: H = head in feet

Values in italics indicate flow below the recommended range of this particular primary device.

Head (feet)	CFS	GPM	MGD	Head (feet)	CFS	GPM	MGD
0.01	*0.0034*	*1.5*	*0.0022*	0.26	0.4464	200.3	0.2885
0.02	*0.0095*	*4.3*	*0.0062*	0.27	0.4724	212.0	0.3053
0.03	*0.0175*	*7.9*	*0.0113*	0.28	0.4989	223.9	0.3224
0.04	*0.0269*	*12.1*	*0.0174*	0.29	0.5258	236.0	0.3398
0.05	*0.0376*	*16.9*	*0.0243*	0.30	0.5533	248.3	0.3576
0.06	*0.0495*	*22.2*	*0.0320*	0.31	0.5811	260.8	0.3756
0.07	*0.0624*	*28.0*	*0.0403*	0.32	0.6095	273.5	0.3939
0.08	*0.0762*	*34.2*	*0.0492*	0.33	0.6383	286.4	0.4125
0.09	*0.0909*	*40.8*	*0.0588*	0.34	0.6675	299.6	0.4314
0.10	*0.1065*	*47.8*	*0.0688*	0.35	0.6972	312.9	0.4506
0.11	*0.1228*	*55.1*	*0.0794*	0.36	0.7273	326.4	0.4700
0.12	*0.1400*	*62.8*	*0.0905*	0.37	0.7578	340.1	0.4897
0.13	*0.1578*	*70.8*	*0.1020*	0.38	0.7887	353.9	0.5097
0.14	*0.1764*	*79.2*	*0.1140*	0.39	0.8200	368.0	0.5300
0.15	*0.1956*	*87.8*	*0.1264*	0.40	0.8518	382.3	0.5505
0.16	*0.2155*	*96.7*	*0.1393*	0.41	0.8839	396.7	0.5713
0.17	*0.2360*	*105.9*	*0.1525*	0.42	0.9165	411.3	0.5923
0.18	*0.2571*	*115.4*	*0.1662*	0.43	0.9494	426.1	0.6136
0.19	*0.2789*	*125.2*	*0.1802*	0.44	0.9827	441.0	0.6351
0.20	0.3012	135.1	0.1946	0.45	1.016	456.1	0.6569
0.21	0.3240	145.4	0.2094	0.46	1.050	471.4	0.6789
0.22	0.3474	155.9	0.2245	0.47	1.085	486.9	0.7011
0.23	0.3714	166.7	0.2400	0.48	1.120	502.5	0.7236
0.24	0.3959	177.7	0.2558	0.49	1.155	518.3	0.7464
0.25	0.4209	188.9	0.2720	0.50	1.190	534.2	0.7693

12

Table 12-2:
1¹/₂ ft. Cipolletti Weir Discharge Table with Head in Feet

Formula: $CFS = 5.051\ H^{1.5}$
$GPM = 2267\ H^{1.5}$
$MGD = 3.264\ H^{1.5}$
Where: H = head in feet

Values in italics indicate flow below the recommended range of this particular primary device.

Table 12-2				Table 12-2 (Continued)			
Head (feet)	CFS	GPM	MGD	Head (feet)	CFS	GPM	MGD
0.01	*0.0051*	*2.3*	*0.0033*	0.39	1.230	552.1	0.7950
0.02	*0.0143*	*6.4*	*0.0092*	0.40	1.278	573.5	0.8257
0.03	*0.0262*	*11.8*	*0.0170*	0.41	1.326	595.2	0.8569
0.04	*0.0404*	*18.1*	*0.0261*	0.42	1.375	617.1	0.8884
0.05	*0.0565*	*25.3*	*0.0365*	0.43	1.424	639.2	0.9203
0.06	*0.0742*	*33.3*	*0.0480*	0.44	1.474	661.7	0.9526
0.07	*0.0935*	*42.0*	*0.0605*	0.45	1.525	684.3	0.9853
0.08	*0.1143*	*51.3*	*0.0739*	0.46	1.576	707.3	1.018
0.09	*0.1364*	*61.2*	*0.0881*	0.47	1.628	730.5	1.052
0.10	*0.1597*	*71.7*	*0.1032*	0.48	1.680	753.9	1.085
0.11	*0.1843*	*82.7*	*0.1191*	0.49	1.732	777.6	1.120
0.12	*0.2099*	*94.2*	*0.1357*	0.50	1.786	801.5	1.154
0.13	*0.2367*	*106.3*	*0.1530*	0.51	1.840	825.7	1.189
0.14	*0.2646*	*118.7*	*0.1710*	0.52	1.894	850.1	1.224
0.15	*0.2934*	*131.7*	*0.1896*	0.53	1.949	874.7	1.259
0.16	*0.3232*	*145.1*	*0.2089*	0.54	2.004	899.6	1.295
0.17	*0.3540*	*158.9*	*0.2288*	0.55	2.060	924.7	1.331
0.18	*0.3857*	*173.1*	*0.2493*	0.56	2.117	950.0	1.368
0.19	*0.4183*	*187.7*	*0.2703*	0.57	2.174	975.6	1.405
0.20	0.4518	202.8	0.2919	0.58	2.231	1001	1.442
0.21	0.4861	218.2	0.3141	0.59	2.289	1027	1.479
0.22	0.5212	233.9	0.3368	0.60	2.347	1054	1.517
0.23	0.5571	250.1	0.3600	0.61	2.406	1080	1.555
0.24	0.5939	266.5	0.3838	0.62	2.466	1107	1.593
0.25	0.6314	283.4	0.4080	0.63	2.526	1134	1.632
0.26	0.6696	300.5	0.4327	0.64	2.586	1161	1.671
0.27	0.7086	318.1	0.4579	0.65	2.647	1188	1.710
0.28	0.7484	335.9	0.4836	0.66	2.708	1216	1.750
0.29	0.7888	354.0	0.5097	0.67	2.770	1243	1.790
0.30	0.8300	372.5	0.5363	0.68	2.832	1271	1.830
0.31	0.8718	391.3	0.5634	0.69	2.895	1299	1.871
0.32	0.9143	410.4	0.5908	0.70	2.958	1328	1.912
0.33	0.9575	429.8	0.6188	0.71	3.022	1356	1.953
0.34	1.001	449.4	0.6471	0.72	3.086	1385	1.994
0.35	1.046	469.4	0.6759	0.73	3.150	1414	2.036
0.36	1.091	489.7	0.7050	0.74	3.215	1443	2.078
0.37	1.137	510.2	0.7346	0.75	3.281	1472	2.120
0.38	1.183	531.0	0.7646				

12

Table 12-3:
2 ft. Cipolletti Weir Discharge Table with Head in Feet

Formula: $\text{CFS} = 6.734\ H^{1.5}$
$\text{GPM} = 3022\ H^{1.5}$
$\text{MGD} = 4.352\ H^{1.5}$
Where: $H = \text{head in feet}$

Values in italics indicate flow below the recommended range of this particular primary device.

Table 12-3				Table 12-3 (Continued)			
Head (feet)	CFS	GPM	MGD	Head (feet)	CFS	GPM	MGD
0.01	*0.0067*	*3.0*	*0.0044*	0.51	2.453	1101	1.585
0.02	*0.0190*	*8.5*	*0.0123*	0.52	2.525	1133	1.632
0.03	*0.0350*	*15.7*	*0.0226*	0.53	2.598	1166	1.679
0.04	*0.0539*	*24.2*	*0.0348*	0.54	2.672	1199	1.727
0.05	*0.0753*	*33.8*	*0.0487*	0.55	2.747	1233	1.775
0.06	*0.0990*	*44.4*	*0.0640*	0.56	2.822	1266	1.824
0.07	*0.1247*	*56.0*	*0.0806*	0.57	2.898	1300	1.873
0.08	*0.1524*	*68.4*	*0.0985*	0.58	2.975	1335	1.922
0.09	*0.1818*	*81.6*	*0.1175*	0.59	3.052	1370	1.972
0.10	*0.2129*	*95.6*	*0.1376*	0.60	3.130	1404	2.023
0.11	*0.2457*	*110.3*	*0.1588*	0.61	3.208	1440	2.073
0.12	*0.2799*	*125.6*	*0.1809*	0.62	3.287	1475	2.125
0.13	*0.3156*	*141.7*	*0.2040*	0.63	3.367	1511	2.176
0.14	*0.3527*	*158.3*	*0.2280*	0.64	3.448	1547	2.228
0.15	*0.3912*	*175.6*	*0.2528*	0.65	3.529	1584	2.281
0.16	*0.4310*	*193.4*	*0.2785*	0.66	3.611	1620	2.333
0.17	*0.4720*	*211.9*	*0.3051*	0.67	3.693	1657	2.387
0.18	*0.5143*	*230.8*	*0.3324*	0.68	3.776	1695	2.440
0.19	*0.5577*	*250.3*	*0.3605*	0.69	3.860	1732	2.494
0.20	0.6023	270.3	0.3893	0.70	3.944	1770	2.549
0.21	0.6480	290.8	0.4188	0.71	4.029	1808	2.604
0.22	0.6949	311.8	0.4491	0.72	4.114	1846	2.659
0.23	0.7428	333.3	0.4800	0.73	4.200	1885	2.714
0.24	0.7918	355.3	0.5117	0.74	4.287	1924	2.770
0.25	0.8418	377.8	0.5440	0.75	4.374	1963	2.827
0.26	0.8928	400.6	0.5770	0.76	4.462	2002	2.883
0.27	0.9448	424.0	0.6106	0.77	4.550	2042	2.941
0.28	0.9977	447.7	0.6448	0.78	4.639	2082	2.998
0.29	1.052	471.9	0.6797	0.79	4.728	2122	3.056
0.30	1.107	496.6	0.7151	0.80	4.818	2162	3.114
0.31	1.162	521.6	0.7512	0.81	4.909	2203	3.173
0.32	1.219	547.0	0.7878	0.82	5.000	2244	3.232
0.33	1.277	572.9	0.8250	0.83	5.092	2285	3.291
0.34	1.335	599.1	0.8628	0.84	5.184	2327	3.350
0.35	1.394	625.7	0.9011	0.85	5.277	2368	3.410
0.36	1.455	652.8	0.9400	0.86	5.371	2410	3.471
0.37	1.516	680.1	0.9795	0.87	5.465	2452	3.532
0.38	1.577	707.9	1.019	0.88	5.559	2495	3.593
0.39	1.640	736.0	1.060	0.89	5.654	2537	3.654
0.40	1.704	764.5	1.101	0.90	5.750	2580	3.716
0.41	1.768	793.4	1.143	0.91	5.846	2623	3.778
0.42	1.833	822.6	1.185	0.92	5.942	2667	3.840
0.43	1.899	852.1	1.227	0.93	6.039	2710	3.903
0.44	1.965	882.0	1.270	0.94	6.137	2754	3.966
0.45	2.033	912.2	1.314	0.95	6.235	2798	4.030
0.46	2.101	942.8	1.358	0.96	6.334	2843	4.094
0.47	2.170	973.7	1.402	0.97	6.433	2887	4.158
0.48	2.239	1005	1.447	0.98	6.533	2932	4.222
0.49	2.310	1037	1.493	0.99	6.633	2977	4.287
0.50	2.381	1068	1.539	1.00	6.734	3022	4.352

12

Table 12-4:
2¹/₂ ft. Cipolletti Weir Discharge Table with Head in Feet

Formula: $CFS = 8.418\ H^{1.5}$
$GPM = 3778\ H^{1.5}$
$MGD = 5.440\ H^{1.5}$
Where: H = head in feet

Values in italics indicate flow below the recommended range of this particular primary device.

Table 12-4				Table 12-4 (Continued)			
Head (feet)	CFS	GPM	MGD	Head (feet)	CFS	GPM	MGD
0.01	*0.0084*	*3.8*	*0.0054*	0.51	3.066	1376	1.981
0.02	*0.0238*	*10.7*	*0.0154*	0.52	3.157	1417	2.040
0.03	*0.0437*	*19.6*	*0.0283*	0.53	3.248	1458	2.099
0.04	*0.0673*	*30.2*	*0.0435*	0.54	3.340	1499	2.159
0.05	*0.0941*	*42.2*	*0.0608*	0.55	3.434	1541	2.219
0.06	*0.1237*	*55.5*	*0.0800*	0.56	3.528	1583	2.280
0.07	*0.1559*	*70.0*	*0.1008*	0.57	3.623	1626	2.341
0.08	*0.1905*	*85.5*	*0.1231*	0.58	3.718	1669	2.403
0.09	*0.2273*	*102.0*	*0.1469*	0.59	3.815	1712	2.465
0.10	*0.2662*	*119.5*	*0.1720*	0.60	3.912	1756	2.528
0.11	*0.3071*	*137.8*	*0.1985*	0.61	4.011	1800	2.592
0.12	*0.3499*	*157.1*	*0.2262*	0.62	4.110	1844	2.656
0.13	*0.3945*	*177.1*	*0.2550*	0.63	4.209	1889	2.720
0.14	*0.4409*	*197.9*	*0.2850*	0.64	4.310	1934	2.785
0.15	*0.4890*	*219.5*	*0.3161*	0.65	4.411	1980	2.851
0.16	*0.5387*	*241.8*	*0.3482*	0.66	4.514	2026	2.917
0.17	*0.5900*	*264.8*	*0.3813*	0.67	4.617	2072	2.983
0.18	*0.6428*	*288.5*	*0.4155*	0.68	4.720	2118	3.050
0.19	*0.6971*	*312.9*	*0.4506*	0.69	4.825	2165	3.118
0.20	0.7529	337.9	0.4866	0.70	4.930	2213	3.186
0.21	0.8101	363.6	0.5235	0.71	5.036	2260	3.255
0.22	0.8686	389.8	0.5613	0.72	5.143	2308	3.324
0.23	0.9285	416.7	0.6001	0.73	5.250	2356	3.393
0.24	0.9898	444.2	0.6396	0.74	5.359	2405	3.463
0.25	1.052	472.3	0.6800	0.75	5.468	2454	3.533
0.26	1.116	500.9	0.7212	0.76	5.577	2503	3.604
0.27	1.181	530.0	0.7632	0.77	5.688	2553	3.676
0.28	1.247	559.8	0.8060	0.78	5.799	2603	3.747
0.29	1.315	590.0	0.8496	0.79	5.911	2653	3.820
0.30	1.383	620.8	0.8939	0.80	6.023	2703	3.893
0.31	1.453	652.1	0.9389	0.81	6.137	2754	3.966
0.32	1.524	683.9	0.9847	0.82	6.251	2805	4.039
0.33	1.596	716.2	1.031	0.83	6.365	2857	4.114
0.34	1.669	749.0	1.078	0.84	6.481	2909	4.188
0.35	1.743	782.3	1.126	0.85	6.597	2961	4.263
0.36	1.818	816.0	1.175	0.86	6.714	3013	4.339
0.37	1.895	850.3	1.224	0.87	6.831	3066	4.414
0.38	1.972	885.0	1.274	0.88	6.949	3119	4.491
0.39	2.050	920.2	1.325	0.89	7.068	3172	4.568
0.40	2.130	955.8	1.376	0.90	7.187	3226	4.645
0.41	2.210	991.8	1.428	0.91	7.308	3280	4.722
0.42	2.291	1028	1.481	0.92	7.428	3334	4.800
0.43	2.374	1065	1.534	0.93	7.550	3388	4.879
0.44	2.457	1103	1.588	0.94	7.672	3443	4.958
0.45	2.541	1140	1.642	0.95	7.795	3498	5.037
0.46	2.626	1179	1.697	0.96	7.918	3554	5.117
0.47	2.712	1217	1.753	0.97	8.042	3609	5.197
0.48	2.799	1256	1.809	0.98	8.167	3665	5.278
0.49	2.887	1296	1.866	0.99	8.292	3721	5.359
0.50	2.976	1336	1.923	1.00	8.418	3778	5.440

12

Table 12-4 (Continued)			
Head (feet)	CFS	GPM	MGD
1.01	8.545	3835	5.522
1.02	8.672	3892	5.604
1.03	8.800	3949	5.687
1.04	8.928	4007	5.770
1.05	9.057	4065	5.853
1.06	9.187	4123	5.937
1.07	9.317	4182	6.021
1.08	9.448	4240	6.106
1.09	9.580	4299	6.191
1.10	9.712	4359	6.276
1.11	9.844	4418	6.362
1.12	9.978	4478	6.448
1.13	10.11	4538	6.535

Table 12-4 (Continued)			
Head (feet)	CFS	GPM	MGD
1.14	10.25	4599	6.621
1.15	10.38	4659	6.709
1.16	10.52	4720	6.797
1.17	10.65	4781	6.885
1.18	10.79	4843	6.973
1.19	10.93	4904	7.062
1.20	11.07	4966	7.151
1.21	11.20	5029	7.241
1.22	11.34	5091	7.331
1.23	11.48	5154	7.421
1.24	11.62	5217	7.512
1.25	11.76	5280	7.603

12

Table 12-5:
3 ft. Cipolletti Weir Discharge Table with Head in Feet

Formula:
$$CFS = 10.10\ H^{1.5}$$
$$GPM = 4533\ H^{1.5}$$
$$MGD = 6.528\ H^{1.5}$$
Where: H = head in feet

Values in italics indicate flow below the recommended range of this particular primary device.

Head (feet)	CFS	GPM	MGD	Head (feet)	CFS	GPM	MGD
0.01	*0.0101*	*4.5*	*0.0065*	0.51	3.679	1651	2.378
0.02	*0.0286*	*12.8*	*0.0185*	0.52	3.787	1700	2.448
0.03	*0.0525*	*23.6*	*0.0339*	0.53	3.897	1749	2.519
0.04	*0.0808*	*36.3*	*0.0522*	0.54	4.008	1799	2.590
0.05	*0.1129*	*50.7*	*0.0730*	0.55	4.120	1849	2.663
0.06	*0.1485*	*66.6*	*0.0959*	0.56	4.233	1900	2.736
0.07	*0.1871*	*84.0*	*0.1209*	0.57	4.346	1951	2.809
0.08	*0.2286*	*102.6*	*0.1477*	0.58	4.461	2002	2.884
0.09	*0.2727*	*122.4*	*0.1763*	0.59	4.577	2054	2.958
0.10	*0.3194*	*143.4*	*0.2064*	0.60	4.694	2107	3.034
0.11	*0.3685*	*165.4*	*0.2382*	0.61	4.812	2160	3.110
0.12	*0.4199*	*188.5*	*0.2714*	0.62	4.931	2213	3.187
0.13	*0.4735*	*212.5*	*0.3060*	0.63	5.050	2267	3.264
0.14	*0.5291*	*237.5*	*0.3420*	0.64	5.171	2321	3.342
0.15	*0.5868*	*263.4*	*0.3793*	0.65	5.293	2376	3.421
0.16	*0.6465*	*290.2*	*0.4178*	0.66	5.415	2431	3.500
0.17	*0.7080*	*317.8*	*0.4576*	0.67	5.539	2486	3.580
0.18	*0.7714*	*346.2*	*0.4986*	0.68	5.663	2542	3.661
0.19	*0.8366*	*375.5*	*0.5407*	0.69	5.789	2598	3.742
0.20	0.9034	405.4	0.5839	0.70	5.915	2655	3.823
0.21	0.9720	436.2	0.6282	0.71	6.042	2712	3.905
0.22	1.042	467.8	0.6736	0.72	6.170	2769	3.988
0.23	1.114	500.0	0.7201	0.73	6.299	2827	4.072
0.24	1.188	533.0	0.7675	0.74	6.429	2886	4.156
0.25	1.263	566.6	0.8160	0.75	6.560	2944	4.240
0.26	1.339	601.0	0.8654	0.76	6.692	3003	4.325
0.27	1.417	636.0	0.9159	0.77	6.824	3063	4.411
0.28	1.496	671.6	0.9672	0.78	6.958	3123	4.497
0.29	1.577	707.9	1.019	0.79	7.092	3183	4.584
0.30	1.660	744.8	1.073	0.80	7.227	3244	4.671
0.31	1.743	782.4	1.127	0.81	7.363	3305	4.759
0.32	1.828	820.6	1.182	0.82	7.500	3366	4.847
0.33	1.915	859.3	1.238	0.83	7.637	3428	4.936
0.34	2.002	898.7	1.294	0.84	7.776	3490	5.026
0.35	2.091	938.6	1.352	0.85	7.915	3552	5.116
0.36	2.182	979.1	1.410	0.86	8.055	3615	5.206
0.37	2.273	1020	1.469	0.87	8.196	3678	5.297
0.38	2.366	1062	1.529	0.88	8.338	3742	5.389
0.39	2.460	1104	1.590	0.89	8.480	3806	5.481
0.40	2.555	1147	1.651	0.90	8.624	3870	5.574
0.41	2.652	1190	1.714	0.91	8.768	3935	5.667
0.42	2.749	1234	1.777	0.92	8.913	4000	5.761
0.43	2.848	1278	1.841	0.93	9.058	4065	5.855
0.44	2.948	1323	1.905	0.94	9.205	4131	5.949
0.45	3.049	1368	1.971	0.95	9.352	4197	6.045
0.46	3.151	1414	2.037	0.96	9.500	4264	6.140
0.47	3.254	1461	2.103	0.97	9.649	4331	6.236
0.48	3.359	1507	2.171	0.98	9.799	4398	6.333
0.49	3.464	1555	2.239	0.99	9.949	4465	6.430
0.50	3.571	1603	2.308	1.00	10.10	4533	6.528

12

Table 12-5 (Continued)				Table 12-5 (Continued)			
Head (feet)	CFS	GPM	MGD	Head (feet)	CFS	GPM	MGD
1.01	10.25	4601	6.626	1.26	14.28	6411	9.233
1.02	10.40	4670	6.725	1.27	14.46	6488	9.343
1.03	10.56	4739	6.824	1.28	14.63	6564	9.454
1.04	10.71	4808	6.924	1.29	14.80	6642	9.565
1.05	10.87	4877	7.024	1.30	14.97	6719	9.676
1.06	11.02	4947	7.124	1.31	15.14	6797	9.788
1.07	11.18	5017	7.225	1.32	15.32	6875	9.900
1.08	11.34	5088	7.327	1.33	15.49	6953	10.01
1.09	11.49	5159	7.429	1.34	15.67	7031	10.13
1.10	11.65	5230	7.531	1.35	15.84	7110	10.24
1.11	11.81	5301	7.634	1.36	16.02	7189	10.35
1.12	11.97	5373	7.738	1.37	16.20	7269	10.47
1.13	12.13	5445	7.841	1.38	16.37	7349	10.58
1.14	12.29	5518	7.946	1.39	16.55	7429	10.70
1.15	12.46	5590	8.051	1.40	16.73	7509	10.81
1.16	12.62	5663	8.156	1.41	16.91	7590	10.93
1.17	12.78	5737	8.262	1.42	17.09	7670	11.05
1.18	12.95	5810	8.368	1.43	17.27	7752	11.16
1.19	13.11	5884	8.474	1.44	17.45	7833	11.28
1.20	13.28	5959	8.581	1.45	17.63	7915	11.40
1.21	13.44	6033	8.689	1.46	17.82	7997	11.52
1.22	13.61	6108	8.797	1.47	18.00	8079	11.63
1.23	13.78	6184	8.905	1.48	18.19	8162	11.75
1.24	13.95	6259	9.014	1.49	18.37	8245	11.87
1.25	14.12	6335	9.123	1.50	18.55	8328	11.99

12

Table 12-6:
4 ft. Cipolletti Weir Discharge Table with Head in Feet

Formula: CFS $= 13.47\ H^{1.5}$
GPM $= 6044\ H^{1.5}$
MGD $= 8.704\ H^{1.5}$
Where: H = head in feet

Values in italics indicate flow below the recommended range of this particular primary device.

Table 12-6				Table 12-6 (Continued)			
Head (feet)	CFS	GPM	MGD	Head (feet)	CFS	GPM	MGD
0.01	*0.013*	*6.0*	*0.0087*	0.51	4.906	2201	3.170
0.02	*0.038*	*17.1*	*0.0246*	0.52	5.051	2266	3.264
0.03	*0.070*	*31.4*	*0.0452*	0.53	5.197	2332	3.358
0.04	*0.108*	*48.4*	*0.0696*	0.54	5.345	2398	3.454
0.05	*0.151*	*67.6*	*0.0973*	0.55	5.494	2465	3.550
0.06	*0.198*	*88.8*	*0.1279*	0.56	5.645	2533	3.648
0.07	*0.249*	*112.0*	*0.1612*	0.57	5.797	2601	3.746
0.08	*0.305*	*136.8*	*0.1970*	0.58	5.950	2670	3.845
0.09	*0.364*	*163.2*	*0.2350*	0.59	6.104	2739	3.945
0.10	*0.426*	*191.2*	*0.2753*	0.60	6.260	2809	4.045
0.11	*0.491*	*220.5*	*0.3176*	0.61	6.417	2880	4.147
0.12	*0.560*	*251.3*	*0.3618*	0.62	6.576	2951	4.249
0.13	*0.631*	*283.3*	*0.4080*	0.63	6.736	3022	4.352
0.14	*0.705*	*316.6*	*0.4560*	0.64	6.897	3095	4.456
0.15	*0.782*	*351.2*	*0.5057*	0.65	7.059	3167	4.561
0.16	*0.862*	*386.9*	*0.5571*	0.66	7.222	3241	4.667
0.17	*0.944*	*423.7*	*0.6101*	0.67	7.387	3315	4.773
0.18	*1.029*	*461.6*	*0.6647*	0.68	7.553	3389	4.881
0.19	*1.115*	*500.6*	*0.7209*	0.69	7.720	3464	4.989
0.20	1.205	540.6	0.7785	0.70	7.889	3540	5.098
0.21	1.296	581.6	0.8376	0.71	8.059	3616	5.207
0.22	1.390	623.7	0.8982	0.72	8.229	3693	5.318
0.23	1.486	666.7	0.9601	0.73	8.401	3770	5.429
0.24	1.584	710.6	1.023	0.74	8.575	3847	5.541
0.25	1.684	755.5	1.088	0.75	8.749	3926	5.653
0.26	1.786	801.3	1.154	0.76	8.925	4004	5.767
0.27	1.890	847.9	1.221	0.77	9.101	4084	5.881
0.28	1.996	895.5	1.290	0.78	9.279	4164	5.996
0.29	2.104	943.9	1.359	0.79	9.458	4244	6.112
0.30	2.213	993.1	1.430	0.80	9.638	4325	6.228
0.31	2.325	1043	1.502	0.81	9.820	4406	6.345
0.32	2.438	1094	1.576	0.82	10.00	4488	6.463
0.33	2.554	1146	1.650	0.83	10.19	4570	6.582
0.34	2.670	1198	1.726	0.84	10.37	4653	6.701
0.35	2.789	1251	1.802	0.85	10.56	4736	6.821
0.36	2.910	1306	1.880	0.86	10.74	4820	6.942
0.37	3.032	1360	1.959	0.87	10.93	4905	7.063
0.38	3.155	1416	2.039	0.88	11.12	4989	7.185
0.39	3.281	1472	2.120	0.89	11.31	5075	7.308
0.40	3.408	1529	2.202	0.90	11.50	5160	7.432
0.41	3.536	1587	2.285	0.91	11.69	5247	7.556
0.42	3.666	1645	2.369	0.92	11.89	5333	7.681
0.43	3.798	1704	2.454	0.93	12.08	5421	7.806
0.44	3.931	1764	2.540	0.94	12.28	5508	7.933
0.45	4.066	1824	2.627	0.95	12.47	5596	8.059
0.46	4.202	1886	2.716	0.96	12.67	5685	8.187
0.47	4.340	1947	2.805	0.97	12.87	5774	8.315
0.48	4.479	2010	2.895	0.98	13.07	5864	8.444
0.49	4.620	2073	2.985	0.99	13.27	5954	8.574
0.50	4.762	2137	3.077	1.00	13.47	6044	8.704

12

Table 12-6 (Continued)				Table 12-6 (Continued)			
Head (feet)	CFS	GPM	MGD	Head (feet)	CFS	GPM	MGD
1.01	13.67	6135	8.835	1.51	24.99	11,210	16.15
1.02	13.88	6226	8.966	1.52	25.24	11,330	16.31
1.03	14.08	6318	9.099	1.53	25.49	11,440	16.47
1.04	14.29	6410	9.231	1.54	25.74	11,550	16.63
1.05	14.49	6503	9.365	1.55	25.99	11,660	16.80
1.06	14.70	6596	9.499	1.56	26.25	11,780	16.96
1.07	14.91	6690	9.634	1.57	26.50	11,890	17.12
1.08	15.12	6784	9.769	1.58	26.75	12,000	17.29
1.09	15.33	6878	9.905	1.59	27.01	12,120	17.45
1.10	15.54	6973	10.04	1.60	27.26	12,230	17.62
1.11	15.75	7068	10.18	1.61	27.52	12,350	17.78
1.12	15.97	7164	10.32	1.62	27.77	12,460	17.95
1.13	16.18	7260	10.46	1.63	28.03	12,580	18.11
1.14	16.40	7357	10.59	1.64	28.29	12,690	18.28
1.15	16.61	7454	10.73	1.65	28.55	12,810	18.45
1.16	16.83	7551	10.87	1.66	28.81	12,930	18.62
1.17	17.05	7649	11.02	1.67	29.07	13,040	18.78
1.18	17.27	7747	11.16	1.68	29.33	13,160	18.95
1.19	17.49	7846	11.30	1.69	29.59	13,280	19.12
1.20	17.71	7945	11.44	1.70	29.86	13,400	19.29
1.21	17.93	8045	11.59	1.71	30.12	13,520	19.46
1.22	18.15	8144	11.73	1.72	30.39	13,630	19.63
1.23	18.37	8245	11.87	1.73	30.65	13,750	19.81
1.24	18.60	8346	12.02	1.74	30.92	13,870	19.98
1.25	18.82	8447	12.16	1.75	31.18	13,990	20.15
1.26	19.05	8548	12.31	1.76	31.45	14,110	20.32
1.27	19.28	8650	12.46	1.77	31.72	14,230	20.50
1.28	19.51	8753	12.60	1.78	31.99	14,350	20.67
1.29	19.74	8855	12.75	1.79	32.26	14,470	20.84
1.30	19.97	8959	12.90	1.80	32.53	14,600	21.02
1.31	20.20	9062	13.05	1.81	32.80	14,720	21.20
1.32	20.43	9166	13.20	1.82	33.07	14,840	21.37
1.33	20.66	9270	13.35	1.83	33.35	14,960	21.55
1.34	20.89	9375	13.50	1.84	33.62	15,090	21.72
1.35	21.13	9480	13.65	1.85	33.89	15,210	21.90
1.36	21.36	9586	13.80	1.86	34.17	15,330	22.08
1.37	21.60	9692	13.96	1.87	34.45	15,460	22.26
1.38	21.84	9798	14.11	1.88	34.72	15,580	22.44
1.39	22.07	9905	14.26	1.89	35.00	15,700	22.62
1.40	22.31	10,010	14.42	1.90	35.28	15,830	22.80
1.41	22.55	10,120	14.57	1.91	35.56	15,950	22.98
1.42	22.79	10,230	14.73	1.92	35.84	16,080	23.16
1.43	23.03	10,340	14.88	1.93	36.12	16,210	23.34
1.44	23.28	10,440	15.04	1.94	36.40	16,330	23.52
1.45	23.52	10,550	15.20	1.95	36.68	16,460	23.70
1.46	23.76	10,660	15.35	1.96	36.96	16,580	23.88
1.47	24.01	10,770	15.51	1.97	37.24	16,710	24.07
1.48	24.25	10,880	15.67	1.98	37.53	16,840	24.25
1.49	24.50	10,990	15.83	1.99	37.81	16,970	24.43
1.50	24.75	11,100	15.99	2.00	38.10	17,100	24.62

Table 12-7:
5 ft. Cipolletti Weir Discharge Table with Head in Feet

Formula: $CFS = 16.84\, H^{1.5}$
$GPM = 7556\, H^{1.5}$
$MGD = 10.88\, H^{1.5}$
Where: H = head in feet

Values in italics indicate flow below the recommended range of this particular primary device.

Table 12-7				Table 12-7 (Continued)			
Head (feet)	CFS	GPM	MGD	Head (feet)	CFS	GPM	MGD
0.01	*0.017*	*7.6*	*0.0109*	0.51	6.133	2752	3.963
0.02	*0.048*	*21.4*	*0.0308*	0.52	6.315	2833	4.080
0.03	*0.087*	*39.3*	*0.0565*	0.53	6.498	2915	4.198
0.04	*0.135*	*60.4*	*0.0870*	0.54	6.682	2998	4.317
0.05	*0.188*	*84.5*	*0.1217*	0.55	6.869	3082	4.438
0.06	*0.247*	*111.1*	*0.1599*	0.56	7.057	3166	4.559
0.07	*0.312*	*139.9*	*0.2015*	0.57	7.247	3252	4.682
0.08	*0.381*	*171.0*	*0.2462*	0.58	7.438	3338	4.806
0.09	*0.455*	*204.0*	*0.2938*	0.59	7.632	3424	4.931
0.10	*0.532*	*238.9*	*0.3441*	0.60	7.827	3512	5.057
0.11	*0.614*	*275.7*	*0.3970*	0.61	8.023	3600	5.184
0.12	*0.700*	*314.1*	*0.4523*	0.62	8.221	3689	5.311
0.13	*0.789*	*354.2*	*0.5100*	0.63	8.421	3778	5.441
0.14	*0.882*	*395.8*	*0.5700*	0.64	8.622	3869	5.571
0.15	*0.978*	*439.0*	*0.6321*	0.65	8.825	3960	5.702
0.16	*1.077*	*483.6*	*0.6964*	0.66	9.029	4051	5.834
0.17	*1.180*	*529.6*	*0.7627*	0.67	9.235	4144	5.967
0.18	*1.286*	*577.0*	*0.8309*	0.68	9.443	4237	6.101
0.19	*1.394*	*625.8*	*0.9011*	0.69	9.652	4331	6.236
0.20	1.506	675.8	0.9731	0.70	9.863	4425	6.372
0.21	1.621	727.1	1.047	0.71	10.07	4520	6.509
0.22	1.738	779.7	1.123	0.72	10.29	4616	6.647
0.23	1.858	833.5	1.200	0.73	10.50	4713	6.786
0.24	1.980	888.4	1.279	0.74	10.72	4810	6.926
0.25	2.105	944.5	1.360	0.75	10.94	4908	7.067
0.26	2.233	1002	1.442	0.76	11.16	5006	7.209
0.27	2.363	1060	1.526	0.77	11.38	5105	7.351
0.28	2.495	1120	1.612	0.78	11.60	5205	7.495
0.29	2.630	1180	1.699	0.79	11.82	5306	7.640
0.30	2.767	1242	1.788	0.80	12.05	5407	7.785
0.31	2.907	1304	1.878	0.81	12.28	5508	7.932
0.32	3.048	1368	1.969	0.82	12.50	5611	8.079
0.33	3.192	1432	2.063	0.83	12.73	5714	8.227
0.34	3.339	1498	2.157	0.84	12.96	5817	8.376
0.35	3.487	1565	2.253	0.85	13.20	5921	8.526
0.36	3.637	1632	2.350	0.86	13.43	6026	8.677
0.37	3.790	1701	2.449	0.87	13.67	6132	8.829
0.38	3.945	1770	2.549	0.88	13.90	6238	8.982
0.39	4.101	1840	2.650	0.89	14.14	6344	9.135
0.40	4.260	1912	2.752	0.90	14.38	6451	9.290
0.41	4.421	1984	2.856	0.91	14.62	6559	9.445
0.42	4.584	2057	2.961	0.92	14.86	6668	9.601
0.43	4.748	2131	3.068	0.93	15.10	6777	9.758
0.44	4.915	2205	3.175	0.94	15.35	6886	9.916
0.45	5.083	2281	3.284	0.95	15.59	6996	10.07
0.46	5.254	2357	3.394	0.96	15.84	7107	10.23
0.47	5.426	2435	3.506	0.97	16.09	7219	10.39
0.48	5.600	2513	3.618	0.98	16.34	7330	10.56
0.49	5.776	2592	3.732	0.99	16.59	7443	10.72
0.50	5.954	2671	3.847	1.00	16.84	7556	10.88

12

Table 12-7 (Continued)				Table 12-7 (Continued)			
Head (feet)	CFS	GPM	MGD	Head (feet)	CFS	GPM	MGD
1.01	17.09	7670	11.04	1.51	31.25	14,020	20.19
1.02	17.35	7784	11.21	1.52	31.56	14,160	20.39
1.03	17.60	7899	11.37	1.53	31.87	14,300	20.59
1.04	17.86	8014	11.54	1.54	32.18	14,440	20.79
1.05	18.12	8130	11.71	1.55	32.50	14,580	21.00
1.06	18.38	8246	11.87	1.56	32.81	14,720	21.20
1.07	18.64	8363	12.04	1.57	33.13	14,860	21.40
1.08	18.90	8481	12.21	1.58	33.44	15,010	21.61
1.09	19.16	8599	12.38	1.59	33.76	15,150	21.81
1.10	19.43	8717	12.55	1.60	34.08	15,290	22.02
1.11	19.69	8836	12.72	1.61	34.40	15,440	22.23
1.12	19.96	8956	12.90	1.62	34.72	15,580	22.43
1.13	20.23	9076	13.07	1.63	35.04	15,720	22.64
1.14	20.50	9197	13.24	1.64	35.37	15,870	22.85
1.15	20.77	9318	13.42	1.65	35.69	16,010	23.06
1.16	21.04	9440	13.59	1.66	36.02	16,160	23.27
1.17	21.31	9562	13.77	1.67	36.34	16,310	23.48
1.18	21.59	9685	13.95	1.68	36.67	16,450	23.69
1.19	21.86	9809	14.12	1.69	37.00	16,600	23.90
1.20	22.14	9933	14.30	1.70	37.33	16,750	24.12
1.21	22.41	10,060	14.48	1.71	37.66	16,900	24.33
1.22	22.69	10,180	14.66	1.72	37.99	17,040	24.54
1.23	22.97	10,310	14.84	1.73	38.32	17,190	24.76
1.24	23.25	10,430	15.02	1.74	38.65	17,340	24.97
1.25	23.53	10,560	15.21	1.75	38.99	17,490	25.19
1.26	23.82	10,690	15.39	1.76	39.32	17,640	25.40
1.27	24.10	10,810	15.57	1.77	39.66	17,790	25.62
1.28	24.39	10,940	15.76	1.78	39.99	17,940	25.84
1.29	24.67	11,070	15.94	1.79	40.33	18,100	26.06
1.30	24.96	11,200	16.13	1.80	40.67	18,250	26.27
1.31	25.25	11,330	16.31	1.81	41.01	18,400	26.49
1.32	25.54	11,460	16.50	1.82	41.35	18,550	26.71
1.33	25.83	11,590	16.69	1.83	41.69	18,710	26.93
1.34	26.12	11,720	16.88	1.84	42.03	18,860	27.16
1.35	26.41	11,850	17.07	1.85	42.37	19,010	27.38
1.36	26.71	11,980	17.26	1.86	42.72	19,170	27.60
1.37	27.00	12,120	17.45	1.87	43.06	19,320	27.82
1.38	27.30	12,250	17.64	1.88	43.41	19,480	28.05
1.39	27.60	12,380	17.83	1.89	43.76	19,630	28.27
1.40	27.90	12,520	18.02	1.90	44.10	19,790	28.49
1.41	28.19	12,650	18.22	1.91	44.45	19,950	28.72
1.42	28.50	12,790	18.41	1.92	44.80	20,100	28.95
1.43	28.80	12,920	18.61	1.93	45.15	20,260	29.17
1.44	29.10	13,060	18.80	1.94	45.50	20,420	29.40
1.45	29.40	13,190	19.00	1.95	45.86	20,580	29.63
1.46	29.71	13,330	19.19	1.96	46.21	20,730	29.85
1.47	30.01	13,470	19.39	1.97	46.56	20,890	30.08
1.48	30.32	13,600	19.59	1.98	46.92	21,050	30.31
1.49	30.63	13,740	19.79	1.99	47.27	21,210	30.54
1.50	30.94	13,880	19.99	2.00	47.63	21,370	30.77

12

Table 12-7 (Continued)			
Head (feet)	CFS	GPM	MGD
2.01	47.99	21,530	31.00
2.02	48.35	21,690	31.24
2.03	48.71	21,850	31.47
2.04	49.07	22,020	31.70
2.05	49.43	22,180	31.93
2.06	49.79	22,340	32.17
2.07	50.15	22,500	32.40
2.08	50.52	22,670	32.64
2.09	50.88	22,830	32.87
2.10	51.25	22,990	33.11
2.11	51.61	23,160	33.35
2.12	51.98	23,320	33.58
2.13	52.35	23,490	33.82
2.14	52.72	23,650	34.06
2.15	53.09	23,820	34.30
2.16	53.46	23,990	34.54
2.17	53.83	24,150	34.78
2.18	54.20	24,320	35.02
2.19	54.58	24,490	35.26
2.20	54.95	24,660	35.50
2.21	55.33	24,820	35.75
2.22	55.70	24,990	35.99
2.23	56.08	25,160	36.23
2.24	56.46	25,330	36.48
2.25	56.83	25,500	36.72

Table 12-7 (Continued)			
Head (feet)	CFS	GPM	MGD
2.26	57.21	25,670	36.97
2.27	57.59	25,840	37.21
2.28	57.98	26,010	37.46
2.29	58.36	26,180	37.70
2.30	58.74	26,360	37.95
2.31	59.12	26,530	38.20
2.32	59.51	26,700	38.45
2.33	59.89	26,870	38.70
2.34	60.28	27,050	38.95
2.35	60.67	27,220	39.20
2.36	61.05	27,390	39.45
2.37	61.44	27,570	39.70
2.38	61.83	27,740	39.95
2.39	62.22	27,920	40.20
2.40	62.61	28,090	40.45
2.41	63.00	28,270	40.71
2.42	63.40	28,450	40.96
2.43	63.79	28,620	41.21
2.44	64.18	28,800	41.47
2.45	64.58	28,980	41.72
2.46	64.97	29,150	41.98
2.47	65.37	29,330	42.24
2.48	65.77	29,510	42.49
2.49	66.17	29,690	42.75
2.50	66.57	29,870	43.01

12

Table 12-8:
6 ft. Cipolletti Weir Discharge Table with Head in Feet

Formula: $CFS = 20.20\,H^{1.5}$
$GPM = 9067\,H^{1.5}$
$MGD = 13.06\,H^{1.5}$
Where: H = head in feet

Values in italics indicate flow below the recommended range of this particular primary device.

Table 12-8				Table 12-8 (Continued)			
Head (feet)	CFS	GPM	MGD	Head (feet)	CFS	GPM	MGD
0.01	*0.020*	*9.1*	*0.013*	0.51	7.357	3302	4.757
0.02	*0.057*	*25.6*	*0.037*	0.52	7.575	3400	4.897
0.03	*0.105*	*47.1*	*0.068*	0.53	7.794	3498	5.039
0.04	*0.162*	*72.5*	*0.104*	0.54	8.016	3598	5.182
0.05	*0.226*	*101.4*	*0.146*	0.55	8.239	3698	5.327
0.06	*0.297*	*133.3*	*0.192*	0.56	8.465	3800	5.473
0.07	*0.374*	*167.9*	*0.242*	0.57	8.693	3902	5.620
0.08	*0.457*	*205.2*	*0.295*	0.58	8.923	4005	5.769
0.09	*0.545*	*244.8*	*0.353*	0.59	9.154	4109	5.919
0.10	*0.639*	*286.7*	*0.413*	0.60	9.388	4214	6.070
0.11	*0.737*	*330.8*	*0.476*	0.61	9.624	4320	6.222
0.12	*0.840*	*376.9*	*0.543*	0.62	9.861	4426	6.376
0.13	*0.947*	*425.0*	*0.612*	0.63	10.10	4534	6.531
0.14	*1.058*	*475.0*	*0.684*	0.64	10.34	4642	6.687
0.15	*1.174*	*526.8*	*0.759*	0.65	10.59	4752	6.844
0.16	*1.293*	*580.3*	*0.836*	0.66	10.83	4862	7.003
0.17	*1.416*	*635.6*	*0.915*	0.67	11.08	4973	7.162
0.18	*1.543*	*692.4*	*0.997*	0.68	11.33	5084	7.323
0.19	*1.673*	*750.9*	*1.081*	0.69	11.58	5197	7.485
0.20	1.807	811.0	1.168	0.70	11.83	5310	7.649
0.21	1.944	872.6	1.257	0.71	12.08	5424	7.813
0.22	2.084	935.6	1.348	0.72	12.34	5539	7.979
0.23	2.228	1000	1.441	0.73	12.60	5655	8.146
0.24	2.375	1066	1.536	0.74	12.86	5772	8.314
0.25	2.525	1133	1.633	0.75	13.12	5889	8.483
0.26	2.678	1202	1.731	0.76	13.38	6007	8.653
0.27	2.834	1272	1.832	0.77	13.65	6126	8.824
0.28	2.993	1343	1.935	0.78	13.92	6246	8.997
0.29	3.155	1416	2.040	0.79	14.18	6367	9.170
0.30	3.319	1490	2.146	0.80	14.45	6488	9.345
0.31	3.487	1565	2.254	0.81	14.73	6610	9.521
0.32	3.657	1641	2.364	0.82	15.00	6733	9.698
0.33	3.829	1719	2.476	0.83	15.27	6856	9.876
0.34	4.005	1798	2.589	0.84	15.55	6980	10.05
0.35	4.183	1877	2.704	0.85	15.83	7105	10.23
0.36	4.363	1958	2.821	0.86	16.11	7231	10.42
0.37	4.546	2041	2.939	0.87	16.39	7358	10.60
0.38	4.732	2124	3.059	0.88	16.68	7485	10.78
0.39	4.920	2208	3.181	0.89	16.96	7613	10.97
0.40	5.110	2294	3.304	0.90	17.25	7742	11.15
0.41	5.303	2380	3.429	0.91	17.54	7871	11.34
0.42	5.498	2468	3.555	0.92	17.83	8001	11.52
0.43	5.696	2557	3.683	0.93	18.12	8132	11.71
0.44	5.896	2646	3.812	0.94	18.41	8263	11.90
0.45	6.098	2737	3.942	0.95	18.70	8396	12.09
0.46	6.302	2829	4.075	0.96	19.00	8528	12.28
0.47	6.509	2922	4.208	0.97	19.30	8662	12.48
0.48	6.718	3015	4.343	0.98	19.60	8796	12.67
0.49	6.929	3110	4.480	0.99	19.90	8931	12.86
0.50	7.142	3206	4.617	1.00	20.20	9067	13.06

12

Table 12-8 (Continued)					Table 12-8 (Continued)			
Head (feet)	CFS	GPM	MGD		Head (feet)	CFS	GPM	MGD
1.01	20.50	9203	13.26		1.51	37.48	16,820	24.23
1.02	20.81	9340	13.45		1.52	37.85	16,990	24.47
1.03	21.12	9478	13.65		1.53	38.23	17,160	24.72
1.04	21.42	9616	13.85		1.54	38.60	17,330	24.96
1.05	21.73	9755	14.05		1.55	38.98	17,500	25.20
1.06	22.05	9895	14.25		1.56	39.36	17,670	25.45
1.07	22.36	10,040	14.46		1.57	39.74	17,840	25.69
1.08	22.67	10,180	14.66		1.58	40.12	18,010	25.94
1.09	22.99	10,320	14.86		1.59	40.50	18,180	26.18
1.10	23.30	10,460	15.07		1.60	40.88	18,350	26.43
1.11	23.62	10,600	15.27		1.61	41.27	18,520	26.68
1.12	23.94	10,750	15.48		1.62	41.65	18,700	26.93
1.13	24.26	10,890	15.69		1.63	42.04	18,870	27.18
1.14	24.59	11,040	15.90		1.64	42.42	19,040	27.43
1.15	24.91	11,180	16.11		1.65	42.81	19,220	27.68
1.16	25.24	11,330	16.32		1.66	43.20	19,390	27.93
1.17	25.56	11,470	16.53		1.67	43.59	19,570	28.18
1.18	25.89	11,620	16.74		1.68	43.99	19,740	28.44
1.19	26.22	11,770	16.95		1.69	44.38	19,920	28.69
1.20	26.55	11,920	17.17		1.70	44.77	20,100	28.95
1.21	26.89	12,070	17.38		1.71	45.17	20,270	29.20
1.22	27.22	12,220	17.60		1.72	45.57	20,450	29.46
1.23	27.56	12,370	17.82		1.73	45.96	20,630	29.72
1.24	27.89	12,520	18.03		1.74	46.36	20,810	29.98
1.25	28.23	12,670	18.25		1.75	46.76	20,990	30.23
1.26	28.57	12,820	18.47		1.76	47.17	21,170	30.49
1.27	28.91	12,980	18.69		1.77	47.57	21,350	30.75
1.28	29.25	13,130	18.91		1.78	47.97	21,530	31.02
1.29	29.60	13,280	19.13		1.79	48.38	21,710	31.28
1.30	29.94	13,440	19.36		1.80	48.78	21,900	31.54
1.31	30.29	13,590	19.58		1.81	49.19	22,080	31.80
1.32	30.63	13,750	19.81		1.82	49.60	22,260	32.07
1.33	30.98	13,910	20.03		1.83	50.01	22,450	32.33
1.34	31.33	14,060	20.26		1.84	50.42	22,630	32.60
1.35	31.68	14,220	20.49		1.85	50.83	22,820	32.86
1.36	32.04	14,380	20.71		1.86	51.24	23,000	33.13
1.37	32.39	14,540	20.94		1.87	51.66	23,190	33.40
1.38	32.75	14,700	21.17		1.88	52.07	23,370	33.67
1.39	33.10	14,860	21.40		1.89	52.49	23,560	33.93
1.40	33.46	15,020	21.63		1.90	52.90	23,750	34.20
1.41	33.82	15,180	21.87		1.91	53.32	23,930	34.47
1.42	34.18	15,340	22.10		1.92	53.74	24,120	34.75
1.43	34.54	15,500	22.33		1.93	54.16	24,310	35.02
1.44	34.91	15,670	22.57		1.94	54.58	24,500	35.29
1.45	35.27	15,830	22.80		1.95	55.01	24,690	35.56
1.46	35.64	16,000	23.04		1.96	55.43	24,880	35.84
1.47	36.00	16,160	23.28		1.97	55.85	25,070	36.11
1.48	36.37	16,330	23.51		1.98	56.28	25,260	36.39
1.49	36.74	16,490	23.75		1.99	56.71	25,450	36.66
1.50	37.11	16,660	23.99		2.00	57.13	25,650	36.94

12

Table 12-8 (Continued)					Table 12-8 (Continued)			
Head (feet)	CFS	GPM	MGD		Head (feet)	CFS	GPM	MGD
2.01	57.56	25,840	37.22		2.51	80.33	36,060	51.93
2.02	57.99	26,030	37.49		2.52	80.81	36,270	52.24
2.03	58.42	26,220	37.77		2.53	81.29	36,490	52.56
2.04	58.86	26,420	38.05		2.54	81.77	36,700	52.87
2.05	59.29	26,610	38.33		2.55	82.25	36,920	53.18
2.06	59.72	26,810	38.61		2.56	82.74	37,140	53.49
2.07	60.16	27,000	38.90		2.57	83.22	37,360	53.81
2.08	60.60	27,200	39.18		2.58	83.71	37,570	54.12
2.09	61.03	27,400	39.46		2.59	84.20	37,790	54.44
2.10	61.47	27,590	39.74		2.60	84.69	38,010	54.75
2.11	61.91	27,790	40.03		2.61	85.17	38,230	55.07
2.12	62.35	27,990	40.31		2.62	85.66	38,450	55.39
2.13	62.79	28,190	40.60		2.63	86.16	38,670	55.70
2.14	63.24	28,380	40.88		2.64	86.65	38,890	56.02
2.15	63.68	28,580	41.17		2.65	87.14	39,110	56.34
2.16	64.13	28,780	41.46		2.66	87.63	39,340	56.66
2.17	64.57	28,980	41.75		2.67	88.13	39,560	56.98
2.18	65.02	29,180	42.04		2.68	88.62	39,780	57.30
2.19	65.47	29,390	42.33		2.69	89.12	40,000	57.62
2.20	65.92	29,590	42.62		2.70	89.62	40,230	57.94
2.21	66.37	29,790	42.91		2.71	90.12	40,450	58.26
2.22	66.82	29,990	43.20		2.72	90.62	40,670	58.59
2.23	67.27	30,190	43.49		2.73	91.12	40,900	58.91
2.24	67.72	30,400	43.78		2.74	91.62	41,120	59.23
2.25	68.17	30,600	44.08		2.75	92.12	41,350	59.56
2.26	68.63	30,810	44.37		2.76	92.62	41,570	59.88
2.27	69.09	31,010	44.67		2.77	93.13	41,800	60.21
2.28	69.54	31,220	44.96		2.78	93.63	42,030	60.54
2.29	70.00	31,420	45.26		2.79	94.14	42,250	60.86
2.30	70.46	31,630	45.55		2.80	94.64	42,480	61.19
2.31	70.92	31,830	45.85		2.81	95.15	42,710	61.52
2.32	71.38	32,040	46.15		2.82	95.66	42,940	61.85
2.33	71.84	32,250	46.45		2.83	96.17	43,170	62.18
2.34	72.31	32,460	46.75		2.84	96.68	43,400	62.51
2.35	72.77	32,660	47.05		2.85	97.19	43,620	62.84
2.36	73.24	32,870	47.35		2.86	97.70	43,850	63.17
2.37	73.70	33,080	47.65		2.87	98.21	44,080	63.50
2.38	74.17	33,290	47.95		2.88	98.73	44,320	63.83
2.39	74.64	33,500	48.25		2.89	99.24	44,550	64.16
2.40	75.10	33,710	48.56		2.90	99.76	44,780	64.50
2.41	75.57	33,920	48.86		2.91	100.3	45,010	64.83
2.42	76.05	34,130	49.17		2.92	100.8	45,240	65.17
2.43	76.52	34,350	49.47		2.93	101.3	45,470	65.50
2.44	76.99	34,560	49.78		2.94	101.8	45,710	65.84
2.45	77.46	34,770	50.08		2.95	102.3	45,940	66.17
2.46	77.94	34,980	50.39		2.96	102.9	46,170	66.51
2.47	78.41	35,200	50.70		2.97	103.4	46,410	66.85
2.48	78.89	35,410	51.01		2.98	103.9	46,640	67.18
2.49	79.37	35,630	51.31		2.99	104.4	46,880	67.52
2.50	79.85	35,840	51.62		3.00	105.0	47,110	67.86

12

Table 12-9:
8 ft. Cipolletti Weir Discharge Table with Head in Feet

Formula: $CFS = 26.94\ H^{1.5}$
$GPM = 12090\ H^{1.5}$
$MGD = 17.41\ H^{1.5}$
Where: H = head in feet

Values in italics indicate flow below the recommended range of this particular primary device.

Table 12-9				Table 12-9 (Continued)			
Head (feet)	CFS	GPM	MGD	Head (feet)	CFS	GPM	MGD
0.01	*0.027*	*12.1*	*0.017*	0.51	9.812	4403	6.341
0.02	*0.076*	*34.2*	*0.049*	0.52	10.10	4533	6.528
0.03	*0.140*	*62.8*	*0.090*	0.53	10.39	4665	6.718
0.04	*0.215*	*96.7*	*0.139*	0.54	10.69	4798	6.909
0.05	*0.301*	*135.2*	*0.195*	0.55	10.99	4931	7.101
0.06	*0.396*	*177.7*	*0.256*	0.56	11.29	5067	7.296
0.07	*0.499*	*223.9*	*0.322*	0.57	11.59	5203	7.492
0.08	*0.609*	*273.6*	*0.394*	0.58	11.90	5340	7.690
0.09	*0.727*	*326.4*	*0.470*	0.59	12.21	5479	7.890
0.10	*0.852*	*382.3*	*0.551*	0.60	12.52	5619	8.091
0.11	*0.983*	*441.1*	*0.635*	0.61	12.83	5760	8.295
0.12	*1.120*	*502.6*	*0.724*	0.62	13.15	5902	8.499
0.13	*1.263*	*566.7*	*0.816*	0.63	13.47	6046	8.706
0.14	*1.411*	*633.3*	*0.912*	0.64	13.79	6190	8.914
0.15	*1.565*	*702.3*	*1.011*	0.65	14.12	6336	9.124
0.16	*1.724*	*773.7*	*1.114*	0.66	14.44	6482	9.335
0.17	*1.888*	*847.4*	*1.220*	0.67	14.77	6630	9.548
0.18	*2.057*	*923.3*	*1.329*	0.68	15.11	6779	9.763
0.19	*2.231*	*1001*	*1.442*	0.69	15.44	6929	9.979
0.20	2.410	1081	1.557	0.70	15.78	7081	10.20
0.21	2.593	1163	1.675	0.71	16.12	7233	10.42
0.22	2.780	1248	1.797	0.72	16.46	7386	10.64
0.23	2.972	1334	1.920	0.73	16.80	7541	10.86
0.24	3.167	1421	2.047	0.74	17.15	7696	11.08
0.25	3.368	1511	2.176	0.75	17.50	7853	11.31
0.26	3.572	1603	2.308	0.76	17.85	8010	11.54
0.27	3.780	1696	2.443	0.77	18.20	8169	11.76
0.28	3.991	1791	2.580	0.78	18.56	8329	11.99
0.29	4.207	1888	2.719	0.79	18.92	8489	12.22
0.30	4.427	1987	2.861	0.80	19.28	8651	12.46
0.31	4.650	2087	3.005	0.81	19.64	8814	12.69
0.32	4.877	2189	3.152	0.82	20.00	8977	12.93
0.33	5.107	2292	3.300	0.83	20.37	9142	13.16
0.34	5.341	2397	3.452	0.84	20.74	9308	13.40
0.35	5.578	2503	3.605	0.85	21.11	9474	13.64
0.36	5.819	2611	3.761	0.86	21.49	9642	13.89
0.37	6.063	2721	3.918	0.87	21.86	9811	14.13
0.38	6.311	2832	4.078	0.88	22.24	9980	14.37
0.39	6.561	2945	4.240	0.89	22.62	10,150	14.62
0.40	6.815	3059	4.404	0.90	23.00	10,320	14.86
0.41	7.073	3174	4.571	0.91	23.39	10,500	15.11
0.42	7.333	3291	4.739	0.92	23.77	10,670	15.36
0.43	7.596	3409	4.909	0.93	24.16	10,840	15.61
0.44	7.863	3529	5.081	0.94	24.55	11,020	15.87
0.45	8.132	3650	5.256	0.95	24.94	11,190	16.12
0.46	8.405	3772	5.432	0.96	25.34	11,370	16.38
0.47	8.680	3896	5.610	0.97	25.74	11,550	16.63
0.48	8.959	4021	5.790	0.98	26.14	11,730	16.89
0.49	9.240	4147	5.972	0.99	26.54	11,910	17.15
0.50	9.525	4274	6.155	1.00	26.94	12,090	17.41

12

Table 12-9 (Continued)				Table 12-9 (Continued)			
Head (feet)	CFS	GPM	MGD	Head (feet)	CFS	GPM	MGD
1.01	27.35	12,270	17.67	1.51	49.99	22,430	32.30
1.02	27.75	12,450	17.93	1.52	50.49	22,660	32.63
1.03	28.16	12,640	18.20	1.53	50.98	22,880	32.95
1.04	28.57	12,820	18.46	1.54	51.48	23,110	33.27
1.05	28.99	13,010	18.73	1.55	51.99	23,330	33.60
1.06	29.40	13,190	19.00	1.56	52.49	23,560	33.92
1.07	29.82	13,380	19.27	1.57	53.00	23,780	34.25
1.08	30.24	13,570	19.54	1.58	53.50	24,010	34.58
1.09	30.66	13,760	19.81	1.59	54.01	24,240	34.91
1.10	31.08	13,950	20.09	1.60	54.52	24,470	35.24
1.11	31.51	14,140	20.36	1.61	55.03	24,700	35.57
1.12	31.93	14,330	20.64	1.62	55.55	24,930	35.90
1.13	32.36	14,520	20.91	1.63	56.06	25,160	36.23
1.14	32.79	14,720	21.19	1.64	56.58	25,390	36.56
1.15	33.22	14,910	21.47	1.65	57.10	25,620	36.90
1.16	33.66	15,100	21.75	1.66	57.62	25,860	37.24
1.17	34.09	15,300	22.03	1.67	58.14	26,090	37.57
1.18	34.53	15,500	22.32	1.68	58.66	26,330	37.91
1.19	34.97	15,690	22.60	1.69	59.19	26,560	38.25
1.20	35.41	15,890	22.89	1.70	59.71	26,800	38.59
1.21	35.86	16,090	23.17	1.71	60.24	27,030	38.93
1.22	36.30	16,290	23.46	1.72	60.77	27,270	39.27
1.23	36.75	16,490	23.75	1.73	61.30	27,510	39.62
1.24	37.20	16,690	24.04	1.74	61.83	27,750	39.96
1.25	37.65	16,900	24.33	1.75	62.37	27,990	40.30
1.26	38.10	17,100	24.62	1.76	62.90	28,230	40.65
1.27	38.56	17,300	24.92	1.77	63.44	28,470	41.00
1.28	39.01	17,510	25.21	1.78	63.98	28,710	41.35
1.29	39.47	17,710	25.51	1.79	64.52	28,950	41.69
1.30	39.93	17,920	25.81	1.80	65.06	29,200	42.04
1.31	40.39	18,130	26.10	1.81	65.60	29,440	42.40
1.32	40.86	18,340	26.40	1.82	66.15	29,680	42.75
1.33	41.32	18,540	26.70	1.83	66.69	29,930	43.10
1.34	41.79	18,750	27.01	1.84	67.24	30,180	43.45
1.35	42.26	18,960	27.31	1.85	67.79	30,420	43.81
1.36	42.73	19,170	27.61	1.86	68.34	30,670	44.16
1.37	43.20	19,390	27.92	1.87	68.89	30,920	44.52
1.38	43.67	19,600	28.22	1.88	69.44	31,160	44.88
1.39	44.15	19,810	28.53	1.89	70.00	31,410	45.24
1.40	44.63	20,030	28.84	1.90	70.56	31,660	45.60
1.41	45.11	20,240	29.15	1.91	71.11	31,910	45.96
1.42	45.59	20,460	29.46	1.92	71.67	32,160	46.32
1.43	46.07	20,670	29.77	1.93	72.23	32,420	46.68
1.44	46.55	20,890	30.08	1.94	72.79	32,670	47.04
1.45	47.04	21,110	30.40	1.95	73.36	32,920	47.41
1.46	47.53	21,330	30.71	1.96	73.92	33,170	47.77
1.47	48.01	21,550	31.03	1.97	74.49	33,430	48.14
1.48	48.51	21,770	31.35	1.98	75.06	33,680	48.51
1.49	49.00	21,990	31.66	1.99	75.63	33,940	48.87
1.50	49.49	22,210	31.98	2.00	76.20	34,200	49.24

Table 12-9 (Continued)				Table 12-9 (Continued)			
Head (feet)	CFS	GPM	MGD	Head (feet)	CFS	GPM	MGD
2.01	76.77	34,450	49.61	2.51	107.1	48,080	69.23
2.02	77.34	34,710	49.98	2.52	107.8	48,360	69.65
2.03	77.92	34,970	50.36	2.53	108.4	48,650	70.06
2.04	78.50	35,230	50.73	2.54	109.1	48,940	70.48
2.05	79.07	35,490	51.10	2.55	109.7	49,230	70.89
2.06	79.65	35,750	51.48	2.56	110.3	49,520	71.31
2.07	80.23	36,010	51.85	2.57	111.0	49,810	71.73
2.08	80.82	36,270	52.23	2.58	111.6	50,100	72.15
2.09	81.40	36,530	52.60	2.59	112.3	50,390	72.57
2.10	81.98	36,790	52.98	2.60	112.9	50,690	72.99
2.11	82.57	37,060	53.36	2.61	113.6	50,980	73.41
2.12	83.16	37,320	53.74	2.62	114.2	51,270	73.83
2.13	83.75	37,580	54.12	2.63	114.9	51,570	74.26
2.14	84.34	37,850	54.50	2.64	115.6	51,860	74.68
2.15	84.93	38,110	54.89	2.65	116.2	52,150	75.10
2.16	85.52	38,380	55.27	2.66	116.9	52,450	75.53
2.17	86.12	38,650	55.65	2.67	117.5	52,750	75.96
2.18	86.71	38,910	56.04	2.68	118.2	53,040	76.38
2.19	87.31	39,180	56.42	2.69	118.9	53,340	76.81
2.20	87.91	39,450	56.81	2.70	119.5	53,640	77.24
2.21	88.51	39,720	57.20	2.71	120.2	53,940	77.67
2.22	89.11	39,990	57.59	2.72	120.9	54,240	78.10
2.23	89.71	40,260	57.98	2.73	121.5	54,530	78.53
2.24	90.32	40,530	58.37	2.74	122.2	54,830	78.96
2.25	90.92	40,800	58.76	2.75	122.9	55,130	79.40
2.26	91.53	41,080	59.15	2.76	123.5	55,440	79.83
2.27	92.14	41,350	59.54	2.77	124.2	55,740	80.26
2.28	92.75	41,620	59.94	2.78	124.9	56,040	80.70
2.29	93.36	41,900	60.33	2.79	125.5	56,340	81.13
2.30	93.97	42,170	60.73	2.80	126.2	56,650	81.57
2.31	94.58	42,450	61.12	2.81	126.9	56,950	82.01
2.32	95.20	42,720	61.52	2.82	127.6	57,250	82.45
2.33	95.81	43,000	61.92	2.83	128.3	57,560	82.89
2.34	96.43	43,280	62.32	2.84	128.9	57,860	83.33
2.35	97.05	43,550	62.72	2.85	129.6	58,170	83.77
2.36	97.67	43,830	63.12	2.86	130.3	58,480	84.21
2.37	98.29	44,110	63.52	2.87	131.0	58,780	84.65
2.38	98.92	44,390	63.92	2.88	131.7	59,090	85.09
2.39	99.54	44,670	64.33	2.89	132.4	59,400	85.54
2.40	100.2	44,950	64.73	2.90	133.0	59,710	85.98
2.41	100.8	45,230	65.14	2.91	133.7	60,020	86.42
2.42	101.4	45,510	65.54	2.92	134.4	60,330	86.87
2.43	102.0	45,800	65.95	2.93	135.1	60,640	87.32
2.44	102.7	46,080	66.36	2.94	135.8	60,950	87.76
2.45	103.3	46,360	66.76	2.95	136.5	61,260	88.21
2.46	103.9	46,650	67.17	2.96	137.2	61,570	88.66
2.47	104.6	46,930	67.58	2.97	137.9	61,880	89.11
2.48	105.2	47,220	67.99	2.98	138.6	62,190	89.56
2.49	105.9	47,500	68.41	2.99	139.3	62,510	90.01
2.50	106.5	47,790	68.82	3.00	140.0	62,820	90.47

12

Table 12-9 (Continued)					Table 12-9 (Continued)			
Head (feet)	CFS	GPM	MGD		Head (feet)	CFS	GPM	MGD
3.01	140.7	63,140	90.92		3.51	177.2	79,500	114.5
3.02	141.4	63,450	91.37		3.52	177.9	79,840	115.0
3.03	142.1	63,770	91.83		3.53	178.7	80,180	115.5
3.04	142.8	64,080	92.28		3.54	179.4	80,530	116.0
3.05	143.5	64,400	92.74		3.55	180.2	80,870	116.5
3.06	144.2	64,720	93.19		3.56	181.0	81,210	116.9
3.07	144.9	65,030	93.65		3.57	181.7	81,550	117.4
3.08	145.6	65,350	94.11		3.58	182.5	81,890	117.9
3.09	146.3	65,670	94.57		3.59	183.2	82,240	118.4
3.10	147.0	65,990	95.03		3.60	184.0	82,580	118.9
3.11	147.8	66,310	95.49		3.61	184.8	82,930	119.4
3.12	148.5	66,630	95.95		3.62	185.5	83,270	119.9
3.13	149.2	66,950	96.41		3.63	186.3	83,620	120.4
3.14	149.9	67,270	96.87		3.64	187.1	83,960	120.9
3.15	150.6	67,590	97.33		3.65	187.9	84,310	121.4
3.16	151.3	67,910	97.80		3.66	188.6	84,650	121.9
3.17	152.1	68,240	98.26		3.67	189.4	85,000	122.4
3.18	152.8	68,560	98.73		3.68	190.2	85,350	122.9
3.19	153.5	68,880	99.19		3.69	191.0	85,700	123.4
3.20	154.2	69,210	99.66		3.70	191.7	86,050	123.9
3.21	154.9	69,530	100.1		3.71	192.5	86,390	124.4
3.22	155.7	69,860	100.6		3.72	193.3	86,740	124.9
3.23	156.4	70,180	101.1		3.73	194.1	87,090	125.4
3.24	157.1	70,510	101.5		3.74	194.9	87,440	125.9
3.25	157.8	70,840	102.0		3.75	195.6	87,800	126.4
3.26	158.6	71,160	102.5		3.76	196.4	88,150	126.9
3.27	159.3	71,490	102.9		3.77	197.2	88,500	127.4
3.28	160.0	71,820	103.4		3.78	198.0	88,850	127.9
3.29	160.8	72,150	103.9		3.79	198.8	89,200	128.5
3.30	161.5	72,480	104.4		3.80	199.6	89,560	129.0
3.31	162.2	72,810	104.8		3.81	200.3	89,910	129.5
3.32	163.0	73,140	105.3		3.82	201.1	90,270	130.0
3.33	163.7	73,470	105.8		3.83	201.9	90,620	130.5
3.34	164.4	73,800	106.3		3.84	202.7	90,980	131.0
3.35	165.2	74,130	106.7		3.85	203.5	91,330	131.5
3.36	165.9	74,460	107.2		3.86	204.3	91,690	132.0
3.37	166.7	74,790	107.7		3.87	205.1	92,040	132.5
3.38	167.4	75,130	108.2		3.88	205.9	92,400	133.1
3.39	168.2	75,460	108.7		3.89	206.7	92,760	133.6
3.40	168.9	75,800	109.1		3.90	207.5	93,120	134.1
3.41	169.6	76,130	109.6		3.91	208.3	93,470	134.6
3.42	170.4	76,470	110.1		3.92	209.1	93,830	135.1
3.43	171.1	76,800	110.6		3.93	209.9	94,190	135.6
3.44	171.9	77,140	111.1		3.94	210.7	94,550	136.2
3.45	172.6	77,470	111.6		3.95	211.5	94,910	136.7
3.46	173.4	77,810	112.1		3.96	212.3	95,270	137.2
3.47	174.1	78,150	112.5		3.97	213.1	95,630	137.7
3.48	174.9	78,490	113.0		3.98	213.9	96,000	138.2
3.49	175.6	78,830	113.5		3.99	214.7	96,360	138.8
3.50	176.4	79,160	114.0		4.00	215.5	96,720	139.3

12

Table 12-10:
10 ft. Cipolletti Weir Discharge Table with Head in Feet

Formula:
$CFS = 33.67\ H^{1.5}$
$GPM = 15110\ H^{1.5}$
$MGD = 21.76\ H^{1.5}$
Where: H = head in feet

Values in italics indicate flow below the recommended range of this particular primary device.

Table 12-10				Table 12-10 (Continued)			
Head (feet)	CFS	GPM	MGD	Head (feet)	CFS	GPM	MGD
0.01	*0.034*	*15*	*0.022*	0.51	12.26	5503	7.925
0.02	*0.095*	*43*	*0.062*	0.52	12.63	5666	8.160
0.03	*0.175*	*79*	*0.113*	0.53	12.99	5830	8.396
0.04	*0.269*	*121*	*0.174*	0.54	13.36	5996	8.635
0.05	*0.376*	*169*	*0.243*	0.55	13.73	6163	8.876
0.06	*0.495*	*222*	*0.320*	0.56	14.11	6332	9.119
0.07	*0.624*	*280*	*0.403*	0.57	14.49	6502	9.364
0.08	*0.762*	*342*	*0.492*	0.58	14.87	6674	9.612
0.09	*0.909*	*408*	*0.588*	0.59	15.26	6848	9.861
0.10	*1.065*	*478*	*0.688*	0.60	15.65	7022	10.11
0.11	*1.228*	*551*	*0.794*	0.61	16.04	7199	10.37
0.12	*1.400*	*628*	*0.905*	0.62	16.44	7377	10.62
0.13	*1.578*	*708*	*1.020*	0.63	16.84	7556	10.88
0.14	*1.764*	*792*	*1.140*	0.64	17.24	7736	11.14
0.15	*1.956*	*878*	*1.264*	0.65	17.64	7918	11.40
0.16	*2.155*	*967*	*1.393*	0.66	18.05	8102	11.67
0.17	*2.360*	*1059*	*1.525*	0.67	18.47	8287	11.93
0.18	*2.571*	*1154*	*1.662*	0.68	18.88	8473	12.20
0.19	*2.789*	*1252*	*1.802*	0.69	19.30	8660	12.47
0.20	3.012	1351	1.946	0.70	19.72	8849	12.74
0.21	3.240	1454	2.094	0.71	20.14	9040	13.02
0.22	3.474	1559	2.245	0.72	20.57	9231	13.29
0.23	3.714	1667	2.400	0.73	21.00	9424	13.57
0.24	3.959	1777	2.558	0.74	21.43	9619	13.85
0.25	4.209	1889	2.720	0.75	21.87	9814	14.13
0.26	4.464	2003	2.885	0.76	22.31	10,010	14.42
0.27	4.724	2120	3.053	0.77	22.75	10,210	14.70
0.28	4.989	2239	3.224	0.78	23.19	10,410	14.99
0.29	5.258	2360	3.398	0.79	23.64	10,610	15.28
0.30	5.533	2483	3.576	0.80	24.09	10,810	15.57
0.31	5.811	2608	3.756	0.81	24.55	11,020	15.86
0.32	6.095	2735	3.939	0.82	25.00	11,220	16.16
0.33	6.383	2864	4.125	0.83	25.46	11,430	16.45
0.34	6.675	2996	4.314	0.84	25.92	11,630	16.75
0.35	6.972	3129	4.506	0.85	26.39	11,840	17.05
0.36	7.273	3264	4.700	0.86	26.85	12,050	17.35
0.37	7.578	3401	4.897	0.87	27.32	12,260	17.66
0.38	7.887	3539	5.097	0.88	27.80	12,470	17.96
0.39	8.200	3680	5.300	0.89	28.27	12,690	18.27
0.40	8.518	3823	5.505	0.90	28.75	12,900	18.58
0.41	8.839	3967	5.713	0.91	29.23	13,120	18.89
0.42	9.165	4113	5.923	0.92	29.71	13,330	19.20
0.43	9.494	4261	6.136	0.93	30.20	13,550	19.52
0.44	9.827	4410	6.351	0.94	30.69	13,770	19.83
0.45	10.16	4561	6.569	0.95	31.18	13,990	20.15
0.46	10.50	4714	6.789	0.96	31.67	14,210	20.47
0.47	10.85	4869	7.011	0.97	32.17	14,440	20.79
0.48	11.20	5025	7.236	0.98	32.66	14,660	21.11
0.49	11.55	5183	7.464	0.99	33.17	14,880	21.43
0.50	11.90	5342	7.693	1.00	33.67	15,110	21.76

12

Table 12-10 (Continued)				Table 12-10 (Continued)			
Head (feet)	CFS	GPM	MGD	Head (feet)	CFS	GPM	MGD
1.01	34.18	15,340	22.09	1.51	62.48	28,040	40.38
1.02	34.69	15,570	22.42	1.52	63.10	28,320	40.78
1.03	35.20	15,800	22.75	1.53	63.72	28,600	41.18
1.04	35.71	16,030	23.08	1.54	64.35	28,880	41.59
1.05	36.23	16,260	23.41	1.55	64.97	29,160	41.99
1.06	36.75	16,490	23.75	1.56	65.60	29,440	42.40
1.07	37.27	16,720	24.08	1.57	66.24	29,720	42.81
1.08	37.79	16,960	24.42	1.58	66.87	30,010	43.22
1.09	38.32	17,200	24.76	1.59	67.51	30,290	43.63
1.10	38.84	17,430	25.10	1.60	68.14	30,580	44.04
1.11	39.38	17,670	25.45	1.61	68.78	30,870	44.45
1.12	39.91	17,910	25.79	1.62	69.42	31,160	44.87
1.13	40.44	18,150	26.14	1.63	70.07	31,440	45.28
1.14	40.98	18,390	26.49	1.64	70.71	31,730	45.70
1.15	41.52	18,630	26.84	1.65	71.36	32,030	46.12
1.16	42.07	18,880	27.19	1.66	72.01	32,320	46.54
1.17	42.61	19,120	27.54	1.67	72.66	32,610	46.96
1.18	43.16	19,370	27.89	1.68	73.32	32,900	47.38
1.19	43.71	19,610	28.25	1.69	73.97	33,200	47.81
1.20	44.26	19,860	28.60	1.70	74.63	33,490	48.23
1.21	44.81	20,110	28.96	1.71	75.29	33,790	48.66
1.22	45.37	20,360	29.32	1.72	75.95	34,080	49.09
1.23	45.93	20,610	29.68	1.73	76.61	34,380	49.51
1.24	46.49	20,860	30.05	1.74	77.28	34,680	49.94
1.25	47.06	21,120	30.41	1.75	77.95	34,980	50.38
1.26	47.62	21,370	30.78	1.76	78.62	35,280	50.81
1.27	48.19	21,630	31.14	1.77	79.29	35,580	51.24
1.28	48.76	21,880	31.51	1.78	79.96	35,880	51.68
1.29	49.33	22,140	31.88	1.79	80.63	36,190	52.11
1.30	49.91	22,400	32.25	1.80	81.31	36,490	52.55
1.31	50.48	22,660	32.63	1.81	81.99	36,790	52.99
1.32	51.06	22,920	33.00	1.82	82.67	37,100	53.43
1.33	51.64	23,180	33.38	1.83	83.35	37,410	53.87
1.34	52.23	23,440	33.75	1.84	84.04	37,710	54.31
1.35	52.81	23,700	34.13	1.85	84.72	38,020	54.75
1.36	53.40	23,960	34.51	1.86	85.41	38,330	55.20
1.37	53.99	24,230	34.89	1.87	86.10	38,640	55.64
1.38	54.58	24,500	35.28	1.88	86.79	38,950	56.09
1.39	55.18	24,760	35.66	1.89	87.49	39,260	56.54
1.40	55.77	25,030	36.05	1.90	88.18	39,570	56.99
1.41	56.37	25,300	36.43	1.91	88.88	39,890	57.44
1.42	56.97	25,570	36.82	1.92	89.58	40,200	57.89
1.43	57.58	25,840	37.21	1.93	90.28	40,510	58.34
1.44	58.18	26,110	37.60	1.94	90.98	40,830	58.80
1.45	58.79	26,380	37.99	1.95	91.68	41,140	59.25
1.46	59.40	26,660	38.39	1.96	92.39	41,460	59.71
1.47	60.01	26,930	38.78	1.97	93.10	41,780	60.17
1.48	60.62	27,210	39.18	1.98	93.81	42,100	60.63
1.49	61.24	27,480	39.58	1.99	94.52	42,420	61.09
1.50	61.86	27,760	39.98	2.00	95.23	42,740	61.55

12

Table 12-10 (Continued)					Table 12-10 (Continued)			
Head (feet)	CFS	GPM	MGD		Head (feet)	CFS	GPM	MGD
2.01	95.95	43,060	62.01		2.51	133.9	60,090	86.53
2.02	96.67	43,380	62.47		2.52	134.7	60,450	87.05
2.03	97.38	43,700	62.94		2.53	135.5	60,810	87.57
2.04	98.10	44,030	63.40		2.54	136.3	61,170	88.09
2.05	98.83	44,350	63.87		2.55	137.1	61,530	88.61
2.06	99.55	44,680	64.34		2.56	137.9	61,890	89.13
2.07	100.3	45,000	64.81		2.57	138.7	62,250	89.65
2.08	101.0	45,330	65.28		2.58	139.5	62,620	90.18
2.09	101.7	45,650	65.75		2.59	140.3	62,980	90.70
2.10	102.5	45,980	66.22		2.60	141.2	63,350	91.23
2.11	103.2	46,310	66.69		2.61	142.0	63,710	91.75
2.12	103.9	46,640	67.17		2.62	142.8	64,080	92.28
2.13	104.7	46,970	67.64		2.63	143.6	64,450	92.81
2.14	105.4	47,300	68.12		2.64	144.4	64,810	93.34
2.15	106.1	47,630	68.60		2.65	145.2	65,180	93.87
2.16	106.9	47,970	69.08		2.66	146.1	65,550	94.40
2.17	107.6	48,300	69.56		2.67	146.9	65,920	94.93
2.18	108.4	48,640	70.04		2.68	147.7	66,290	95.47
2.19	109.1	48,970	70.52		2.69	148.5	66,660	96.00
2.20	109.9	49,310	71.01		2.70	149.4	67,040	96.54
2.21	110.6	49,640	71.49		2.71	150.2	67,410	97.08
2.22	111.4	49,980	71.98		2.72	151.0	67,780	97.61
2.23	112.1	50,320	72.46		2.73	151.9	68,160	98.15
2.24	112.9	50,660	72.95		2.74	152.7	68,530	98.69
2.25	113.6	51,000	73.44		2.75	153.5	68,910	99.23
2.26	114.4	51,340	73.93		2.76	154.4	69,280	99.78
2.27	115.2	51,680	74.42		2.77	155.2	69,660	100.3
2.28	115.9	52,020	74.91		2.78	156.1	70,040	100.9
2.29	116.7	52,360	75.41		2.79	156.9	70,420	101.4
2.30	117.4	52,710	75.90		2.80	157.8	70,790	102.0
2.31	118.2	53,050	76.40		2.81	158.6	71,170	102.5
2.32	119.0	53,390	76.89		2.82	159.4	71,550	103.0
2.33	119.8	53,740	77.39		2.83	160.3	71,940	103.6
2.34	120.5	54,090	77.89		2.84	161.1	72,320	104.1
2.35	121.3	54,430	78.39		2.85	162.0	72,700	104.7
2.36	122.1	54,780	78.89		2.86	162.9	73,080	105.2
2.37	122.8	55,130	79.39		2.87	163.7	73,470	105.8
2.38	123.6	55,480	79.90		2.88	164.6	73,850	106.4
2.39	124.4	55,830	80.40		2.89	165.4	74,240	106.9
2.40	125.2	56,180	80.91		2.90	166.3	74,620	107.5
2.41	126.0	56,530	81.41		2.91	167.1	75,010	108.0
2.42	126.8	56,880	81.92		2.92	168.0	75,390	108.6
2.43	127.5	57,240	82.43		2.93	168.9	75,780	109.1
2.44	128.3	57,590	82.94		2.94	169.7	76,170	109.7
2.45	129.1	57,940	83.45		2.95	170.6	76,560	110.3
2.46	129.9	58,300	83.96		2.96	171.5	76,950	110.8
2.47	130.7	58,660	84.47		2.97	172.3	77,340	111.4
2.48	131.5	59,010	84.98		2.98	173.2	77,730	111.9
2.49	132.3	59,370	85.50		2.99	174.1	78,120	112.5
2.50	133.1	59,730	86.01		3.00	175.0	78,510	113.1

12

Cipolletti Weir Discharge Tables • 281

Table 12-10 (Continued)				Table 12-10 (Continued)			
Head (feet)	CFS	GPM	MGD	Head (feet)	CFS	GPM	MGD
3.01	175.8	78,910	113.6	3.51	221.4	99,360	143.1
3.02	176.7	79,300	114.2	3.52	222.4	99,790	143.7
3.03	177.6	79,690	114.8	3.53	223.3	100,200	144.3
3.04	178.5	80,090	115.3	3.54	224.3	100,600	144.9
3.05	179.3	80,480	115.9	3.55	225.2	101,100	145.5
3.06	180.2	80,880	116.5	3.56	226.2	101,500	146.2
3.07	181.1	81,280	117.0	3.57	227.1	101,900	146.8
3.08	182.0	81,680	117.6	3.58	228.1	102,400	147.4
3.09	182.9	82,070	118.2	3.59	229.0	102,800	148.0
3.10	183.8	82,470	118.8	3.60	230.0	103,200	148.6
3.11	184.7	82,870	119.3	3.61	230.9	103,600	149.3
3.12	185.6	83,270	119.9	3.62	231.9	104,100	149.9
3.13	186.4	83,670	120.5	3.63	232.9	104,500	150.5
3.14	187.3	84,070	121.1	3.64	233.8	104,900	151.1
3.15	188.2	84,480	121.7	3.65	234.8	105,400	151.7
3.16	189.1	84,880	122.2	3.66	235.8	105,800	152.4
3.17	190.0	85,280	122.8	3.67	236.7	106,200	153.0
3.18	190.9	85,690	123.4	3.68	237.7	106,700	153.6
3.19	191.8	86,090	124.0	3.69	238.7	107,100	154.2
3.20	192.7	86,490	124.6	3.70	239.6	107,500	154.9
3.21	193.6	86,900	125.1	3.71	240.6	108,000	155.5
3.22	194.5	87,310	125.7	3.72	241.6	108,400	156.1
3.23	195.5	87,710	126.3	3.73	242.6	108,800	156.8
3.24	196.4	88,120	126.9	3.74	243.5	109,300	157.4
3.25	197.3	88,530	127.5	3.75	244.5	109,700	158.0
3.26	198.2	88,940	128.1	3.76	245.5	110,200	158.7
3.27	199.1	89,350	128.7	3.77	246.5	110,600	159.3
3.28	200.0	89,760	129.3	3.78	247.4	111,000	159.9
3.29	200.9	90,170	129.9	3.79	248.4	111,500	160.6
3.30	201.8	90,580	130.4	3.80	249.4	111,900	161.2
3.31	202.8	90,990	131.0	3.81	250.4	112,400	161.8
3.32	203.7	91,410	131.6	3.82	251.4	112,800	162.5
3.33	204.6	91,820	132.2	3.83	252.4	113,300	163.1
3.34	205.5	92,230	132.8	3.84	253.4	113,700	163.7
3.35	206.4	92,650	133.4	3.85	254.4	114,100	164.4
3.36	207.4	93,060	134.0	3.86	255.3	114,600	165.0
3.37	208.3	93,480	134.6	3.87	256.3	115,000	165.7
3.38	209.2	93,890	135.2	3.88	257.3	115,500	166.3
3.39	210.2	94,310	135.8	3.89	258.3	115,900	166.9
3.40	211.1	94,730	136.4	3.90	259.3	116,400	167.6
3.41	212.0	95,150	137.0	3.91	260.3	116,800	168.2
3.42	213.0	95,570	137.6	3.92	261.3	117,300	168.9
3.43	213.9	95,990	138.2	3.93	262.3	117,700	169.5
3.44	214.8	96,410	138.8	3.94	263.3	118,200	170.2
3.45	215.8	96,830	139.4	3.95	264.3	118,600	170.8
3.46	216.7	97,250	140.0	3.96	265.3	119,100	171.5
3.47	217.6	97,670	140.7	3.97	266.3	119,500	172.1
3.48	218.6	98,090	141.3	3.98	267.3	120,000	172.8
3.49	219.5	98,520	141.9	3.99	268.4	120,400	173.4
3.50	220.5	98,940	142.5	4.00	269.4	120,900	174.1

Head (feet)	CFS	GPM	MGD	Head (feet)	CFS	GPM	MGD
	Table 12-10 (Continued)				Table 12-10 (Continued)		
4.01	270.4	121,300	174.7	4.51	322.5	144,700	208.4
4.02	271.4	121,800	175.4	4.52	323.6	145,200	209.1
4.03	272.4	122,200	176.0	4.53	324.6	145,700	209.8
4.04	273.4	122,700	176.7	4.54	325.7	146,200	210.5
4.05	274.4	123,200	177.4	4.55	326.8	146,600	211.2
4.06	275.4	123,600	178.0	4.56	327.9	147,100	211.9
4.07	276.5	124,100	178.7	4.57	328.9	147,600	212.6
4.08	277.5	124,500	179.3	4.58	330.0	148,100	213.3
4.09	278.5	125,000	180.0	4.59	331.1	148,600	214.0
4.10	279.5	125,400	180.6	4.60	332.2	149,100	214.7
4.11	280.5	125,900	181.3	4.61	333.3	149,600	215.4
4.12	281.6	126,400	182.0	4.62	334.4	150,000	216.1
4.13	282.6	126,800	182.6	4.63	335.4	150,500	216.8
4.14	283.6	127,300	183.3	4.64	336.5	151,000	217.5
4.15	284.7	127,700	184.0	4.65	337.6	151,500	218.2
4.16	285.7	128,200	184.6	4.66	338.7	152,000	218.9
4.17	286.7	128,700	185.3	4.67	339.8	152,500	219.6
4.18	287.7	129,100	186.0	4.68	340.9	153,000	220.3
4.19	288.8	129,600	186.6	4.69	342.0	153,500	221.0
4.20	289.8	130,100	187.3	4.70	343.1	154,000	221.7
4.21	290.8	130,500	188.0	4.71	344.2	154,500	222.4
4.22	291.9	131,000	188.6	4.72	345.3	154,900	223.1
4.23	292.9	131,500	189.3	4.73	346.4	155,400	223.8
4.24	294.0	131,900	190.0	4.74	347.5	155,900	224.6
4.25	295.0	132,400	190.7	4.75	348.6	156,400	225.3
4.26	296.0	132,900	191.3	4.76	349.7	156,900	226.0
4.27	297.1	133,300	192.0	4.77	350.8	157,400	226.7
4.28	298.1	133,800	192.7	4.78	351.9	157,900	227.4
4.29	299.2	134,300	193.4	4.79	353.0	158,400	228.1
4.30	300.2	134,700	194.0	4.80	354.1	158,900	228.8
4.31	301.3	135,200	194.7	4.81	355.2	159,400	229.5
4.32	302.3	135,700	195.4	4.82	356.3	159,900	230.3
4.33	303.4	136,100	196.1	4.83	357.4	160,400	231.0
4.34	304.4	136,600	196.7	4.84	358.5	160,900	231.7
4.35	305.5	137,100	197.4	4.85	359.6	161,400	232.4
4.36	306.5	137,600	198.1	4.86	360.7	161,900	233.1
4.37	307.6	138,000	198.8	4.87	361.9	162,400	233.9
4.38	308.6	138,500	199.5	4.88	363.0	162,900	234.6
4.39	309.7	139,000	200.2	4.89	364.1	163,400	235.3
4.40	310.8	139,500	200.8	4.90	365.2	163,900	236.0
4.41	311.8	139,900	201.5	4.91	366.3	164,400	236.7
4.42	312.9	140,400	202.2	4.92	367.4	164,900	237.5
4.43	313.9	140,900	202.9	4.93	368.6	165,400	238.2
4.44	315.0	141,400	203.6	4.94	369.7	165,900	238.9
4.45	316.1	141,800	204.3	4.95	370.8	166,400	239.6
4.46	317.1	142,300	205.0	4.96	371.9	166,900	240.4
4.47	318.2	142,800	205.6	4.97	373.1	167,400	241.1
4.48	319.3	143,300	206.3	4.98	374.2	167,900	241.8
4.49	320.3	143,800	207.0	4.99	375.3	168,400	242.6
4.50	321.4	144,200	207.7	5.00	376.4	168,900	243.3

12

Table 12-11:
0.3 m Cipolletti Weir Discharge Table with Head in Meters

Formula: l/s = 557.7 H$^{1.5}$
m^3/hr = 2008 H$^{1.5}$
Where: H = head in meters

Values in italics indicate flow below the recommended range of this particular primary device.

Table 12-11			Table 12-11 (Continued)		
Head (meters)	l/s	m^3/hr	Head (meters)	l/s	m^3/hr
0.005	*0.20*	*0.71*	0.080	12.62	45.44
0.010	*0.56*	*2.01*	0.085	13.82	49.76
0.015	*1.02*	*3.69*	0.090	15.06	54.22
0.020	*1.58*	*5.68*	0.095	16.33	58.80
0.025	*2.20*	*7.94*	0.100	17.64	63.50
0.030	*2.90*	*10.43*	0.105	18.98	68.32
0.035	*3.65*	*13.15*	0.110	20.35	73.26
0.040	*4.46*	*16.06*	0.115	21.75	78.31
0.045	*5.32*	*19.16*	0.120	23.18	83.47
0.050	*6.23*	*22.45*	0.125	24.65	88.74
0.055	*7.19*	*25.90*	0.130	26.14	94.12
0.060	8.196	29.51	0.135	27.66	99.60
0.065	9.242	33.28	0.140	29.21	105.2
0.070	10.33	37.19	0.145	30.79	110.9
0.075	11.45	41.24	0.150	32.40	116.7

Table 12-12:
0.4 m Cipolletti Weir Discharge Table with Head in Meters

Formula: l/s = 743.6 H$^{1.5}$
m^3/hr = 2677 H$^{1.5}$
Where: H = head in meters

Values in italics indicate flow below the recommended range of this particular primary device.

12

Table 12-12			Table 12-12 (Continued)		
Head (meters)	l/s	m^3/hr	Head (meters)	l/s	m^3/hr
0.005	*0.26*	*0.95*	0.105	25.30	91.08
0.010	*0.74*	*2.68*	0.110	27.13	97.66
0.015	*1.37*	*4.92*	0.115	29.00	104.4
0.020	*2.10*	*7.57*	0.120	30.91	111.3
0.025	*2.94*	*10.58*	0.125	32.86	118.3
0.030	*3.86*	*13.91*	0.130	34.85	125.5
0.035	*4.87*	*17.53*	0.135	36.88	132.8
0.040	*5.95*	*21.41*	0.140	38.95	140.2
0.045	*7.10*	*25.55*	0.145	41.06	147.8
0.050	*8.31*	*29.93*	0.150	43.20	155.5
0.055	*9.59*	*34.53*	0.155	45.38	163.4
0.060	10.93	39.34	0.160	47.59	171.3
0.065	12.32	44.36	0.165	49.84	179.4
0.070	13.77	49.58	0.170	52.12	187.6
0.075	15.27	54.98	0.175	54.44	196.0
0.080	16.83	60.57	0.180	56.79	204.4
0.085	18.43	66.34	0.185	59.17	213.0
0.090	20.08	72.28	0.190	61.58	221.7
0.095	21.77	78.39	0.195	64.03	230.5
0.100	23.51	84.65	0.200	66.51	239.4

Table 12-13:
0.5 m Cipolletti Weir Discharge Table with Head in Meters

Formula: $l/s = 929.4\ H^{1.5}$
$m^3/hr = 3346\ H^{1.5}$

Where: H = head in meters

Values in italics indicate flow below the recommended range of this particular primary device.

Table 12-13			Table 12-13 (Continued)		
Head (meters)	l/s	m³/hr	Head (meters)	l/s	m³/hr
0.005	*0.33*	*1.18*	0.130	43.56	156.8
0.010	*0.93*	*3.35*	0.135	46.10	166.0
0.015	*1.71*	*6.15*	0.140	48.68	175.3
0.020	*2.63*	*9.46*	0.145	51.32	184.7
0.025	*3.67*	*13.23*	0.150	53.99	194.4
0.030	*4.83*	*17.39*	0.155	56.72	204.2
0.035	*6.09*	*21.91*	0.160	59.48	214.1
0.040	*7.44*	*26.77*	0.165	62.29	224.3
0.045	*8.87*	*31.94*	0.170	65.14	234.5
0.050	*10.39*	*37.41*	0.175	68.04	245.0
0.055	*11.99*	*43.16*	0.180	70.98	255.5
0.060	13.66	49.18	0.185	73.95	266.2
0.065	15.40	55.45	0.190	76.97	277.1
0.070	17.21	61.97	0.195	80.03	288.1
0.075	19.09	68.73	0.200	83.13	299.3
0.080	21.03	75.71	0.205	86.26	310.6
0.085	23.03	82.92	0.210	89.44	322.0
0.090	25.09	90.34	0.215	92.65	333.6
0.095	27.21	97.97	0.220	95.90	345.3
0.100	29.39	105.8	0.225	99.19	357.1
0.105	31.62	113.8	0.230	102.5	369.1
0.110	33.91	122.1	0.235	105.9	381.2
0.115	36.25	130.5	0.240	109.3	393.4
0.120	38.63	139.1	0.245	112.7	405.8
0.125	41.07	147.9	0.250	116.2	418.3

12

Table 12-14:
0.6 m Cipolletti Weir Discharge Table with Head in Meters

Formula: l/s $= 1115\,H^{1.5}$
$m^3/hr = 4015\,H^{1.5}$
Where: H = head in meters

Values in italics indicate flow below the recommended range of this particular primary device.

Table 12-14			Table 12-14 (Continued)		
Head (meters)	l/s	m³/hr	Head (meters)	l/s	m³/hr
0.005	*0.39*	*1.42*	0.155	68.04	245.0
0.010	*1.12*	*4.02*	0.160	71.36	257.0
0.015	*2.05*	*7.38*	0.165	74.73	269.1
0.020	*3.15*	*11.36*	0.170	78.15	281.4
0.025	*4.41*	*15.87*	0.175	81.63	293.9
0.030	*5.80*	*20.86*	0.180	85.15	306.6
0.035	*7.30*	*26.29*	0.185	88.72	319.5
0.040	*8.92*	*32.12*	0.190	92.34	332.5
0.045	*10.65*	*38.33*	0.195	96.01	345.7
0.050	*12.47*	*44.89*	0.200	99.73	359.1
0.055	*14.39*	*51.79*	0.205	103.5	372.7
0.060	16.39	59.01	0.210	107.3	386.4
0.065	18.48	66.54	0.215	111.2	400.3
0.070	20.65	74.36	0.220	115.1	414.3
0.075	22.90	82.47	0.225	119.0	428.5
0.080	25.23	90.85	0.230	123.0	442.9
0.085	27.63	99.50	0.235	127.0	457.4
0.090	30.11	108.4	0.240	131.1	472.1
0.095	32.65	117.6	0.245	135.2	486.9
0.100	35.26	127.0	0.250	139.4	501.9
0.105	37.94	136.6	0.255	143.6	517.0
0.110	40.68	146.5	0.260	147.8	532.3
0.115	43.48	156.6	0.265	152.1	547.7
0.120	46.35	166.9	0.270	156.4	563.3
0.125	49.28	177.4	0.275	160.8	579.0
0.130	52.26	188.2	0.280	165.2	594.9
0.135	55.31	199.2	0.285	169.6	610.9
0.140	58.41	210.3	0.290	174.1	627.0
0.145	61.56	221.7	0.295	178.7	643.3
0.150	64.78	233.3	0.300	183.2	659.7

12

Table 12-15:
0.8 m Cipolletti Weir Discharge Table with Head in Meters

Formula: $l/s = 1487 \, H^{1.5}$
$m^3/hr = 5354 \, H^{1.5}$
Where: H = head in meters

Values in italics indicate flow below the recommended range of this particular primary device.

Table 12-15			Table 12-15 (Continued)		
Head (meters)	l/s	m³/hr	Head (meters)	l/s	m³/hr
0.005	*0.53*	*1.89*	0.205	138.0	496.9
0.010	*1.49*	*5.35*	0.210	143.1	515.2
0.015	*2.73*	*9.84*	0.215	148.2	533.7
0.020	*4.21*	*15.14*	0.220	153.4	552.5
0.025	*5.88*	*21.16*	0.225	158.7	571.4
0.030	*7.73*	*27.82*	0.230	164.0	590.6
0.035	*9.74*	*35.05*	0.235	169.4	609.9
0.040	*11.90*	*42.83*	0.240	174.8	629.5
0.045	*14.20*	*51.10*	0.245	180.3	649.3
0.050	*16.63*	*59.85*	0.250	185.9	669.3
0.055	*19.18*	*69.05*	0.255	191.5	689.4
0.060	21.85	78.69	0.260	197.1	709.8
0.065	24.64	88.73	0.265	202.9	730.4
0.070	27.54	99.16	0.270	208.6	751.1
0.075	30.54	110.0	0.275	214.4	772.1
0.080	33.65	121.1	0.280	220.3	793.3
0.085	36.85	132.7	0.285	226.2	814.6
0.090	40.15	144.6	0.290	232.2	836.1
0.095	43.54	156.8	0.295	238.3	857.9
0.100	47.02	169.3	0.300	244.3	879.8
0.105	50.59	182.2	0.305	250.5	901.8
0.110	54.25	195.3	0.310	256.7	924.1
0.115	57.99	208.8	0.315	262.9	946.6
0.120	61.81	222.6	0.320	269.2	969.2
0.125	65.72	236.6	0.325	275.5	992.0
0.130	69.70	251.0	0.330	281.9	1015
0.135	73.76	265.6	0.335	288.3	1038
0.140	77.89	280.5	0.340	294.8	1061
0.145	82.10	295.6	0.345	301.3	1085
0.150	86.39	311.0	0.350	307.9	1109
0.155	90.74	326.7	0.355	314.5	1132
0.160	95.17	342.7	0.360	321.2	1156
0.165	99.66	358.8	0.365	327.9	1181
0.170	104.2	375.3	0.370	334.7	1205
0.175	108.9	392.0	0.375	341.5	1229
0.180	113.6	408.9	0.380	348.3	1254
0.185	118.3	426.0	0.385	355.2	1279
0.190	123.2	443.4	0.390	362.2	1304
0.195	128.0	461.0	0.395	369.2	1329
0.200	133.0	478.9	0.400	376.2	1354

12

Table 12-16:
1 m Cipolletti Weir Discharge Table with Head in Meters

Formula: l/s $= 1859\,H^{1.5}$
$m^3/hr = 6692\,H^{1.5}$
Where: H = head in meters

Values in italics indicate flow below the recommended range of this particular primary device.

Table 12-16			Table 12-16 (Continued)		
Head (meters)	l/s	m³/hr	Head (meters)	l/s	m³/hr
0.005	*0.66*	*2.37*	0.255	239.4	861.7
0.010	*1.86*	*6.69*	0.260	246.5	887.2
0.015	*3.41*	*12.29*	0.265	253.6	912.9
0.020	*5.26*	*18.93*	0.270	260.8	938.9
0.025	*7.35*	*26.45*	0.275	268.1	965.1
0.030	*9.66*	*34.77*	0.280	275.4	991.5
0.035	*12.17*	*43.82*	0.285	282.8	1018
0.040	*14.87*	*53.54*	0.290	290.3	1045
0.045	*17.74*	*63.88*	0.295	297.9	1072
0.050	*20.78*	*74.82*	0.300	305.5	1100
0.055	*23.98*	*86.32*	0.305	313.1	1127
0.060	27.32	98.35	0.310	320.9	1155
0.065	30.81	110.9	0.315	328.7	1183
0.070	34.43	123.9	0.320	336.5	1211
0.075	38.18	137.5	0.325	344.4	1240
0.080	42.06	151.4	0.330	352.4	1269
0.085	46.07	165.8	0.335	360.5	1298
0.090	50.19	180.7	0.340	368.6	1327
0.095	54.43	195.9	0.345	376.7	1356
0.100	58.79	211.6	0.350	384.9	1386
0.105	63.25	227.7	0.355	393.2	1415
0.110	67.82	244.1	0.360	401.5	1445
0.115	72.50	261.0	0.365	409.9	1476
0.120	77.28	278.2	0.370	418.4	1506
0.125	82.16	295.7	0.375	426.9	1537
0.130	87.14	313.7	0.380	435.5	1568
0.135	92.21	331.9	0.385	444.1	1599
0.140	97.38	350.5	0.390	452.8	1630
0.145	102.6	369.5	0.395	461.5	1661
0.150	108.0	388.8	0.400	470.3	1693
0.155	113.4	408.4	0.405	479.1	1725
0.160	119.0	428.3	0.410	488.0	1757
0.165	124.6	448.5	0.415	497.0	1789
0.170	130.3	469.1	0.420	506.0	1822
0.175	136.1	489.9	0.425	515.1	1854
0.180	142.0	511.1	0.430	524.2	1887
0.185	147.9	532.5	0.435	533.4	1920
0.190	154.0	554.2	0.440	542.6	1953
0.195	160.1	576.2	0.445	551.8	1987
0.200	166.3	598.6	0.450	561.2	2020
0.205	172.5	621.1	0.455	570.6	2054
0.210	178.9	644.0	0.460	580.0	2088
0.215	185.3	667.1	0.465	589.5	2122
0.220	191.8	690.5	0.470	599.0	2156
0.225	198.4	714.2	0.475	608.6	2191
0.230	205.1	738.2	0.480	618.2	2225
0.235	211.8	762.4	0.485	627.9	2260
0.240	218.6	786.8	0.490	637.6	2295
0.245	225.4	811.5	0.495	647.4	2331
0.250	232.4	836.5	0.500	657.3	2366

12

Table 12-17:
1.5 m Cipolletti Weir Discharge Table with Head in Meters

Formula: $l/s = 2788\,H^{1.5}$
$m^3/hr = 10040\,H^{1.5}$
Where: H = head in meters

Values in italics indicate flow below the recommended range of this particular primary device.

Table 12-17			Table 12-17 (Continued)		
Head (meters)	l/s	m³/hr	Head (meters)	l/s	m³/hr
0.005	*0.99*	*3.5*	0.255	359.0	1293
0.010	*2.79*	*10.0*	0.260	369.6	1331
0.015	*5.12*	*18.4*	0.265	380.3	1370
0.020	*7.89*	*28.4*	0.270	391.1	1409
0.025	*11.02*	*39.7*	0.275	402.1	1448
0.030	*14.49*	*52.2*	0.280	413.1	1488
0.035	*18.26*	*65.7*	0.285	424.2	1528
0.040	*22.31*	*80.3*	0.290	435.4	1568
0.045	*26.62*	*95.8*	0.295	446.7	1609
0.050	*31.17*	*112.2*	0.300	458.1	1650
0.055	*35.97*	*129.5*	0.305	469.6	1691
0.060	40.98	147.6	0.310	481.2	1733
0.065	46.20	166.4	0.315	492.9	1775
0.070	51.63	185.9	0.320	504.7	1817
0.075	57.26	206.2	0.325	516.6	1860
0.080	63.09	227.2	0.330	528.5	1903
0.085	69.09	248.8	0.335	540.6	1947
0.090	75.28	271.1	0.340	552.7	1990
0.095	81.64	294.0	0.345	565.0	2035
0.100	88.16	317.5	0.350	577.3	2079
0.105	94.86	341.6	0.355	589.7	2124
0.110	101.7	366.3	0.360	602.2	2169
0.115	108.7	391.5	0.365	614.8	2214
0.120	115.9	417.4	0.370	627.5	2260
0.125	123.2	443.7	0.375	640.2	2306
0.130	130.7	470.6	0.380	653.1	2352
0.135	138.3	498.0	0.385	666.0	2398
0.140	146.0	525.9	0.390	679.0	2445
0.145	153.9	554.4	0.395	692.1	2492
0.150	162.0	583.3	0.400	705.3	2540
0.155	170.1	612.7	0.405	718.6	2588
0.160	178.4	642.6	0.410	731.9	2636
0.165	186.9	672.9	0.415	745.4	2684
0.170	195.4	703.7	0.420	758.9	2733
0.175	204.1	735.0	0.425	772.5	2782
0.180	212.9	766.7	0.430	786.1	2831
0.185	221.8	798.9	0.435	799.9	2880
0.190	230.9	831.5	0.440	813.7	2930
0.195	240.1	864.5	0.445	827.6	2980
0.200	249.4	898.0	0.450	841.6	3031
0.205	258.8	931.9	0.455	855.7	3081
0.210	268.3	966.2	0.460	869.8	3132
0.215	277.9	1001	0.465	884.0	3184
0.220	287.7	1036	0.470	898.3	3235
0.225	297.6	1072	0.475	912.7	3287
0.230	307.5	1107	0.480	927.2	3339
0.235	317.6	1144	0.485	941.7	3391
0.240	327.8	1180	0.490	956.3	3444
0.245	338.1	1218	0.495	971.0	3497
0.250	348.5	1255	0.500	985.7	3550

12

Table 12-17 (Continued)		
Head (meters)	l/s	m³/hr
0.505	1001	3603
0.510	1015	3657
0.515	1030	3711
0.520	1045	3765
0.525	1061	3819
0.530	1076	3874
0.535	1091	3929
0.540	1106	3984
0.545	1122	4040
0.550	1137	4095
0.555	1153	4151
0.560	1168	4207
0.565	1184	4264
0.570	1200	4321
0.575	1216	4378
0.580	1232	4435
0.585	1247	4492
0.590	1263	4550
0.595	1280	4608
0.600	1296	4666
0.605	1312	4725
0.610	1328	4783
0.615	1345	4842
0.620	1361	4901
0.625	1378	4961

Table 12-17 (Continued)		
Head (meters)	l/s	m³/hr
0.630	1394	5020
0.635	1411	5080
0.640	1427	5140
0.645	1444	5201
0.650	1461	5261
0.655	1478	5322
0.660	1495	5383
0.665	1512	5445
0.670	1529	5506
0.675	1546	5568
0.680	1563	5630
0.685	1581	5692
0.690	1598	5754
0.695	1615	5817
0.700	1633	5880
0.705	1650	5943
0.710	1668	6006
0.715	1686	6070
0.720	1703	6134
0.725	1721	6198
0.730	1739	6262
0.735	1757	6327
0.740	1775	6391
0.745	1793	6456
0.750	1811	6521

12

Table 12-18:
2 m Cipolletti Weir Discharge Table with Head in Meters

Formula: l/s $= 3718\,H^{1.5}$
$m^3/hr = 13380\,H^{1.5}$
Where: H = head in meters

Values in italics indicate flow below the recommended range of this particular primary device.

Head (meters)	l/s	m³/hr	Head (meters)	l/s	m³/hr
0.005	*1.31*	*4.7*	0.255	478.8	1723
0.010	*3.72*	*13.4*	0.260	492.9	1774
0.015	*6.83*	*24.6*	0.265	507.2	1825
0.020	*10.52*	*37.9*	0.270	521.6	1877
0.025	*14.70*	*52.9*	0.275	536.2	1930
0.030	*19.32*	*69.5*	0.280	550.9	1982
0.035	*24.34*	*87.6*	0.285	565.7	2036
0.040	*29.74*	*107.1*	0.290	580.6	2090
0.045	*35.49*	*127.8*	0.295	595.7	2144
0.050	*41.57*	*149.8*	0.300	610.9	2199
0.055	*47.95*	*172.6*	0.305	626.3	2254
0.060	54.64	196.6	0.310	641.7	2309
0.065	61.61	221.7	0.315	657.3	2365
0.070	68.86	247.8	0.320	673.0	2422
0.075	76.37	274.8	0.325	688.9	2479
0.080	84.13	302.8	0.330	704.8	2536
0.085	92.14	331.6	0.335	720.9	2594
0.090	100.4	361.3	0.340	737.1	2653
0.095	108.9	391.8	0.345	753.4	2711
0.100	117.6	423.1	0.350	769.9	2771
0.105	126.5	455.2	0.355	786.4	2830
0.110	135.6	488.1	0.360	803.1	2890
0.115	145.0	521.8	0.365	819.9	2950
0.120	154.6	556.2	0.370	836.8	3011
0.125	164.3	591.3	0.375	853.8	3073
0.130	174.3	627.1	0.380	870.9	3134
0.135	184.4	663.7	0.385	888.2	3196
0.140	194.8	700.9	0.390	905.5	3259
0.145	205.3	738.8	0.395	923.0	3322
0.150	216.0	777.3	0.400	940.6	3385
0.155	226.9	816.5	0.405	958.3	3449
0.160	238.0	856.3	0.410	976.1	3513
0.165	249.2	896.8	0.415	994.0	3577
0.170	260.6	937.8	0.420	1012	3642
0.175	272.2	979.5	0.425	1030	3707
0.180	283.9	1022	0.430	1048	3773
0.185	295.8	1065	0.435	1067	3839
0.190	307.9	1108	0.440	1085	3905
0.195	320.2	1152	0.445	1104	3972
0.200	332.5	1197	0.450	1122	4039
0.205	345.1	1242	0.455	1141	4107
0.210	357.8	1288	0.460	1160	4174
0.215	370.7	1334	0.465	1179	4243
0.220	383.7	1381	0.470	1198	4311
0.225	396.8	1428	0.475	1217	4380
0.230	410.1	1476	0.480	1236	4450
0.235	423.6	1524	0.485	1256	4519
0.240	437.1	1573	0.490	1275	4589
0.245	450.9	1623	0.495	1295	4660
0.250	464.8	1673	0.500	1315	4731

12

Table 12-18 (Continued)			Table 12-18 (Continued)		
Head (meters)	l/s	m³/hr	Head (meters)	l/s	m³/hr
0.505	1334	4802	0.755	2439	8778
0.510	1354	4873	0.760	2463	8865
0.515	1374	4945	0.765	2488	8953
0.520	1394	5017	0.770	2512	9040
0.525	1414	5090	0.775	2537	9129
0.530	1435	5163	0.780	2561	9217
0.535	1455	5236	0.785	2586	9306
0.540	1475	5309	0.790	2611	9395
0.545	1496	5383	0.795	2635	9484
0.550	1517	5458	0.800	2660	9574
0.555	1537	5532	0.805	2685	9664
0.560	1558	5607	0.810	2710	9754
0.565	1579	5682	0.815	2736	9844
0.570	1600	5758	0.820	2761	9935
0.575	1621	5834	0.825	2786	10,030
0.580	1642	5910	0.830	2811	10,120
0.585	1664	5987	0.835	2837	10,210
0.590	1685	6064	0.840	2862	10,300
0.595	1706	6141	0.845	2888	10,390
0.600	1728	6218	0.850	2914	10,490
0.605	1750	6296	0.855	2939	10,580
0.610	1771	6375	0.860	2965	10,670
0.615	1793	6453	0.865	2991	10,760
0.620	1815	6532	0.870	3017	10,860
0.625	1837	6611	0.875	3043	10,950
0.630	1859	6691	0.880	3069	11,050
0.635	1881	6770	0.885	3095	11,140
0.640	1904	6851	0.890	3122	11,230
0.645	1926	6931	0.895	3148	11,330
0.650	1948	7012	0.900	3174	11,420
0.655	1971	7093	0.905	3201	11,520
0.660	1994	7174	0.910	3228	11,610
0.665	2016	7256	0.915	3254	11,710
0.670	2039	7338	0.920	3281	11,810
0.675	2062	7420	0.925	3308	11,900
0.680	2085	7503	0.930	3335	12,000
0.685	2108	7586	0.935	3361	12,100
0.690	2131	7669	0.940	3388	12,190
0.695	2154	7752	0.945	3416	12,290
0.700	2177	7836	0.950	3443	12,390
0.705	2201	7920	0.955	3470	12,490
0.710	2224	8005	0.960	3497	12,590
0.715	2248	8089	0.965	3525	12,680
0.720	2271	8174	0.970	3552	12,780
0.725	2295	8260	0.975	3579	12,880
0.730	2319	8345	0.980	3607	12,980
0.735	2343	8431	0.985	3635	13,080
0.740	2367	8517	0.990	3662	13,180
0.745	2391	8604	0.995	3690	13,280
0.750	2415	8691	1.000	3718	13,380

12

Table 12-19:
3 m Cipolletti Weir Discharge Table with Head in Meters

Formula: $l/s = 5577\ H^{1.5}$
$m^3/hr = 20080\ H^{1.5}$

Where: H = head in meters

Values in italics indicate flow below the recommended range of this particular primary device.

Table 12-19			Table 12-19 (Continued)		
Head (meters)	l/s	m³/hr	Head (meters)	l/s	m³/hr
0.005	*1.97*	*7.1*	0.255	718.1	2586
0.010	*5.58*	*20.1*	0.260	739.4	2662
0.015	*10.24*	*36.9*	0.265	760.8	2739
0.020	*15.77*	*56.8*	0.270	782.4	2817
0.025	*22.04*	*79.4*	0.275	804.3	2896
0.030	*28.98*	*104.3*	0.280	826.3	2975
0.035	*36.52*	*131.5*	0.285	848.5	3055
0.040	*44.61*	*160.6*	0.290	871.0	3136
0.045	*53.23*	*191.6*	0.295	893.6	3217
0.050	*62.35*	*224.5*	0.300	916.4	3299
0.055	*71.93*	*259.0*	0.305	939.4	3382
0.060	81.96	295.1	0.310	962.6	3466
0.065	92.42	332.8	0.315	986.0	3550
0.070	103.3	371.9	0.320	1010	3635
0.075	114.5	412.4	0.325	1033	3720
0.080	126.2	454.4	0.330	1057	3807
0.085	138.2	497.6	0.335	1081	3893
0.090	150.6	542.2	0.340	1106	3981
0.095	163.3	588.0	0.345	1130	4069
0.100	176.4	635.0	0.350	1155	4158
0.105	189.8	683.2	0.355	1180	4247
0.110	203.5	732.6	0.360	1205	4337
0.115	217.5	783.1	0.365	1230	4428
0.120	231.8	834.7	0.370	1255	4519
0.125	246.5	887.4	0.375	1281	4611
0.130	261.4	941.2	0.380	1306	4704
0.135	276.6	996.0	0.385	1332	4797
0.140	292.1	1052	0.390	1358	4891
0.145	307.9	1109	0.395	1385	4985
0.150	324.0	1167	0.400	1411	5080
0.155	340.3	1225	0.405	1437	5175
0.160	356.9	1285	0.410	1464	5272
0.165	373.8	1346	0.415	1491	5368
0.170	390.9	1407	0.420	1518	5466
0.175	408.3	1470	0.425	1545	5563
0.180	425.9	1533	0.430	1573	5662
0.185	443.8	1598	0.435	1600	5761
0.190	461.9	1663	0.440	1628	5861
0.195	480.2	1729	0.445	1656	5961
0.200	498.8	1796	0.450	1684	6062
0.205	517.6	1864	0.455	1712	6163
0.210	536.7	1932	0.460	1740	6265
0.215	556.0	2002	0.465	1768	6367
0.220	575.5	2072	0.470	1797	6470
0.225	595.2	2143	0.475	1826	6574
0.230	615.2	2215	0.480	1855	6678
0.235	635.3	2288	0.485	1884	6782
0.240	655.7	2361	0.490	1913	6887
0.245	676.3	2435	0.495	1942	6993
0.250	697.1	2510	0.500	1972	7099

12

Table 12-19 (Continued)			Table 12-19 (Continued)		
Head (meters)	l/s	m³/hr	Head (meters)	l/s	m³/hr
0.505	2001	7206	0.755	3659	13,170
0.510	2031	7313	0.760	3695	13,300
0.515	2061	7421	0.765	3732	13,440
0.520	2091	7530	0.770	3768	13,570
0.525	2121	7638	0.775	3805	13,700
0.530	2152	7748	0.780	3842	13,830
0.535	2182	7858	0.785	3879	13,970
0.540	2213	7968	0.790	3916	14,100
0.545	2244	8079	0.795	3953	14,230
0.550	2275	8190	0.800	3991	14,370
0.555	2306	8302	0.805	4028	14,500
0.560	2337	8415	0.810	4066	14,640
0.565	2368	8528	0.815	4103	14,770
0.570	2400	8641	0.820	4141	14,910
0.575	2432	8755	0.825	4179	15,050
0.580	2463	8870	0.830	4217	15,180
0.585	2495	8985	0.835	4255	15,320
0.590	2527	9100	0.840	4294	15,460
0.595	2560	9216	0.845	4332	15,600
0.600	2592	9332	0.850	4370	15,740
0.605	2624	9449	0.855	4409	15,870
0.610	2657	9567	0.860	4448	16,010
0.615	2690	9684	0.865	4487	16,150
0.620	2723	9803	0.870	4526	16,290
0.625	2756	9922	0.875	4565	16,440
0.630	2789	10,040	0.880	4604	16,580
0.635	2822	10,160	0.885	4643	16,720
0.640	2855	10,280	0.890	4683	16,860
0.645	2889	10,400	0.895	4722	17,000
0.650	2923	10,520	0.900	4762	17,140
0.655	2956	10,640	0.905	4801	17,290
0.660	2990	10,770	0.910	4841	17,430
0.665	3024	10,890	0.915	4881	17,580
0.670	3059	11,010	0.920	4921	17,720
0.675	3093	11,140	0.925	4962	17,860
0.680	3127	11,260	0.930	5002	18,010
0.685	3162	11,380	0.935	5042	18,150
0.690	3196	11,510	0.940	5083	18,300
0.695	3231	11,630	0.945	5123	18,450
0.700	3266	11,760	0.950	5164	18,590
0.705	3301	11,890	0.955	5205	18,740
0.710	3336	12,010	0.960	5246	18,890
0.715	3372	12,140	0.965	5287	19,040
0.720	3407	12,270	0.970	5328	19,180
0.725	3443	12,400	0.975	5369	19,330
0.730	3478	12,520	0.980	5411	19,480
0.735	3514	12,650	0.985	5452	19,630
0.740	3550	12,780	0.990	5494	19,780
0.745	3586	12,910	0.995	5535	19,930
0.750	3622	13,040	1.000	5577	20,080

12

Table 12-19 (Continued)		
Head (meters)	l/s	m³/hr
1.005	5619	20,230
1.010	5661	20,380
1.015	5703	20,530
1.020	5745	20,690
1.025	5787	20,840
1.030	5830	20,990
1.035	5872	21,140
1.040	5915	21,300
1.045	5958	21,450
1.050	6000	21,600
1.055	6043	21,760
1.060	6086	21,910
1.065	6130	22,070
1.070	6173	22,220
1.075	6216	22,380
1.080	6259	22,540
1.085	6303	22,690
1.090	6347	22,850
1.095	6390	23,010
1.100	6434	23,170
1.105	6478	23,320
1.110	6522	23,480
1.115	6566	23,640
1.120	6610	23,800
1.125	6655	23,960
1.130	6699	24,120
1.135	6744	24,280
1.140	6788	24,440
1.145	6833	24,600
1.150	6878	24,760
1.155	6923	24,930
1.160	6968	25,090
1.165	7013	25,250
1.170	7058	25,410
1.175	7103	25,580
1.180	7149	25,740
1.185	7194	25,900
1.190	7240	26,070
1.195	7285	26,230
1.200	7331	26,400
1.205	7377	26,560
1.210	7423	26,730
1.215	7469	26,890
1.220	7515	27,060
1.225	7561	27,220
1.230	7608	27,390
1.235	7654	27,560
1.240	7701	27,730
1.245	7747	27,890
1.250	7794	28,060

Table 12-19 (Continued)		
Head (meters)	l/s	m³/hr
1.255	7841	28,230
1.260	7888	28,400
1.265	7935	28,570
1.270	7982	28,740
1.275	8029	28,910
1.280	8076	29,080
1.285	8124	29,250
1.290	8171	29,420
1.295	8219	29,590
1.300	8266	29,760
1.305	8314	29,940
1.310	8362	30,110
1.315	8410	30,280
1.320	8458	30,450
1.325	8506	30,630
1.330	8554	30,800
1.335	8602	30,970
1.340	8651	31,150
1.345	8699	31,320
1.350	8748	31,500
1.355	8796	31,670
1.360	8845	31,850
1.365	8894	32,020
1.370	8943	32,200
1.375	8992	32,380
1.380	9041	32,550
1.385	9090	32,730
1.390	9140	32,910
1.395	9189	33,080
1.400	9238	33,260
1.405	9288	33,440
1.410	9337	33,620
1.415	9387	33,800
1.420	9437	33,980
1.425	9487	34,160
1.430	9537	34,340
1.435	9587	34,520
1.440	9637	34,700
1.445	9687	34,880
1.450	9738	35,060
1.455	9788	35,240
1.460	9839	35,420
1.465	9889	35,610
1.470	9940	35,790
1.475	9991	35,970
1.480	10,040	36,150
1.485	10,090	36,340
1.490	10,140	36,520
1.495	10,190	36,710
1.500	10,250	36,890

12

12

CHAPTER

13

Parshall Flume Discharge Tables

Overview

This chapter contains discharge (head vs. flow rate) tables for Parshall Flumes. Note that all of the tabular data is for free flow. If the flow is submerged, corrections will have to be made to determine the discharge, as discussed in Chapter 4.

Discharge tables for Parshall flumes with head in feet

13-1:	1 in.	13-6:	1 ft.	13-11:	5 ft.
13-2:	2 in.	13-7:	$1^1/_2$ ft.	13-12:	6 ft.
13-3:	3 in.	13-8:	2 ft.	13-13:	8 ft.
13-4:	6 in.	13-9:	3 ft.	13-14:	10 ft.
13-5:	9 in.	13-10:	4 ft	13-15:	12 ft.

The flume discharges are listed in three different units of measure:
CFS - cubic feet per second   GPM - gallons per minute
MGD - million gallons per day

Discharge tables for Parshall flumes with head in meters

13-16:	0.025 m	13-21:	0.305 m	13-26:	1.52 m
13-17:	0.051 m	13-22:	0.457 m	13-27:	1.83 m
13-18:	0.076 m	13-23:	0.610 m	13-28:	2.44 m
13-19:	0.152 m	13-24:	0.914 m	13-29:	3.05 m
13-20:	0.229 m	13-25:	1.22 m	13-30:	3.66 m

The discharges of the flumes are listed in two different units of measure:
l/s - liters per second m^3/hr - cubic meters per hour

The formulas used to develop each table are listed on the table. Values in italics indicate flow below the recommended range of this particular primary device.

Table 13-1:
1 in. Parshall Flume Discharge Table with Head in Feet

Formula: $\text{CFS} = 0.3380\ H^{1.550}$
$\text{GPM} = 151.7\ H^{1.550}$
$\text{MGD} = 0.2184\ H^{1.550}$

Where: H = head in feet

Values in italics indicate flow below the recommended range of this particular primary device.

Head (feet)	CFS	GPM	MGD	Head (feet)	CFS	GPM	MGD
	Table 13-1				*Table 13-1 (Continued)*		
0.01	*0.0003*	*0.121*	*0.0002*	0.36	0.0694	31.14	0.0448
0.02	*0.0008*	*0.353*	*0.0005*	0.37	0.0724	32.49	0.0468
0.03	*0.0015*	*0.662*	*0.0010*	0.38	0.0754	33.86	0.0487
0.04	*0.0023*	*1.033*	*0.0015*	0.39	0.0785	35.25	0.0507
0.05	*0.0033*	*1.460*	*0.0021*	0.40	0.0817	36.66	0.0528
0.06	*0.0043*	*1.937*	*0.0028*	0.41	0.0849	38.09	0.0548
0.07	*0.0055*	*2.460*	*0.0035*	0.42	0.0881	39.54	0.0569
0.08	*0.0067*	*3.025*	*0.0044*	0.43	0.0914	41.01	0.0590
0.09	*0.0081*	*3.631*	*0.0052*	0.44	0.0947	42.49	0.0612
0.10	0.0095	4.275	0.0062	0.45	0.0980	44.00	0.0633
0.11	0.0110	4.956	0.0071	0.46	0.1014	45.53	0.0655
0.12	0.0126	5.672	0.0082	0.47	0.1049	47.07	0.0678
0.13	0.0143	6.421	0.0092	0.48	0.1084	48.63	0.0700
0.14	0.0160	7.203	0.0104	0.49	0.1119	50.21	0.0723
0.15	0.0179	8.015	0.0115	0.50	0.1154	51.81	0.0746
0.16	0.0197	8.859	0.0128	0.51	0.1190	53.42	0.0769
0.17	0.0217	9.732	0.0140	0.52	0.1227	55.05	0.0793
0.18	0.0237	10.63	0.0153	0.53	0.1263	56.70	0.0816
0.19	0.0258	11.56	0.0166	0.54	0.1301	58.37	0.0840
0.20	0.0279	12.52	0.0180	0.55	0.1338	60.05	0.0865
0.21	0.0301	13.50	0.0194	0.56	0.1376	61.76	0.0889
0.22	0.0323	14.51	0.0209	0.57	0.1414	63.47	0.0914
0.23	0.0346	15.55	0.0224	0.58	0.1453	65.21	0.0939
0.24	0.0370	16.61	0.0239	0.59	0.1492	66.96	0.0964
0.25	0.0394	17.69	0.0255	0.60	0.1531	68.73	0.0989
0.26	0.0419	18.80	0.0271	0.61	0.1571	70.51	0.1015
0.27	0.0444	19.93	0.0287	0.62	0.1611	72.31	0.1041
0.28	0.0470	21.09	0.0304	0.63	0.1652	74.12	0.1067
0.29	0.0496	22.27	0.0321	0.64	0.1692	75.96	0.1094
0.30	0.0523	23.47	0.0338	0.65	0.1734	77.80	0.1120
0.31	0.0550	24.69	0.0356	0.66	0.1775	79.67	0.1147
0.32	0.0578	25.94	0.0373	0.67	0.1817	81.55	0.1174
0.33	0.0606	27.21	0.0392	0.68	0.1859	83.44	0.1201
0.34	0.0635	28.50	0.0410	0.69	0.1902	85.35	0.1229
0.35	0.0664	29.81	0.0429	0.70	0.1945	87.27	0.1256

13

Table 13-2:
2 in. Parshall Flume Discharge Table with Head in Feet

Formula:
$$CFS = 0.6760\ H^{1.550}$$
$$GPM = 303.4\ H^{1.550}$$
$$MGD = 0.4369\ H^{1.550}$$

Where: H = head in feet

Values in italics indicate flow below the recommended range of this particular primary device.

Table 13-2				Table 13-2 (Continued)			
Head (feet)	CFS	GPM	MGD	Head (feet)	CFS	GPM	MGD
0.01	*0.0005*	*0.241*	*0.0003*	0.41	0.1697	76.18	0.1097
0.02	*0.0016*	*0.706*	*0.0010*	0.42	0.1762	79.08	0.1139
0.03	*0.0029*	*1.323*	*0.0019*	0.43	0.1827	82.01	0.1181
0.04	*0.0046*	*2.066*	*0.0030*	0.44	0.1894	84.99	0.1224
0.05	*0.0065*	*2.920*	*0.0042*	0.45	0.1961	88.00	0.1267
0.06	*0.0086*	*3.874*	*0.0056*	0.46	0.2029	91.05	0.1311
0.07	*0.0110*	*4.920*	*0.0071*	0.47	0.2097	94.14	0.1356
0.08	*0.0135*	*6.051*	*0.0087*	0.48	0.2167	97.26	0.1401
0.09	*0.0162*	*7.263*	*0.0105*	0.49	0.2237	100.4	0.1446
0.10	0.0191	8.551	0.0123	0.50	0.2309	103.6	0.1492
0.11	0.0221	9.912	0.0143	0.51	0.2381	106.8	0.1539
0.12	0.0253	11.34	0.0163	0.52	0.2453	110.1	0.1586
0.13	0.0286	12.84	0.0185	0.53	0.2527	113.4	0.1633
0.14	0.0321	14.41	0.0207	0.54	0.2601	116.7	0.1681
0.15	0.0357	16.03	0.0231	0.55	0.2676	120.1	0.1730
0.16	0.0395	17.72	0.0255	0.56	0.2752	123.5	0.1779
0.17	0.0434	19.46	0.0280	0.57	0.2828	126.9	0.1828
0.18	0.0474	21.27	0.0306	0.58	0.2906	130.4	0.1878
0.19	0.0515	23.13	0.0333	0.59	0.2984	133.9	0.1928
0.20	0.0558	25.04	0.0361	0.60	0.3063	137.5	0.1979
0.21	0.0602	27.01	0.0389	0.61	0.3142	141.0	0.2031
0.22	0.0647	29.02	0.0418	0.62	0.3222	144.6	0.2083
0.23	0.0693	31.10	0.0448	0.63	0.3303	148.2	0.2135
0.24	0.0740	33.22	0.0478	0.64	0.3385	151.9	0.2188
0.25	0.0788	35.39	0.0510	0.65	0.3467	155.6	0.2241
0.26	0.0838	37.60	0.0541	0.66	0.3550	159.3	0.2294
0.27	0.0888	39.87	0.0574	0.67	0.3634	163.1	0.2349
0.28	0.0940	42.18	0.0607	0.68	0.3718	166.9	0.2403
0.29	0.0992	44.54	0.0641	0.69	0.3803	170.7	0.2458
0.30	0.1046	46.94	0.0676	0.70	0.3889	174.5	0.2514
0.31	0.1100	49.39	0.0711	0.71	0.3976	178.4	0.2569
0.32	0.1156	51.88	0.0747	0.72	0.4063	182.3	0.2626
0.33	0.1212	54.41	0.0784	0.73	0.4150	186.3	0.2682
0.34	0.1270	56.99	0.0821	0.74	0.4239	190.3	0.2740
0.35	0.1328	59.61	0.0858	0.75	0.4328	194.2	0.2797
0.36	0.1387	62.27	0.0897	0.76	0.4418	198.3	0.2855
0.37	0.1448	64.97	0.0936	0.77	0.4508	202.3	0.2914
0.38	0.1509	67.71	0.0975	0.78	0.4599	206.4	0.2973
0.39	0.1571	70.50	0.1015	0.79	0.4691	210.5	0.3032
0.40	0.1634	73.32	0.1056	0.80	0.4783	214.7	0.3092

13

Table 13-3:
3 in. Parshall Flume Discharge Table with Head in Feet

Formula: CFS $= 0.9920\,H^{1.547}$
GPM $= 445.2\,H^{1.547}$
MGD $= 0.6411\,H^{1.547}$
Where: H = head in feet

Values in italics indicate flow below the recommended range of this particular primary device.

Head (feet)	CFS	GPM	MGD	Head (feet)	CFS	GPM	MGD
0.01	*0.0008*	*0.359*	*0.0005*	0.51	0.3500	157.1	0.2262
0.02	*0.0023*	*1.048*	*0.0015*	0.52	0.3607	161.9	0.2331
0.03	*0.0044*	*1.962*	*0.0028*	0.53	0.3715	166.7	0.2401
0.04	*0.0068*	*3.062*	*0.0044*	0.54	0.3824	171.6	0.2471
0.05	*0.0096*	*4.324*	*0.0062*	0.55	0.3934	176.6	0.2543
0.06	*0.0128*	*5.733*	*0.0083*	0.56	0.4045	181.6	0.2614
0.07	*0.0162*	*7.277*	*0.0105*	0.57	0.4158	186.6	0.2687
0.08	*0.0199*	*8.947*	*0.0129*	0.58	0.4271	191.7	0.2760
0.09	*0.0239*	*10.73*	*0.0155*	0.59	0.4386	196.8	0.2834
0.10	0.0282	12.63	0.0182	0.60	0.4501	202.0	0.2909
0.11	0.0326	14.64	0.0211	0.61	0.4618	207.2	0.2984
0.12	0.0373	16.75	0.0241	0.62	0.4735	212.5	0.3060
0.13	0.0422	18.96	0.0273	0.63	0.4854	217.8	0.3137
0.14	0.0474	21.26	0.0306	0.64	0.4974	223.2	0.3214
0.15	0.0527	23.66	0.0341	0.65	0.5094	228.6	0.3292
0.16	0.0582	26.14	0.0376	0.66	0.5216	234.1	0.3371
0.17	0.0640	28.71	0.0413	0.67	0.5339	239.6	0.3450
0.18	0.0699	31.37	0.0452	0.68	0.5463	245.2	0.3530
0.19	0.0760	34.10	0.0491	0.69	0.5587	250.8	0.3611
0.20	0.0823	36.92	0.0532	0.70	0.5713	256.4	0.3692
0.21	0.0887	39.81	0.0573	0.71	0.5840	262.1	0.3774
0.22	0.0953	42.78	0.0616	0.72	0.5968	267.8	0.3857
0.23	0.1021	45.83	0.0660	0.73	0.6096	273.6	0.3940
0.24	0.1091	48.95	0.0705	0.74	0.6226	279.4	0.4024
0.25	0.1162	52.14	0.0751	0.75	0.6357	285.3	0.4108
0.26	0.1234	55.40	0.0798	0.76	0.6488	291.2	0.4193
0.27	0.1309	58.73	0.0846	0.77	0.6621	297.1	0.4279
0.28	0.1384	62.13	0.0895	0.78	0.6754	303.1	0.4365
0.29	0.1462	65.60	0.0945	0.79	0.6889	309.2	0.4452
0.30	0.1540	69.13	0.0995	0.80	0.7024	315.2	0.4539
0.31	0.1620	72.73	0.1047	0.81	0.7160	321.4	0.4628
0.32	0.1702	76.39	0.1100	0.82	0.7298	327.5	0.4716
0.33	0.1785	80.11	0.1154	0.83	0.7436	333.7	0.4806
0.34	0.1869	83.90	0.1208	0.84	0.7575	340.0	0.4895
0.35	0.1955	87.75	0.1264	0.85	0.7715	346.2	0.4986
0.36	0.2042	91.65	0.1320	0.86	0.7856	352.6	0.5077
0.37	0.2131	95.62	0.1377	0.87	0.7997	358.9	0.5168
0.38	0.2220	99.65	0.1435	0.88	0.8140	365.3	0.5261
0.39	0.2311	103.7	0.1494	0.89	0.8284	371.8	0.5353
0.40	0.2404	107.9	0.1554	0.90	0.8428	378.2	0.5447
0.41	0.2497	112.1	0.1614	0.91	0.8573	384.8	0.5541
0.42	0.2592	116.3	0.1675	0.92	0.8719	391.3	0.5635
0.43	0.2688	120.7	0.1737	0.93	0.8867	397.9	0.5730
0.44	0.2786	125.0	0.1800	0.94	0.9014	404.6	0.5826
0.45	0.2884	129.4	0.1864	0.95	0.9163	411.2	0.5922
0.46	0.2984	133.9	0.1928	0.96	0.9313	418.0	0.6019
0.47	0.3085	138.4	0.1994	0.97	0.9463	424.7	0.6116
0.48	0.3187	143.0	0.2060	0.98	0.9615	431.5	0.6214
0.49	0.3290	147.7	0.2126	0.99	0.9767	438.3	0.6312
0.50	0.3395	152.4	0.2194	1.00	0.9920	445.2	0.6411

13

Table 13-3 (Continued)			
Head (feet)	CFS	GPM	MGD
1.01	1.007	452.1	0.6510
1.02	1.023	459.0	0.6610
1.03	1.038	466.0	0.6711
1.04	1.054	473.0	0.6812
1.05	1.070	480.1	0.6914

Table 13-3 (Continued)			
Head (feet)	CFS	GPM	MGD
1.06	1.086	487.2	0.7016
1.07	1.101	494.3	0.7118
1.08	1.117	501.5	0.7222
1.09	1.133	508.7	0.7325
1.10	1.150	515.9	0.7430

13

Table 13-4:
6 in. Parshall Flume Discharge Table with Head In Feet

Formula: CFS $= 2.060\ H^{1.580}$
GPM $= 924.5\ H^{1.580}$
MGD $= 1.331\ H^{1.580}$

Where: H = head in feet

Values in italics indicate flow below the recommended range of this particular primary device.

Head (feet)	CFS	GPM	MGD	Head (feet)	CFS	GPM	MGD
0.01	*0.0014*	*0.64*	*0.0009*	0.51	0.7109	319.1	0.4593
0.02	*0.0043*	*1.91*	*0.0028*	0.52	0.7331	329.0	0.4737
0.03	*0.0081*	*3.63*	*0.0052*	0.53	0.7555	339.0	0.4881
0.04	*0.0127*	*5.72*	*0.0082*	0.54	0.7781	349.2	0.5028
0.05	*0.0181*	*8.13*	*0.0117*	0.55	0.8010	359.5	0.5175
0.06	*0.0242*	*10.85*	*0.0156*	0.56	0.8241	369.9	0.5325
0.07	*0.0308*	*13.84*	*0.0199*	0.57	0.8475	380.4	0.5476
0.08	*0.0381*	*17.09*	*0.0246*	0.58	0.8711	391.0	0.5629
0.09	*0.0459*	*20.59*	*0.0296*	0.59	0.8950	401.7	0.5783
0.10	0.0542	24.32	0.0350	0.60	0.9191	412.5	0.5938
0.11	0.0630	28.27	0.0407	0.61	0.9434	423.4	0.6095
0.12	0.0723	32.43	0.0467	0.62	0.9679	434.4	0.6254
0.13	0.0820	36.81	0.0530	0.63	0.9927	445.5	0.6414
0.14	0.0922	41.38	0.0596	0.64	1.018	456.7	0.6576
0.15	0.1028	46.15	0.0664	0.65	1.043	468.1	0.6739
0.16	0.1139	51.10	0.0736	0.66	1.068	479.5	0.6903
0.17	0.1253	56.24	0.0810	0.67	1.094	491.0	0.7069
0.18	0.1372	61.55	0.0886	0.68	1.120	502.7	0.7237
0.19	0.1494	67.04	0.0965	0.69	1.146	514.4	0.7406
0.20	0.1620	72.70	0.1047	0.70	1.173	526.2	0.7576
0.21	0.1750	78.53	0.1131	0.71	1.199	538.1	0.7748
0.22	0.1883	84.52	0.1217	0.72	1.226	550.2	0.7921
0.23	0.2020	90.66	0.1305	0.73	1.253	562.3	0.8095
0.24	0.2161	96.97	0.1396	0.74	1.280	574.5	0.8271
0.25	0.2305	103.4	0.1489	0.75	1.308	586.8	0.8448
0.26	0.2452	110.0	0.1584	0.76	1.335	599.2	0.8627
0.27	0.2603	116.8	0.1682	0.77	1.363	611.7	0.8807
0.28	0.2757	123.7	0.1781	0.78	1.391	624.3	0.8989
0.29	0.2914	130.8	0.1883	0.79	1.419	637.0	0.9171
0.30	0.3074	138.0	0.1986	0.80	1.448	649.8	0.9355
0.31	0.3238	145.3	0.2092	0.81	1.477	662.7	0.9541
0.32	0.3404	152.8	0.2199	0.82	1.506	675.7	0.9728
0.33	0.3574	160.4	0.2309	0.83	1.535	688.7	0.9916
0.34	0.3746	168.1	0.2421	0.84	1.564	701.9	1.011
0.35	0.3922	176.0	0.2534	0.85	1.593	715.1	1.030
0.36	0.4100	184.0	0.2649	0.86	1.623	728.5	1.049
0.37	0.4282	192.2	0.2767	0.87	1.653	741.9	1.068
0.38	0.4466	200.4	0.2886	0.88	1.683	755.4	1.088
0.39	0.4653	208.8	0.3006	0.89	1.714	769.0	1.107
0.40	0.4843	217.4	0.3129	0.90	1.744	782.7	1.127
0.41	0.5036	226.0	0.3254	0.91	1.775	796.5	1.147
0.42	0.5231	234.8	0.3380	0.92	1.806	810.4	1.167
0.43	0.5429	243.7	0.3508	0.93	1.837	824.3	1.187
0.44	0.5630	252.7	0.3638	0.94	1.868	838.4	1.207
0.45	0.5834	261.8	0.3769	0.95	1.900	852.5	1.227
0.46	0.6040	271.1	0.3902	0.96	1.931	866.8	1.248
0.47	0.6249	280.4	0.4037	0.97	1.963	881.1	1.268
0.48	0.6460	289.9	0.4174	0.98	1.995	895.5	1.289
0.49	0.6674	299.5	0.4312	0.99	2.028	909.9	1.310
0.50	0.6890	309.2	0.4452	1.00	2.060	924.5	1.331

13

Table 13-4 (Continued)				Table 13-4 (Continued)			
Head (feet)	CFS	GPM	MGD	Head (feet)	CFS	GPM	MGD
1.01	2.093	939.1	1.352	1.26	2.968	1332	1.918
1.02	2.125	953.9	1.373	1.27	3.005	1349	1.942
1.03	2.158	968.7	1.395	1.28	3.043	1366	1.966
1.04	2.192	983.6	1.416	1.29	3.080	1382	1.990
1.05	2.225	998.6	1.438	1.30	3.118	1399	2.015
1.06	2.259	1014	1.459	1.31	3.156	1416	2.039
1.07	2.292	1029	1.481	1.32	3.194	1434	2.064
1.08	2.326	1044	1.503	1.33	3.233	1451	2.089
1.09	2.360	1059	1.525	1.34	3.271	1468	2.114
1.10	2.395	1075	1.547	1.35	3.310	1485	2.138
1.11	2.429	1090	1.570	1.36	3.349	1503	2.164
1.12	2.464	1106	1.592	1.37	3.388	1520	2.189
1.13	2.499	1121	1.615	1.38	3.427	1538	2.214
1.14	2.534	1137	1.637	1.39	3.466	1556	2.239
1.15	2.569	1153	1.660	1.40	3.505	1573	2.265
1.16	2.604	1169	1.683	1.41	3.545	1591	2.291
1.17	2.640	1185	1.706	1.42	3.585	1609	2.316
1.18	2.676	1201	1.729	1.43	3.625	1627	2.342
1.19	2.712	1217	1.752	1.44	3.665	1645	2.368
1.20	2.748	1233	1.775	1.45	3.705	1663	2.394
1.21	2.784	1249	1.799	1.46	3.746	1681	2.420
1.22	2.820	1266	1.822	1.47	3.786	1699	2.446
1.23	2.857	1282	1.846	1.48	3.827	1718	2.473
1.24	2.894	1299	1.870	1.49	3.868	1736	2.499
1.25	2.931	1315	1.894	1.50	3.909	1754	2.526

13

Table 13-5:
9 in. Parshall Flume Discharge Table with Head in Feet

Formula: CFS $= 3.070\ H^{1.530}$
GPM $= 1378\ H^{1.530}$
MGD $= 1.984\ H^{1.530}$
Where: H = head in feet

Values in italics indicate flow below the recommended range of this particular primary device.

Table 13-5				Table 13-5 (Continued)			
Head (feet)	CFS	GPM	MGD	Head (feet)	CFS	GPM	MGD
0.01	*0.0027*	*1.20*	*0.0017*	0.51	1.096	491.8	0.7081
0.02	*0.0077*	*3.47*	*0.0050*	0.52	1.129	506.7	0.7295
0.03	*0.0144*	*6.45*	*0.0093*	0.53	1.162	521.7	0.7511
0.04	*0.0223*	*10.01*	*0.0144*	0.54	1.196	536.8	0.7729
0.05	*0.0314*	*14.08*	*0.0203*	0.55	1.230	552.1	0.7949
0.06	*0.0415*	*18.61*	*0.0268*	0.56	1.264	567.5	0.8171
0.07	*0.0525*	*23.56*	*0.0339*	0.57	1.299	583.1	0.8395
0.08	*0.0644*	*28.90*	*0.0416*	0.58	1.334	598.8	0.8622
0.09	*0.0771*	*34.61*	*0.0498*	0.59	1.369	614.7	0.8850
0.10	0.0906	40.67	0.0586	0.60	1.405	630.7	0.9081
0.11	0.1048	47.05	0.0677	0.61	1.441	646.9	0.9313
0.12	0.1198	53.75	0.0774	0.62	1.477	663.1	0.9548
0.13	0.1354	60.76	0.0875	0.63	1.514	679.6	0.9784
0.14	0.1516	68.05	0.0980	0.64	1.551	696.2	1.002
0.15	0.1685	75.63	0.1089	0.65	1.588	712.9	1.026
0.16	0.1860	83.47	0.1202	0.66	1.626	729.7	1.051
0.17	0.2040	91.59	0.1319	0.67	1.664	746.7	1.075
0.18	0.2227	99.96	0.1439	0.68	1.702	763.8	1.100
0.19	0.2419	108.6	0.1563	0.69	1.740	781.1	1.125
0.20	0.2616	117.4	0.1691	0.70	1.779	798.5	1.150
0.21	0.2819	126.5	0.1822	0.71	1.818	816.0	1.175
0.22	0.3027	135.9	0.1956	0.72	1.857	833.6	1.200
0.23	0.3240	145.4	0.2094	0.73	1.897	851.4	1.226
0.24	0.3458	155.2	0.2235	0.74	1.937	869.3	1.252
0.25	0.3681	165.2	0.2379	0.75	1.977	887.3	1.278
0.26	0.3909	175.5	0.2526	0.76	2.017	905.5	1.304
0.27	0.4141	185.9	0.2676	0.77	2.058	923.8	1.330
0.28	0.4378	196.5	0.2829	0.78	2.099	942.2	1.357
0.29	0.4620	207.4	0.2985	0.79	2.140	960.8	1.383
0.30	0.4866	218.4	0.3144	0.80	2.182	979.4	1.410
0.31	0.5116	229.6	0.3306	0.81	2.224	998.2	1.437
0.32	0.5371	241.1	0.3471	0.82	2.266	1017	1.464
0.33	0.5629	252.7	0.3638	0.83	2.308	1036	1.492
0.34	0.5893	264.5	0.3808	0.84	2.351	1055	1.519
0.35	0.6160	276.5	0.3981	0.85	2.394	1075	1.547
0.36	0.6431	288.7	0.4156	0.86	2.437	1094	1.575
0.37	0.6706	301.0	0.4334	0.87	2.481	1114	1.603
0.38	0.6986	313.6	0.4515	0.88	2.525	1133	1.632
0.39	0.7269	326.3	0.4698	0.89	2.569	1153	1.660
0.40	0.7556	339.2	0.4883	0.90	2.613	1173	1.689
0.41	0.7847	352.2	0.5071	0.91	2.657	1193	1.717
0.42	0.8142	365.4	0.5262	0.92	2.702	1213	1.746
0.43	0.8440	378.8	0.5454	0.93	2.747	1233	1.775
0.44	0.8742	392.4	0.5650	0.94	2.793	1254	1.805
0.45	0.9048	406.1	0.5847	0.95	2.838	1274	1.834
0.46	0.9357	420.0	0.6047	0.96	2.884	1295	1.864
0.47	0.9670	434.1	0.6250	0.97	2.930	1315	1.894
0.48	0.9987	448.3	0.6454	0.98	2.977	1336	1.924
0.49	1.031	462.6	0.6661	0.99	3.023	1357	1.954
0.50	1.063	477.2	0.6870	1.00	3.070	1378	1.984

13

Table 13-5 (Continued)				Table 13-5 (Continued)			
Head (feet)	CFS	GPM	MGD	Head (feet)	CFS	GPM	MGD
1.01	3.117	1399	2.014	1.51	5.767	2589	3.727
1.02	3.164	1420	2.045	1.52	5.826	2615	3.765
1.03	3.212	1442	2.076	1.53	5.885	2641	3.803
1.04	3.260	1463	2.107	1.54	5.944	2668	3.841
1.05	3.308	1485	2.138	1.55	6.003	2694	3.879
1.06	3.356	1506	2.169	1.56	6.062	2721	3.918
1.07	3.405	1528	2.200	1.57	6.122	2748	3.956
1.08	3.454	1550	2.232	1.58	6.181	2775	3.995
1.09	3.503	1572	2.264	1.59	6.241	2801	4.033
1.10	3.552	1594	2.295	1.60	6.301	2828	4.072
1.11	3.601	1617	2.327	1.61	6.362	2856	4.111
1.12	3.651	1639	2.360	1.62	6.422	2883	4.150
1.13	3.701	1661	2.392	1.63	6.483	2910	4.190
1.14	3.751	1684	2.424	1.64	6.544	2937	4.229
1.15	3.802	1707	2.457	1.65	6.605	2965	4.269
1.16	3.853	1729	2.490	1.66	6.667	2992	4.308
1.17	3.904	1752	2.523	1.67	6.728	3020	4.348
1.18	3.955	1775	2.556	1.68	6.790	3048	4.388
1.19	4.006	1798	2.589	1.69	6.852	3076	4.428
1.20	4.058	1821	2.622	1.70	6.914	3103	4.468
1.21	4.110	1845	2.656	1.71	6.976	3131	4.508
1.22	4.162	1868	2.690	1.72	7.039	3159	4.549
1.23	4.214	1891	2.723	1.73	7.101	3188	4.589
1.24	4.267	1915	2.757	1.74	7.164	3216	4.630
1.25	4.319	1939	2.791	1.75	7.227	3244	4.671
1.26	4.372	1963	2.826	1.76	7.291	3273	4.712
1.27	4.425	1986	2.860	1.77	7.354	3301	4.753
1.28	4.479	2010	2.894	1.78	7.418	3330	4.794
1.29	4.533	2034	2.929	1.79	7.482	3358	4.835
1.30	4.586	2059	2.964	1.80	7.546	3387	4.877
1.31	4.640	2083	2.999	1.81	7.610	3416	4.918
1.32	4.695	2107	3.034	1.82	7.674	3445	4.960
1.33	4.749	2132	3.069	1.83	7.739	3474	5.001
1.34	4.804	2156	3.105	1.84	7.804	3503	5.043
1.35	4.859	2181	3.140	1.85	7.869	3532	5.085
1.36	4.914	2206	3.176	1.86	7.934	3561	5.127
1.37	4.970	2231	3.212	1.87	7.999	3591	5.170
1.38	5.025	2256	3.248	1.88	8.065	3620	5.212
1.39	5.081	2281	3.284	1.89	8.131	3650	5.254
1.40	5.137	2306	3.320	1.90	8.197	3679	5.297
1.41	5.193	2331	3.356	1.91	8.263	3709	5.340
1.42	5.250	2356	3.393	1.92	8.329	3739	5.383
1.43	5.306	2382	3.429	1.93	8.395	3768	5.426
1.44	5.363	2407	3.466	1.94	8.462	3798	5.469
1.45	5.420	2433	3.503	1.95	8.529	3828	5.512
1.46	5.478	2459	3.540	1.96	8.596	3858	5.555
1.47	5.535	2485	3.577	1.97	8.663	3889	5.599
1.48	5.593	2510	3.614	1.98	8.730	3919	5.642
1.49	5.651	2536	3.652	1.99	8.798	3949	5.686
1.50	5.709	2563	3.689	2.00	8.866	3979	5.730

13

Table 13-6:
1 ft. Parshall Flume Discharge Table with Head in Feet

Formula: CFS $= 4.000\ H^{1.522}$
GPM $= 1795\ H^{1.522}$
MGD $= 2.585\ H^{1.522}$
Where: H = head in feet

Values in italics indicate flow below the recommended range of this particular primary device.

Table 13-6				Table 13-6 (Continued)			
Head (feet)	CFS	GPM	MGD	Head (feet)	CFS	GPM	MGD
0.01	*0.0036*	*1.62*	*0.0023*	0.51	1.435	644.1	0.9276
0.02	*0.0104*	*4.66*	*0.0067*	0.52	1.478	663.5	0.9555
0.03	*0.0192*	*8.64*	*0.0124*	0.53	1.522	683.0	0.9836
0.04	*0.0298*	*13.38*	*0.0193*	0.54	1.566	702.7	1.012
0.05	*0.0419*	*18.79*	*0.0271*	0.55	1.610	722.6	1.041
0.06	*0.0553*	*24.80*	*0.0357*	0.56	1.655	742.7	1.070
0.07	*0.0699*	*31.36*	*0.0452*	0.57	1.700	763.0	1.099
0.08	*0.0856*	*38.43*	*0.0553*	0.58	1.746	783.4	1.128
0.09	*0.1024*	*45.97*	*0.0662*	0.59	1.792	804.1	1.158
0.10	0.1202	53.96	0.0777	0.60	1.838	824.9	1.188
0.11	0.1390	62.38	0.0898	0.61	1.885	845.9	1.218
0.12	0.1587	71.22	0.1026	0.62	1.932	867.1	1.249
0.13	0.1793	80.44	0.1158	0.63	1.980	888.5	1.280
0.14	0.2007	90.05	0.1297	0.64	2.028	910.1	1.311
0.15	0.2229	100.0	0.1440	0.65	2.076	931.8	1.342
0.16	0.2459	110.3	0.1589	0.66	2.125	953.7	1.373
0.17	0.2697	121.0	0.1743	0.67	2.174	975.8	1.405
0.18	0.2942	132.0	0.1901	0.68	2.224	998.0	1.437
0.19	0.3194	143.3	0.2064	0.69	2.274	1020	1.470
0.20	0.3453	155.0	0.2232	0.70	2.324	1043	1.502
0.21	0.3719	166.9	0.2404	0.71	2.375	1066	1.535
0.22	0.3992	179.2	0.2580	0.72	2.426	1089	1.568
0.23	0.4272	191.7	0.2761	0.73	2.478	1112	1.601
0.24	0.4558	204.5	0.2945	0.74	2.529	1135	1.635
0.25	0.4850	217.6	0.3134	0.75	2.582	1159	1.668
0.26	0.5148	231.0	0.3327	0.76	2.634	1182	1.702
0.27	0.5452	244.7	0.3524	0.77	2.687	1206	1.737
0.28	0.5763	258.6	0.3724	0.78	2.740	1230	1.771
0.29	0.6079	272.8	0.3929	0.79	2.794	1254	1.806
0.30	0.6401	287.2	0.4137	0.80	2.848	1278	1.841
0.31	0.6728	301.9	0.4348	0.81	2.903	1303	1.876
0.32	0.7062	316.9	0.4564	0.82	2.957	1327	1.911
0.33	0.7400	332.1	0.4782	0.83	3.012	1352	1.947
0.34	0.7744	347.5	0.5005	0.84	3.068	1377	1.983
0.35	0.8093	363.2	0.5230	0.85	3.123	1402	2.019
0.36	0.8448	379.1	0.5460	0.86	3.180	1427	2.055
0.37	0.8808	395.2	0.5692	0.87	3.236	1452	2.091
0.38	0.9173	411.6	0.5928	0.88	3.293	1478	2.128
0.39	0.9542	428.2	0.6167	0.89	3.350	1503	2.165
0.40	0.9917	445.0	0.6409	0.90	3.407	1529	2.202
0.41	1.030	462.1	0.6655	0.91	3.465	1555	2.239
0.42	1.068	479.3	0.6903	0.92	3.523	1581	2.277
0.43	1.107	496.8	0.7155	0.93	3.582	1607	2.315
0.44	1.147	514.5	0.7410	0.94	3.640	1634	2.353
0.45	1.186	532.4	0.7667	0.95	3.700	1660	2.391
0.46	1.227	550.5	0.7928	0.96	3.759	1687	2.429
0.47	1.268	568.8	0.8192	0.97	3.819	1714	2.468
0.48	1.309	587.4	0.8459	0.98	3.879	1741	2.507
0.49	1.351	606.1	0.8728	0.99	3.939	1768	2.546
0.50	1.393	625.0	0.9001	1.00	4.000	1795	2.585

13

Table 13-6 (Continued)				Table 13-6 (Continued)			
Head (feet)	CFS	GPM	MGD	Head (feet)	CFS	GPM	MGD
1.01	4.061	1822	2.624	1.51	7.490	3361	4.840
1.02	4.122	1850	2.664	1.52	7.565	3395	4.889
1.03	4.184	1878	2.704	1.53	7.641	3429	4.938
1.04	4.246	1905	2.744	1.54	7.717	3463	4.987
1.05	4.308	1933	2.784	1.55	7.794	3497	5.037
1.06	4.371	1961	2.825	1.56	7.870	3532	5.086
1.07	4.434	1990	2.865	1.57	7.947	3566	5.136
1.08	4.497	2018	2.906	1.58	8.024	3601	5.186
1.09	4.561	2047	2.947	1.59	8.102	3636	5.236
1.10	4.624	2075	2.989	1.60	8.180	3671	5.286
1.11	4.689	2104	3.030	1.61	8.258	3706	5.336
1.12	4.753	2133	3.072	1.62	8.336	3741	5.387
1.13	4.818	2162	3.113	1.63	8.414	3776	5.438
1.14	4.883	2191	3.156	1.64	8.493	3811	5.488
1.15	4.948	2220	3.198	1.65	8.572	3847	5.540
1.16	5.014	2250	3.240	1.66	8.651	3882	5.591
1.17	5.080	2280	3.283	1.67	8.730	3918	5.642
1.18	5.146	2309	3.326	1.68	8.810	3954	5.694
1.19	5.212	2339	3.369	1.69	8.890	3989	5.745
1.20	5.279	2369	3.412	1.70	8.970	4025	5.797
1.21	5.346	2399	3.455	1.71	9.051	4061	5.849
1.22	5.414	2429	3.499	1.72	9.131	4098	5.901
1.23	5.481	2460	3.542	1.73	9.212	4134	5.953
1.24	5.549	2490	3.586	1.74	9.293	4170	6.006
1.25	5.618	2521	3.630	1.75	9.375	4207	6.058
1.26	5.686	2552	3.675	1.76	9.456	4244	6.111
1.27	5.755	2583	3.719	1.77	9.538	4280	6.164
1.28	5.824	2614	3.764	1.78	9.621	4317	6.217
1.29	5.894	2645	3.809	1.79	9.703	4354	6.271
1.30	5.963	2676	3.854	1.80	9.786	4391	6.324
1.31	6.033	2707	3.899	1.81	9.868	4428	6.377
1.32	6.103	2739	3.944	1.82	9.952	4466	6.431
1.33	6.174	2771	3.990	1.83	10.03	4503	6.485
1.34	6.245	2802	4.036	1.84	10.12	4541	6.539
1.35	6.316	2834	4.082	1.85	10.20	4578	6.593
1.36	6.387	2866	4.128	1.86	10.29	4616	6.648
1.37	6.459	2898	4.174	1.87	10.37	4654	6.702
1.38	6.531	2931	4.220	1.88	10.46	4692	6.757
1.39	6.603	2963	4.267	1.89	10.54	4730	6.811
1.40	6.675	2996	4.314	1.90	10.62	4768	6.866
1.41	6.748	3028	4.361	1.91	10.71	4806	6.921
1.42	6.821	3061	4.408	1.92	10.80	4844	6.977
1.43	6.894	3094	4.455	1.93	10.88	4883	7.032
1.44	6.968	3127	4.503	1.94	10.97	4922	7.088
1.45	7.041	3160	4.551	1.95	11.05	4960	7.143
1.46	7.115	3193	4.598	1.96	11.14	4999	7.199
1.47	7.190	3226	4.646	1.97	11.23	5038	7.255
1.48	7.264	3260	4.695	1.98	11.31	5077	7.311
1.49	7.339	3293	4.743	1.99	11.40	5116	7.367
1.50	7.414	3327	4.791	2.00	11.49	5155	7.424

13

Table 13-6 (Continued)			
Head (feet)	CFS	GPM	MGD
2.01	11.58	5194	7.480
2.02	11.66	5234	7.537
2.03	11.75	5273	7.594
2.04	11.84	5313	7.651
2.05	11.93	5352	7.708
2.06	12.02	5392	7.765
2.07	12.11	5432	7.823
2.08	12.19	5472	7.880
2.09	12.28	5512	7.938
2.10	12.37	5552	7.996
2.11	12.46	5593	8.054
2.12	12.55	5633	8.112
2.13	12.64	5674	8.171
2.14	12.73	5714	8.229
2.15	12.82	5755	8.288
2.16	12.92	5796	8.346
2.17	13.01	5837	8.405
2.18	13.10	5878	8.464
2.19	13.19	5919	8.523
2.20	13.28	5960	8.583
2.21	13.37	6001	8.642
2.22	13.47	6042	8.702
2.23	13.56	6084	8.762
2.24	13.65	6126	8.821
2.25	13.74	6167	8.881

Table 13-6 (Continued)			
Head (feet)	CFS	GPM	MGD
2.26	13.84	6209	8.942
2.27	13.93	6251	9.002
2.28	14.02	6293	9.062
2.29	14.12	6335	9.123
2.30	14.21	6377	9.184
2.31	14.30	6419	9.244
2.32	14.40	6462	9.305
2.33	14.49	6504	9.366
2.34	14.59	6547	9.428
2.35	14.68	6589	9.489
2.36	14.78	6632	9.551
2.37	14.87	6675	9.612
2.38	14.97	6718	9.674
2.39	15.07	6761	9.736
2.40	15.16	6804	9.798
2.41	15.26	6847	9.860
2.42	15.35	6890	9.923
2.43	15.45	6934	9.985
2.44	15.55	6977	10.05
2.45	15.64	7021	10.11
2.46	15.74	7064	10.17
2.47	15.84	7108	10.24
2.48	15.94	7152	10.30
2.49	16.04	7196	10.36
2.50	16.13	7240	10.43

13

Table 13-7:

1 1/2 ft. Parshall Flume Discharge Table with Head in Feet

Formula: CFS $= 6.000\ H^{1.538}$
$\quad\quad\quad$ GPM $= 2693\ H^{1.538}$
$\quad\quad\quad$ MGD $= 3.878\ H^{1.538}$
Where: H = head in feet

Values in italics indicate flow below the recommended range of this particular primary device.

Head (feet)	CFS	GPM	MGD	Head (feet)	CFS	GPM	MGD
0.01	*0.0050*	*2.26*	*0.0033*	0.51	2.130	956.0	1.377
0.02	*0.0146*	*6.57*	*0.0095*	0.52	2.195	985.0	1.418
0.03	*0.0273*	*12.25*	*0.0176*	0.53	2.260	1014	1.461
0.04	*0.0425*	*19.06*	*0.0275*	0.54	2.326	1044	1.503
0.05	*0.0599*	*26.87*	*0.0387*	0.55	2.392	1074	1.546
0.06	*0.0792*	*35.57*	*0.0512*	0.56	2.460	1104	1.590
0.07	*0.1004*	*45.08*	*0.0649*	0.57	2.527	1134	1.634
0.08	*0.1233*	*55.36*	*0.0797*	0.58	2.596	1165	1.678
0.09	*0.1478*	*66.35*	*0.0955*	0.59	2.665	1196	1.723
0.10	0.1738	78.03	0.1124	0.60	2.735	1228	1.768
0.11	0.2013	90.34	0.1301	0.61	2.805	1259	1.813
0.12	0.2301	103.3	0.1487	0.62	2.876	1291	1.859
0.13	0.2603	116.8	0.1682	0.63	2.948	1323	1.905
0.14	0.2917	130.9	0.1885	0.64	3.020	1356	1.952
0.15	0.3243	145.6	0.2096	0.65	3.093	1388	1.999
0.16	0.3582	160.8	0.2315	0.66	3.167	1421	2.047
0.17	0.3932	176.5	0.2541	0.67	3.241	1455	2.095
0.18	0.4293	192.7	0.2775	0.68	3.316	1488	2.143
0.19	0.4665	209.4	0.3015	0.69	3.391	1522	2.192
0.20	0.5048	226.6	0.3263	0.70	3.467	1556	2.241
0.21	0.5442	244.2	0.3517	0.71	3.543	1590	2.290
0.22	0.5845	262.4	0.3778	0.72	3.620	1625	2.340
0.23	0.6259	280.9	0.4045	0.73	3.698	1660	2.390
0.24	0.6682	299.9	0.4319	0.74	3.776	1695	2.441
0.25	0.7115	319.4	0.4599	0.75	3.855	1730	2.491
0.26	0.7558	339.2	0.4885	0.76	3.934	1766	2.543
0.27	0.8009	359.5	0.5177	0.77	4.014	1802	2.594
0.28	0.8470	380.2	0.5474	0.78	4.094	1838	2.646
0.29	0.8940	401.2	0.5778	0.79	4.175	1874	2.699
0.30	0.9418	422.7	0.6087	0.80	4.257	1911	2.751
0.31	0.9905	444.6	0.6402	0.81	4.339	1948	2.805
0.32	1.040	466.8	0.6722	0.82	4.422	1985	2.858
0.33	1.091	489.5	0.7048	0.83	4.505	2022	2.912
0.34	1.142	512.4	0.7379	0.84	4.589	2060	2.966
0.35	1.194	535.8	0.7716	0.85	4.673	2097	3.020
0.36	1.247	559.5	0.8058	0.86	4.758	2135	3.075
0.37	1.300	583.6	0.8404	0.87	4.843	2174	3.130
0.38	1.355	608.1	0.8756	0.88	4.929	2212	3.186
0.39	1.410	632.8	0.9113	0.89	5.015	2251	3.242
0.40	1.466	658.0	0.9475	0.90	5.102	2290	3.298
0.41	1.523	683.4	0.9842	0.91	5.190	2329	3.354
0.42	1.580	709.2	1.021	0.92	5.278	2369	3.411
0.43	1.638	735.4	1.059	0.93	5.366	2409	3.468
0.44	1.697	761.8	1.097	0.94	5.455	2449	3.526
0.45	1.757	788.6	1.136	0.95	5.545	2489	3.584
0.46	1.817	815.8	1.175	0.96	5.635	2529	3.642
0.47	1.879	843.2	1.214	0.97	5.725	2570	3.701
0.48	1.940	870.9	1.254	0.98	5.816	2611	3.759
0.49	2.003	899.0	1.295	0.99	5.908	2652	3.819
0.50	2.066	927.4	1.335	1.00	6.000	2693	3.878

13

Table 13-7 (Continued)				Table 13-7 (Continued)			
Head (feet)	CFS	GPM	MGD	Head (feet)	CFS	GPM	MGD
1.01	6.093	2735	3.938	1.51	11.31	5076	7.309
1.02	6.186	2776	3.998	1.52	11.42	5128	7.384
1.03	6.279	2818	4.058	1.53	11.54	5180	7.459
1.04	6.373	2860	4.119	1.54	11.66	5232	7.534
1.05	6.468	2903	4.180	1.55	11.77	5284	7.609
1.06	6.563	2945	4.242	1.56	11.89	5337	7.685
1.07	6.658	2988	4.303	1.57	12.01	5389	7.761
1.08	6.754	3031	4.365	1.58	12.13	5442	7.837
1.09	6.850	3075	4.428	1.59	12.24	5495	7.913
1.10	6.947	3118	4.490	1.60	12.36	5548	7.990
1.11	7.045	3162	4.553	1.61	12.48	5602	8.067
1.12	7.142	3206	4.616	1.62	12.60	5655	8.144
1.13	7.241	3250	4.680	1.63	12.72	5709	8.222
1.14	7.340	3294	4.744	1.64	12.84	5763	8.299
1.15	7.439	3339	4.808	1.65	12.96	5817	8.377
1.16	7.539	3384	4.872	1.66	13.08	5872	8.455
1.17	7.639	3429	4.937	1.67	13.20	5926	8.534
1.18	7.739	3474	5.002	1.68	13.33	5981	8.613
1.19	7.840	3519	5.068	1.69	13.45	6036	8.692
1.20	7.942	3565	5.133	1.70	13.57	6091	8.771
1.21	8.044	3610	5.199	1.71	13.69	6146	8.850
1.22	8.147	3656	5.265	1.72	13.82	6201	8.930
1.23	8.249	3703	5.332	1.73	13.94	6257	9.010
1.24	8.353	3749	5.399	1.74	14.06	6312	9.090
1.25	8.457	3796	5.466	1.75	14.19	6368	9.171
1.26	8.561	3842	5.533	1.76	14.31	6424	9.251
1.27	8.666	3889	5.601	1.77	14.44	6481	9.332
1.28	8.771	3937	5.669	1.78	14.56	6537	9.414
1.29	8.876	3984	5.737	1.79	14.69	6594	9.495
1.30	8.982	4032	5.806	1.80	14.82	6650	9.577
1.31	9.089	4079	5.875	1.81	14.94	6707	9.659
1.32	9.196	4127	5.944	1.82	15.07	6764	9.741
1.33	9.303	4176	6.013	1.83	15.20	6822	9.823
1.34	9.411	4224	6.083	1.84	15.33	6879	9.906
1.35	9.519	4273	6.153	1.85	15.45	6937	9.989
1.36	9.628	4321	6.223	1.86	15.58	6994	10.07
1.37	9.737	4370	6.293	1.87	15.71	7052	10.16
1.38	9.847	4419	6.364	1.88	15.84	7110	10.24
1.39	9.957	4469	6.435	1.89	15.97	7169	10.32
1.40	10.07	4518	6.507	1.90	16.10	7227	10.41
1.41	10.18	4568	6.578	1.91	16.23	7286	10.49
1.42	10.29	4618	6.650	1.92	16.36	7344	10.58
1.43	10.40	4668	6.722	1.93	16.49	7403	10.66
1.44	10.51	4718	6.795	1.94	16.63	7462	10.75
1.45	10.63	4769	6.867	1.95	16.76	7522	10.83
1.46	10.74	4820	6.940	1.96	16.89	7581	10.92
1.47	10.85	4870	7.014	1.97	17.02	7641	11.00
1.48	10.97	4922	7.087	1.98	17.16	7700	11.09
1.49	11.08	4973	7.161	1.99	17.29	7760	11.17
1.50	11.19	5024	7.235	2.00	17.42	7820	11.26

13

Table 13-7 (Continued)			
Head (feet)	CFS	GPM	MGD
2.01	17.56	7880	11.35
2.02	17.69	7941	11.44
2.03	17.83	8001	11.52
2.04	17.96	8062	11.61
2.05	18.10	8123	11.70
2.06	18.23	8184	11.79
2.07	18.37	8245	11.87
2.08	18.51	8306	11.96
2.09	18.64	8368	12.05
2.10	18.78	8430	12.14
2.11	18.92	8491	12.23
2.12	19.06	8553	12.32
2.13	19.20	8616	12.41
2.14	19.33	8678	12.50
2.15	19.47	8740	12.59
2.16	19.61	8803	12.68
2.17	19.75	8866	12.77
2.18	19.89	8929	12.86
2.19	20.03	8992	12.95
2.20	20.17	9055	13.04
2.21	20.32	9118	13.13
2.22	20.46	9182	13.22
2.23	20.60	9245	13.31
2.24	20.74	9309	13.41
2.25	20.88	9373	13.50

Table 13-7 (Continued)			
Head (feet)	CFS	GPM	MGD
2.26	21.03	9437	13.59
2.27	21.17	9502	13.68
2.28	21.31	9566	13.78
2.29	21.46	9631	13.87
2.30	21.60	9696	13.96
2.31	21.75	9760	14.06
2.32	21.89	9826	14.15
2.33	22.04	9891	14.24
2.34	22.18	9956	14.34
2.35	22.33	10,020	14.43
2.36	22.47	10,090	14.53
2.37	22.62	10,150	14.62
2.38	22.77	10,220	14.72
2.39	22.92	10,290	14.81
2.40	23.06	10,350	14.91
2.41	23.21	10,420	15.00
2.42	23.36	10,480	15.10
2.43	23.51	10,550	15.19
2.44	23.66	10,620	15.29
2.45	23.81	10,680	15.39
2.46	23.96	10,750	15.48
2.47	24.11	10,820	15.58
2.48	24.26	10,890	15.68
2.49	24.41	10,950	15.77
2.50	24.56	11,020	15.87

13

Table 13-8:
2 ft. Parshall Flume Discharge Table with Head in Feet

Formula: $CFS = 8.000\ H^{1.550}$
$GPM = 3590\ H^{1.550}$
$MGD = 5.170\ H^{1.550}$

Where: H = head in feet

Values in italics indicate flow below the recommended range of this particular primary device.

Head (feet)	CFS	GPM	MGD	Head (feet)	CFS	GPM	MGD
0.01	*0.0064*	*2.85*	*0.0041*	0.51	2.817	1264	1.821
0.02	*0.0186*	*8.35*	*0.0120*	0.52	2.903	1303	1.876
0.03	*0.0349*	*15.66*	*0.0225*	0.53	2.990	1342	1.932
0.04	*0.0545*	*24.46*	*0.0352*	0.54	3.078	1381	1.989
0.05	*0.0770*	*34.56*	*0.0498*	0.55	3.167	1421	2.047
0.06	*0.1021*	*45.85*	*0.0660*	0.56	3.257	1461	2.105
0.07	*0.1297*	*58.22*	*0.0838*	0.57	3.347	1502	2.163
0.08	*0.1595*	*71.61*	*0.1031*	0.58	3.439	1543	2.222
0.09	*0.1915*	*85.95*	*0.1238*	0.59	3.531	1585	2.282
0.10	*0.2255*	*101.2*	*0.1457*	0.60	3.624	1626	2.342
0.11	*0.2614*	*117.3*	*0.1689*	0.61	3.718	1669	2.403
0.12	*0.2991*	*134.2*	*0.1933*	0.62	3.813	1711	2.464
0.13	*0.3386*	*152.0*	*0.2189*	0.63	3.909	1754	2.526
0.14	*0.3798*	*170.5*	*0.2455*	0.64	4.006	1798	2.589
0.15	0.4227	189.7	0.2732	0.65	4.103	1841	2.652
0.16	0.4672	209.6	0.3019	0.66	4.201	1885	2.715
0.17	0.5132	230.3	0.3317	0.67	4.300	1930	2.779
0.18	0.5607	251.6	0.3624	0.68	4.400	1975	2.844
0.19	0.6098	273.6	0.3941	0.69	4.501	2020	2.909
0.20	0.6602	296.3	0.4267	0.70	4.602	2065	2.974
0.21	0.7121	319.5	0.4602	0.71	4.705	2111	3.040
0.22	0.7653	343.4	0.4946	0.72	4.808	2158	3.107
0.23	0.8199	367.9	0.5299	0.73	4.912	2204	3.174
0.24	0.8758	393.0	0.5660	0.74	5.016	2251	3.242
0.25	0.9330	418.7	0.6030	0.75	5.122	2298	3.310
0.26	0.9915	444.9	0.6408	0.76	5.228	2346	3.379
0.27	1.051	471.7	0.6794	0.77	5.335	2394	3.448
0.28	1.112	499.1	0.7188	0.78	5.443	2443	3.518
0.29	1.174	527.0	0.7589	0.79	5.552	2491	3.588
0.30	1.238	555.4	0.7999	0.80	5.661	2540	3.658
0.31	1.302	584.4	0.8416	0.81	5.771	2590	3.729
0.32	1.368	613.9	0.8840	0.82	5.882	2639	3.801
0.33	1.435	643.9	0.9272	0.83	5.993	2689	3.873
0.34	1.503	674.4	0.9711	0.84	6.106	2740	3.946
0.35	1.572	705.3	1.016	0.85	6.219	2791	4.019
0.36	1.642	736.8	1.061	0.86	6.332	2842	4.092
0.37	1.713	768.8	1.107	0.87	6.447	2893	4.166
0.38	1.785	801.2	1.154	0.88	6.562	2945	4.241
0.39	1.859	834.2	1.201	0.89	6.678	2997	4.316
0.40	1.933	867.5	1.249	0.90	6.795	3049	4.391
0.41	2.009	901.4	1.298	0.91	6.912	3102	4.467
0.42	2.085	935.7	1.347	0.92	7.030	3155	4.543
0.43	2.163	970.4	1.398	0.93	7.149	3208	4.620
0.44	2.241	1006	1.448	0.94	7.268	3262	4.697
0.45	2.320	1041	1.500	0.95	7.389	3316	4.775
0.46	2.401	1077	1.552	0.96	7.509	3370	4.853
0.47	2.482	1114	1.604	0.97	7.631	3424	4.932
0.48	2.565	1151	1.657	0.98	7.753	3479	5.011
0.49	2.648	1188	1.711	0.99	7.876	3535	5.090
0.50	2.732	1226	1.766	1.00	8.000	3590	5.170

13

Table 13-8 (Continued)				Table 13-8 (Continued)			
Head (feet)	CFS	GPM	MGD	Head (feet)	CFS	GPM	MGD
1.01	8.124	3646	5.250	1.51	15.15	6800	9.793
1.02	8.249	3702	5.331	1.52	15.31	6870	9.893
1.03	8.375	3758	5.412	1.53	15.47	6940	9.995
1.04	8.501	3815	5.494	1.54	15.62	7011	10.10
1.05	8.628	3872	5.576	1.55	15.78	7081	10.20
1.06	8.756	3929	5.659	1.56	15.94	7152	10.30
1.07	8.885	3987	5.742	1.57	16.10	7223	10.40
1.08	9.014	4045	5.825	1.58	16.26	7295	10.51
1.09	9.143	4103	5.909	1.59	16.42	7366	10.61
1.10	9.274	4162	5.993	1.60	16.58	7438	10.71
1.11	9.405	4220	6.078	1.61	16.74	7511	10.82
1.12	9.536	4279	6.163	1.62	16.90	7583	10.92
1.13	9.669	4339	6.248	1.63	17.06	7656	11.03
1.14	9.801	4398	6.334	1.64	17.22	7729	11.13
1.15	9.935	4458	6.421	1.65	17.39	7802	11.24
1.16	10.07	4519	6.507	1.66	17.55	7875	11.34
1.17	10.20	4579	6.594	1.67	17.71	7949	11.45
1.18	10.34	4640	6.682	1.68	17.88	8023	11.55
1.19	10.48	4701	6.770	1.69	18.04	8097	11.66
1.20	10.61	4762	6.858	1.70	18.21	8171	11.77
1.21	10.75	4824	6.947	1.71	18.38	8246	11.88
1.22	10.89	4886	7.036	1.72	18.54	8321	11.98
1.23	11.03	4948	7.126	1.73	18.71	8396	12.09
1.24	11.17	5011	7.216	1.74	18.88	8471	12.20
1.25	11.31	5073	7.306	1.75	19.05	8547	12.31
1.26	11.45	5137	7.397	1.76	19.21	8623	12.42
1.27	11.59	5200	7.488	1.77	19.38	8699	12.53
1.28	11.73	5263	7.580	1.78	19.55	8775	12.64
1.29	11.87	5327	7.672	1.79	19.72	8851	12.75
1.30	12.01	5391	7.764	1.80	19.90	8928	12.86
1.31	12.16	5456	7.857	1.81	20.07	9005	12.97
1.32	12.30	5521	7.950	1.82	20.24	9082	13.08
1.33	12.45	5586	8.044	1.83	20.41	9160	13.19
1.34	12.59	5651	8.138	1.84	20.59	9238	13.30
1.35	12.74	5716	8.232	1.85	20.76	9316	13.42
1.36	12.88	5782	8.327	1.86	20.93	9394	13.53
1.37	13.03	5848	8.422	1.87	21.11	9472	13.64
1.38	13.18	5914	8.517	1.88	21.28	9551	13.75
1.39	13.33	5981	8.613	1.89	21.46	9630	13.87
1.40	13.48	6048	8.709	1.90	21.64	9709	13.98
1.41	13.63	6115	8.806	1.91	21.81	9788	14.10
1.42	13.78	6182	8.903	1.92	21.99	9868	14.21
1.43	13.93	6250	9.000	1.93	22.17	9947	14.33
1.44	14.08	6318	9.098	1.94	22.35	10,030	14.44
1.45	14.23	6386	9.196	1.95	22.52	10,110	14.56
1.46	14.38	6454	9.295	1.96	22.70	10,190	14.67
1.47	14.54	6523	9.394	1.97	22.88	10,270	14.79
1.48	14.69	6592	9.493	1.98	23.06	10,350	14.90
1.49	14.84	6661	9.592	1.99	23.24	10,430	15.02
1.50	15.00	6730	9.692	2.00	23.43	10,510	15.14

13

Parshall Flume Discharge Tables • 313

Table 13-8 (Continued)				Table 13-8 (Continued)			
Head (feet)	CFS	GPM	MGD	Head (feet)	CFS	GPM	MGD
2.01	23.61	10,590	15.26	2.26	28.31	12,700	18.30
2.02	23.79	10,680	15.37	2.27	28.51	12,790	18.42
2.03	23.97	10,760	15.49	2.28	28.70	12,880	18.55
2.04	24.16	10,840	15.61	2.29	28.90	12,970	18.67
2.05	24.34	10,920	15.73	2.30	29.09	13,050	18.80
2.06	24.52	11,000	15.85	2.31	29.29	13,140	18.93
2.07	24.71	11,090	15.97	2.32	29.48	13,230	19.05
2.08	24.89	11,170	16.09	2.33	29.68	13,320	19.18
2.09	25.08	11,250	16.21	2.34	29.88	13,410	19.31
2.10	25.27	11,340	16.33	2.35	30.08	13,500	19.44
2.11	25.45	11,420	16.45	2.36	30.28	13,590	19.57
2.12	25.64	11,510	16.57	2.37	30.48	13,680	19.69
2.13	25.83	11,590	16.69	2.38	30.67	13,770	19.82
2.14	26.02	11,670	16.81	2.39	30.87	13,860	19.95
2.15	26.20	11,760	16.93	2.40	31.08	13,950	20.08
2.16	26.39	11,840	17.06	2.41	31.28	14,040	20.21
2.17	26.58	11,930	17.18	2.42	31.48	14,130	20.34
2.18	26.77	12,010	17.30	2.43	31.68	14,220	20.47
2.19	26.96	12,100	17.43	2.44	31.88	14,310	20.60
2.20	27.15	12,190	17.55	2.45	32.08	14,400	20.73
2.21	27.35	12,270	17.67	2.46	32.29	14,490	20.87
2.22	27.54	12,360	17.80	2.47	32.49	14,580	21.00
2.23	27.73	12,440	17.92	2.48	32.70	14,670	21.13
2.24	27.92	12,530	18.05	2.49	32.90	14,760	21.26
2.25	28.12	12,620	18.17	2.50	33.11	14,860	21.39

13

Table 13-9:
3 ft. Parshall Flume Discharge Table with Head in Feet

Formula: $CFS = 12.00\ H^{1.566}$
$GPM = 5386\ H^{1.566}$
$MGD = 7.756\ H^{1.566}$
Where: H = head in feet

Values in italics indicate flow below the recommended range of this particular primary device.

Table 13-9				Table 13-9 (Continued)			
Head (feet)	CFS	GPM	MGD	Head (feet)	CFS	GPM	MGD
0.01	*0.0089*	*4.0*	*0.0057*	0.51	4.181	1876	2.702
0.02	*0.0262*	*11.8*	*0.0169*	0.52	4.310	1934	2.785
0.03	*0.0495*	*22.2*	*0.0320*	0.53	4.440	1993	2.870
0.04	*0.0776*	*34.8*	*0.0502*	0.54	4.572	2052	2.955
0.05	*0.1101*	*49.4*	*0.0712*	0.55	4.705	2112	3.041
0.06	*0.1465*	*65.7*	*0.0947*	0.56	4.840	2172	3.128
0.07	*0.1865*	*83.7*	*0.1205*	0.57	4.976	2233	3.216
0.08	*0.2298*	*103.2*	*0.1485*	0.58	5.113	2295	3.305
0.09	*0.2764*	*124.1*	*0.1786*	0.59	5.252	2357	3.395
0.10	*0.3260*	*146.3*	*0.2107*	0.60	5.392	2420	3.485
0.11	*0.3784*	*169.9*	*0.2446*	0.61	5.534	2484	3.577
0.12	*0.4337*	*194.7*	*0.2803*	0.62	5.676	2548	3.669
0.13	*0.4916*	*220.6*	*0.3177*	0.63	5.820	2612	3.762
0.14	*0.5521*	*247.8*	*0.3568*	0.64	5.966	2678	3.856
0.15	0.6151	276.1	0.3976	0.65	6.112	2743	3.951
0.16	0.6805	305.4	0.4398	0.66	6.260	2810	4.046
0.17	0.7483	335.9	0.4836	0.67	6.409	2877	4.143
0.18	0.8183	367.3	0.5289	0.68	6.560	2944	4.240
0.19	0.8907	399.8	0.5757	0.69	6.711	3012	4.338
0.20	0.9651	433.2	0.6238	0.70	6.864	3081	4.437
0.21	1.042	467.6	0.6733	0.71	7.019	3150	4.536
0.22	1.121	502.9	0.7242	0.72	7.174	3220	4.637
0.23	1.201	539.2	0.7764	0.73	7.331	3290	4.738
0.24	1.284	576.3	0.8299	0.74	7.489	3361	4.840
0.25	1.369	614.4	0.8847	0.75	7.648	3433	4.943
0.26	1.456	653.3	0.9408	0.76	7.808	3504	5.047
0.27	1.544	693.1	0.9981	0.77	7.969	3577	5.151
0.28	1.635	733.7	1.057	0.78	8.132	3650	5.256
0.29	1.727	775.1	1.116	0.79	8.296	3723	5.362
0.30	1.821	817.4	1.177	0.80	8.461	3798	5.469
0.31	1.917	860.5	1.239	0.81	8.627	3872	5.576
0.32	2.015	904.3	1.302	0.82	8.795	3947	5.684
0.33	2.114	949.0	1.367	0.83	8.963	4023	5.793
0.34	2.216	994.4	1.432	0.84	9.133	4099	5.903
0.35	2.318	1041	1.498	0.85	9.304	4176	6.013
0.36	2.423	1088	1.566	0.86	9.476	4253	6.124
0.37	2.529	1135	1.635	0.87	9.649	4331	6.236
0.38	2.637	1184	1.704	0.88	9.823	4409	6.349
0.39	2.747	1233	1.775	0.89	9.998	4488	6.462
0.40	2.858	1283	1.847	0.90	10.17	4567	6.576
0.41	2.970	1333	1.920	0.91	10.35	4646	6.691
0.42	3.085	1384	1.994	0.92	10.53	4727	6.807
0.43	3.200	1436	2.068	0.93	10.71	4807	6.923
0.44	3.318	1489	2.144	0.94	10.89	4889	7.040
0.45	3.436	1542	2.221	0.95	11.07	4970	7.157
0.46	3.557	1596	2.299	0.96	11.26	5052	7.276
0.47	3.679	1651	2.378	0.97	11.44	5135	7.395
0.48	3.802	1706	2.457	0.98	11.63	5218	7.514
0.49	3.927	1762	2.538	0.99	11.81	5302	7.635
0.50	4.053	1819	2.620	1.00	12.00	5386	7.756

13

Table 13-9 (Continued)				Table 13-9 (Continued)			
Head (feet)	CFS	GPM	MGD	Head (feet)	CFS	GPM	MGD
1.01	12.19	5471	7.878	1.51	22.88	10,270	14.79
1.02	12.38	5556	8.000	1.52	23.12	10,380	14.94
1.03	12.57	5641	8.123	1.53	23.36	10,480	15.10
1.04	12.76	5727	8.247	1.54	23.60	10,590	15.25
1.05	12.95	5814	8.372	1.55	23.84	10,700	15.41
1.06	13.15	5901	8.497	1.56	24.08	10,810	15.56
1.07	13.34	5988	8.623	1.57	24.32	10,920	15.72
1.08	13.54	6076	8.749	1.58	24.56	11,020	15.88
1.09	13.73	6164	8.877	1.59	24.81	11,130	16.03
1.10	13.93	6253	9.004	1.60	25.05	11,240	16.19
1.11	14.13	6342	9.133	1.61	25.30	11,350	16.35
1.12	14.33	6432	9.262	1.62	25.54	11,460	16.51
1.13	14.53	6522	9.392	1.63	25.79	11,580	16.67
1.14	14.73	6613	9.522	1.64	26.04	11,690	16.83
1.15	14.94	6704	9.654	1.65	26.29	11,800	16.99
1.16	15.14	6795	9.785	1.66	26.54	11,910	17.15
1.17	15.34	6887	9.918	1.67	26.79	12,020	17.31
1.18	15.55	6980	10.05	1.68	27.04	12,140	17.48
1.19	15.76	7072	10.18	1.69	27.29	12,250	17.64
1.20	15.97	7166	10.32	1.70	27.55	12,360	17.80
1.21	16.17	7260	10.45	1.71	27.80	12,480	17.97
1.22	16.38	7354	10.59	1.72	28.06	12,590	18.13
1.23	16.59	7448	10.73	1.73	28.31	12,710	18.30
1.24	16.81	7543	10.86	1.74	28.57	12,820	18.46
1.25	17.02	7639	11.00	1.75	28.83	12,940	18.63
1.26	17.23	7735	11.14	1.76	29.08	13,050	18.80
1.27	17.45	7831	11.28	1.77	29.34	13,170	18.97
1.28	17.66	7928	11.42	1.78	29.60	13,290	19.13
1.29	17.88	8025	11.56	1.79	29.86	13,400	19.30
1.30	18.10	8123	11.70	1.80	30.13	13,520	19.47
1.31	18.32	8221	11.84	1.81	30.39	13,640	19.64
1.32	18.54	8319	11.98	1.82	30.65	13,760	19.81
1.33	18.76	8418	12.12	1.83	30.92	13,880	19.98
1.34	18.98	8518	12.27	1.84	31.18	13,990	20.15
1.35	19.20	8617	12.41	1.85	31.45	14,110	20.32
1.36	19.42	8717	12.55	1.86	31.71	14,230	20.50
1.37	19.65	8818	12.70	1.87	31.98	14,350	20.67
1.38	19.87	8919	12.84	1.88	32.25	14,470	20.84
1.39	20.10	9020	12.99	1.89	32.52	14,600	21.02
1.40	20.32	9122	13.14	1.90	32.79	14,720	21.19
1.41	20.55	9225	13.28	1.91	33.06	14,840	21.37
1.42	20.78	9327	13.43	1.92	33.33	14,960	21.54
1.43	21.01	9430	13.58	1.93	33.60	15,080	21.72
1.44	21.24	9534	13.73	1.94	33.87	15,200	21.89
1.45	21.47	9638	13.88	1.95	34.15	15,330	22.07
1.46	21.70	9742	14.03	1.96	34.42	15,450	22.25
1.47	21.94	9847	14.18	1.97	34.70	15,570	22.43
1.48	22.17	9952	14.33	1.98	34.98	15,700	22.61
1.49	22.41	10,060	14.48	1.99	35.25	15,820	22.78
1.50	22.64	10,160	14.64	2.00	35.53	15,950	22.96

13

Table 13-9 (Continued)			
Head (feet)	CFS	GPM	MGD
2.01	35.81	16,070	23.14
2.02	36.09	16,200	23.32
2.03	36.37	16,320	23.51
2.04	36.65	16,450	23.69
2.05	36.93	16,580	23.87
2.06	37.21	16,700	24.05
2.07	37.50	16,830	24.24
2.08	37.78	16,960	24.42
2.09	38.07	17,090	24.60
2.10	38.35	17,210	24.79
2.11	38.64	17,340	24.97
2.12	38.92	17,470	25.16
2.13	39.21	17,600	25.34
2.14	39.50	17,730	25.53
2.15	39.79	17,860	25.72
2.16	40.08	17,990	25.91
2.17	40.37	18,120	26.09
2.18	40.66	18,250	26.28
2.19	40.96	18,380	26.47
2.20	41.25	18,510	26.66
2.21	41.54	18,650	26.85
2.22	41.84	18,780	27.04
2.23	42.13	18,910	27.23
2.24	42.43	19,040	27.42
2.25	42.73	19,180	27.62

Table 13-9 (Continued)			
Head (feet)	CFS	GPM	MGD
2.26	43.02	19,310	27.81
2.27	43.32	19,440	28.00
2.28	43.62	19,580	28.19
2.29	43.92	19,710	28.39
2.30	44.22	19,850	28.58
2.31	44.52	19,980	28.78
2.32	44.83	20,120	28.97
2.33	45.13	20,260	29.17
2.34	45.43	20,390	29.36
2.35	45.74	20,530	29.56
2.36	46.04	20,670	29.76
2.37	46.35	20,800	29.96
2.38	46.66	20,940	30.15
2.39	46.96	21,080	30.35
2.40	47.27	21,220	30.55
2.41	47.58	21,360	30.75
2.42	47.89	21,490	30.95
2.43	48.20	21,630	31.15
2.44	48.51	21,770	31.35
2.45	48.82	21,910	31.56
2.46	49.13	22,050	31.76
2.47	49.45	22,190	31.96
2.48	49.76	22,330	32.16
2.49	50.08	22,480	32.37
2.50	50.39	22,620	32.57

13

Table 13-10:
4 ft. Parshall Flume Discharge Table with Head in Feet

Formula: CFS $= 16.00\ H^{1.578}$
GPM $= 7181\ H^{1.578}$
MGD $= 10.34\ H^{1.578}$
Where: H = head in feet

Values in italics indicate flow below the recommended range of this particular primary device.

Table 13-10				Table 13-10 (Continued)			
Head (feet)	CFS	GPM	MGD	Head (feet)	CFS	GPM	MGD
0.01	*0.0112*	*5.0*	*0.0072*	0.51	5.529	2482	3.573
0.02	*0.0334*	*15.0*	*0.0216*	0.52	5.701	2559	3.684
0.03	*0.0632*	*28.4*	*0.0409*	0.53	5.875	2637	3.797
0.04	*0.0996*	*44.7*	*0.0644*	0.54	6.051	2716	3.911
0.05	*0.1416*	*63.6*	*0.0915*	0.55	6.229	2796	4.025
0.06	*0.1888*	*84.8*	*0.1220*	0.56	6.409	2876	4.142
0.07	*0.2408*	*108.1*	*0.1556*	0.57	6.590	2958	4.259
0.08	*0.2973*	*133.4*	*0.1922*	0.58	6.773	3040	4.377
0.09	*0.3580*	*160.7*	*0.2314*	0.59	6.959	3123	4.497
0.10	*0.4228*	*189.8*	*0.2733*	0.60	7.146	3207	4.618
0.11	*0.4914*	*220.6*	*0.3176*	0.61	7.334	3292	4.740
0.12	*0.5637*	*253.0*	*0.3643*	0.62	7.525	3377	4.863
0.13	*0.6396*	*287.1*	*0.4134*	0.63	7.718	3464	4.987
0.14	*0.7190*	*322.7*	*0.4647*	0.64	7.912	3551	5.113
0.15	*0.8017*	*359.8*	*0.5181*	0.65	8.108	3639	5.240
0.16	*0.8876*	*398.4*	*0.5737*	0.66	8.305	3728	5.367
0.17	*0.9767*	*438.4*	*0.6313*	0.67	8.505	3817	5.496
0.18	*1.069*	*479.8*	*0.6909*	0.68	8.706	3907	5.626
0.19	*1.164*	*522.5*	*0.7524*	0.69	8.909	3998	5.757
0.20	1.262	566.5	0.8157	0.70	9.113	4090	5.890
0.21	1.363	611.9	0.8810	0.71	9.320	4183	6.023
0.22	1.467	658.5	0.9481	0.72	9.528	4276	6.157
0.23	1.574	706.3	1.017	0.73	9.737	4370	6.293
0.24	1.683	755.4	1.088	0.74	9.949	4465	6.429
0.25	1.795	805.6	1.160	0.75	10.16	4561	6.567
0.26	1.910	857.1	1.234	0.76	10.38	4657	6.706
0.27	2.027	909.7	1.310	0.77	10.59	4754	6.845
0.28	2.147	963.4	1.387	0.78	10.81	4852	6.986
0.29	2.269	1018	1.466	0.79	11.03	4950	7.128
0.30	2.393	1074	1.547	0.80	11.25	5050	7.271
0.31	2.521	1131	1.629	0.81	11.47	5150	7.415
0.32	2.650	1189	1.713	0.82	11.70	5250	7.560
0.33	2.782	1249	1.798	0.83	11.92	5352	7.706
0.34	2.916	1309	1.884	0.84	12.15	5454	7.853
0.35	3.053	1370	1.973	0.85	12.38	5557	8.001
0.36	3.191	1432	2.062	0.86	12.61	5660	8.150
0.37	3.332	1496	2.153	0.87	12.84	5764	8.300
0.38	3.476	1560	2.246	0.88	13.08	5869	8.451
0.39	3.621	1625	2.340	0.89	13.31	5975	8.603
0.40	3.769	1691	2.435	0.90	13.55	6081	8.756
0.41	3.918	1759	2.532	0.91	13.79	6188	8.910
0.42	4.070	1827	2.630	0.92	14.03	6296	9.065
0.43	4.224	1896	2.730	0.93	14.27	6404	9.221
0.44	4.380	1966	2.831	0.94	14.51	6513	9.378
0.45	4.538	2037	2.933	0.95	14.76	6623	9.536
0.46	4.698	2109	3.036	0.96	15.00	6733	9.695
0.47	4.861	2182	3.141	0.97	15.25	6844	9.855
0.48	5.025	2255	3.247	0.98	15.50	6956	10.02
0.49	5.191	2330	3.355	0.99	15.75	7068	10.18
0.50	5.359	2405	3.463	1.00	16.00	7181	10.34

13

Table 13-10 (Continued)				Table 13-10 (Continued)			
Head (feet)	CFS	GPM	MGD	Head (feet)	CFS	GPM	MGD
1.01	16.25	7295	10.50	1.51	30.66	13,760	19.81
1.02	16.51	7409	10.67	1.52	30.98	13,900	20.02
1.03	16.76	7524	10.83	1.53	31.30	14,050	20.23
1.04	17.02	7639	11.00	1.54	31.62	14,190	20.44
1.05	17.28	7756	11.17	1.55	31.95	14,340	20.65
1.06	17.54	7873	11.34	1.56	32.28	14,490	20.86
1.07	17.80	7990	11.51	1.57	32.60	14,630	21.07
1.08	18.07	8108	11.68	1.58	32.93	14,780	21.28
1.09	18.33	8227	11.85	1.59	33.26	14,930	21.49
1.10	18.60	8346	12.02	1.60	33.59	15,080	21.71
1.11	18.86	8467	12.19	1.61	33.92	15,220	21.92
1.12	19.13	8587	12.36	1.62	34.26	15,370	22.14
1.13	19.40	8708	12.54	1.63	34.59	15,520	22.35
1.14	19.68	8830	12.72	1.64	34.93	15,680	22.57
1.15	19.95	8953	12.89	1.65	35.26	15,830	22.79
1.16	20.22	9076	13.07	1.66	35.60	15,980	23.01
1.17	20.50	9200	13.25	1.67	35.94	16,130	23.23
1.18	20.78	9324	13.43	1.68	36.28	16,280	23.45
1.19	21.05	9449	13.61	1.69	36.62	16,440	23.67
1.20	21.33	9575	13.79	1.70	36.96	16,590	23.89
1.21	21.62	9701	13.97	1.71	37.31	16,740	24.11
1.22	21.90	9828	14.15	1.72	37.65	16,900	24.33
1.23	22.18	9955	14.33	1.73	38.00	17,050	24.56
1.24	22.47	10,080	14.52	1.74	38.34	17,210	24.78
1.25	22.75	10,210	14.70	1.75	38.69	17,370	25.01
1.26	23.04	10,340	14.89	1.76	39.04	17,520	25.23
1.27	23.33	10,470	15.08	1.77	39.39	17,680	25.46
1.28	23.62	10,600	15.27	1.78	39.75	17,840	25.69
1.29	23.91	10,730	15.45	1.79	40.10	18,000	25.91
1.30	24.21	10,860	15.64	1.80	40.45	18,160	26.14
1.31	24.50	11,000	15.83	1.81	40.81	18,310	26.37
1.32	24.80	11,130	16.02	1.82	41.16	18,470	26.60
1.33	25.09	11,260	16.22	1.83	41.52	18,640	26.83
1.34	25.39	11,400	16.41	1.84	41.88	18,800	27.06
1.35	25.69	11,530	16.60	1.85	42.24	18,960	27.30
1.36	25.99	11,670	16.80	1.86	42.60	19,120	27.53
1.37	26.29	11,800	16.99	1.87	42.96	19,280	27.76
1.38	26.60	11,940	17.19	1.88	43.33	19,440	28.00
1.39	26.90	12,070	17.39	1.89	43.69	19,610	28.23
1.40	27.21	12,210	17.58	1.90	44.05	19,770	28.47
1.41	27.52	12,350	17.78	1.91	44.42	19,940	28.71
1.42	27.82	12,490	17.98	1.92	44.79	20,100	28.94
1.43	28.13	12,630	18.18	1.93	45.16	20,270	29.18
1.44	28.45	12,770	18.38	1.94	45.53	20,430	29.42
1.45	28.76	12,910	18.58	1.95	45.90	20,600	29.66
1.46	29.07	13,050	18.79	1.96	46.27	20,770	29.90
1.47	29.39	13,190	18.99	1.97	46.64	20,930	30.14
1.48	29.70	13,330	19.20	1.98	47.02	21,100	30.38
1.49	30.02	13,470	19.40	1.99	47.39	21,270	30.63
1.50	30.34	13,620	19.61	2.00	47.77	21,440	30.87

13

Table 13-10 (Continued)				Table 13-10 (Continued)			
Head (feet)	CFS	GPM	MGD	Head (feet)	CFS	GPM	MGD
2.01	48.15	21,610	31.11	2.26	57.93	26,000	37.44
2.02	48.52	21,780	31.36	2.27	58.33	26,180	37.70
2.03	48.90	21,950	31.60	2.28	58.74	26,360	37.96
2.04	49.29	22,120	31.85	2.29	59.15	26,550	38.22
2.05	49.67	22,290	32.10	2.30	59.56	26,730	38.49
2.06	50.05	22,460	32.34	2.31	59.97	26,910	38.75
2.07	50.43	22,640	32.59	2.32	60.38	27,100	39.02
2.08	50.82	22,810	32.84	2.33	60.79	27,280	39.28
2.09	51.20	22,980	33.09	2.34	61.20	27,470	39.55
2.10	51.59	23,160	33.34	2.35	61.61	27,650	39.82
2.11	51.98	23,330	33.59	2.36	62.03	27,840	40.08
2.12	52.37	23,500	33.84	2.37	62.44	28,020	40.35
2.13	52.76	23,680	34.10	2.38	62.86	28,210	40.62
2.14	53.15	23,850	34.35	2.39	63.27	28,400	40.89
2.15	53.54	24,030	34.60	2.40	63.69	28,590	41.16
2.16	53.94	24,210	34.86	2.41	64.11	28,770	41.43
2.17	54.33	24,380	35.11	2.42	64.53	28,960	41.70
2.18	54.73	24,560	35.37	2.43	64.95	29,150	41.98
2.19	55.12	24,740	35.62	2.44	65.38	29,340	42.25
2.20	55.52	24,920	35.88	2.45	65.80	29,530	42.52
2.21	55.92	25,100	36.14	2.46	66.22	29,720	42.80
2.22	56.32	25,280	36.40	2.47	66.65	29,910	43.07
2.23	56.72	25,460	36.66	2.48	67.08	30,100	43.35
2.24	57.12	25,640	36.92	2.49	67.50	30,300	43.62
2.25	57.53	25,820	37.18	2.50	67.93	30,490	43.90

13

Table 13-11:
5 ft. Parshall Flume Discharge Table with Head in Feet

Formula: CFS $= 20.00\ H^{1.587}$
GPM $= 8976\ H^{1.587}$
MGD $= 12.93\ H^{1.587}$
Where: H = head in feet

Values in italics indicate flow below the recommended range of this particular primary device.

Head (feet)	CFS	GPM	MGD	Head (feet)	CFS	GPM	MGD
0.01	*0.013*	*6.0*	*0.009*	0.51	6.870	3083	4.441
0.02	*0.040*	*18.1*	*0.026*	0.52	7.085	3180	4.580
0.03	*0.077*	*34.4*	*0.050*	0.53	7.302	3277	4.721
0.04	*0.121*	*54.3*	*0.078*	0.54	7.522	3376	4.863
0.05	*0.172*	*77.3*	*0.111*	0.55	7.744	3476	5.007
0.06	*0.230*	*103.3*	*0.149*	0.56	7.969	3576	5.152
0.07	*0.294*	*131.9*	*0.190*	0.57	8.196	3678	5.299
0.08	*0.363*	*163.0*	*0.235*	0.58	8.425	3781	5.447
0.09	*0.438*	*196.6*	*0.283*	0.59	8.657	3885	5.597
0.10	*0.518*	*232.3*	*0.335*	0.60	8.891	3990	5.748
0.11	*0.602*	*270.3*	*0.389*	0.61	9.127	4096	5.901
0.12	*0.691*	*310.3*	*0.447*	0.62	9.366	4203	6.055
0.13	*0.785*	*352.3*	*0.507*	0.63	9.607	4312	6.211
0.14	*0.883*	*396.3*	*0.571*	0.64	9.850	4421	6.368
0.15	*0.985*	*442.2*	*0.637*	0.65	10.10	4531	6.527
0.16	*1.091*	*489.8*	*0.705*	0.66	10.34	4642	6.687
0.17	*1.202*	*539.3*	*0.777*	0.67	10.59	4754	6.848
0.18	*1.316*	*590.5*	*0.850*	0.68	10.84	4867	7.011
0.19	*1.434*	*643.4*	*0.927*	0.69	11.10	4981	7.175
0.20	1.555	697.9	1.005	0.70	11.36	5096	7.341
0.21	1.680	754.1	1.086	0.71	11.61	5212	7.508
0.22	1.809	811.9	1.170	0.72	11.87	5329	7.677
0.23	1.941	871.3	1.255	0.73	12.14	5447	7.847
0.24	2.077	932.1	1.343	0.74	12.40	5566	8.018
0.25	2.216	994.5	1.433	0.75	12.67	5686	8.191
0.26	2.358	1058	1.525	0.76	12.94	5807	8.365
0.27	2.504	1124	1.619	0.77	13.21	5928	8.540
0.28	2.653	1190	1.715	0.78	13.48	6051	8.717
0.29	2.805	1259	1.813	0.79	13.76	6175	8.895
0.30	2.960	1328	1.913	0.80	14.04	6299	9.074
0.31	3.118	1399	2.016	0.81	14.32	6425	9.255
0.32	3.279	1471	2.120	0.82	14.60	6551	9.437
0.33	3.443	1545	2.226	0.83	14.88	6678	9.620
0.34	3.610	1620	2.334	0.84	15.17	6806	9.805
0.35	3.780	1696	2.444	0.85	15.45	6935	9.990
0.36	3.953	1774	2.555	0.86	15.74	7065	10.18
0.37	4.128	1853	2.669	0.87	16.03	7196	10.37
0.38	4.307	1933	2.784	0.88	16.33	7328	10.56
0.39	4.488	2014	2.901	0.89	16.62	7460	10.75
0.40	4.672	2097	3.020	0.90	16.92	7594	10.94
0.41	4.859	2181	3.141	0.91	17.22	7728	11.13
0.42	5.048	2266	3.264	0.92	17.52	7863	11.33
0.43	5.240	2352	3.388	0.93	17.82	8000	11.52
0.44	5.435	2439	3.514	0.94	18.13	8136	11.72
0.45	5.632	2528	3.641	0.95	18.44	8274	11.92
0.46	5.832	2617	3.770	0.96	18.75	8413	12.12
0.47	6.035	2708	3.901	0.97	19.06	8552	12.32
0.48	6.240	2800	4.034	0.98	19.37	8693	12.52
0.49	6.447	2894	4.168	0.99	19.68	8834	12.73
0.50	6.657	2988	4.304	1.00	20.00	8976	12.93

13

Table 13-11 (Continued)				Table 13-11 (Continued)			
Head (feet)	CFS	GPM	MGD	Head (feet)	CFS	GPM	MGD
1.01	20.32	9119	13.14	1.51	38.47	17,260	24.87
1.02	20.64	9263	13.34	1.52	38.87	17,440	25.13
1.03	20.96	9407	13.55	1.53	39.28	17,630	25.39
1.04	21.28	9552	13.76	1.54	39.68	17,810	25.66
1.05	21.61	9699	13.97	1.55	40.09	17,990	25.92
1.06	21.94	9846	14.18	1.56	40.51	18,180	26.19
1.07	22.27	9993	14.40	1.57	40.92	18,360	26.45
1.08	22.60	10,140	14.61	1.58	41.33	18,550	26.72
1.09	22.93	10,290	14.82	1.59	41.75	18,740	26.99
1.10	23.27	10,440	15.04	1.60	42.17	18,920	27.26
1.11	23.60	10,590	15.26	1.61	42.59	19,110	27.53
1.12	23.94	10,740	15.48	1.62	43.01	19,300	27.80
1.13	24.28	10,900	15.70	1.63	43.43	19,490	28.08
1.14	24.62	11,050	15.92	1.64	43.85	19,680	28.35
1.15	24.97	11,200	16.14	1.65	44.28	19,870	28.63
1.16	25.31	11,360	16.36	1.66	44.70	20,060	28.90
1.17	25.66	11,520	16.59	1.67	45.13	20,260	29.18
1.18	26.01	11,670	16.81	1.68	45.56	20,450	29.46
1.19	26.36	11,830	17.04	1.69	45.99	20,640	29.73
1.20	26.71	11,990	17.27	1.70	46.43	20,840	30.01
1.21	27.07	12,150	17.50	1.71	46.86	21,030	30.29
1.22	27.42	12,310	17.73	1.72	47.29	21,230	30.58
1.23	27.78	12,470	17.96	1.73	47.73	21,420	30.86
1.24	28.14	12,630	18.19	1.74	48.17	21,620	31.14
1.25	28.50	12,790	18.42	1.75	48.61	21,820	31.43
1.26	28.86	12,950	18.66	1.76	49.05	22,010	31.71
1.27	29.23	13,120	18.89	1.77	49.50	22,210	32.00
1.28	29.59	13,280	19.13	1.78	49.94	22,410	32.29
1.29	29.96	13,450	19.37	1.79	50.39	22,610	32.57
1.30	30.33	13,610	19.61	1.80	50.83	22,810	32.86
1.31	30.70	13,780	19.85	1.81	51.28	23,020	33.15
1.32	31.07	13,950	20.09	1.82	51.73	23,220	33.45
1.33	31.45	14,110	20.33	1.83	52.18	23,420	33.74
1.34	31.82	14,280	20.57	1.84	52.64	23,620	34.03
1.35	32.20	14,450	20.82	1.85	53.09	23,830	34.32
1.36	32.58	14,620	21.06	1.86	53.55	24,030	34.62
1.37	32.96	14,790	21.31	1.87	54.01	24,240	34.91
1.38	33.34	14,960	21.56	1.88	54.47	24,440	35.21
1.39	33.73	15,140	21.81	1.89	54.93	24,650	35.51
1.40	34.11	15,310	22.05	1.90	55.39	24,860	35.81
1.41	34.50	15,480	22.31	1.91	55.85	25,070	36.11
1.42	34.89	15,660	22.56	1.92	56.32	25,270	36.41
1.43	35.28	15,830	22.81	1.93	56.78	25,480	36.71
1.44	35.67	16,010	23.06	1.94	57.25	25,690	37.01
1.45	36.07	16,190	23.32	1.95	57.72	25,900	37.32
1.46	36.46	16,360	23.57	1.96	58.19	26,120	37.62
1.47	36.86	16,540	23.83	1.97	58.66	26,330	37.92
1.48	37.26	16,720	24.09	1.98	59.13	26,540	38.23
1.49	37.66	16,900	24.35	1.99	59.61	26,750	38.54
1.50	38.06	17,080	24.61	2.00	60.08	26,970	38.84

13

Table 13-11 (Continued)					Table 13-11 (Continued)			
Head (feet)	CFS	GPM	MGD		Head (feet)	CFS	GPM	MGD
2.01	60.56	27,180	39.15		2.26	72.95	32,740	47.16
2.02	61.04	27,400	39.46		2.27	73.46	32,970	47.49
2.03	61.52	27,610	39.77		2.28	73.97	33,200	47.82
2.04	62.00	27,830	40.08		2.29	74.49	33,430	48.16
2.05	62.49	28,040	40.40		2.30	75.01	33,660	48.49
2.06	62.97	28,260	40.71		2.31	75.52	33,890	48.83
2.07	63.46	28,480	41.02		2.32	76.04	34,130	49.16
2.08	63.94	28,700	41.34		2.33	76.56	34,360	49.50
2.09	64.43	28,920	41.66		2.34	77.09	34,600	49.84
2.10	64.92	29,140	41.97		2.35	77.61	34,830	50.17
2.11	65.41	29,360	42.29		2.36	78.13	35,070	50.51
2.12	65.91	29,580	42.61		2.37	78.66	35,300	50.85
2.13	66.40	29,800	42.93		2.38	79.19	35,540	51.19
2.14	66.90	30,020	43.25		2.39	79.72	35,780	51.54
2.15	67.39	30,250	43.57		2.40	80.25	36,010	51.88
2.16	67.89	30,470	43.89		2.41	80.78	36,250	52.22
2.17	68.39	30,690	44.21		2.42	81.31	36,490	52.57
2.18	68.89	30,920	44.54		2.43	81.84	36,730	52.91
2.19	69.39	31,140	44.86		2.44	82.38	36,970	53.26
2.20	69.90	31,370	45.19		2.45	82.92	37,210	53.60
2.21	70.40	31,600	45.51		2.46	83.45	37,450	53.95
2.22	70.91	31,820	45.84		2.47	83.99	37,700	54.30
2.23	71.42	32,050	46.17		2.48	84.53	37,940	54.65
2.24	71.92	32,280	46.50		2.49	85.07	38,180	55.00
2.25	72.43	32,510	46.83		2.50	85.62	38,420	55.35

13

Table 13-12:
6 ft. Parshall Flume Discharge Table with Head in Feet

Formula: CFS $= 24.00\ H^{1.595}$
 GPM $= 10770\ H^{1.595}$
 MGD $= 15.51\ H^{1.595}$
Where: H = head in feet

Values in italics indicate flow below the recommended range of this particular primary device.

Table 13-12				Table 13-12 (Continued)			
Head (feet)	CFS	GPM	MGD	Head (feet)	CFS	GPM	MGD
0.01	*0.016*	*7*	*0.010*	0.51	8.199	3680	5.299
0.02	*0.047*	*21*	*0.030*	0.52	8.457	3795	5.466
0.03	*0.089*	*40*	*0.058*	0.53	8.718	3912	5.634
0.04	*0.141*	*63*	*0.091*	0.54	8.982	4031	5.805
0.05	*0.202*	*91*	*0.131*	0.55	9.249	4150	5.977
0.06	*0.270*	*121*	*0.175*	0.56	9.519	4271	6.151
0.07	*0.345*	*155*	*0.223*	0.57	9.791	4394	6.328
0.08	*0.427*	*192*	*0.276*	0.58	10.07	4517	6.505
0.09	*0.516*	*231*	*0.333*	0.59	10.34	4642	6.685
0.10	*0.610*	*274*	*0.394*	0.60	10.63	4768	6.867
0.11	*0.710*	*319*	*0.459*	0.61	10.91	4896	7.050
0.12	*0.816*	*366*	*0.527*	0.62	11.20	5024	7.236
0.13	*0.927*	*416*	*0.599*	0.63	11.49	5154	7.423
0.14	*1.043*	*468*	*0.674*	0.64	11.78	5285	7.611
0.15	*1.164*	*523*	*0.753*	0.65	12.07	5418	7.802
0.16	*1.291*	*579*	*0.834*	0.66	12.37	5551	7.994
0.17	*1.422*	*638*	*0.919*	0.67	12.67	5686	8.188
0.18	*1.557*	*699*	*1.007*	0.68	12.97	5822	8.384
0.19	*1.698*	*762*	*1.097*	0.69	13.28	5959	8.582
0.20	*1.842*	*827*	*1.191*	0.70	13.59	6097	8.781
0.21	*1.991*	*894*	*1.287*	0.71	13.90	6237	8.982
0.22	*2.145*	*963*	*1.386*	0.72	14.21	6378	9.185
0.23	*2.302*	*1033*	*1.488*	0.73	14.53	6520	9.389
0.24	*2.464*	*1106*	*1.593*	0.74	14.85	6663	9.595
0.25	2.630	1180	1.700	0.75	15.17	6807	9.802
0.26	2.800	1256	1.809	0.76	15.49	6952	10.01
0.27	2.973	1334	1.921	0.77	15.82	7099	10.22
0.28	3.151	1414	2.036	0.78	16.15	7246	10.44
0.29	3.332	1495	2.153	0.79	16.48	7395	10.65
0.30	3.517	1578	2.273	0.80	16.81	7545	10.87
0.31	3.706	1663	2.395	0.81	17.15	7696	11.08
0.32	3.899	1750	2.520	0.82	17.49	7848	11.30
0.33	4.095	1838	2.646	0.83	17.83	8001	11.52
0.34	4.295	1927	2.775	0.84	18.17	8155	11.74
0.35	4.498	2018	2.907	0.85	18.52	8311	11.97
0.36	4.705	2111	3.040	0.86	18.87	8467	12.19
0.37	4.915	2205	3.176	0.87	19.22	8625	12.42
0.38	5.128	2301	3.314	0.88	19.57	8783	12.65
0.39	5.345	2399	3.454	0.89	19.93	8943	12.88
0.40	5.565	2497	3.597	0.90	20.29	9104	13.11
0.41	5.789	2598	3.741	0.91	20.65	9266	13.34
0.42	6.016	2700	3.888	0.92	21.01	9429	13.58
0.43	6.246	2803	4.036	0.93	21.38	9593	13.81
0.44	6.479	2908	4.187	0.94	21.74	9758	14.05
0.45	6.716	3014	4.340	0.95	22.11	9924	14.29
0.46	6.955	3121	4.495	0.96	22.49	10,090	14.53
0.47	7.198	3230	4.652	0.97	22.86	10,260	14.77
0.48	7.444	3340	4.811	0.98	23.24	10,430	15.02
0.49	7.693	3452	4.971	0.99	23.62	10,600	15.26
0.50	7.945	3565	5.134	1.00	24.00	10,770	15.51

13

Table 13-12 (Continued)				Table 13-12 (Continued)			
Head (feet)	CFS	GPM	MGD	Head (feet)	CFS	GPM	MGD
1.01	24.38	10,940	15.76	1.51	46.31	20,780	29.93
1.02	24.77	11,120	16.01	1.52	46.80	21,000	30.24
1.03	25.16	11,290	16.26	1.53	47.29	21,220	30.56
1.04	25.55	11,470	16.51	1.54	47.79	21,440	30.88
1.05	25.94	11,640	16.77	1.55	48.28	21,670	31.20
1.06	26.34	11,820	17.02	1.56	48.78	21,890	31.52
1.07	26.73	12,000	17.28	1.57	49.28	22,110	31.85
1.08	27.13	12,180	17.54	1.58	49.78	22,340	32.17
1.09	27.54	12,360	17.80	1.59	50.29	22,570	32.50
1.10	27.94	12,540	18.06	1.60	50.79	22,790	32.82
1.11	28.35	12,720	18.32	1.61	51.30	23,020	33.15
1.12	28.76	12,900	18.58	1.62	51.81	23,250	33.48
1.13	29.17	13,090	18.85	1.63	52.32	23,480	33.81
1.14	29.58	13,270	19.12	1.64	52.83	23,710	34.14
1.15	29.99	13,460	19.38	1.65	53.35	23,940	34.47
1.16	30.41	13,650	19.65	1.66	53.86	24,170	34.81
1.17	30.83	13,830	19.92	1.67	54.38	24,400	35.14
1.18	31.25	14,020	20.20	1.68	54.90	24,640	35.48
1.19	31.67	14,210	20.47	1.69	55.42	24,870	35.82
1.20	32.10	14,400	20.74	1.70	55.95	25,110	36.16
1.21	32.53	14,600	21.02	1.71	56.47	25,340	36.50
1.22	32.96	14,790	21.30	1.72	57.00	25,580	36.84
1.23	33.39	14,980	21.58	1.73	57.53	25,820	37.18
1.24	33.82	15,180	21.86	1.74	58.06	26,060	37.52
1.25	34.26	15,370	22.14	1.75	58.59	26,290	37.87
1.26	34.70	15,570	22.42	1.76	59.13	26,530	38.21
1.27	35.14	15,770	22.71	1.77	59.67	26,780	38.56
1.28	35.58	15,970	22.99	1.78	60.20	27,020	38.91
1.29	36.02	16,170	23.28	1.79	60.75	27,260	39.26
1.30	36.47	16,370	23.57	1.80	61.29	27,500	39.61
1.31	36.92	16,570	23.86	1.81	61.83	27,750	39.96
1.32	37.37	16,770	24.15	1.82	62.38	27,990	40.31
1.33	37.82	16,970	24.44	1.83	62.92	28,240	40.67
1.34	38.28	17,180	24.74	1.84	63.47	28,480	41.02
1.35	38.73	17,380	25.03	1.85	64.03	28,730	41.38
1.36	39.19	17,590	25.33	1.86	64.58	28,980	41.73
1.37	39.65	17,790	25.63	1.87	65.13	29,230	42.09
1.38	40.12	18,000	25.93	1.88	65.69	29,480	42.45
1.39	40.58	18,210	26.23	1.89	66.25	29,730	42.81
1.40	41.05	18,420	26.53	1.90	66.81	29,980	43.17
1.41	41.52	18,630	26.83	1.91	67.37	30,230	43.54
1.42	41.99	18,840	27.13	1.92	67.93	30,480	43.90
1.43	42.46	19,050	27.44	1.93	68.50	30,740	44.27
1.44	42.93	19,270	27.75	1.94	69.06	30,990	44.63
1.45	43.41	19,480	28.05	1.95	69.63	31,250	45.00
1.46	43.89	19,700	28.36	1.96	70.20	31,500	45.37
1.47	44.37	19,910	28.67	1.97	70.78	31,760	45.74
1.48	44.85	20,130	28.99	1.98	71.35	32,020	46.11
1.49	45.34	20,340	29.30	1.99	71.93	32,280	46.48
1.50	45.82	20,560	29.61	2.00	72.50	32,540	46.85

13

Table 13-12 (Continued)				Table 13-12 (Continued)			
Head (feet)	CFS	GPM	MGD	Head (feet)	CFS	GPM	MGD
2.01	73.08	32,800	47.23	2.26	88.11	39,540	56.94
2.02	73.66	33,060	47.60	2.27	88.73	39,820	57.34
2.03	74.25	33,320	47.98	2.28	89.35	40,100	57.75
2.04	74.83	33,580	48.36	2.29	89.98	40,380	58.15
2.05	75.42	33,840	48.74	2.30	90.61	40,660	58.56
2.06	76.00	34,110	49.12	2.31	91.24	40,940	58.96
2.07	76.59	34,370	49.50	2.32	91.87	41,230	59.37
2.08	77.18	34,640	49.88	2.33	92.50	41,510	59.78
2.09	77.78	34,900	50.26	2.34	93.13	41,790	60.19
2.10	78.37	35,170	50.65	2.35	93.77	42,080	60.60
2.11	78.97	35,440	51.03	2.36	94.41	42,370	61.01
2.12	79.56	35,700	51.42	2.37	95.05	42,650	61.42
2.13	80.16	35,970	51.81	2.38	95.69	42,940	61.84
2.14	80.76	36,240	52.19	2.39	96.33	43,230	62.25
2.15	81.37	36,510	52.58	2.40	96.97	43,520	62.67
2.16	81.97	36,780	52.97	2.41	97.62	43,810	63.09
2.17	82.58	37,060	53.37	2.42	98.26	44,100	63.50
2.18	83.19	37,330	53.76	2.43	98.91	44,390	63.92
2.19	83.80	37,600	54.15	2.44	99.56	44,680	64.34
2.20	84.41	37,880	54.55	2.45	100.2	44,970	64.76
2.21	85.02	38,150	54.94	2.46	100.9	45,260	65.19
2.22	85.63	38,430	55.34	2.47	101.5	45,560	65.61
2.23	86.25	38,700	55.74	2.48	102.2	45,850	66.03
2.24	86.87	38,980	56.14	2.49	102.8	46,150	66.46
2.25	87.49	39,260	56.54	2.50	103.5	46,440	66.88

13

Table 13-13:
8 ft. Parshall Flume Discharge Table with Head in Feet

Formula: CFS $= 32.00\ H^{1.607}$
GPM $= 14360\ H^{1.607}$
MGD $= 20.68\ H^{1.607}$
Where: H = head in feet

Values in italics indicate flow below the recommended range of this particular primary device.

Head (feet)	CFS	GPM	MGD	Head (feet)	CFS	GPM	MGD
0.01	*0.020*	*9*	*0.013*	0.51	10.84	4867	7.008
0.02	*0.060*	*27*	*0.039*	0.52	11.19	5021	7.230
0.03	*0.114*	*51*	*0.074*	0.53	11.54	5177	7.455
0.04	*0.181*	*81*	*0.117*	0.54	11.89	5335	7.683
0.05	*0.260*	*117*	*0.168*	0.55	12.24	5494	7.912
0.06	*0.348*	*156*	*0.225*	0.56	12.60	5656	8.145
0.07	*0.446*	*200*	*0.288*	0.57	12.97	5819	8.380
0.08	*0.553*	*248*	*0.357*	0.58	13.33	5984	8.617
0.09	*0.668*	*300*	*0.432*	0.59	13.71	6151	8.857
0.10	*0.791*	*355*	*0.511*	0.60	14.08	6319	9.100
0.11	*0.922*	*414*	*0.596*	0.61	14.46	6489	9.345
0.12	*1.060*	*476*	*0.685*	0.62	14.84	6661	9.592
0.13	*1.206*	*541*	*0.779*	0.63	15.23	6834	9.842
0.14	*1.358*	*610*	*0.878*	0.64	15.62	7009	10.09
0.15	*1.518*	*681*	*0.981*	0.65	16.01	7186	10.35
0.16	*1.683*	*756*	*1.088*	0.66	16.41	7365	10.61
0.17	*1.856*	*833*	*1.199*	0.67	16.81	7545	10.87
0.18	2.034	913	1.315	0.68	17.22	7727	11.13
0.19	2.219	996	1.434	0.69	17.63	7910	11.39
0.20	2.409	1081	1.557	0.70	18.04	8095	11.66
0.21	2.606	1170	1.684	0.71	18.46	8282	11.93
0.22	2.808	1260	1.815	0.72	18.87	8470	12.20
0.23	3.016	1354	1.949	0.73	19.30	8660	12.47
0.24	3.230	1450	2.087	0.74	19.72	8851	12.75
0.25	3.449	1548	2.229	0.75	20.15	9044	13.02
0.26	3.673	1648	2.374	0.76	20.59	9239	13.31
0.27	3.903	1751	2.522	0.77	21.03	9435	13.59
0.28	4.137	1857	2.674	0.78	21.47	9633	13.87
0.29	4.377	1964	2.829	0.79	21.91	9832	14.16
0.30	4.623	2074	2.987	0.80	22.36	10,030	14.45
0.31	4.873	2187	3.149	0.81	22.81	10,240	14.74
0.32	5.128	2301	3.314	0.82	23.26	10,440	15.03
0.33	5.388	2418	3.482	0.83	23.72	10,640	15.33
0.34	5.652	2537	3.653	0.84	24.18	10,850	15.63
0.35	5.922	2657	3.827	0.85	24.64	11,060	15.93
0.36	6.196	2781	4.004	0.86	25.11	11,270	16.23
0.37	6.475	2906	4.185	0.87	25.58	11,480	16.53
0.38	6.759	3033	4.368	0.88	26.06	11,690	16.84
0.39	7.047	3162	4.554	0.89	26.54	11,910	17.15
0.40	7.339	3294	4.743	0.90	27.02	12,120	17.46
0.41	7.636	3427	4.935	0.91	27.50	12,340	17.77
0.42	7.938	3562	5.130	0.92	27.99	12,560	18.09
0.43	8.244	3699	5.328	0.93	28.48	12,780	18.40
0.44	8.554	3839	5.528	0.94	28.97	13,000	18.72
0.45	8.869	3980	5.731	0.95	29.47	13,220	19.04
0.46	9.188	4123	5.937	0.96	29.97	13,450	19.37
0.47	9.511	4268	6.146	0.97	30.47	13,670	19.69
0.48	9.838	4415	6.358	0.98	30.98	13,900	20.02
0.49	10.17	4564	6.572	0.99	31.49	14,130	20.35
0.50	10.50	4714	6.789	1.00	32.00	14,360	20.68

13

Table 13-13 (Continued)					Table 13-13 (Continued)			
Head (feet)	CFS	GPM	MGD		Head (feet)	CFS	GPM	MGD
1.01	32.52	14,590	21.01		1.51	62.05	27,850	40.10
1.02	33.03	14,820	21.35		1.52	62.72	28,140	40.53
1.03	33.56	15,060	21.69		1.53	63.38	28,440	40.96
1.04	34.08	15,290	22.03		1.54	64.05	28,740	41.39
1.05	34.61	15,530	22.37		1.55	64.72	29,040	41.82
1.06	35.14	15,770	22.71		1.56	65.39	29,340	42.26
1.07	35.68	16,010	23.06		1.57	66.06	29,650	42.69
1.08	36.21	16,250	23.40		1.58	66.74	29,950	43.13
1.09	36.75	16,490	23.75		1.59	67.42	30,260	43.57
1.10	37.30	16,740	24.10		1.60	68.10	30,560	44.01
1.11	37.84	16,980	24.46		1.61	68.79	30,870	44.45
1.12	38.39	17,230	24.81		1.62	69.48	31,180	44.90
1.13	38.94	17,480	25.17		1.63	70.17	31,490	45.35
1.14	39.50	17,730	25.53		1.64	70.86	31,800	45.79
1.15	40.06	17,980	25.89		1.65	71.56	32,110	46.24
1.16	40.62	18,230	26.25		1.66	72.25	32,420	46.69
1.17	41.18	18,480	26.61		1.67	72.96	32,740	47.15
1.18	41.75	18,740	26.98		1.68	73.66	33,050	47.60
1.19	42.32	18,990	27.35		1.69	74.36	33,370	48.06
1.20	42.89	19,250	27.72		1.70	75.07	33,690	48.52
1.21	43.47	19,510	28.09		1.71	75.78	34,010	48.98
1.22	44.05	19,770	28.47		1.72	76.50	34,330	49.44
1.23	44.63	20,030	28.84		1.73	77.21	34,650	49.90
1.24	45.21	20,290	29.22		1.74	77.93	34,970	50.36
1.25	45.80	20,550	29.60		1.75	78.65	35,300	50.83
1.26	46.39	20,820	29.98		1.76	79.38	35,620	51.30
1.27	46.99	21,080	30.36		1.77	80.10	35,950	51.77
1.28	47.58	21,350	30.75		1.78	80.83	36,270	52.24
1.29	48.18	21,620	31.14		1.79	81.56	36,600	52.71
1.30	48.78	21,890	31.53		1.80	82.29	36,930	53.18
1.31	49.39	22,160	31.92		1.81	83.03	37,260	53.66
1.32	49.99	22,430	32.31		1.82	83.77	37,590	54.14
1.33	50.60	22,710	32.70		1.83	84.51	37,920	54.61
1.34	51.22	22,980	33.10		1.84	85.25	38,260	55.10
1.35	51.83	23,260	33.50		1.85	86.00	38,590	55.58
1.36	52.45	23,540	33.90		1.86	86.75	38,930	56.06
1.37	53.07	23,820	34.30		1.87	87.50	39,260	56.55
1.38	53.70	24,100	34.70		1.88	88.25	39,600	57.03
1.39	54.32	24,380	35.11		1.89	89.01	39,940	57.52
1.40	54.95	24,660	35.51		1.90	89.76	40,280	58.01
1.41	55.58	24,940	35.92		1.91	90.53	40,620	58.50
1.42	56.22	25,230	36.33		1.92	91.29	40,970	59.00
1.43	56.86	25,510	36.74		1.93	92.05	41,310	59.49
1.44	57.50	25,800	37.16		1.94	92.82	41,650	59.99
1.45	58.14	26,090	37.57		1.95	93.59	42,000	60.48
1.46	58.78	26,380	37.99		1.96	94.36	42,350	60.98
1.47	59.43	26,670	38.41		1.97	95.14	42,690	61.48
1.48	60.08	26,960	38.83		1.98	95.92	43,040	61.99
1.49	60.74	27,260	39.25		1.99	96.70	43,390	62.49
1.50	61.39	27,550	39.68		2.00	97.48	43,740	62.99

Table 13-13 (Continued)				Table 13-13 (Continued)			
Head (feet)	CFS	GPM	MGD	Head (feet)	CFS	GPM	MGD
2.01	98.26	44,100	63.50	2.26	118.6	53,240	76.67
2.02	99.05	44,450	64.01	2.27	119.5	53,620	77.21
2.03	99.84	44,800	64.52	2.28	120.3	54,000	77.76
2.04	100.6	45,160	65.03	2.29	121.2	54,380	78.31
2.05	101.4	45,510	65.54	2.30	122.0	54,760	78.86
2.06	102.2	45,870	66.06	2.31	122.9	55,140	79.41
2.07	103.0	46,230	66.58	2.32	123.7	55,530	79.96
2.08	103.8	46,590	67.09	2.33	124.6	55,910	80.52
2.09	104.6	46,950	67.61	2.34	125.5	56,300	81.07
2.10	105.4	47,310	68.13	2.35	126.3	56,680	81.63
2.11	106.2	47,670	68.66	2.36	127.2	57,070	82.19
2.12	107.0	48,040	69.18	2.37	128.0	57,460	82.75
2.13	107.9	48,400	69.70	2.38	128.9	57,850	83.31
2.14	108.7	48,770	70.23	2.39	129.8	58,240	83.88
2.15	109.5	49,130	70.76	2.40	130.7	58,630	84.44
2.16	110.3	49,500	71.29	2.41	131.5	59,030	85.01
2.17	111.1	49,870	71.82	2.42	132.4	59,420	85.57
2.18	112.0	50,240	72.35	2.43	133.3	59,820	86.14
2.19	112.8	50,610	72.89	2.44	134.2	60,210	86.71
2.20	113.6	50,980	73.42	2.45	135.1	60,610	87.29
2.21	114.4	51,360	73.96	2.46	136.0	61,010	87.86
2.22	115.3	51,730	74.50	2.47	136.8	61,410	88.43
2.23	116.1	52,110	75.04	2.48	137.7	61,810	89.01
2.24	116.9	52,480	75.58	2.49	138.6	62,210	89.59
2.25	117.8	52,860	76.12	2.50	139.5	62,610	90.17

13

Table 13-14:
10 ft. Parshall Flume Discharge Table with Head in Feet

Formula: CFS $= 39.38\ H^{1.600}$
GPM $= 17670\ H^{1.600}$
MGD $= 25.45\ H^{1.600}$
Where: H = head in feet

Values in italics indicate flow below the recommended range of this particular primary device.

Table 13-14				Table 13-14 (Continued)			
Head (feet)	CFS	GPM	MGD	Head (feet)	CFS	GPM	MGD
0.01	*0.025*	*11*	*0.016*	0.51	13.41	6017	8.666
0.02	*0.075*	*34*	*0.049*	0.52	13.83	6206	8.939
0.03	*0.144*	*65*	*0.093*	0.53	14.26	6398	9.216
0.04	*0.228*	*103*	*0.148*	0.54	14.69	6593	9.495
0.05	*0.326*	*147*	*0.211*	0.55	15.13	6789	9.778
0.06	*0.437*	*196*	*0.282*	0.56	15.57	6988	10.06
0.07	*0.559*	*251*	*0.361*	0.57	16.02	7188	10.35
0.08	*0.692*	*311*	*0.447*	0.58	16.47	7391	10.65
0.09	*0.836*	*375*	*0.540*	0.59	16.93	7596	10.94
0.10	*0.989*	*444*	*0.639*	0.60	17.39	7803	11.24
0.11	*1.152*	*517*	*0.745*	0.61	17.86	8012	11.54
0.12	*1.324*	*594*	*0.856*	0.62	18.33	8224	11.84
0.13	*1.505*	*676*	*0.973*	0.63	18.80	8437	12.15
0.14	*1.695*	*761*	*1.095*	0.64	19.28	8652	12.46
0.15	*1.892*	*849*	*1.223*	0.65	19.77	8869	12.77
0.16	*2.098*	*942*	*1.356*	0.66	20.26	9089	13.09
0.17	*2.312*	*1038*	*1.494*	0.67	20.75	9310	13.41
0.18	*2.533*	*1137*	*1.637*	0.68	21.25	9533	13.73
0.19	*2.762*	*1240*	*1.785*	0.69	21.75	9759	14.06
0.20	*2.999*	*1346*	*1.938*	0.70	22.26	9986	14.38
0.21	*3.242*	*1455*	*2.095*	0.71	22.77	10,220	14.71
0.22	*3.493*	*1568*	*2.257*	0.72	23.28	10,450	15.05
0.23	*3.750*	*1683*	*2.424*	0.73	23.80	10,680	15.38
0.24	*4.014*	*1802*	*2.595*	0.74	24.32	10,910	15.72
0.25	*4.285*	*1923*	*2.770*	0.75	24.85	11,150	16.06
0.26	*4.563*	*2048*	*2.949*	0.76	25.39	11,390	16.41
0.27	*4.847*	*2175*	*3.133*	0.77	25.92	11,630	16.75
0.28	*5.137*	*2306*	*3.320*	0.78	26.46	11,870	17.10
0.29	*5.434*	*2439*	*3.512*	0.79	27.01	12,120	17.45
0.30	5.737	2574	3.708	0.80	27.56	12,360	17.81
0.31	6.046	2713	3.907	0.81	28.11	12,610	18.17
0.32	6.361	2854	4.111	0.82	28.67	12,860	18.53
0.33	6.682	2998	4.318	0.83	29.23	13,110	18.89
0.34	7.009	3145	4.530	0.84	29.79	13,370	19.25
0.35	7.341	3294	4.745	0.85	30.36	13,620	19.62
0.36	7.680	3446	4.963	0.86	30.94	13,880	19.99
0.37	8.024	3600	5.186	0.87	31.51	14,140	20.37
0.38	8.374	3757	5.412	0.88	32.10	14,400	20.74
0.39	8.729	3917	5.641	0.89	32.68	14,660	21.12
0.40	9.090	4079	5.875	0.90	33.27	14,930	21.50
0.41	9.456	4243	6.111	0.91	33.86	15,200	21.89
0.42	9.828	4410	6.352	0.92	34.46	15,460	22.27
0.43	10.21	4579	6.595	0.93	35.06	15,730	22.66
0.44	10.59	4751	6.842	0.94	35.67	16,000	23.05
0.45	10.98	4925	7.093	0.95	36.28	16,280	23.44
0.46	11.37	5101	7.347	0.96	36.89	16,550	23.84
0.47	11.77	5280	7.604	0.97	37.51	16,830	24.24
0.48	12.17	5460	7.865	0.98	38.13	17,110	24.64
0.49	12.58	5644	8.128	0.99	38.75	17,390	25.04
0.50	12.99	5829	8.395	1.00	39.38	17,670	25.45

13

Table 13-14 (Continued)

Head (feet)	CFS	GPM	MGD
1.01	40.01	17,950	25.86
1.02	40.65	18,240	26.27
1.03	41.29	18,530	26.68
1.04	41.93	18,810	27.10
1.05	42.58	19,100	27.52
1.06	43.23	19,400	27.94
1.07	43.88	19,690	28.36
1.08	44.54	19,990	28.78
1.09	45.20	20,280	29.21
1.10	45.87	20,580	29.64
1.11	46.54	20,880	30.07
1.12	47.21	21,180	30.51
1.13	47.89	21,490	30.95
1.14	48.57	21,790	31.39
1.15	49.25	22,100	31.83
1.16	49.94	22,410	32.27
1.17	50.63	22,720	32.72
1.18	51.32	23,030	33.17
1.19	52.02	23,340	33.62
1.20	52.72	23,660	34.07
1.21	53.42	23,970	34.53
1.22	54.13	24,290	34.98
1.23	54.84	24,610	35.44
1.24	55.56	24,930	35.91
1.25	56.28	25,250	36.37
1.26	57.00	25,580	36.84
1.27	57.72	25,900	37.31
1.28	58.45	26,230	37.78
1.29	59.19	26,560	38.25
1.30	59.92	26,890	38.73
1.31	60.66	27,220	39.20
1.32	61.40	27,550	39.68
1.33	62.15	27,890	40.17
1.34	62.90	28,220	40.65
1.35	63.65	28,560	41.14
1.36	64.41	28,900	41.62
1.37	65.17	29,240	42.12
1.38	65.93	29,580	42.61
1.39	66.70	29,930	43.10
1.40	67.47	30,270	43.60
1.41	68.24	30,620	44.10
1.42	69.01	30,970	44.60
1.43	69.79	31,320	45.11
1.44	70.58	31,670	45.61
1.45	71.36	32,020	46.12
1.46	72.15	32,370	46.63
1.47	72.94	32,730	47.14
1.48	73.74	33,090	47.65
1.49	74.54	33,450	48.17
1.50	75.34	33,810	48.69

Table 13-14 (Continued)

Head (feet)	CFS	GPM	MGD
1.51	76.14	34,170	49.21
1.52	76.95	34,530	49.73
1.53	77.76	34,890	50.26
1.54	78.58	35,260	50.78
1.55	79.40	35,630	51.31
1.56	80.22	35,990	51.84
1.57	81.04	36,360	52.38
1.58	81.87	36,740	52.91
1.59	82.70	37,110	53.45
1.60	83.53	37,480	53.99
1.61	84.37	37,860	54.53
1.62	85.21	38,230	55.07
1.63	86.05	38,610	55.61
1.64	86.90	38,990	56.16
1.65	87.75	39,370	56.71
1.66	88.60	39,760	57.26
1.67	89.46	40,140	57.81
1.68	90.32	40,530	58.37
1.69	91.18	40,910	58.93
1.70	92.04	41,300	59.48
1.71	92.91	41,690	60.05
1.72	93.78	42,080	60.61
1.73	94.66	42,470	61.17
1.74	95.53	42,870	61.74
1.75	96.41	43,260	62.31
1.76	97.30	43,660	62.88
1.77	98.18	44,050	63.45
1.78	99.07	44,450	64.03
1.79	99.96	44,850	64.60
1.80	100.9	45,260	65.18
1.81	101.8	45,660	65.76
1.82	102.7	46,060	66.34
1.83	103.6	46,470	66.93
1.84	104.5	46,880	67.51
1.85	105.4	47,280	68.10
1.86	106.3	47,690	68.69
1.87	107.2	48,100	69.28
1.88	108.1	48,520	69.88
1.89	109.0	48,930	70.47
1.90	110.0	49,340	71.07
1.91	110.9	49,760	71.67
1.92	111.8	50,180	72.27
1.93	112.8	50,600	72.88
1.94	113.7	51,020	73.48
1.95	114.6	51,440	74.09
1.96	115.6	51,860	74.70
1.97	116.5	52,290	75.31
1.98	117.5	52,710	75.92
1.99	118.4	53,140	76.53
2.00	119.4	53,570	77.15

13

Table 13-14 (Continued)				Table 13-14 (Continued)			
Head (feet)	CFS	GPM	MGD	Head (feet)	CFS	GPM	MGD
2.01	120.3	53,990	77.77	2.39	158.7	71,230	102.6
2.02	121.3	54,430	78.39	2.40	159.8	71,710	103.3
2.03	122.3	54,860	79.01	2.41	160.9	72,190	104.0
2.04	123.2	55,290	79.63	2.42	161.9	72,670	104.7
2.05	124.2	55,720	80.26	2.43	163.0	73,150	105.4
2.06	125.2	56,160	80.89	2.44	164.1	73,630	106.1
2.07	126.1	56,600	81.52	2.45	165.2	74,110	106.7
2.08	127.1	57,030	82.15	2.46	166.3	74,600	107.4
2.09	128.1	57,470	82.78	2.47	167.3	75,080	108.1
2.10	129.1	57,910	83.41	2.48	168.4	75,570	108.8
2.11	130.1	58,360	84.05	2.49	169.5	76,060	109.5
2.12	131.0	58,800	84.69	2.50	170.6	76,550	110.3
2.13	132.0	59,240	85.33	2.51	171.7	77,040	111.0
2.14	133.0	59,690	85.97	2.52	172.8	77,530	111.7
2.15	134.0	60,140	86.61	2.53	173.9	78,020	112.4
2.16	135.0	60,580	87.26	2.54	175.0	78,520	113.1
2.17	136.0	61,030	87.91	2.55	176.1	79,010	113.8
2.18	137.0	61,480	88.56	2.56	177.2	79,510	114.5
2.19	138.0	61,940	89.21	2.57	178.3	80,010	115.2
2.20	139.0	62,390	89.86	2.58	179.4	80,510	116.0
2.21	140.1	62,840	90.51	2.59	180.5	81,010	116.7
2.22	141.1	63,300	91.17	2.60	181.6	81,510	117.4
2.23	142.1	63,760	91.83	2.61	182.8	82,010	118.1
2.24	143.1	64,210	92.49	2.62	183.9	82,510	118.8
2.25	144.1	64,670	93.15	2.63	185.0	83,020	119.6
2.26	145.2	65,130	93.81	2.64	186.1	83,520	120.3
2.27	146.2	65,600	94.48	2.65	187.3	84,030	121.0
2.28	147.2	66,060	95.14	2.66	188.4	84,540	121.8
2.29	148.3	66,520	95.81	2.67	189.5	85,050	122.5
2.30	149.3	66,990	96.48	2.68	190.7	85,560	123.2
2.31	150.3	67,460	97.16	2.69	191.8	86,070	124.0
2.32	151.4	67,920	97.83	2.70	193.0	86,580	124.7
2.33	152.4	68,390	98.50	2.71	194.1	87,090	125.4
2.34	153.5	68,860	99.18	2.72	195.2	87,610	126.2
2.35	154.5	69,330	99.86	2.73	196.4	88,120	126.9
2.36	155.6	69,810	100.5	2.74	197.5	88,640	127.7
2.37	156.6	70,280	101.2	2.75	198.7	89,160	128.4
2.38	157.7	70,760	101.9				

13

Table 13-15:
12 ft. Parshall Flume Discharge Table with Head in Feet

Formula: $\text{CFS} = 46.75\ H^{1.600}$
$\text{GPM} = 20980\ H^{1.600}$
$\text{MGD} = 30.21\ H^{1.600}$
Where: H = head in feet

Values in italics indicate flow below the recommended range of this particular primary device.

Table 13-15				Table 13-15 (Continued)			
Head (feet)	CFS	GPM	MGD	Head (feet)	CFS	GPM	MGD
0.01	*0.030*	*13.24*	*0.019*	0.51	15.92	7144	10.29
0.02	*0.089*	*40.13*	*0.058*	0.52	16.42	7369	10.61
0.03	*0.171*	*76.78*	*0.111*	0.53	16.93	7597	10.94
0.04	*0.271*	*121.7*	*0.175*	0.54	17.44	7828	11.27
0.05	*0.387*	*173.9*	*0.250*	0.55	17.96	8061	11.61
0.06	*0.519*	*232.8*	*0.335*	0.56	18.49	8297	11.95
0.07	*0.664*	*297.9*	*0.429*	0.57	19.02	8535	12.29
0.08	*0.822*	*368.8*	*0.531*	0.58	19.56	8776	12.64
0.09	*0.992*	*445.3*	*0.641*	0.59	20.10	9019	12.99
0.10	*1.174*	*527.1*	*0.759*	0.60	20.65	9265	13.34
0.11	*1.368*	*613.9*	*0.884*	0.61	21.20	9513	13.70
0.12	*1.572*	*705.6*	*1.016*	0.62	21.76	9764	14.06
0.13	*1.787*	*802.0*	*1.155*	0.63	22.32	10,020	14.42
0.14	*2.012*	*903.0*	*1.300*	0.64	22.89	10,270	14.79
0.15	*2.247*	*1008*	*1.452*	0.65	23.47	10,530	15.16
0.16	*2.491*	*1118*	*1.610*	0.66	24.05	10,790	15.54
0.17	*2.745*	*1232*	*1.774*	0.67	24.63	11,050	15.92
0.18	*3.008*	*1350*	*1.944*	0.68	25.22	11,320	16.30
0.19	*3.279*	*1472*	*2.120*	0.69	25.82	11,590	16.68
0.20	*3.560*	*1598*	*2.301*	0.70	26.42	11,860	17.07
0.21	*3.849*	*1727*	*2.488*	0.71	27.03	12,130	17.46
0.22	*4.146*	*1861*	*2.680*	0.72	27.64	12,400	17.86
0.23	*4.452*	*1998*	*2.877*	0.73	28.26	12,680	18.26
0.24	*4.766*	*2139*	*3.080*	0.74	28.88	12,960	18.66
0.25	*5.087*	*2283*	*3.288*	0.75	29.50	13,240	19.07
0.26	*5.417*	*2431*	*3.501*	0.76	30.14	13,520	19.47
0.27	*5.754*	*2583*	*3.719*	0.77	30.77	13,810	19.89
0.28	*6.099*	*2737*	*3.942*	0.78	31.41	14,100	20.30
0.29	*6.451*	*2895*	*4.169*	0.79	32.06	14,390	20.72
0.30	*6.810*	*3057*	*4.402*	0.80	32.71	14,680	21.14
0.31	*7.177*	*3221*	*4.639*	0.81	33.37	14,980	21.56
0.32	*7.551*	*3389*	*4.881*	0.82	34.03	15,270	21.99
0.33	7.932	3560	5.126	0.83	34.70	15,570	22.42
0.34	8.320	3734	5.377	0.84	35.37	15,870	22.86
0.35	8.715	3911	5.632	0.85	36.05	16,180	23.29
0.36	9.117	4092	5.892	0.86	36.73	16,480	23.73
0.37	9.526	4275	6.156	0.87	37.41	16,790	24.18
0.38	9.941	4461	6.424	0.88	38.10	17,100	24.62
0.39	10.36	4651	6.697	0.89	38.80	17,410	25.07
0.40	10.79	4843	6.973	0.90	39.50	17,730	25.52
0.41	11.23	5038	7.254	0.91	40.20	18,040	25.98
0.42	11.67	5236	7.540	0.92	40.91	18,360	26.44
0.43	12.12	5437	7.829	0.93	41.63	18,680	26.90
0.44	12.57	5641	8.122	0.94	42.34	19,000	27.36
0.45	13.03	5847	8.420	0.95	43.07	19,330	27.83
0.46	13.50	6056	8.721	0.96	43.79	19,650	28.30
0.47	13.97	6268	9.026	0.97	44.53	19,980	28.77
0.48	14.45	6483	9.335	0.98	45.26	20,310	29.25
0.49	14.93	6701	9.649	0.99	46.00	20,650	29.73
0.50	15.42	6921	9.966	1.00	46.75	20,980	30.21

13

Table 13-15 (Continued)				Table 13-15 (Continued)		
Head (feet)	CFS	GPM	MGD	Head (feet)	CFS	GPM	MGD
1.01	47.50	21,320	30.69	1.51	90.40	40,570	58.41
1.02	48.25	21,660	31.18	1.52	91.35	41,000	59.03
1.03	49.01	22,000	31.67	1.53	92.32	41,430	59.66
1.04	49.78	22,340	32.17	1.54	93.29	41,860	60.28
1.05	50.55	22,680	32.66	1.55	94.26	42,300	60.91
1.06	51.32	23,030	33.16	1.56	95.23	42,740	61.54
1.07	52.09	23,380	33.66	1.57	96.21	43,180	62.17
1.08	52.88	23,730	34.17	1.58	97.19	43,620	62.81
1.09	53.66	24,080	34.68	1.59	98.18	44,060	63.44
1.10	54.45	24,440	35.19	1.60	99.17	44,500	64.08
1.11	55.25	24,790	35.70	1.61	100.2	44,950	64.73
1.12	56.04	25,150	36.22	1.62	101.2	45,400	65.37
1.13	56.85	25,510	36.73	1.63	102.2	45,850	66.02
1.14	57.65	25,870	37.26	1.64	103.2	46,300	66.67
1.15	58.47	26,240	37.78	1.65	104.2	46,750	67.32
1.16	59.28	26,600	38.31	1.66	105.2	47,200	67.97
1.17	60.10	26,970	38.84	1.67	106.2	47,660	68.63
1.18	60.92	27,340	39.37	1.68	107.2	48,120	69.29
1.19	61.75	27,710	39.90	1.69	108.2	48,580	69.95
1.20	62.59	28,090	40.44	1.70	109.3	49,040	70.61
1.21	63.42	28,460	40.98	1.71	110.3	49,500	71.28
1.22	64.26	28,840	41.53	1.72	111.3	49,960	71.94
1.23	65.11	29,220	42.07	1.73	112.4	50,430	72.61
1.24	65.96	29,600	42.62	1.74	113.4	50,900	73.29
1.25	66.81	29,980	43.17	1.75	114.5	51,360	73.96
1.26	67.67	30,370	43.73	1.76	115.5	51,840	74.64
1.27	68.53	30,750	44.28	1.77	116.6	52,310	75.32
1.28	69.39	31,140	44.84	1.78	117.6	52,780	76.00
1.29	70.26	31,530	45.40	1.79	118.7	53,260	76.69
1.30	71.14	31,920	45.97	1.80	119.7	53,730	77.37
1.31	72.01	32,320	46.54	1.81	120.8	54,210	78.06
1.32	72.90	32,710	47.11	1.82	121.9	54,690	78.75
1.33	73.78	33,110	47.68	1.83	122.9	55,170	79.45
1.34	74.67	33,510	48.25	1.84	124.0	55,660	80.14
1.35	75.56	33,910	48.83	1.85	125.1	56,140	80.84
1.36	76.46	34,310	49.41	1.86	126.2	56,630	81.54
1.37	77.36	34,720	49.99	1.87	127.3	57,120	82.24
1.38	78.27	35,120	50.58	1.88	128.4	57,600	82.95
1.39	79.18	35,530	51.17	1.89	129.5	58,100	83.65
1.40	80.09	35,940	51.76	1.90	130.6	58,590	84.36
1.41	81.01	36,350	52.35	1.91	131.7	59,080	85.08
1.42	81.93	36,770	52.94	1.92	132.8	59,580	85.79
1.43	82.86	37,180	53.54	1.93	133.9	60,080	86.51
1.44	83.78	37,600	54.14	1.94	135.0	60,570	87.22
1.45	84.72	38,020	54.74	1.95	136.1	61,070	87.94
1.46	85.65	38,440	55.35	1.96	137.2	61,580	88.67
1.47	86.59	38,860	55.96	1.97	138.3	62,080	89.39
1.48	87.54	39,280	56.57	1.98	139.5	62,580	90.12
1.49	88.49	39,710	57.18	1.99	140.6	63,090	90.85
1.50	89.44	40,140	57.80	2.00	141.7	63,600	91.58

13

Head (feet)	CFS	GPM	MGD		Head (feet)	CFS	GPM	MGD
			Table 13-15 (Continued)				Table 13-15 (Continued)	
2.01	142.9	64110	92.31		2.51	203.8	91,470	131.7
2.02	144.0	64,620	93.05		2.52	205.1	92,050	132.6
2.03	145.1	65,130	93.79		2.53	206.4	92,640	133.4
2.04	146.3	65,650	94.53		2.54	207.7	93,230	134.2
2.05	147.4	66,160	95.27		2.55	209.0	93,810	135.1
2.06	148.6	66,680	96.01		2.56	210.4	94,400	135.9
2.07	149.7	67,200	96.76		2.57	211.7	94,990	136.8
2.08	150.9	67,720	97.51		2.58	213.0	95,590	137.6
2.09	152.1	68,240	98.26		2.59	214.3	96,180	138.5
2.10	153.2	68,760	99.02		2.60	215.6	96,770	139.4
2.11	154.4	69,290	99.77		2.61	217.0	97,370	140.2
2.12	155.6	69,810	100.5		2.62	218.3	97,970	141.1
2.13	156.7	70,340	101.3		2.63	219.6	98,570	141.9
2.14	157.9	70,870	102.0		2.64	221.0	99,170	142.8
2.15	159.1	71,400	102.8		2.65	222.3	99,770	143.7
2.16	160.3	71,930	103.6		2.66	223.7	100,400	144.5
2.17	161.5	72,470	104.3		2.67	225.0	101,000	145.4
2.18	162.7	73,000	105.1		2.68	226.4	101,600	146.3
2.19	163.9	73,540	105.9		2.69	227.7	102,200	147.1
2.20	165.1	74,080	106.7		2.70	229.1	102,800	148.0
2.21	166.3	74,620	107.4		2.71	230.4	103,400	148.9
2.22	167.5	75,160	108.2		2.72	231.8	104,000	149.8
2.23	168.7	75,700	109.0		2.73	233.2	104,600	150.7
2.24	169.9	76,240	109.8		2.74	234.5	105,200	151.5
2.25	171.1	76,790	110.6		2.75	235.9	105,900	152.4
2.26	172.3	77,340	111.4		2.76	237.3	106,500	153.3
2.27	173.5	77,880	112.1		2.77	238.6	107,100	154.2
2.28	174.8	78,430	112.9		2.78	240.0	107,700	155.1
2.29	176.0	78,980	113.7		2.79	241.4	108,300	156.0
2.30	177.2	79,540	114.5		2.80	242.8	109,000	156.9
2.31	178.5	80,090	115.3		2.81	244.2	109,600	157.8
2.32	179.7	80,650	116.1		2.82	245.6	110,200	158.7
2.33	180.9	81,200	116.9		2.83	247.0	110,800	159.6
2.34	182.2	81,760	117.7		2.84	248.4	111,500	160.5
2.35	183.4	82,320	118.5		2.85	249.8	112,100	161.4
2.36	184.7	82,880	119.3		2.86	251.2	112,700	162.3
2.37	185.9	83,450	120.2		2.87	252.6	113,300	163.2
2.38	187.2	84,010	121.0		2.88	254.0	114,000	164.1
2.39	188.5	84,580	121.8		2.89	255.4	114,600	165.0
2.40	189.7	85,140	122.6		2.90	256.8	115,300	166.0
2.41	191.0	85,710	123.4		2.91	258.2	115,900	166.9
2.42	192.3	86,280	124.2		2.92	259.7	116,500	167.8
2.43	193.5	86,850	125.1		2.93	261.1	117,200	168.7
2.44	194.8	87,420	125.9		2.94	262.5	117,800	169.6
2.45	196.1	88,000	126.7		2.95	263.9	118,400	170.6
2.46	197.4	88,570	127.5		2.96	265.4	119,100	171.5
2.47	198.7	89,150	128.4		2.97	266.8	119,700	172.4
2.48	199.9	89,730	129.2		2.98	268.2	120,400	173.3
2.49	201.2	90,310	130.0		2.99	269.7	121,000	174.3
2.50	202.5	90,890	130.9		3.00	271.1	121,700	175.2

13

Table 13-15 (Continued)				Table 13-15 (Continued)			
Head (feet)	CFS	GPM	MGD	Head (feet)	CFS	GPM	MGD
3.01	272.6	122,300	176.1	3.26	309.7	139,000	200.1
3.02	274.0	123,000	177.1	3.27	311.2	139,700	201.1
3.03	275.5	123,600	178.0	3.28	312.7	140,300	202.1
3.04	276.9	124,300	179.0	3.29	314.3	141,000	203.1
3.05	278.4	124,900	179.9	3.30	315.8	141,700	204.1
3.06	279.9	125,600	180.8	3.31	317.3	142,400	205.1
3.07	281.3	126,200	181.8	3.32	318.9	143,100	206.0
3.08	282.8	126,900	182.7	3.33	320.4	143,800	207.0
3.09	284.3	127,600	183.7	3.34	321.9	144,500	208.0
3.10	285.7	128,200	184.6	3.35	323.5	145,200	209.0
3.11	287.2	128,900	185.6	3.36	325.0	145,900	210.0
3.12	288.7	129,600	186.6	3.37	326.6	146,600	211.0
3.13	290.2	130,200	187.5	3.38	328.1	147,300	212.0
3.14	291.7	130,900	188.5	3.39	329.7	148,000	213.0
3.15	293.1	131,600	189.4	3.40	331.2	148,700	214.1
3.16	294.6	132,200	190.4	3.41	332.8	149,400	215.1
3.17	296.1	132,900	191.4	3.42	334.4	150,100	216.1
3.18	297.6	133,600	192.3	3.43	335.9	150,800	217.1
3.19	299.1	134,200	193.3	3.44	337.5	151,500	218.1
3.20	300.6	134,900	194.3	3.45	339.1	152,200	219.1
3.21	302.1	135,600	195.2	3.46	340.6	152,900	220.1
3.22	303.6	136,300	196.2	3.47	342.2	153,600	221.1
3.23	305.1	136,900	197.2	3.48	343.8	154,300	222.2
3.24	306.7	137,600	198.2	3.49	345.4	155,000	223.2
3.25	308.2	138,300	199.1	3.50	347.0	155,700	224.2

13

Table 13-16:
0.025 m Parshall Flume Discharge Table with Head in Meters

Formula: $l/s = 60.36 \ H^{1.550}$
$m^3/hr = 217.3 \ H^{1.550}$

Where: H = head in meters

Values in italics indicate flow below the recommended range of this particular primary device.

Head (meters)	l/s	m³/hr	Head (meters)	l/s	m³/hr
	Table 13-16			Table 13-16 (Continued)	
0.005	*0.0164*	*0.0590*	0.105	1.835	6.605
0.010	*0.0479*	*0.1730*	0.110	1.972	7.099
0.015	*0.0899*	*0.3240*	0.115	2.113	7.606
0.020	*0.1404*	*0.5050*	0.120	2.257	8.124
0.025	*0.1984*	*0.7140*	0.125	2.404	8.655
0.030	0.2632	0.9475	0.130	2.555	9.198
0.035	0.3342	1.203	0.135	2.709	9.752
0.040	0.4111	1.480	0.140	2.866	10.32
0.045	0.4934	1.776	0.145	3.026	10.89
0.050	0.5810	2.092	0.150	3.189	11.48
0.055	0.6735	2.424	0.155	3.356	12.08
0.060	0.7707	2.775	0.160	3.525	12.69
0.065	0.8725	3.141	0.165	3.697	13.31
0.070	0.9787	3.523	0.170	3.872	13.94
0.075	1.089	3.921	0.175	4.050	14.58
0.080	1.204	4.334	0.180	4.231	15.23
0.085	1.322	4.761	0.185	4.414	15.89
0.090	1.445	5.202	0.190	4.601	16.56
0.095	1.571	5.656	0.195	4.790	17.24
0.100	1.701	6.124	0.200	4.981	17.93

13

Table 13-17:
0.051 m Parshall Flume Discharge Table with Head in Meters

Formula: $l/s = 120.7 \, H^{1.550}$
$m^3/hr = 434.6 \, H^{1.550}$

Where: H = head in meters

Values in italics indicate flow below the recommended range of this particular primary device.

Table 13-17			Table 13-17 (Continued)		
Head (meters)	l/s	m³/hr	Head (meters)	l/s	m³/hr
0.005	*0.0327*	*0.118*	0.130	5.109	18.40
0.010	*0.0959*	*0.345*	0.135	5.417	19.50
0.015	*0.1798*	*0.647*	0.140	5.731	20.63
0.020	*0.2808*	*1.011*	0.145	6.051	21.79
0.025	*0.3968*	*1.428*	0.150	6.377	22.96
0.030	0.5263	1.895	0.155	6.710	24.16
0.035	0.6684	2.407	0.160	7.048	25.38
0.040	0.8221	2.960	0.165	7.393	26.62
0.045	0.9867	3.553	0.170	7.743	27.88
0.050	1.162	4.183	0.175	8.099	29.16
0.055	1.347	4.849	0.180	8.460	30.46
0.060	1.541	5.549	0.185	8.827	31.78
0.065	1.745	6.282	0.190	9.200	33.13
0.070	1.957	7.047	0.195	9.578	34.49
0.075	2.178	7.842	0.200	9.961	35.87
0.080	2.407	8.667	0.205	10.35	37.27
0.085	2.644	9.521	0.210	10.74	38.68
0.090	2.889	10.40	0.215	11.14	40.12
0.095	3.142	11.31	0.220	11.55	41.58
0.100	3.402	12.25	0.225	11.96	43.05
0.105	3.669	13.21	0.230	12.37	44.54
0.110	3.943	14.20	0.235	12.79	46.05
0.115	4.225	15.21	0.240	13.21	47.58
0.120	4.513	16.25	0.245	13.64	49.12
0.125	4.807	17.31	0.250	14.08	50.69

13

Table 13-18:
0.076 m Parshall Flume Discharge Table with Head in Meters

Formula: $l/s = 176.5\ H^{1.547}$
$m^3/hr = 635.5\ H^{1.547}$
Where: H = head in meters

Values in italics indicate flow below the recommended range of this particular primary device.

Table 13-18			Table 13-18 (Continued)		
Head (meters)	l/s	m³/hr	Head (meters)	l/s	m³/hr
0.005	*0.0487*	*0.175*	0.180	12.44	44.77
0.010	*0.1422*	*0.512*	0.185	12.97	46.71
0.015	*0.2662*	*0.958*	0.190	13.52	48.68
0.020	*0.4154*	*1.495*	0.195	14.07	50.68
0.025	*0.5867*	*2.112*	0.200	14.64	52.70
0.030	0.7778	2.800	0.205	15.21	54.75
0.035	0.9872	3.555	0.210	15.78	56.83
0.040	1.214	4.370	0.215	16.37	58.94
0.045	1.456	5.244	0.220	16.96	61.07
0.050	1.714	6.172	0.225	17.56	63.23
0.055	1.986	7.152	0.230	18.17	65.42
0.060	2.273	8.183	0.235	18.78	67.63
0.065	2.572	9.262	0.240	19.41	69.87
0.070	2.885	10.39	0.245	20.03	72.14
0.075	3.210	11.56	0.250	20.67	74.43
0.080	3.547	12.77	0.255	21.31	76.74
0.085	3.895	14.03	0.260	21.96	79.08
0.090	4.256	15.32	0.265	22.62	81.45
0.095	4.627	16.66	0.270	23.28	83.84
0.100	5.009	18.03	0.275	23.95	86.25
0.105	5.402	19.45	0.280	24.63	88.69
0.110	5.805	20.90	0.285	25.32	91.15
0.115	6.218	22.39	0.290	26.01	93.64
0.120	6.641	23.91	0.295	26.70	96.15
0.125	7.074	25.47	0.300	27.41	98.68
0.130	7.516	27.06	0.305	28.12	101.2
0.135	7.968	28.69	0.310	28.83	103.8
0.140	8.430	30.35	0.315	29.56	106.4
0.145	8.900	32.04	0.320	30.28	109.0
0.150	9.379	33.77	0.325	31.02	111.7
0.155	9.867	35.53	0.330	31.76	114.4
0.160	10.36	37.32	0.335	32.51	117.0
0.165	10.87	39.13	0.340	33.26	119.8
0.170	11.38	40.98	0.345	34.02	122.5
0.175	11.90	42.86	0.350	34.79	125.3

13

Table 13-19:
0.152 m Parshall Flume Discharge Table with Head in Meters

Formula: $l/s = 381.2\ H^{1.580}$
$m^3/hr = 1372\ H^{1.580}$
Where: H = head in meters

Values in italics indicate flow below the recommended range of this particular primary device.

Table 13-19			Table 13-19 (Continued)		
Head (meters)	l/s	m³/hr	Head (meters)	l/s	m³/hr
0.005	*0.088*	*0.318*	0.230	37.38	134.6
0.010	*0.264*	*0.949*	0.235	38.68	139.2
0.015	*0.501*	*1.802*	0.240	39.98	143.9
0.020	*0.789*	*2.839*	0.245	41.31	148.7
0.025	*1.122*	*4.038*	0.250	42.65	153.5
0.030	1.496	5.385	0.255	44.00	158.4
0.035	1.909	6.870	0.260	45.37	163.3
0.040	2.357	8.484	0.265	46.76	168.3
0.045	2.839	10.22	0.270	48.16	173.3
0.050	3.354	12.07	0.275	49.58	178.4
0.055	3.899	14.03	0.280	51.01	183.6
0.060	4.473	16.10	0.285	52.46	188.8
0.065	5.076	18.27	0.290	53.92	194.1
0.070	5.707	20.54	0.295	55.40	199.4
0.075	6.364	22.91	0.300	56.89	204.7
0.080	7.047	25.37	0.305	58.39	210.2
0.085	7.756	27.91	0.310	59.91	215.6
0.090	8.489	30.55	0.315	61.44	221.1
0.095	9.246	33.28	0.320	62.99	226.7
0.100	10.03	36.09	0.325	64.55	232.3
0.105	10.83	38.98	0.330	66.13	238.0
0.110	11.66	41.95	0.335	67.72	243.7
0.115	12.50	45.00	0.340	69.32	249.5
0.120	13.37	48.13	0.345	70.94	255.3
0.125	14.26	51.34	0.350	72.57	261.2
0.130	15.18	54.62	0.355	74.22	267.1
0.135	16.11	57.98	0.360	75.88	273.1
0.140	17.06	61.41	0.365	77.55	279.1
0.145	18.03	64.91	0.370	79.23	285.2
0.150	19.03	68.48	0.375	80.93	291.3
0.155	20.04	72.12	0.380	82.64	297.4
0.160	21.07	75.83	0.385	84.37	303.7
0.165	22.12	79.61	0.390	86.11	309.9
0.170	23.19	83.46	0.395	87.86	316.2
0.175	24.27	87.37	0.400	89.62	322.6
0.180	25.38	91.34	0.405	91.40	329.0
0.185	26.50	95.39	0.410	93.19	335.4
0.190	27.64	99.49	0.415	94.99	341.9
0.195	28.80	103.7	0.420	96.80	348.4
0.200	29.98	107.9	0.425	98.63	355.0
0.205	31.17	112.2	0.430	100.5	361.6
0.210	32.38	116.5	0.435	102.3	368.3
0.215	33.61	121.0	0.440	104.2	375.0
0.220	34.85	125.4	0.445	106.1	381.7
0.225	36.11	130.0	0.450	108.0	388.5

13

Table 13-20:
0.229 m Parshall Flume Discharge Table with Head in Meters

Formula: $l/s = 535.4\ H^{1.530}$
$m^3/hr = 1927\ H^{1.530}$

Where: H = head in meters

Values in italics indicate flow below the recommended range of this particular primary device.

Table 13-20			Table 13-20 (Continued)		
Head (meters)	l/s	m³/hr	Head (meters)	l/s	m³/hr
0.005	*0.162*	*0.581*	0.255	66.17	238.2
0.010	*0.466*	*1.679*	0.260	68.17	245.4
0.015	*0.867*	*3.121*	0.265	70.19	252.6
0.020	*1.347*	*4.848*	0.270	72.22	259.9
0.025	*1.895*	*6.820*	0.275	74.28	267.3
0.030	2.504	9.013	0.280	76.35	274.8
0.035	3.170	11.41	0.285	78.45	282.4
0.040	3.889	14.00	0.290	80.57	290.0
0.045	4.657	16.76	0.295	82.70	297.7
0.050	5.471	19.69	0.300	84.85	305.4
0.055	6.330	22.78	0.305	87.03	313.2
0.060	7.232	26.03	0.310	89.22	321.1
0.065	8.174	29.42	0.315	91.43	329.1
0.070	9.155	32.95	0.320	93.66	337.1
0.075	10.17	36.62	0.325	95.91	345.2
0.080	11.23	40.42	0.330	98.18	353.4
0.085	12.32	44.35	0.335	100.5	361.6
0.090	13.45	48.40	0.340	102.8	369.9
0.095	14.61	52.58	0.345	105.1	378.2
0.100	15.80	56.87	0.350	107.4	386.6
0.105	17.03	61.28	0.355	109.8	395.1
0.110	18.28	65.80	0.360	112.2	403.7
0.115	19.57	70.43	0.365	114.5	412.3
0.120	20.88	75.17	0.370	117.0	420.9
0.125	22.23	80.01	0.375	119.4	429.7
0.130	23.61	84.96	0.380	121.8	438.5
0.135	25.01	90.01	0.385	124.3	447.3
0.140	26.44	95.16	0.390	126.8	456.3
0.145	27.90	100.4	0.395	129.3	465.2
0.150	29.38	105.8	0.400	131.8	474.3
0.155	30.89	111.2	0.405	134.3	483.4
0.160	32.43	116.7	0.410	136.8	492.5
0.165	34.00	122.4	0.415	139.4	501.8
0.170	35.58	128.1	0.420	142.0	511.0
0.175	37.20	133.9	0.425	144.6	520.4
0.180	38.84	139.8	0.430	147.2	529.8
0.185	40.50	145.8	0.435	149.8	539.2
0.190	42.19	151.8	0.440	152.5	548.7
0.195	43.90	158.0	0.445	155.1	558.3
0.200	45.63	164.2	0.450	157.8	567.9
0.205	47.39	170.6	0.455	160.5	577.6
0.210	49.17	177.0	0.460	163.2	587.4
0.215	50.97	183.4	0.465	165.9	597.2
0.220	52.79	190.0	0.470	168.7	607.0
0.225	54.64	196.7	0.475	171.4	616.9
0.230	56.51	203.4	0.480	174.2	626.9
0.235	58.40	210.2	0.485	177.0	636.9
0.240	60.31	217.1	0.490	179.8	647.0
0.245	62.24	224.0	0.495	182.6	657.1
0.250	64.20	231.1	0.500	185.4	667.3

13

Table 13-20 (Continued)			Table 13-20 (Continued)		
Head (meters)	l/s	m³/hr	Head (meters)	l/s	m³/hr
0.505	188.2	677.5	0.555	217.5	782.8
0.510	191.1	687.8	0.560	220.5	793.6
0.515	194.0	698.1	0.565	223.5	804.5
0.520	196.9	708.5	0.570	226.6	815.4
0.525	199.8	719.0	0.575	229.6	826.4
0.530	202.7	729.5	0.580	232.7	837.4
0.535	205.6	740.1	0.585	235.7	848.5
0.540	208.6	750.7	0.590	238.8	859.6
0.545	211.5	761.3	0.595	241.9	870.7
0.550	214.5	772.0	0.600	245.0	882.0

Table 13-21:
0.305 m Parshall Flume Discharge Table with Head in Meters

Formula: l/s = 690.9 H$^{1.522}$
m^3/hr = 2487 H$^{1.522}$
Where: H = head in meters

Values in italics indicate flow below the recommended range of this particular primary device.

Table 13-21			Table 13-21 (Continued)		
Head (meters)	l/s	m^3/hr	Head (meters)	l/s	m^3/hr
0.005	*0.217*	*0.78*	0.255	86.33	310.8
0.010	*0.624*	*2.25*	0.260	88.92	320.1
0.015	*1.157*	*4.17*	0.265	91.54	329.5
0.020	*1.793*	*6.46*	0.270	94.18	339.0
0.025	*2.518*	*9.07*	0.275	96.85	348.6
0.030	3.323	11.96	0.280	99.54	358.3
0.035	4.202	15.13	0.285	102.3	368.1
0.040	5.149	18.54	0.290	105.0	378.0
0.045	6.160	22.18	0.295	107.8	387.9
0.050	7.232	26.03	0.300	110.6	398.0
0.055	8.361	30.10	0.305	113.4	408.1
0.060	9.545	34.36	0.310	116.2	418.3
0.065	10.78	38.81	0.315	119.1	428.7
0.070	12.07	43.44	0.320	122.0	439.1
0.075	13.40	48.25	0.325	124.9	449.5
0.080	14.79	53.23	0.330	127.8	460.1
0.085	16.22	58.38	0.335	130.8	470.8
0.090	17.69	63.68	0.340	133.8	481.5
0.095	19.21	69.15	0.345	136.8	492.3
0.100	20.77	74.76	0.350	139.8	503.2
0.105	22.37	80.52	0.355	142.8	514.2
0.110	24.01	86.43	0.360	145.9	525.3
0.115	25.69	92.48	0.365	149.0	536.4
0.120	27.41	98.67	0.370	152.1	547.6
0.125	29.17	105.0	0.375	155.3	558.9
0.130	30.96	111.5	0.380	158.4	570.3
0.135	32.79	118.0	0.385	161.6	581.8
0.140	34.66	124.8	0.390	164.8	593.3
0.145	36.56	131.6	0.395	168.0	604.9
0.150	38.50	138.6	0.400	171.3	616.6
0.155	40.47	145.7	0.405	174.6	628.4
0.160	42.47	152.9	0.410	177.9	640.2
0.165	44.51	160.2	0.415	181.2	652.1
0.170	46.58	167.7	0.420	184.5	664.1
0.175	48.68	175.2	0.425	187.9	676.2
0.180	50.81	182.9	0.430	191.2	688.4
0.185	52.97	190.7	0.435	194.6	700.6
0.190	55.17	198.6	0.440	198.0	712.9
0.195	57.39	206.6	0.445	201.5	725.2
0.200	59.65	214.7	0.450	204.9	737.7
0.205	61.93	222.9	0.455	208.4	750.2
0.210	64.24	231.3	0.460	211.9	762.8
0.215	66.59	239.7	0.465	215.4	775.4
0.220	68.96	248.2	0.470	219.0	788.1
0.225	71.36	256.9	0.475	222.5	800.9
0.230	73.78	265.6	0.480	226.1	813.8
0.235	76.24	274.4	0.485	229.7	826.8
0.240	78.72	283.4	0.490	233.3	839.8
0.245	81.23	292.4	0.495	236.9	852.8
0.250	83.77	301.5	0.500	240.6	866.0

13

Table 13-21 (Continued)		
Head (meters)	l/s	m³/hr
0.505	244.2	879.2
0.510	247.9	892.5
0.515	251.6	905.8
0.520	255.4	919.2
0.525	259.1	932.7
0.530	262.9	946.3
0.535	266.7	959.9
0.540	270.5	973.6
0.545	274.3	987.4
0.550	278.1	1001
0.555	282.0	1015
0.560	285.9	1029
0.565	289.8	1043
0.570	293.7	1057
0.575	297.6	1071
0.580	301.5	1085
0.585	305.5	1100
0.590	309.5	1114
0.595	313.5	1128
0.600	317.5	1143
0.605	321.5	1157
0.610	325.6	1172
0.615	329.7	1187
0.620	333.8	1201
0.625	337.9	1216

Table 13-21 (Continued)		
Head (meters)	l/s	m³/hr
0.630	342.0	1231
0.635	346.1	1246
0.640	350.3	1261
0.645	354.5	1276
0.650	358.6	1291
0.655	362.9	1306
0.660	367.1	1321
0.665	371.3	1337
0.670	375.6	1352
0.675	379.9	1367
0.680	384.1	1383
0.685	388.5	1398
0.690	392.8	1414
0.695	397.1	1429
0.700	401.5	1445
0.705	405.8	1461
0.710	410.2	1477
0.715	414.6	1493
0.720	419.1	1508
0.725	423.5	1524
0.730	427.9	1540
0.735	432.4	1557
0.740	436.9	1573
0.745	441.4	1589
0.750	445.9	1605

13

Table 13-22:
0.457 m Parshall Flume Discharge Table with Head in Meters

Formula: $l/s = 1056\ H^{1.538}$
$m^3/hr = 3803\ H^{1.538}$
Where: H = head in meters

Values in italics indicate flow below the recommended range of this particular primary device.

Table 13-22			Table 13-22 (Continued)		
Head (meters)	l/s	m³/hr	Head (meters)	l/s	m³/hr
0.005	*0.305*	*1.10*	0.255	129.1	464.9
0.010	*0.887*	*3.19*	0.260	133.0	479.0
0.015	*1.654*	*5.96*	0.265	137.0	493.3
0.020	*2.575*	*9.27*	0.270	141.0	507.6
0.025	*3.629*	*13.07*	0.275	145.0	522.2
0.030	4.803	17.30	0.280	149.1	536.9
0.035	6.088	21.92	0.285	153.2	551.7
0.040	7.475	26.92	0.290	157.3	566.6
0.045	8.960	32.27	0.295	161.5	581.7
0.050	10.54	37.94	0.300	165.8	597.0
0.055	12.20	43.93	0.305	170.0	612.3
0.060	13.95	50.23	0.310	174.3	627.8
0.065	15.77	56.81	0.315	178.7	643.5
0.070	17.68	63.66	0.320	183.1	659.2
0.075	19.66	70.79	0.325	187.5	675.2
0.080	21.71	78.18	0.330	191.9	691.2
0.085	23.83	85.82	0.335	196.4	707.4
0.090	26.02	93.70	0.340	200.9	723.7
0.095	28.28	101.8	0.345	205.5	740.1
0.100	30.60	110.2	0.350	210.1	756.7
0.105	32.98	118.8	0.355	214.7	773.4
0.110	35.43	127.6	0.360	219.4	790.2
0.115	37.93	136.6	0.365	224.1	807.1
0.120	40.50	145.9	0.370	228.9	824.2
0.125	43.12	155.3	0.375	233.6	841.4
0.130	45.80	165.0	0.380	238.4	858.7
0.135	48.54	174.8	0.385	243.3	876.1
0.140	51.33	184.9	0.390	248.2	893.7
0.145	54.18	195.1	0.395	253.1	911.4
0.150	57.08	205.6	0.400	258.0	929.2
0.155	60.03	216.2	0.405	263.0	947.1
0.160	63.04	227.0	0.410	268.0	965.1
0.165	66.09	238.0	0.415	273.0	983.3
0.170	69.20	249.2	0.420	278.1	1002
0.175	72.35	260.6	0.425	283.2	1020
0.180	75.56	272.1	0.430	288.4	1038
0.185	78.81	283.8	0.435	293.5	1057
0.190	82.11	295.7	0.440	298.7	1076
0.195	85.45	307.8	0.445	304.0	1095
0.200	88.85	320.0	0.450	309.2	1114
0.205	92.29	332.4	0.455	314.5	1133
0.210	95.77	344.9	0.460	319.9	1152
0.215	99.30	357.6	0.465	325.2	1171
0.220	102.9	370.5	0.470	330.6	1191
0.225	106.5	383.5	0.475	336.1	1210
0.230	110.2	396.7	0.480	341.5	1230
0.235	113.9	410.0	0.485	347.0	1250
0.240	117.6	423.5	0.490	352.5	1270
0.245	121.4	437.2	0.495	358.1	1290
0.250	125.2	451.0	0.500	363.6	1310

13

Table 13-22 (Continued)		
Head (meters)	l/s	m³/hr
0.505	369.3	1330
0.510	374.9	1350
0.515	380.6	1371
0.520	386.3	1391
0.525	392.0	1412
0.530	397.7	1432
0.535	403.5	1453
0.540	409.3	1474
0.545	415.2	1495
0.550	421.1	1516
0.555	427.0	1538
0.560	432.9	1559
0.565	438.8	1580
0.570	444.8	1602
0.575	450.9	1624
0.580	456.9	1645
0.585	463.0	1667
0.590	469.1	1689
0.595	475.2	1711
0.600	481.3	1733
0.605	487.5	1756
0.610	493.7	1778
0.615	500.0	1801
0.620	506.2	1823
0.625	512.5	1846

Table 13-22 (Continued)		
Head (meters)	l/s	m³/hr
0.630	518.9	1869
0.635	525.2	1891
0.640	531.6	1914
0.645	538.0	1937
0.650	544.4	1961
0.655	550.9	1984
0.660	557.3	2007
0.665	563.9	2031
0.670	570.4	2054
0.675	576.9	2078
0.680	583.5	2101
0.685	590.1	2125
0.690	596.8	2149
0.695	603.4	2173
0.700	610.1	2197
0.705	616.8	2221
0.710	623.6	2246
0.715	630.4	2270
0.720	637.1	2295
0.725	644.0	2319
0.730	650.8	2344
0.735	657.7	2369
0.740	664.6	2393
0.745	671.5	2418
0.750	678.4	2443

13

Table 13-23:
0.610 m Parshall Flume Discharge Table with Head in Meters

Formula: l/s = 1429 H$^{1.550}$
m^3/hr = 5143 H$^{1.550}$

Where: H = head in meters

Values in italics indicate flow below the recommended range of this particular primary device.

Table 13-23			Table 13-23 (Continued)		
Head (meters)	l/s	m³/hr	Head (meters)	l/s	m³/hr
0.005	*0.388*	*1.40*	0.255	171.9	618.5
0.010	*1.135*	*4.09*	0.260	177.1	637.4
0.015	*2.127*	*7.66*	0.265	182.4	656.5
0.020	*3.323*	*11.96*	0.270	187.8	675.8
0.025	*4.696*	*16.91*	0.275	193.2	695.3
0.030	*6.229*	*22.43*	0.280	198.7	715.0
0.035	*7.911*	*28.48*	0.285	204.2	734.9
0.040	*9.730*	*35.03*	0.290	209.8	755.0
0.045	11.68	42.04	0.295	215.4	775.2
0.050	13.75	49.50	0.300	221.1	795.7
0.055	15.94	57.38	0.305	226.8	816.4
0.060	18.25	65.67	0.310	232.6	837.2
0.065	20.66	74.34	0.315	238.5	858.2
0.070	23.17	83.39	0.320	244.4	879.4
0.075	25.79	92.80	0.325	250.3	900.8
0.080	28.50	102.6	0.330	256.3	922.4
0.085	31.31	112.7	0.335	262.3	944.1
0.090	34.21	123.1	0.340	268.4	966.1
0.095	37.20	133.9	0.345	274.6	988.2
0.100	40.27	144.9	0.350	280.8	1010
0.105	43.44	156.3	0.355	287.0	1033
0.110	46.69	168.0	0.360	293.3	1056
0.115	50.02	180.0	0.365	299.6	1078
0.120	53.43	192.3	0.370	306.0	1101
0.125	56.92	204.8	0.375	312.5	1125
0.130	60.48	217.7	0.380	318.9	1148
0.135	64.13	230.8	0.385	325.5	1171
0.140	67.85	244.2	0.390	332.0	1195
0.145	71.64	257.8	0.395	338.7	1219
0.150	75.50	271.7	0.400	345.3	1243
0.155	79.44	285.9	0.405	352.0	1267
0.160	83.45	300.3	0.410	358.8	1291
0.165	87.53	315.0	0.415	365.6	1316
0.170	91.67	329.9	0.420	372.5	1340
0.175	95.88	345.1	0.425	379.3	1365
0.180	100.2	360.5	0.430	386.3	1390
0.185	104.5	376.1	0.435	393.3	1415
0.190	108.9	392.0	0.440	400.3	1441
0.195	113.4	408.1	0.445	407.4	1466
0.200	117.9	424.4	0.450	414.5	1492
0.205	122.5	441.0	0.455	421.6	1518
0.210	127.2	457.8	0.460	428.9	1543
0.215	131.9	474.8	0.465	436.1	1570
0.220	136.7	492.0	0.470	443.4	1596
0.225	141.6	509.4	0.475	450.7	1622
0.230	146.5	527.1	0.480	458.1	1649
0.235	151.4	545.0	0.485	465.5	1675
0.240	156.4	563.0	0.490	473.0	1702
0.245	161.5	581.3	0.495	480.5	1729
0.250	166.7	599.8	0.500	488.0	1756

13

Table 13-23 (Continued)			Table 13-23 (Continued)		
Head (meters)	l/s	m³/hr	Head (meters)	l/s	m³/hr
0.505	495.6	1784	0.630	698.2	2513
0.510	503.2	1811	0.635	706.9	2544
0.515	510.9	1839	0.640	715.5	2575
0.520	518.6	1866	0.645	724.2	2606
0.525	526.4	1894	0.650	732.9	2638
0.530	534.1	1922	0.655	741.7	2669
0.535	542.0	1951	0.660	750.5	2701
0.540	549.8	1979	0.665	759.3	2733
0.545	557.8	2007	0.670	768.2	2765
0.550	565.7	2036	0.675	777.1	2797
0.555	573.7	2065	0.680	786.0	2829
0.560	581.7	2094	0.685	795.0	2861
0.565	589.8	2123	0.690	804.0	2894
0.570	597.9	2152	0.695	813.0	2926
0.575	606.1	2181	0.700	822.1	2959
0.580	614.3	2211	0.705	831.2	2992
0.585	622.5	2240	0.710	840.4	3025
0.590	630.7	2270	0.715	849.6	3058
0.595	639.0	2300	0.720	858.8	3091
0.600	647.4	2330	0.725	868.1	3124
0.605	655.8	2360	0.730	877.4	3158
0.610	664.2	2390	0.735	886.7	3191
0.615	672.6	2421	0.740	896.1	3225
0.620	681.1	2451	0.745	905.5	3259
0.625	689.7	2482	0.750	914.9	3293

13

Table 13-24:
0.914 m Parshall Flume Discharge Table with Head in Meters

Formula: l/s = 2184 H$^{1.566}$
m^3/hr = 7863 H$^{1.566}$
Where: H = head in meters

Values in italics indicate flow below the recommended range of this particular primary device.

Table 13-24			Table 13-24 (Continued)		
Head (meters)	l/s	m^3/hr	Head (meters)	l/s	m^3/hr
0.005	*0.544*	*1.96*	0.255	257.0	925.2
0.010	*1.612*	*5.80*	0.260	264.9	953.8
0.015	*3.041*	*10.95*	0.265	272.9	982.6
0.020	*4.772*	*17.18*	0.270	281.0	1012
0.025	*6.768*	*24.36*	0.275	289.2	1041
0.030	*9.004*	*32.41*	0.280	297.5	1071
0.035	*11.46*	*41.26*	0.285	305.9	1101
0.040	*14.13*	*50.86*	0.290	314.3	1132
0.045	16.99	61.17	0.295	322.8	1162
0.050	20.04	72.14	0.300	331.5	1193
0.055	23.26	83.75	0.305	340.1	1225
0.060	26.66	95.98	0.310	348.9	1256
0.065	30.22	108.8	0.315	357.8	1288
0.070	33.94	122.2	0.320	366.7	1320
0.075	37.81	136.1	0.325	375.7	1353
0.080	41.83	150.6	0.330	384.8	1385
0.085	46.00	165.6	0.335	394.0	1418
0.090	50.30	181.1	0.340	403.2	1452
0.095	54.75	197.1	0.345	412.6	1485
0.100	59.33	213.6	0.350	422.0	1519
0.105	64.04	230.6	0.355	431.4	1553
0.110	68.88	248.0	0.360	441.0	1588
0.115	73.84	265.9	0.365	450.6	1622
0.120	78.93	284.2	0.370	460.3	1657
0.125	84.14	302.9	0.375	470.1	1692
0.130	89.47	322.1	0.380	479.9	1728
0.135	94.92	341.7	0.385	489.9	1764
0.140	100.5	361.8	0.390	499.9	1800
0.145	106.2	382.2	0.395	509.9	1836
0.150	111.9	403.0	0.400	520.1	1872
0.155	117.8	424.3	0.405	530.3	1909
0.160	123.9	445.9	0.410	540.6	1946
0.165	130.0	467.9	0.415	551.0	1984
0.170	136.2	490.3	0.420	561.4	2021
0.175	142.5	513.1	0.425	571.9	2059
0.180	148.9	536.2	0.430	582.5	2097
0.185	155.5	559.7	0.435	593.1	2135
0.190	162.1	583.6	0.440	603.8	2174
0.195	168.8	607.8	0.445	614.6	2213
0.200	175.7	632.4	0.450	625.4	2252
0.205	182.6	657.3	0.455	636.4	2291
0.210	189.6	682.6	0.460	647.3	2331
0.215	196.7	708.3	0.465	658.4	2370
0.220	203.9	734.2	0.470	669.5	2410
0.225	211.2	760.5	0.475	680.7	2451
0.230	218.6	787.1	0.480	692.0	2491
0.235	226.1	814.1	0.485	703.3	2532
0.240	233.7	841.4	0.490	714.7	2573
0.245	241.4	869.0	0.495	726.1	2614
0.250	249.1	896.9	0.500	737.6	2656

13

Table 13-24 (Continued)			Table 13-24 (Continued)		
Head (meters)	l/s	m³/hr	Head (meters)	l/s	m³/hr
0.505	749.2	2697	0.630	1059	3814
0.510	760.9	2739	0.635	1072	3861
0.515	772.6	2781	0.640	1086	3909
0.520	784.4	2824	0.645	1099	3957
0.525	796.2	2867	0.650	1112	4005
0.530	808.1	2909	0.655	1126	4053
0.535	820.1	2953	0.660	1139	4102
0.540	832.1	2996	0.665	1153	4151
0.545	844.2	3039	0.670	1167	4200
0.550	856.4	3083	0.675	1180	4249
0.555	868.6	3127	0.680	1194	4298
0.560	880.9	3171	0.685	1208	4348
0.565	893.2	3216	0.690	1221	4398
0.570	905.6	3261	0.695	1235	4448
0.575	918.1	3305	0.700	1249	4498
0.580	930.6	3351	0.705	1263	4548
0.585	943.2	3396	0.710	1277	4599
0.590	955.9	3441	0.715	1292	4650
0.595	968.6	3487	0.720	1306	4701
0.600	981.4	3533	0.725	1320	4752
0.605	994.2	3579	0.730	1334	4803
0.610	1007	3626	0.735	1349	4855
0.615	1020	3673	0.740	1363	4907
0.620	1033	3719	0.745	1377	4959
0.625	1046	3766	0.750	1392	5011

13

Table 13-25:
1.22 m Parshall Flume Discharge Table with Head in Meters

Formula: l/s = 2954 H$^{1.578}$
m^3/hr = 10630 H$^{1.578}$

Where: H = head in meters

Values in italics indicate flow below the recommended range of this particular primary device.

Table 13-25			Table 13-25 (Continued)		
Head (meters)	l/s	m^3/hr	Head (meters)	l/s	m^3/hr
0.005	0.691	2.5	0.255	341.9	1230
0.010	2.063	7.4	0.260	352.6	1269
0.015	3.911	14.1	0.265	363.3	1307
0.020	6.158	22.2	0.270	374.2	1347
0.025	8.757	31.5	0.275	385.2	1386
0.030	11.68	42.0	0.280	396.3	1426
0.035	14.89	53.6	0.285	407.5	1466
0.040	18.38	66.2	0.290	418.9	1507
0.045	22.14	79.7	0.295	430.3	1549
0.050	26.14	94.1	0.300	441.9	1590
0.055	30.39	109.4	0.305	453.6	1632
0.060	34.86	125.4	0.310	465.3	1675
0.065	39.55	142.3	0.315	477.2	1717
0.070	44.46	160.0	0.320	489.3	1761
0.075	49.57	178.4	0.325	501.4	1804
0.080	54.89	197.5	0.330	513.6	1848
0.085	60.40	217.3	0.335	525.9	1893
0.090	66.10	237.9	0.340	538.4	1937
0.095	71.99	259.0	0.345	550.9	1982
0.100	78.06	280.9	0.350	563.6	2028
0.105	84.30	303.4	0.355	576.3	2074
0.110	90.73	326.5	0.360	589.2	2120
0.115	97.32	350.2	0.365	602.2	2167
0.120	104.1	374.5	0.370	615.2	2214
0.125	111.0	399.4	0.375	628.4	2261
0.130	118.1	424.9	0.380	641.7	2309
0.135	125.3	451.0	0.385	655.0	2357
0.140	132.7	477.7	0.390	668.5	2406
0.145	140.3	504.9	0.395	682.1	2455
0.150	148.0	532.6	0.400	695.8	2504
0.155	155.9	560.9	0.405	709.5	2553
0.160	163.9	589.7	0.410	723.4	2603
0.165	172.0	619.0	0.415	737.4	2653
0.170	180.3	648.9	0.420	751.4	2704
0.175	188.8	679.3	0.425	765.6	2755
0.180	197.3	710.2	0.430	779.9	2806
0.185	206.1	741.5	0.435	794.2	2858
0.190	214.9	773.4	0.440	808.7	2910
0.195	223.9	805.8	0.445	823.2	2962
0.200	233.0	838.6	0.450	837.9	3015
0.205	242.3	871.9	0.455	852.6	3068
0.210	251.7	905.7	0.460	867.4	3122
0.215	261.2	940.0	0.465	882.4	3175
0.220	270.9	974.7	0.470	897.4	3229
0.225	280.6	1010	0.475	912.5	3284
0.230	290.5	1046	0.480	927.7	3338
0.235	300.6	1082	0.485	943.0	3393
0.240	310.7	1118	0.490	958.4	3449
0.245	321.0	1155	0.495	973.9	3504
0.250	331.4	1193	0.500	989.4	3560

13

Table 13-25 (Continued)			Table 13-25 (Continued)		
Head (meters)	l/s	m³/hr	Head (meters)	l/s	m³/hr
0.505	1005	3617	0.630	1425	5127
0.510	1021	3673	0.635	1443	5192
0.515	1037	3730	0.640	1461	5256
0.520	1053	3788	0.645	1479	5321
0.525	1069	3845	0.650	1497	5387
0.530	1085	3903	0.655	1515	5452
0.535	1101	3962	0.660	1533	5518
0.540	1117	4020	0.665	1552	5584
0.545	1134	4079	0.670	1570	5650
0.550	1150	4138	0.675	1589	5717
0.555	1167	4198	0.680	1607	5784
0.560	1183	4258	0.685	1626	5851
0.565	1200	4318	0.690	1645	5919
0.570	1217	4378	0.695	1664	5987
0.575	1234	4439	0.700	1683	6055
0.580	1251	4500	0.705	1702	6123
0.585	1268	4561	0.710	1721	6192
0.590	1285	4623	0.715	1740	6261
0.595	1302	4685	0.720	1759	6330
0.600	1319	4747	0.725	1778	6400
0.605	1337	4810	0.730	1798	6469
0.610	1354	4873	0.735	1817	6539
0.615	1372	4936	0.740	1837	6610
0.620	1389	5000	0.745	1856	6680
0.625	1407	5063	0.750	1876	6751

13

Table 13-26:
1.52 m Parshall Flume Discharge Table with Head in Meters

Formula: $l/s = 3732\ H^{1.587}$
$m^3/hr = 13440\ H^{1.587}$
Where: H = head in meters

Values in italics indicate flow below the recommended range of this particular primary device.

Table 13-26			Table 13-26 (Continued)		
Head (meters)	l/s	m³/hr	Head (meters)	l/s	m³/hr
0.005	*0.832*	*3.0*	0.255	426.7	1537
0.010	*2.500*	*9.0*	0.260	440.1	1585
0.015	*4.758*	*17.1*	0.265	453.6	1633
0.020	*7.511*	*27.0*	0.270	467.2	1683
0.025	*10.70*	*38.5*	0.275	481.0	1732
0.030	*14.29*	*51.5*	0.280	495.0	1783
0.035	*18.26*	*65.7*	0.285	509.1	1833
0.040	*22.56*	*81.2*	0.290	523.3	1885
0.045	*27.20*	*97.9*	0.295	537.7	1936
0.050	*32.16*	*115.7*	0.300	552.2	1989
0.055	*37.40*	*134.6*	0.305	566.9	2042
0.060	42.94	154.6	0.310	581.7	2095
0.065	48.76	175.6	0.315	596.7	2149
0.070	54.84	197.5	0.320	611.8	2203
0.075	61.19	220.4	0.325	627.0	2258
0.080	67.79	244.1	0.330	642.4	2314
0.085	74.63	268.8	0.335	657.9	2369
0.090	81.72	294.3	0.340	673.6	2426
0.095	89.04	320.7	0.345	689.4	2483
0.100	96.59	347.9	0.350	705.3	2540
0.105	104.4	375.9	0.355	721.4	2598
0.110	112.4	404.7	0.360	737.6	2656
0.115	120.6	434.2	0.365	753.9	2715
0.120	129.0	464.6	0.370	770.3	2774
0.125	137.6	495.7	0.375	786.9	2834
0.130	146.5	527.5	0.380	803.6	2894
0.135	155.5	560.1	0.385	820.5	2955
0.140	164.8	593.3	0.390	837.5	3016
0.145	174.2	627.3	0.395	854.6	3078
0.150	183.8	662.0	0.400	871.8	3140
0.155	193.6	697.4	0.405	889.1	3202
0.160	203.6	733.4	0.410	906.6	3265
0.165	213.8	770.1	0.415	924.2	3328
0.170	224.2	807.5	0.420	942.0	3392
0.175	234.8	845.5	0.425	959.8	3457
0.180	245.5	884.1	0.430	977.8	3521
0.185	256.4	923.4	0.435	995.9	3587
0.190	267.5	963.3	0.440	1014	3652
0.195	278.8	1004	0.445	1032	3718
0.200	290.2	1045	0.450	1051	3785
0.205	301.8	1087	0.455	1070	3852
0.210	313.5	1129	0.460	1088	3919
0.215	325.5	1172	0.465	1107	3987
0.220	337.6	1216	0.470	1126	4055
0.225	349.8	1260	0.475	1145	4124
0.230	362.2	1305	0.480	1164	4193
0.235	374.8	1350	0.485	1184	4263
0.240	387.6	1396	0.490	1203	4333
0.245	400.4	1442	0.495	1223	4403
0.250	413.5	1489	0.500	1242	4474

13

Table 13-26 (Continued)		
Head (meters)	l/s	m³/hr
0.505	1262	4545
0.510	1282	4617
0.515	1302	4689
0.520	1322	4761
0.525	1342	4834
0.530	1363	4907
0.535	1383	4981
0.540	1404	5055
0.545	1424	5129
0.550	1445	5204
0.555	1466	5279
0.560	1487	5355
0.565	1508	5431
0.570	1529	5508
0.575	1551	5585
0.580	1572	5662
0.585	1594	5740
0.590	1615	5818
0.595	1637	5896
0.600	1659	5975
0.605	1681	6054
0.610	1703	6134
0.615	1725	6214
0.620	1748	6294
0.625	1770	6375

Table 13-26 (Continued)		
Head (meters)	l/s	m³/hr
0.630	1793	6456
0.635	1815	6537
0.640	1838	6619
0.645	1861	6701
0.650	1884	6784
0.655	1907	6867
0.660	1930	6950
0.665	1953	7034
0.670	1977	7118
0.675	2000	7203
0.680	2024	7288
0.685	2047	7373
0.690	2071	7459
0.695	2095	7544
0.700	2119	7631
0.705	2143	7717
0.710	2167	7805
0.715	2191	7892
0.720	2216	7980
0.725	2240	8068
0.730	2265	8156
0.735	2289	8245
0.740	2314	8334
0.745	2339	8424
0.750	2364	8514

13

Table 13-27:
1.83 m Parshall Flume Discharge Table with Head in Meters

Formula: $l/s = 4521\ H^{1.595}$
$m^3/hr = 16280\ H^{1.595}$
Where: H = head in meters

Values in italics indicate flow below the recommended range of this particular primary device.

Table 13-27			Table 13-27 (Continued)		
Head (meters)	l/s	m³/hr	Head (meters)	l/s	m³/hr
0.005	*0.966*	*3.48*	0.255	511.3	1841
0.010	*2.919*	*10.5*	0.260	527.4	1899
0.015	*5.573*	*20.1*	0.265	543.6	1958
0.020	*8.819*	*31.8*	0.270	560.1	2017
0.025	*12.59*	*45.3*	0.275	576.7	2077
0.030	*16.84*	*60.6*	0.280	593.5	2137
0.035	*21.53*	*77.5*	0.285	610.5	2199
0.040	*26.64*	*95.9*	0.290	627.7	2260
0.045	*32.15*	*115.7*	0.295	645.1	2323
0.050	*38.03*	*136.9*	0.300	662.6	2386
0.055	*44.27*	*159.4*	0.305	680.3	2450
0.060	*50.86*	*183.1*	0.310	698.2	2514
0.065	*57.79*	*208.0*	0.315	716.2	2579
0.070	*65.04*	*234.1*	0.320	734.4	2645
0.075	72.60	261.4	0.325	752.8	2711
0.080	80.48	289.8	0.330	771.4	2778
0.085	88.65	319.2	0.335	790.1	2845
0.090	97.11	349.7	0.340	809.0	2913
0.095	105.9	381.2	0.345	828.0	2982
0.100	114.9	413.7	0.350	847.3	3051
0.105	124.2	447.1	0.355	866.7	3121
0.110	133.7	481.6	0.360	886.2	3191
0.115	143.6	517.0	0.365	905.9	3262
0.120	153.6	553.3	0.370	925.8	3334
0.125	164.0	590.5	0.375	945.8	3406
0.130	174.6	628.6	0.380	966.0	3479
0.135	185.4	667.6	0.385	986.4	3552
0.140	196.5	707.5	0.390	1007	3626
0.145	207.8	748.2	0.395	1028	3700
0.150	219.3	789.8	0.400	1048	3775
0.155	231.1	832.2	0.405	1069	3851
0.160	243.1	875.4	0.410	1090	3927
0.165	255.3	919.5	0.415	1112	4004
0.170	267.8	964.3	0.420	1133	4081
0.175	280.5	1010	0.425	1155	4158
0.180	293.4	1056	0.430	1177	4237
0.185	306.5	1104	0.435	1198	4316
0.190	319.8	1152	0.440	1221	4395
0.195	333.3	1200	0.445	1243	4475
0.200	347.0	1250	0.450	1265	4555
0.205	361.0	1300	0.455	1288	4636
0.210	375.1	1351	0.460	1310	4718
0.215	389.5	1402	0.465	1333	4800
0.220	404.0	1455	0.470	1356	4883
0.225	418.8	1508	0.475	1379	4966
0.230	433.7	1562	0.480	1402	5049
0.235	448.8	1616	0.485	1426	5133
0.240	464.2	1671	0.490	1449	5218
0.245	479.7	1727	0.495	1473	5303
0.250	495.4	1784	0.500	1497	5389

13

Table 13-27 (Continued)			Table 13-27 (Continued)		
Head (meters)	l/s	m³/hr	Head (meters)	l/s	m³/hr
0.505	1520	5475	0.630	2164	7791
0.510	1545	5562	0.635	2191	7890
0.515	1569	5649	0.640	2219	7989
0.520	1593	5737	0.645	2246	8089
0.525	1618	5825	0.650	2274	8189
0.530	1642	5914	0.655	2302	8290
0.535	1667	6003	0.660	2330	8391
0.540	1692	6093	0.665	2358	8493
0.545	1717	6183	0.670	2387	8595
0.550	1742	6274	0.675	2415	8697
0.555	1768	6365	0.680	2444	8800
0.560	1793	6457	0.685	2473	8904
0.565	1819	6549	0.690	2501	9008
0.570	1844	6642	0.695	2530	9112
0.575	1870	6735	0.700	2560	9217
0.580	1896	6828	0.705	2589	9322
0.585	1922	6923	0.710	2618	9428
0.590	1949	7017	0.715	2648	9534
0.595	1975	7112	0.720	2677	9641
0.600	2002	7208	0.725	2707	9748
0.605	2028	7304	0.730	2737	9855
0.610	2055	7400	0.735	2767	9963
0.615	2082	7497	0.740	2797	10,070
0.620	2109	7595	0.745	2827	10,180
0.625	2136	7693	0.750	2857	10,290

13

Table 13-28:
2.44 m Parshall Flume Discharge Table with Head in Meters

Formula: $l/s = 6115\ H^{1.607}$
$m^3/hr = 22010\ H^{1.607}$
Where: H = head in meters

Values in italics indicate flow below the recommended range of this particular primary device.

Table 13-28			Table 13-28 (Continued)		
Head (meters)	l/s	m³/hr	Head (meters)	l/s	m³/hr
0.005	*1.226*	*4.4*	0.255	680.3	2449
0.010	*3.736*	*13.5*	0.260	701.9	2526
0.015	*7.167*	*25.8*	0.265	723.7	2605
0.020	*11.38*	*41.0*	0.270	745.8	2684
0.025	*16.29*	*58.6*	0.275	768.1	2765
0.030	*21.83*	*78.6*	0.280	790.6	2846
0.035	*27.97*	*100.7*	0.285	813.5	2928
0.040	*34.67*	*124.8*	0.290	836.5	3011
0.045	*41.89*	*150.8*	0.295	859.8	3095
0.050	*49.62*	*178.6*	0.300	883.3	3179
0.055	*57.83*	*208.2*	0.305	907.1	3265
0.060	*66.51*	*239.4*	0.310	931.1	3351
0.065	*75.64*	*272.3*	0.315	955.4	3439
0.070	*85.20*	*306.7*	0.320	979.9	3527
0.075	95.20	342.6	0.325	1005	3616
0.080	105.6	380.1	0.330	1030	3706
0.085	116.4	419.0	0.335	1055	3796
0.090	127.6	459.3	0.340	1080	3888
0.095	139.2	501.0	0.345	1106	3980
0.100	151.1	544.0	0.350	1132	4073
0.105	163.5	588.4	0.355	1158	4167
0.110	176.2	634.1	0.360	1184	4262
0.115	189.2	681.0	0.365	1211	4357
0.120	202.6	729.2	0.370	1237	4454
0.125	216.3	778.7	0.375	1264	4551
0.130	230.4	829.3	0.380	1292	4649
0.135	244.8	881.2	0.385	1319	4747
0.140	259.6	934.2	0.390	1347	4847
0.145	274.6	988.4	0.395	1374	4947
0.150	290.0	1044	0.400	1403	5048
0.155	305.7	1100	0.405	1431	5150
0.160	321.7	1158	0.410	1459	5252
0.165	338.0	1217	0.415	1488	5356
0.170	354.6	1276	0.420	1517	5460
0.175	371.5	1337	0.425	1546	5565
0.180	388.7	1399	0.430	1575	5670
0.185	406.2	1462	0.435	1605	5777
0.190	424.0	1526	0.440	1635	5884
0.195	442.1	1591	0.445	1665	5991
0.200	460.4	1657	0.450	1695	6100
0.205	479.1	1724	0.455	1725	6209
0.210	498.0	1792	0.460	1756	6319
0.215	517.2	1861	0.465	1786	6430
0.220	536.6	1931	0.470	1817	6542
0.225	556.4	2003	0.475	1849	6654
0.230	576.4	2075	0.480	1880	6767
0.235	596.6	2147	0.485	1912	6880
0.240	617.2	2221	0.490	1943	6995
0.245	637.9	2296	0.495	1975	7110
0.250	659.0	2372	0.500	2007	7225

13

Table 13-28 (Continued)		
Head (meters)	l/s	m³/hr
0.505	2040	7342
0.510	2072	7459
0.515	2105	7577
0.520	2138	7696
0.525	2171	7815
0.530	2204	7935
0.535	2238	8055
0.540	2272	8177
0.545	2306	8299
0.550	2340	8421
0.555	2374	8545
0.560	2408	8669
0.565	2443	8794
0.570	2478	8919
0.575	2513	9045
0.580	2548	9172
0.585	2584	9299
0.590	2619	9427
0.595	2655	9556
0.600	2691	9685
0.605	2727	9815
0.610	2763	9946
0.615	2800	10,080
0.620	2836	10,210
0.625	2873	10,340

Table 13-28 (Continued)		
Head (meters)	l/s	m³/hr
0.630	2910	10,480
0.635	2948	10,610
0.640	2985	10,740
0.645	3022	10,880
0.650	3060	11,010
0.655	3098	11,150
0.660	3136	11,290
0.665	3174	11,430
0.670	3213	11,560
0.675	3252	11,700
0.680	3290	11,840
0.685	3329	11,980
0.690	3368	12,120
0.695	3408	12,270
0.700	3447	12,410
0.705	3487	12,550
0.710	3527	12,690
0.715	3567	12,840
0.720	3607	12,980
0.725	3647	13,130
0.730	3688	13,270
0.735	3728	13,420
0.740	3769	13,570
0.745	3810	13,710
0.750	3851	13,860

13

Table 13-29:
3.05 m Parshall Flume Discharge Table with Head in Meters

Formula: l/s = 7463 H$^{1.600}$
m^3/hr = 26870 H$^{1.600}$
Where: H = head in meters

Values in italics indicate flow below the recommended range of this particular primary device.

Table 13-29			Table 13-29 (Continued)		
Head (meters)	l/s	m^3/hr	Head (meters)	l/s	m^3/hr
0.005	*1.6*	*5.6*	0.255	838.3	3018
0.010	*4.7*	*17.0*	0.260	864.7	3113
0.015	*9.0*	*32.4*	0.265	891.5	3210
0.020	*14.3*	*51.4*	0.270	918.5	3307
0.025	*20.4*	*73.4*	0.275	945.9	3406
0.030	*27.3*	*98.3*	0.280	973.6	3505
0.035	*34.9*	*125.8*	0.285	1002	3606
0.040	*43.3*	*155.8*	0.290	1030	3708
0.045	*52.2*	*188.1*	0.295	1058	3811
0.050	*61.8*	*222.6*	0.300	1087	3914
0.055	*72.0*	*259.3*	0.305	1116	4019
0.060	*82.8*	*298.0*	0.310	1146	4125
0.065	*94.1*	*338.7*	0.315	1175	4232
0.070	*105.9*	*381.4*	0.320	1205	4340
0.075	*118.3*	*425.9*	0.325	1236	4449
0.080	*131.2*	*472.2*	0.330	1266	4559
0.085	*144.5*	*520.3*	0.335	1297	4670
0.090	158.4	570.2	0.340	1328	4782
0.095	172.7	621.8	0.345	1360	4895
0.100	187.5	674.9	0.350	1391	5009
0.105	202.7	729.7	0.355	1423	5124
0.110	218.3	786.1	0.360	1455	5240
0.115	234.4	844.1	0.365	1488	5357
0.120	251.0	903.6	0.370	1521	5475
0.125	267.9	964.5	0.375	1554	5594
0.130	285.2	1027	0.380	1587	5714
0.135	303.0	1091	0.385	1621	5835
0.140	321.2	1156	0.390	1654	5956
0.145	339.7	1223	0.395	1688	6079
0.150	358.6	1291	0.400	1723	6202
0.155	378.0	1361	0.405	1757	6327
0.160	397.7	1432	0.410	1792	6452
0.165	417.7	1504	0.415	1827	6579
0.170	438.2	1578	0.420	1863	6706
0.175	459.0	1652	0.425	1898	6834
0.180	480.1	1729	0.430	1934	6963
0.185	501.6	1806	0.435	1970	7093
0.190	523.5	1885	0.440	2006	7224
0.195	545.7	1965	0.445	2043	7356
0.200	568.3	2046	0.450	2080	7489
0.205	591.2	2129	0.455	2117	7622
0.210	614.4	2212	0.460	2154	7757
0.215	638.0	2297	0.465	2192	7892
0.220	661.9	2383	0.470	2230	8028
0.225	686.1	2470	0.475	2268	8165
0.230	710.7	2559	0.480	2306	8303
0.235	735.6	2648	0.485	2345	8442
0.240	760.8	2739	0.490	2384	8582
0.245	786.3	2831	0.495	2423	8722
0.250	812.1	2924	0.500	2462	8864

13

Table 13-29 (Continued)		
Head (meters)	l/s	m³/hr
0.505	2501	9006
0.510	2541	9149
0.515	2581	9293
0.520	2621	9438
0.525	2662	9583
0.530	2702	9730
0.535	2743	9877
0.540	2784	10,030
0.545	2826	10,170
0.550	2867	10,320
0.555	2909	10,470
0.560	2951	10,630
0.565	2994	10,780
0.570	3036	10,930
0.575	3079	11,090
0.580	3122	11,240
0.585	3165	11,400
0.590	3208	11,550
0.595	3252	11,710
0.600	3296	11,870
0.605	3340	12,020
0.610	3384	12,180
0.615	3429	12,340
0.620	3473	12,510
0.625	3518	12,670
0.630	3563	12,830
0.635	3609	12,990
0.640	3654	13,160
0.645	3700	13,320
0.650	3746	13,490
0.655	3792	13,650
0.660	3839	13,820
0.665	3885	13,990
0.670	3932	14,160
0.675	3979	14,330

Table 13-29 (Continued)		
Head (meters)	l/s	m³/hr
0.680	4026	14,500
0.685	4074	14,670
0.690	4122	14,840
0.695	4170	15,010
0.700	4218	15,190
0.705	4266	15,360
0.710	4314	15,530
0.715	4363	15,710
0.720	4412	15,890
0.725	4461	16,060
0.730	4511	16,240
0.735	4560	16,420
0.740	4610	16,600
0.745	4660	16,780
0.750	4710	16,960
0.755	4760	17,140
0.760	4811	17,320
0.765	4862	17,500
0.770	4912	17,690
0.775	4964	17,870
0.780	5015	18,060
0.785	5066	18,240
0.790	5118	18,430
0.795	5170	18,610
0.800	5222	18,800
0.805	5275	18,990
0.810	5327	19,180
0.815	5380	19,370
0.820	5433	19,560
0.825	5486	19,750
0.830	5539	19,940
0.835	5593	20,140
0.840	5646	20,330
0.845	5700	20,520
0.850	5754	20,720

13

Table 13-30:
3.66 m Parshall Flume Discharge Table with Head in Meters

Formula: l/s = 8859 H$^{1.600}$
           m^3/hr = 31890 H$^{1.600}$
Where: H = head in meters

Values in italics indicate flow below the recommended range of this particular primary device.

Head (meters)	l/s	m³/hr	Head (meters)	l/s	m³/hr
	Table 13-30			Table 13-30 (Continued)	
0.005	*1.8*	*6.6*	0.255	995.1	3582
0.010	*5.6*	*20.1*	0.260	1026	3695
0.015	*10.7*	*38.5*	0.265	1058	3809
0.020	*16.9*	*61.0*	0.270	1090	3925
0.025	*24.2*	*87.2*	0.275	1123	4042
0.030	*32.4*	*116.7*	0.280	1156	4160
0.035	*41.5*	*149.4*	0.285	1189	4280
0.040	*51.4*	*184.9*	0.290	1222	4400
0.045	*62.0*	*223.3*	0.295	1256	4522
0.050	*73.4*	*264.3*	0.300	1291	4646
0.055	*85.5*	*307.8*	0.305	1325	4770
0.060	*98.3*	*353.8*	0.310	1360	4896
0.065	*111.7*	*402.1*	0.315	1395	5023
0.070	*125.8*	*452.8*	0.320	1431	5151
0.075	*140.4*	*505.6*	0.325	1467	5280
0.080	*155.7*	*560.6*	0.330	1503	5411
0.085	*171.6*	*617.7*	0.335	1540	5543
0.090	*188.0*	*676.9*	0.340	1577	5676
0.095	*205.0*	*738.0*	0.345	1614	5810
0.100	222.5	801.0	0.350	1652	5945
0.105	240.6	866.1	0.355	1689	6082
0.110	259.2	933.0	0.360	1728	6219
0.115	278.3	1002	0.365	1766	6358
0.120	297.9	1072	0.370	1805	6498
0.125	318.0	1145	0.375	1844	6639
0.130	338.6	1219	0.380	1884	6781
0.135	359.7	1295	0.385	1924	6925
0.140	381.2	1372	0.390	1964	7069
0.145	403.2	1452	0.395	2004	7215
0.150	425.7	1533	0.400	2045	7361
0.155	448.7	1615	0.405	2086	7509
0.160	472.0	1699	0.410	2127	7658
0.165	495.9	1785	0.415	2169	7808
0.170	520.1	1872	0.420	2211	7959
0.175	544.8	1961	0.425	2253	8111
0.180	569.9	2052	0.430	2296	8264
0.185	595.5	2144	0.435	2339	8419
0.190	621.4	2237	0.440	2382	8574
0.195	647.8	2332	0.445	2425	8730
0.200	674.6	2428	0.450	2469	8888
0.205	701.8	2526	0.455	2513	9046
0.210	729.3	2625	0.460	2557	9206
0.215	757.3	2726	0.465	2602	9367
0.220	785.7	2828	0.470	2647	9528
0.225	814.5	2932	0.475	2692	9691
0.230	843.6	3037	0.480	2738	9855
0.235	873.2	3143	0.485	2783	10,020
0.240	903.1	3251	0.490	2829	10,190
0.245	933.4	3360	0.495	2876	10,350
0.250	964.0	3470	0.500	2922	10,520

13

0.505	2969	10,690	0.755	5651	20,340
0.510	3016	10,860	0.760	5711	20,560
0.515	3064	11,030	0.765	5771	20,770
0.520	3112	11,200	0.770	5831	20,990
0.525	3160	11,370	0.775	5892	21,210
0.530	3208	11,550	0.780	5953	21,430
0.535	3256	11,720	0.785	6014	21,650
0.540	3305	11,900	0.790	6076	21,870
0.545	3354	12,080	0.795	6137	22,090
0.550	3404	12,250	0.800	6199	22,320
0.555	3453	12,430	0.805	6261	22,540
0.560	3503	12,610	0.810	6324	22,760
0.565	3554	12,790	0.815	6386	22,990
0.570	3604	12,970	0.820	6449	23,210
0.575	3655	13,160	0.825	6512	23,440
0.580	3706	13,340	0.830	6575	23,670
0.585	3757	13,520	0.835	6639	23,900
0.590	3808	13,710	0.840	6702	24,130
0.595	3860	13,900	0.845	6766	24,360
0.600	3912	14,080	0.850	6831	24,590
0.605	3965	14,270	0.855	6895	24,820
0.610	4017	14,460	0.860	6960	25,050
0.615	4070	14,650	0.865	7024	25,290
0.620	4123	14,840	0.870	7089	25,520
0.625	4176	15,030	0.875	7155	25,760
0.630	4230	15,230	0.880	7220	25,990
0.635	4284	15,420	0.885	7286	26,230
0.640	4338	15,620	0.890	7352	26,470
0.645	4392	15,810	0.895	7418	26,700
0.650	4447	16,010	0.900	7485	26,940
0.655	4502	16,200	0.905	7551	27,180
0.660	4557	16,400	0.910	7618	27,420
0.665	4612	16,600	0.915	7685	27,660
0.670	4668	16,800	0.920	7753	27,910
0.675	4724	17,000	0.925	7820	28,150
0.680	4780	17,210	0.930	7888	28,390
0.685	4836	17,410	0.935	7956	28,640
0.690	4893	17,610	0.940	8024	28,880
0.695	4949	17,820	0.945	8092	29,130
0.700	5007	18,020	0.950	8161	29,380
0.705	5064	18,230	0.955	8230	29,630
0.710	5122	18,440	0.960	8299	29,870
0.715	5179	18,640	0.965	8368	30,120
0.720	5237	18,850	0.970	8438	30,370
0.725	5296	19,060	0.975	8507	30,620
0.730	5354	19,270	0.980	8577	30,880
0.735	5413	19,490	0.985	8647	31,130
0.740	5472	19,700	0.990	8718	31,380
0.745	5531	19,910	0.995	8788	31,640
0.750	5591	20,130	1.000	8859	31,890

13

Table 13-30 (Continued)		
Head (meters)	l/s	m³/hr
1.005	8930	32,150
1.010	9001	32,400
1.015	9073	32,660
1.020	9144	32,920
1.025	9216	33,180

Table 13-30 (Continued)		
Head (meters)	l/s	m³/hr
1.030	9288	33,430
1.035	9360	33,690
1.040	9433	33,960
1.045	9505	34,220
1.050	9578	34,480

13

13

Palmer-Bowlus Flume Discharge Tables

Overview

This chapter contains discharge (head vs. flow rate) tables for Palmer-Bowlus flumes (manufactured by Plasti-Fab, Inc.). Note that all of the tabular data is for free flow. [1]

Discharge tables for Palmer Bowlus flumes with head in feet

14-1: 4 in.	14-5: 12 in.	14-9: 24 in.
14-2: 6 in.	14-6: 15 in.	14-10: 27 in.
14-3: 8 in.	14-7: 18 in.	14-11: 30 in.
14-4: 10 in.	14-8: 21 in.	

The discharges of the flumes are listed in three different units of measure:

CFS - cubic feet per second   GPM - gallons per minute
MGD - million gallons per day

Discharge tables for Palmer-Bowlus flumes with head in meters

14-12: 0.102 m	14-16: 0.305 m	14-20: 0.610 m
14-13: 0.152 m	14-17: 0.381 m	14-21: 0.686 m
14-14: 0.203 m	14-18: 0.457 m	14-22: 0.762 m
14-15: 0.254 m	14-19: 0.533 m	

The discharges of the flumes are listed in two different units of measure:

l/s - liters per second m^3/hr - cubic meters per hour

The data in the tables are provided by Plasti-Fab, Inc. The formulas listed after each table are approximation formulas which fit that data within 1% of full scale. Values in italics indicate flow below the recommended range of this particular primary device.

---

1. All Palmer-Bowlus flume data, © Copyright Plasti-Fab, Inc., Taulatin, Oregon

Table 14-1:
4 in. Palmer-Bowlus Flume Discharge Table with Head in Feet

Data in table from Plasti-Fab, Inc.

Values in italics indicate flow below the recommended range of this particular primary device.

Table 14-1				Table 14-1 (Continued)			
Head (feet)	CFS	GPM	MGD	Head (feet)	CFS	GPM	MGD
0.01				0.14	0.0392	17.57	0.0253
0.02				0.15	0.0447	20.08	0.0289
0.03				0.16	0.0508	22.78	0.0328
0.04	*0.0043*	*1.937*	*0.0028*	0.17	0.0572	25.68	0.0370
0.05	*0.0063*	*2.833*	*0.0041*	0.18	0.0641	28.76	0.0414
0.06	0.0086	3.865	0.0056	0.19	0.0714	32.03	0.0461
0.07	0.0112	5.036	0.0073	0.20	0.0790	35.46	0.0511
0.08	0.0141	6.348	0.0091	0.21	0.0870	39.05	0.0562
0.09	0.0174	7.806	0.0112	0.22	0.0953	42.76	0.0616
0.10	0.0210	9.418	0.0136	0.23	0.1038	46.58	0.0671
0.11	0.0249	11.19	0.0161	0.24	0.1125	50.48	0.0727
0.12	0.0293	13.14	0.0189	0.25	0.1213	54.45	0.0784
0.13	0.0340	15.26	0.0220				

The approximation formulas below fit the data in the table within 1% of full scale.

Formula: $CFS = 1.68\ H^{1.9}$ $GPM = 754.1\ H^{1.9}$ $MGD = 1.08\ H^{1.9}$ *Where:* H = head in feet

14

Table 14-2:
6 in. Palmer-Bowlus Flume Discharge Table with Head in Feet

Data in table from Plasti-Fab, Inc.

Values in italics indicate flow below the recommended range of this particular primary device.

Head (feet)	CFS	GPM	MGD	Head (feet)	CFS	GPM	MGD
	Table 14-2				Table 14-2 (Continued)		
0.01				0.19	0.0898	40.31	0.0581
0.02				0.20	0.0989	44.39	0.0639
0.03				0.21	0.1085	48.70	0.0701
0.04	*0.0061*	*2.719*	*0.0039*	0.22	0.1186	53.25	0.0767
0.05	*0.0088*	*3.963*	*0.0057*	0.23	0.1293	58.04	0.0836
0.06	*0.0120*	*5.399*	*0.0078*	0.24	0.1405	63.07	0.0908
0.07	0.0156	7.017	0.0101	0.25	0.1523	68.35	0.0984
0.08	0.0196	8.811	0.0127	0.26	0.1646	73.87	0.1064
0.09	0.0240	10.78	0.0155	0.27	0.1774	79.62	0.1147
0.10	0.0288	12.92	0.0186	0.28	0.1907	85.60	0.1233
0.11	0.0339	15.22	0.0219	0.29	0.2045	91.79	0.1322
0.12	0.0394	17.70	0.0255	0.30	0.2187	98.17	0.1414
0.13	0.0454	20.35	0.0293	0.31	0.2334	104.7	0.1508
0.14	0.0517	23.19	0.0334	0.32	0.2484	111.5	0.1605
0.15	0.0584	26.21	0.0377	0.33	0.2637	118.3	0.1704
0.16	0.0656	29.42	0.0424	0.34	0.2793	125.3	0.1805
0.17	0.0732	32.84	0.0473	0.35	0.2951	132.4	0.1907
0.18	0.0813	36.47	0.0525				

The approximation formulas below fit the data in the table within 1% of full scale.

Formula: $CFS = 2.18\,H^{1.9}$ $GPM = 978.4\,H^{1.9}$ $MGD = 1.41\,H^{1.9}$ *Where:* H = head in feet

14

Table 14-3:
8 in. Palmer-Bowlus Flume Discharge Table with Head in Feet

Data in table from Plasti-Fab, Inc.

Values in italics indicate flow below the recommended range of this particular primary device.

Head (feet)	CFS	GPM	MGD	Head (feet)	CFS	GPM	MGD
0.01				0.26	0.1943	87.18	0.1256
0.02				0.27	0.2086	93.62	0.1348
0.03				0.28	0.2235	100.3	0.1445
0.04	*0.0076*	*3.42*	*0.0049*	0.29	0.2391	107.3	0.1545
0.05	*0.0113*	*5.08*	*0.0073*	0.30	0.2553	114.6	0.1650
0.06	*0.0155*	*6.94*	*0.0100*	0.31	0.2720	122.1	0.1758
0.07	*0.0201*	*9.00*	*0.0130*	0.32	0.2895	129.9	0.1871
0.08	*0.0251*	*11.27*	*0.0162*	0.33	0.3075	138.0	0.1987
0.09	0.0306	13.73	0.0198	0.34	0.3261	146.4	0.2108
0.10	0.0365	16.39	0.0236	0.35	0.3454	155.0	0.2232
0.11	0.0429	19.24	0.0277	0.36	0.3652	163.9	0.2360
0.12	0.0497	22.29	0.0321	0.37	0.3856	173.1	0.2492
0.13	0.0569	25.53	0.0368	0.38	0.4066	182.5	0.2628
0.14	0.0646	28.97	0.0417	0.39	0.4281	192.1	0.2767
0.15	0.0727	32.61	0.0470	0.40	0.4500	202.0	0.2909
0.16	0.0812	36.46	0.0525	0.41	0.4725	212.1	0.3054
0.17	0.0903	40.51	0.0583	0.42	0.4954	222.3	0.3202
0.18	0.0997	44.77	0.0645	0.43	0.5187	232.8	0.3352
0.19	0.1097	49.25	0.0709	0.44	0.5423	243.4	0.3505
0.20	0.1202	53.95	0.0777	0.45	0.5663	254.2	0.3660
0.21	0.1312	58.88	0.0848	0.46	0.5906	265.1	0.3817
0.22	0.1427	64.04	0.0922	0.47	0.6151	276.1	0.3976
0.23	0.1547	69.45	0.1000	0.48	0.6399	287.2	0.4136
0.24	0.1673	75.10	0.1082	0.49	0.6648	298.4	0.4297
0.25	0.1805	81.01	0.1167	0.50	0.6900	309.7	0.4459

The approximation formulas below fit the data in the table within 1% of full scale.

Formula: $CFS = 2.59\,H^{1.9}$ $GPM = 1162.4\,H^{1.9}$ $MGD = 1.67\,H^{1.9}$ *Where:* H = head in feet

14

Table 14-4:
10 in. Palmer-Bowlus Flume Discharge Table with Head in Feet

Data in table from Plasti-Fab, Inc.

Values in italics indicate flow below the recommended range of this particular primary device.

Head (feet)	CFS	GPM	MGD	Head (feet)	CFS	GPM	MGD
0.01				0.31	0.3083	138.4	0.1992
0.02				0.32	0.3272	146.9	0.2115
0.03				0.33	0.3469	155.7	0.2242
0.04	*0.0092*	*4.14*	*0.0060*	0.34	0.3673	164.9	0.2374
0.05	*0.0138*	*6.17*	*0.0089*	0.35	0.3884	174.3	0.2510
0.06	*0.0188*	*8.45*	*0.0122*	0.36	0.4102	184.1	0.2651
0.07	*0.0245*	*10.98*	*0.0158*	0.37	0.4328	194.2	0.2797
0.08	*0.0306*	*13.74*	*0.0198*	0.38	0.4560	204.7	0.2947
0.09	*0.0373*	*16.72*	*0.0241*	0.39	0.4800	215.5	0.3103
0.10	*0.4440*	*19.92*	*0.0287*	0.40	0.5047	226.5	0.3262
0.11	0.0520	23.34	0.0336	0.41	0.5302	238.0	0.3427
0.12	0.0601	26.96	0.0388	0.42	0.5563	249.7	0.3595
0.13	0.0686	30.79	0.0443	0.43	0.5831	261.7	0.3769
0.14	0.0776	34.82	0.0501	0.44	0.6106	274.1	0.3946
0.15	0.0870	39.06	0.0562	0.45	0.6387	286.7	0.4128
0.16	0.0969	43.50	0.0626	0.46	0.6675	299.6	0.4314
0.17	0.1073	48.15	0.0693	0.47	0.6968	312.8	0.4504
0.18	0.1181	53.02	0.0764	0.48	0.7268	326.2	0.4697
0.19	0.1295	58.10	0.0837	0.49	0.7573	339.9	0.4894
0.20	0.1413	63.40	0.0913	0.50	0.7883	353.8	0.5095
0.21	0.1536	68.93	0.0993	0.51	0.8197	367.9	0.5298
0.22	0.1664	74.70	0.1076	0.52	0.8517	382.3	0.5505
0.23	0.1798	80.70	0.1162	0.53	0.8840	396.8	0.5714
0.24	0.1938	86.96	0.1252	0.54	0.9167	411.5	0.5925
0.25	0.2083	93.47	0.1346	0.55	0.9498	426.3	0.6139
0.26	0.2234	100.3	0.1444	0.56	0.9832	441.3	0.6354
0.27	0.2391	107.3	0.1545	0.57	1.017	456.4	0.6572
0.28	0.2554	114.6	0.1651	0.58	1.051	471.6	0.6791
0.29	0.2723	122.2	0.1760	0.59	1.085	486.9	0.7012
0.30	0.2900	130.1	0.1874	0.60	1.119	502.4	0.7234

14

The approximation formulas below fit the data in the table within 1% of full scale.

Formula: $CFS = 2.96\ H^{1.9}$ $GPM = 1328.4\ H^{1.9}$ $MGD = 1.93\ H^{1.9}$ *Where:* H = head in feet

Table 14-5:
12 in. Palmer-Bowlus Flume Discharge Table with Head in Feet

Data in table from Plasti-Fab, Inc.

Values in italics indicate flow below the recommended range of this particular primary device.

Table 14-5				Table 14-5 (Continued)			
Head (feet)	CFS	GPM	MGD	Head (feet)	CFS	GPM	MGD
0.01				0.36	0.4631	207.9	0.2993
0.02				0.37	0.4871	218.6	0.3149
0.03				0.38	0.5119	229.8	0.3308
0.04				0.39	0.5374	241.2	0.3473
0.05	*0.0164*	*7.35*	*0.0106*	0.40	0.5635	252.9	0.3642
0.06	*0.0221*	*9.90*	*0.0143*	0.41	0.5905	265.0	0.3816
0.07	*0.0284*	*12.75*	*0.0184*	0.42	0.6181	277.4	0.3995
0.08	*0.0354*	*15.89*	*0.0229*	0.43	0.6466	290.2	0.4179
0.09	*0.0430*	*19.31*	*0.0278*	0.44	0.6757	303.3	0.4367
0.10	*0.0513*	*23.00*	*0.0331*	0.45	0.7057	316.7	0.4561
0.11	*0.0601*	*26.96*	*0.0388*	0.46	0.7364	330.5	0.4759
0.12	0.0695	31.18	0.0449	0.47	0.7679	344.6	0.4963
0.13	0.0795	35.66	0.0514	0.48	0.8001	359.1	0.5171
0.14	0.0900	40.39	0.0582	0.49	0.8331	373.9	0.5384
0.15	0.1011	45.37	0.0653	0.50	0.8669	389.1	0.5603
0.16	0.1127	50.59	0.0729	0.51	0.9014	404.6	0.5826
0.17	0.1249	56.05	0.0807	0.52	0.9366	420.4	0.6053
0.18	0.1376	61.76	0.0889	0.53	0.9726	436.5	0.6286
0.19	0.1509	67.71	0.0975	0.54	1.009	453.0	0.6523
0.20	0.1646	73.89	0.1064	0.55	1.047	469.8	0.6765
0.21	0.1790	80.32	0.1157	0.56	1.085	486.9	0.7011
0.22	0.1938	86.99	0.1253	0.57	1.124	504.3	0.7262
0.23	0.2092	93.91	0.1352	0.58	1.163	522.0	0.7516
0.24	0.2252	101.1	0.1456	0.59	1.203	539.9	0.7775
0.25	0.2417	108.5	0.1562	0.60	1.244	558.2	0.8038
0.26	0.2588	116.2	0.1673	0.61	1.285	576.7	0.8304
0.27	0.2765	124.1	0.1787	0.62	1.327	595.4	0.8573
0.28	0.2947	132.3	0.1905	0.63	1.369	614.3	0.8847
0.29	0.3135	140.7	0.2027	0.64	1.412	633.5	0.9123
0.30	0.3330	149.5	0.2152	0.65	1.455	652.9	0.9402
0.31	0.3531	158.5	0.2282	0.66	1.498	672.5	0.9684
0.32	0.3738	167.8	0.2416	0.67	1.542	692.2	0.9968
0.33	0.3951	177.3	0.2554	0.68	1.587	712.1	1.026
0.34	0.4171	187.2	0.2696	0.69	1.631	732.2	1.054
0.35	0.4398	197.4	0.2842	0.70	1.676	752.4	1.084

The approximation formulas below fit the data in the table within 1% of full scale.

Formula: $CFS = 3.31\ H^{1.9}$ $GPM = 1485.5\ H^{1.9}$ $MGD = 2.14\ H^{1.9}$ *Where:* H = head in feet

Table 14-6:
15 in. Palmer-Bowlus Flume Discharge Table with Head in Feet

Data in table from Plasti-Fab, Inc.

Values in italics indicate flow below the recommended range of this particular primary device.

Head (feet)	CFS	GPM	MGD	Head (feet)	CFS	GPM	MGD
0.01				0.46	0.8441	378.9	0.5456
0.02				0.47	0.8783	394.2	0.5677
0.03				0.48	0.9133	409.9	0.5903
0.04				0.49	0.9492	426.0	0.6135
0.05				0.50	0.9858	442.5	0.6371
0.06	*0.0269*	*12.08*	*0.0174*	0.51	1.023	459.3	0.6613
0.07	*0.0348*	*15.61*	*0.0225*	0.52	1.062	476.4	0.6861
0.08	*0.0433*	*19.45*	*0.0280*	0.53	1.101	494.0	0.7114
0.09	*0.0526*	*23.60*	*0.0340*	0.54	1.141	512.0	0.7372
0.10	*0.0625*	*28.05*	*0.0404*	0.55	1.182	530.3	0.7636
0.11	*0.0731*	*32.80*	*0.0472*	0.56	1.223	549.0	0.7906
0.12	*0.0843*	*37.84*	*0.0545*	0.57	1.266	568.1	0.8181
0.13	*0.0962*	*43.18*	*0.0622*	0.58	1.309	587.6	0.8461
0.14	0.1088	48.82	0.0703	0.59	1.354	607.5	0.8748
0.15	0.1220	54.74	0.0788	0.60	1.399	627.8	0.9040
0.16	0.1358	60.94	0.0878	0.61	1.445	648.4	0.9337
0.17	0.1503	67.44	0.0971	0.62	1.492	669.5	0.9641
0.18	0.1653	74.21	0.1069	0.63	1.539	690.9	0.9949
0.19	0.1811	81.27	0.1170	0.64	1.588	712.8	1.026
0.20	0.1974	88.60	0.1276	0.65	1.638	735.0	1.058
0.21	0.2144	96.21	0.1385	0.66	1.688	757.5	1.091
0.22	0.2319	104.1	0.1499	0.67	1.739	780.5	1.124
0.23	0.2501	112.3	0.1617	0.68	1.791	803.8	1.157
0.24	0.2689	120.7	0.1738	0.69	1.844	827.4	1.192
0.25	0.2883	129.4	0.1863	0.70	1.897	851.4	1.226
0.26	0.3083	138.4	0.1993	0.71	1.951	875.8	1.261
0.27	0.3290	147.6	0.2126	0.72	2.006	900.4	1.297
0.28	0.3502	157.2	0.2263	0.73	2.062	925.4	1.333
0.29	0.3720	167.0	0.2405	0.74	2.118	950.7	1.369
0.30	0.3945	177.1	0.2550	0.75	2.175	976.2	1.406
0.31	0.4176	187.4	0.2699	0.76	2.233	1002	1.443
0.32	0.4414	198.1	0.2853	0.77	2.291	1028	1.481
0.33	0.4657	209.0	0.3010	0.78	2.349	1054	1.519
0.34	0.4907	220.3	0.3172	0.79	2.409	1081	1.557
0.35	0.5164	231.8	0.3337	0.80	2.468	1108	1.595
0.36	0.5427	243.6	0.3507	0.81	2.528	1135	1.634
0.37	0.5697	255.7	0.3682	0.82	2.589	1162	1.673
0.38	0.5973	268.1	0.3860	0.83	2.650	1189	1.713
0.39	0.6256	280.8	0.4044	0.84	2.711	1217	1.752
0.40	0.6547	293.8	0.4231	0.85	2.773	1245	1.792
0.41	0.6844	307.2	0.4423	0.86	2.835	1272	1.832
0.42	0.7149	320.9	0.4620	0.87	2.897	1300	1.873
0.43	0.7460	334.8	0.4822	0.88	2.960	1328	1.913
0.44	0.7780	349.2	0.5028	0.89	3.023	1357	1.954
0.45	0.8106	363.8	0.5239	0.90	3.086	1385	1.994

14

The approximation formulas below fit the data in the table within 1% of full scale.

Formula: $CFS = 3.79\ H^{1.9}$ $GPM = 1701\ H^{1.9}$ $MGD = 2.45\ H^{1.9}$ *Where:* H = head in feet

Table 14-7:
18 in. Palmer-Bowlus Flume Discharge Table with Head in Feet

Data in table from Plasti-Fab, Inc.

Values in italics indicate flow below the recommended range of this particular primary device.

Head (feet)	CFS	GPM	MGD	Head (feet)	CFS	GPM	MGD
0.01				0.46	0.9586	430.3	0.6196
0.02				0.47	0.9958	446.9	0.6436
0.03				0.48	1.034	464.0	0.6681
0.04				0.49	1.073	481.4	0.6931
0.05				0.50	1.112	499.1	0.7187
0.06				0.51	1.152	517.2	0.7447
0.07				0.52	1.193	535.6	0.7713
0.08	*0.0505*	*22.66*	*0.0326*	0.53	1.235	554.4	0.7984
0.09	*0.0604*	*27.12*	*0.0391*	0.54	1.278	573.6	0.8260
0.10	*0.0713*	*32.01*	*0.0461*	0.55	1.322	593.2	0.8542
0.11	*0.0832*	*37.34*	*0.0538*	0.56	1.366	613.2	0.8830
0.12	*0.0960*	*43.07*	*0.0620*	0.57	1.412	633.5	0.9123
0.13	*0.1096*	*49.21*	*0.0709*	0.58	1.458	654.3	0.9422
0.14	*0.1242*	*55.73*	*0.0803*	0.59	1.505	675.4	0.9726
0.15	*0.1395*	*62.63*	*0.0902*	0.60	1.553	697.0	1.004
0.16	0.1557	69.89	0.1007	0.61	1.602	719.0	1.035
0.17	0.1727	77.51	0.1116	0.62	1.652	741.4	1.068
0.18	0.1904	85.47	0.1231	0.63	1.703	764.2	1.100
0.19	0.2089	93.77	0.1350	0.64	1.754	787.4	1.134
0.20	0.2281	102.4	0.1474	0.65	1.807	811.1	1.168
0.21	0.2481	111.3	0.1603	0.66	1.861	835.2	1.203
0.22	0.2687	120.6	0.1736	0.67	1.916	859.7	1.238
0.23	0.2900	130.2	0.1874	0.68	1.971	884.7	1.274
0.24	0.3120	140.0	0.2016	0.69	2.028	910.1	1.311
0.25	0.3346	150.2	0.2163	0.70	2.085	935.9	1.348
0.26	0.3579	160.6	0.2313	0.71	2.144	962.2	1.386
0.27	0.3818	171.4	0.2468	0.72	2.203	988.8	1.424
0.28	0.4064	182.4	0.2626	0.73	2.264	1016	1.463
0.29	0.4316	193.7	0.2789	0.74	2.325	1044	1.503
0.30	0.4574	205.3	0.2956	0.75	2.387	1072	1.543
0.31	0.4839	217.2	0.3127	0.76	2.451	1100	1.584
0.32	0.5110	229.3	0.3302	0.77	2.515	1129	1.625
0.33	0.5387	241.8	0.3482	0.78	2.580	1158	1.667
0.34	0.5670	254.5	0.3665	0.79	2.646	1188	1.710
0.35	0.5960	267.5	0.3852	0.80	2.713	1218	1.753
0.36	0.6256	280.8	0.4044	0.81	2.781	1248	1.797
0.37	0.6560	294.4	0.4239	0.82	2.849	1279	1.842
0.38	0.6868	308.3	0.4439	0.83	2.919	1310	1.886
0.39	0.7184	322.4	0.4643	0.84	2.989	1342	1.932
0.40	0.7506	336.9	0.4851	0.85	3.060	1374	1.978
0.41	0.7835	351.7	0.5064	0.86	3.132	1406	2.024
0.42	0.8171	366.8	0.5281	0.87	3.205	1438	2.071
0.43	0.8514	382.2	0.5503	0.88	3.278	1471	2.119
0.44	0.8864	397.9	0.5729	0.89	3.352	1505	2.167
0.45	0.9222	413.9	0.5960	0.90	3.427	1538	2.215

14

Table 14-7 (Continued)					Table 14-7 (Continued)			
Head (feet)	CFS	GPM	MGD		Head (feet)	CFS	GPM	MGD
0.91	3.503	1572	2.264		0.99	4.127	1852	2.667
0.92	3.579	1606	2.313		1.00	4.207	1888	2.719
0.93	3.656	1641	2.363		1.01	4.288	1925	2.771
0.94	3.733	1675	2.413		1.02	4.369	1961	2.824
0.95	3.811	1710	2.463		1.03	4.450	1998	2.876
0.96	3.889	1746	2.514		1.04	4.532	2034	2.929
0.97	3.968	1781	2.565		1.05	4.614	2071	2.982
0.98	4.047	1817	2.616					

The approximation formulas below fit the data in the table within 1% of full scale.

Formula: $CFS = 4.23\ H^{1.9}$ $GPM = 1898.4\ H^{1.9}$ $MGD = 2.73\ H^{1.9}$ *Where:* H = head in feet

14

Table 14-8:
21 in. Palmer-Bowlus Flume Discharge Table with Head in Feet

Data in table from Plasti-Fab, Inc.

Values in italics indicate flow below the recommended range of this particular primary device.

Head (feet)	CFS	GPM	MGD	Head (feet)	CFS	GPM	MGD
0.01				0.51	1.283	575.7	0.8290
0.02				0.52	1.327	595.8	0.8579
0.03				0.53	1.373	616.3	0.8874
0.04				0.54	1.420	637.1	0.9175
0.05				0.55	1.467	658.4	0.9480
0.06				0.56	1.515	680.0	0.9792
0.07				0.57	1.564	702.0	1.011
0.08				0.58	1.614	724.4	1.043
0.09	*0.0670*	*30.03*	*0.0432*	0.59	1.665	747.2	1.076
0.10	*0.0813*	*36.47*	*0.0525*	0.60	1.716	770.4	1.109
0.11	*0.0963*	*43.24*	*0.0623*	0.61	1.769	793.9	1.143
0.12	*0.1122*	*50.34*	*0.0725*	0.62	1.822	817.9	1.178
0.13	*0.1287*	*57.77*	*0.0832*	0.63	1.877	842.3	1.213
0.14	*0.1460*	*65.53*	*0.0944*	0.64	1.932	867.1	1.249
0.15	*0.1640*	*73.61*	*0.1060*	0.65	1.988	892.4	1.285
0.16	*0.1827*	*82.00*	*0.1181*	0.66	2.045	918.0	1.322
0.17	*0.2021*	*90.72*	*0.1306*	0.67	2.103	944.1	1.359
0.18	0.2223	99.76	0.1437	0.68	2.162	970.5	1.398
0.19	0.2431	109.1	0.1571	0.69	2.222	997.4	1.436
0.20	0.2646	118.8	0.1710	0.70	2.283	1025	1.476
0.21	0.2869	128.8	0.1854	0.71	2.345	1053	1.516
0.22	0.3098	139.1	0.2002	0.72	2.408	1081	1.556
0.23	0.3334	149.7	0.2155	0.73	2.472	1110	1.598
0.24	0.3577	160.6	0.2312	0.74	2.537	1139	1.640
0.25	0.3827	171.8	0.2474	0.75	2.603	1168	1.682
0.26	0.4084	183.3	0.2640	0.76	2.669	1198	1.725
0.27	0.4348	195.2	0.2810	0.77	2.737	1229	1.769
0.28	0.4619	207.3	0.2985	0.78	2.806	1259	1.814
0.29	0.4897	219.8	0.3165	0.79	2.876	1291	1.859
0.30	0.5181	232.6	0.3349	0.80	2.947	1323	1.905
0.31	0.5473	245.6	0.3537	0.81	3.019	1355	1.951
0.32	0.5772	259.0	0.3730	0.82	3.091	1388	1.998
0.33	0.6077	272.8	0.3928	0.83	3.165	1421	2.046
0.34	0.6390	286.8	0.4130	0.84	3.240	1454	2.094
0.35	0.6709	301.1	0.4336	0.85	3.316	1488	2.143
0.36	0.7036	315.8	0.4548	0.86	3.393	1523	2.193
0.37	0.7370	330.8	0.4763	0.87	3.470	1558	2.243
0.38	0.7711	346.1	0.4984	0.88	3.549	1593	2.294
0.39	0.8059	361.7	0.5209	0.89	3.629	1629	2.345
0.40	0.8415	377.7	0.5439	0.90	3.710	1665	2.398
0.41	0.8778	394.0	0.5673	0.91	3.791	1702	2.450
0.42	0.9148	410.6	0.5913	0.92	3.874	1739	2.504
0.43	0.9526	427.6	0.6157	0.93	3.958	1776	2.558
0.44	0.9911	444.9	0.6406	0.94	4.042	1814	2.613
0.45	1.030	462.5	0.6660	0.95	4.128	1853	2.668
0.46	1.071	480.5	0.6919	0.96	4.214	1891	2.724
0.47	1.111	498.8	0.7183	0.97	4.301	1931	2.780
0.48	1.153	517.5	0.7452	0.98	4.390	1970	2.837
0.49	1.195	536.5	0.7726	0.99	4.479	2010	2.895
0.50	1.239	555.9	0.8005	1.00	4.569	2051	2.953

14

Table 14-8 (Continued)				Table 14-8 (Continued)			
Head (feet)	CFS	GPM	MGD	Head (feet)	CFS	GPM	MGD
1.01	4.659	2091	3.011	1.14	5.909	2652	3.819
1.02	4.751	2132	3.071	1.15	6.009	2697	3.884
1.03	4.843	2174	3.130	1.16	6.111	2743	3.949
1.04	4.937	2216	3.191	1.17	6.212	2788	4.015
1.05	5.031	2258	3.251	1.18	6.315	2834	4.081
1.06	5.126	2301	3.313	1.19	6.417	2880	4.148
1.07	5.221	2343	3.374	1.20	6.521	2927	4.214
1.08	5.317	2387	3.437	1.21	6.624	2973	4.281
1.09	5.414	2430	3.499	1.22	6.728	3020	4.349
1.10	5.512	2474	3.562	1.23	6.833	3067	4.416
1.11	5.610	2518	3.626	1.24	6.937	3114	4.484
1.12	5.709	2562	3.690	1.25	7.043	3161	4.552
1.13	5.809	2607	3.754				

The approximation formulas below fit the data in the table within 1% of full scale.

Formula: $CFS = 4.61\ H^{1.9}$ $GPM = 2069\ H^{1.9}$ $MGD = 2.98\ H^{1.9}$ *Where:* H = head in feet

14

Table 14-9:
24 in. Palmer-Bowlus Flume Discharge Table with Head in Feet

Data in table from Plasti-Fab, Inc.

Values in italics indicate flow below the recommended range of this particular primary device.

Table 14-9				Table 14-9 (Continued)			
Head (feet)	CFS	GPM	MGD	Head (feet)	CFS	GPM	MGD
0.01				0.51	1.419	636.9	0.9172
0.02				0.52	1.468	658.7	0.9486
0.03				0.53	1.517	680.9	0.9805
0.04				0.54	1.567	703.4	1.013
0.05				0.55	1.618	726.3	1.046
0.06				0.56	1.670	749.5	1.079
0.07				0.57	1.723	773.2	1.113
0.08				0.58	1.776	797.2	1.148
0.09				0.59	1.830	821.6	1.183
0.10	*0.0958*	*43.00*	*0.0619*	0.60	1.886	846.3	1.219
0.11	*0.1114*	*49.99*	*0.0720*	0.61	1.942	871.5	1.255
0.12	*0.1279*	*57.41*	*0.0827*	0.62	1.999	897.1	1.292
0.13	*0.1454*	*65.27*	*0.0940*	0.63	2.057	923.0	1.329
0.14	*0.1639*	*73.55*	*0.1060*	0.64	2.115	949.4	1.367
0.15	*0.1832*	*82.24*	*0.1184*	0.65	2.175	976.1	1.406
0.16	*0.2035*	*91.35*	*0.1315*	0.66	2.235	1003	1.445
0.17	*0.2247*	*100.9*	*0.1452*	0.67	2.297	1031	1.485
0.18	*0.2468*	*110.8*	*0.1595*	0.68	2.359	1059	1.525
0.19	*0.2697*	*121.1*	*0.1743*	0.69	2.423	1087	1.566
0.20	0.2935	131.7	0.1897	0.70	2.487	1116	1.607
0.21	0.3182	142.8	0.2056	0.71	2.552	1146	1.650
0.22	0.3436	154.2	0.2221	0.72	2.619	1175	1.692
0.23	0.3699	166.0	0.2391	0.73	2.686	1206	1.736
0.24	0.3971	178.2	0.2566	0.74	2.754	1236	1.780
0.25	0.4250	190.7	0.2747	0.75	2.823	1267	1.825
0.26	0.4537	203.6	0.2932	0.76	2.894	1299	1.870
0.27	0.4832	216.9	0.3123	0.77	2.965	1331	1.916
0.28	0.5135	230.5	0.3319	0.78	3.037	1363	1.963
0.29	0.5446	244.4	0.3520	0.79	3.110	1396	2.010
0.30	0.5764	258.7	0.3725	0.80	3.185	1429	2.058
0.31	0.6090	273.3	0.3936	0.81	3.260	1463	2.107
0.32	0.6424	288.3	0.4152	0.82	3.337	1498	2.156
0.33	0.6765	303.6	0.4372	0.83	3.414	1532	2.207
0.34	0.7113	319.3	0.4598	0.84	3.493	1568	2.257
0.35	0.7470	335.3	0.4828	0.85	3.572	1603	2.309
0.36	0.7833	351.6	0.5063	0.86	3.653	1640	2.361
0.37	0.8204	368.2	0.5303	0.87	3.735	1676	2.414
0.38	0.8583	385.2	0.5547	0.88	3.818	1713	2.467
0.39	0.8969	402.6	0.5797	0.89	3.901	1751	2.522
0.40	0.9362	420.2	0.6051	0.90	3.986	1789	2.577
0.41	0.9762	438.2	0.6310	0.91	4.073	1828	2.632
0.42	1.017	456.5	0.6574	0.92	4.160	1867	2.689
0.43	1.059	475.2	0.6843	0.93	4.248	1907	2.746
0.44	1.101	494.2	0.7117	0.94	4.337	1947	2.803
0.45	1.144	513.6	0.7396	0.95	4.428	1987	2.862
0.46	1.188	533.3	0.7679	0.96	4.519	2028	2.921
0.47	1.233	553.3	0.7968	0.97	4.612	2070	2.981
0.48	1.278	573.7	0.8261	0.98	4.706	2112	3.041
0.49	1.324	594.4	0.8560	0.99	4.800	2155	3.103
0.50	1.371	615.5	0.8863	1.00	4.896	2198	3.165

14

Table 14-9 (Continued)				Table 14-9 (Continued)			
Head (feet)	CFS	GPM	MGD	Head (feet)	CFS	GPM	MGD
1.01	4.993	2241	3.227	1.21	7.139	3204	4.614
1.02	5.091	2285	3.291	1.22	7.256	3257	4.690
1.03	5.190	2330	3.354	1.23	7.373	3309	4.765
1.04	5.290	2374	3.419	1.24	7.491	3362	4.842
1.05	5.391	2420	3.484	1.25	7.610	3416	4.919
1.06	5.493	2466	3.550	1.26	7.730	3469	4.996
1.07	5.596	2512	3.617	1.27	7.850	3523	5.074
1.08	5.701	2559	3.684	1.28	7.971	3578	5.152
1.09	5.806	2606	3.752	1.29	8.092	3632	5.230
1.10	5.912	2653	3.821	1.30	8.215	3687	5.309
1.11	6.019	2701	3.890	1.31	8.337	3742	5.389
1.12	6.127	2750	3.960	1.32	8.461	3797	5.468
1.13	6.236	2799	4.030	1.33	8.585	3853	5.548
1.14	6.346	2848	4.101	1.34	8.709	3909	5.629
1.15	6.456	2898	4.173	1.35	8.834	3965	5.709
1.16	6.568	2948	4.245	1.36	8.959	4021	5.791
1.17	6.681	2998	4.318	1.37	9.085	4078	5.872
1.18	6.794	3049	4.391	1.38	9.211	4134	5.954
1.19	6.908	3101	4.465	1.39	9.338	4191	6.035
1.20	7.023	3152	4.539	1.40	9.465	4248	6.118

The approximation formulas below fit the data in the table within 1% of full scale.

Formula: $CFS = 5.03 \, H^{1.9}$ $GPM = 2257.4 \, H^{1.9}$ $MGD = 3.25 \, H^{1.9}$ *Where:* H = head in feet

14

Table 14-10:
27 in. Palmer-Bowlus Flume Discharge Table with Head in Feet

Data in table from Plasti-Fab, Inc.

Values in italics indicate flow below the recommended range of this particular primary device.

Head (feet)	CFS	GPM	MGD	Head (feet)	CFS	GPM	MGD
0.01				0.51	1.555	697.8	1.005
0.02				0.52	1.608	721.5	1.039
0.03				0.53	1.661	745.5	1.074
0.04				0.54	1.715	769.9	1.109
0.05				0.55	1.770	794.6	1.144
0.06				0.56	1.826	819.7	1.180
0.07				0.57	1.883	845.2	1.217
0.08				0.58	1.941	871.0	1.254
0.09				0.59	1.999	897.3	1.292
0.10				0.60	2.058	923.9	1.330
0.11	*0.1257*	*56.43*	*0.0813*	0.61	2.119	950.9	1.369
0.12	*0.1434*	*64.35*	*0.0927*	0.62	2.180	978.3	1.409
0.13	*0.1621*	*72.77*	*0.1048*	0.63	2.241	1006	1.449
0.14	*0.1820*	*81.68*	*0.1176*	0.64	2.304	1034	1.489
0.15	*0.2029*	*91.06*	*0.1311*	0.65	2.368	1063	1.530
0.16	*0.2248*	*100.9*	*0.1453*	0.66	2.432	1092	1.572
0.17	*0.2478*	*111.2*	*0.1601*	0.67	2.498	1121	1.614
0.18	*0.2718*	*122.0*	*0.1756*	0.68	2.564	1151	1.657
0.19	*0.2967*	*133.2*	*0.1918*	0.69	2.631	1181	1.701
0.20	*0.3227*	*144.8*	*0.2085*	0.70	2.700	1212	1.745
0.21	*0.3496*	*156.9*	*0.2259*	0.71	2.769	1243	1.790
0.22	0.3774	169.4	0.2439	0.72	2.839	1274	1.835
0.23	0.4062	182.3	0.2625	0.73	2.910	1306	1.881
0.24	0.4359	195.6	0.2817	0.74	2.982	1338	1.927
0.25	0.4665	209.4	0.3015	0.75	3.055	1371	1.974
0.26	0.4980	223.5	0.3219	0.76	3.129	1404	2.022
0.27	0.5304	238.0	0.3428	0.77	3.204	1438	2.071
0.28	0.5636	253.0	0.3643	0.78	3.280	1472	2.120
0.29	0.5978	268.3	0.3863	0.79	3.357	1507	2.170
0.30	0.6327	284.0	0.4089	0.80	3.435	1542	2.220
0.31	0.6686	300.1	0.4321	0.81	3.514	1577	2.271
0.32	0.7052	316.5	0.4558	0.82	3.594	1613	2.323
0.33	0.7427	333.4	0.4800	0.83	3.675	1649	2.375
0.34	0.7810	350.5	0.5048	0.84	3.757	1686	2.428
0.35	0.8201	368.1	0.5301	0.85	3.840	1724	2.482
0.36	0.8601	386.0	0.5559	0.86	3.925	1762	2.537
0.37	0.9008	404.3	0.5822	0.87	4.010	1800	2.592
0.38	0.9424	423.0	0.6091	0.88	4.097	1839	2.648
0.39	0.9847	442.0	0.6365	0.89	4.184	1878	2.704
0.40	1.028	461.4	0.6643	0.90	4.273	1918	2.762
0.41	1.072	481.1	0.6927	0.91	4.363	1958	2.820
0.42	1.117	501.2	0.7217	0.92	4.454	1999	2.878
0.43	1.162	521.6	0.7511	0.93	4.546	2040	2.938
0.44	1.208	542.4	0.7810	0.94	4.639	2082	2.998
0.45	1.256	563.5	0.8115	0.95	4.733	2124	3.059
0.46	1.303	585.0	0.8424	0.96	4.829	2167	3.121
0.47	1.352	606.9	0.8739	0.97	4.925	2211	3.183
0.48	1.402	629.1	0.9059	0.98	5.023	2254	3.246
0.49	1.452	651.6	0.9384	0.99	5.122	2299	3.310
0.50	1.503	674.6	0.9714	1.00	5.222	2344	3.375

14

Table 14-10 (Continued)				Table 14-10 (Continued)			
Head (feet)	CFS	GPM	MGD	Head (feet)	CFS	GPM	MGD
1.01	5.323	2389	3.440	1.31	8.882	3987	5.741
1.02	5.425	2435	3.506	1.32	9.017	4047	5.828
1.03	5.529	2482	3.573	1.33	9.152	4108	5.915
1.04	5.633	2528	3.641	1.34	9.289	4169	6.004
1.05	5.739	2576	3.709	1.35	9.426	4231	6.092
1.06	5.846	2624	3.779	1.36	9.565	4293	6.182
1.07	5.954	2673	3.848	1.37	9.704	4355	6.272
1.08	6.064	2722	3.919	1.38	9.844	4418	6.362
1.09	6.174	2771	3.990	1.39	9.984	4481	6.453
1.10	6.286	2821	4.063	1.40	10.13	4545	6.545
1.11	6.398	2872	4.135	1.41	10.27	4609	6.637
1.12	6.512	2923	4.209	1.42	10.41	4673	6.729
1.13	6.627	2975	4.283	1.43	10.56	4737	6.822
1.14	6.743	3027	4.358	1.44	10.70	4802	6.915
1.15	6.861	3079	4.434	1.45	10.84	4867	7.009
1.16	6.979	3132	4.511	1.46	10.99	4933	7.103
1.17	7.098	3186	4.588	1.47	11.14	4998	7.197
1.18	7.219	3240	4.666	1.48	11.28	5064	7.292
1.19	7.341	3295	4.744	1.49	11.43	5130	7.388
1.20	7.464	3350	4.824	1.50	11.58	5197	7.483
1.21	7.587	3405	4.904	1.51	11.73	5264	7.579
1.22	7.712	3462	4.985	1.52	11.88	5330	7.676
1.23	7.838	3518	5.066	1.53	12.03	5398	7.773
1.24	7.965	3575	5.148	1.54	12.18	5465	7.870
1.25	8.093	3633	5.231	1.55	12.33	5533	7.967
1.26	8.222	3690	5.314	1.56	12.48	5600	8.065
1.27	8.352	3749	5.398	1.57	12.63	5668	8.162
1.28	8.483	3808	5.483	1.58	12.78	5737	8.260
1.29	8.615	3867	5.568	1.59	12.93	5805	8.359
1.30	8.748	3926	5.654	1.60	13.09	5874	8.458

14

The approximation formulas below fit the data in the table within 1% of full scale.

Formula: $CFS = 5.39\,H^{1.9}$ $GPM = 2419\,H^{1.9}$ $MGD = 3.49\,H^{1.9}$ *Where:* H = head in feet

Table 14-11:
30 in. Palmer-Bowlus Flume Discharge Table with Head in Feet

Data in table from Plasti-Fab, Inc.

Values in italics indicate flow below the recommended range of this particular primary device.

Head (feet)	CFS	GPM	MGD	Head (feet)	CFS	GPM	MGD
0.01				0.51	1.689	757.9	1.091
0.02				0.52	1.744	782.9	1.127
0.03				0.53	1.801	808.2	1.164
0.04				0.54	1.858	834.0	1.201
0.05				0.55	1.916	860.1	1.239
0.06				0.56	1.976	886.7	1.277
0.07				0.57	2.036	913.6	1.316
0.08				0.58	2.097	941.0	1.355
0.09				0.59	2.158	968.8	1.395
0.10				0.60	2.221	996.9	1.436
0.11				0.61	2.285	1026	1.477
0.12				0.62	2.350	1055	1.519
0.13	*0.1309*	*58.75*	*0.0846*	0.63	2.415	1084	1.561
0.14	*0.1599*	*71.78*	*0.1034*	0.64	2.482	1114	1.604
0.15	*0.1895*	*85.05*	*0.1225*	0.65	2.549	1144	1.648
0.16	*0.2196*	*98.57*	*0.1420*	0.66	2.618	1175	1.692
0.17	*0.2503*	*112.4*	*0.1618*	0.67	2.687	1206	1.737
0.18	*0.2816*	*126.4*	*0.1820*	0.68	2.757	1238	1.782
0.19	*0.3134*	*140.7*	*0.2026*	0.69	2.829	1270	1.828
0.20	*0.3459*	*155.2*	*0.2235*	0.70	2.901	1302	1.875
0.21	*0.3789*	*170.1*	*0.2249*	0.71	2.975	1335	1.923
0.22	*0.4125*	*185.2*	*0.2666*	0.72	3.049	1368	1.971
0.23	*0.4468*	*200.5*	*0.2888*	0.73	3.124	1402	2.019
0.24	0.4817	216.2	0.3113	0.74	3.201	1437	2.069
0.25	0.5172	232.1	0.3342	0.75	3.278	1471	2.119
0.26	0.5533	248.3	0.3576	0.76	3.357	1507	2.170
0.27	0.5901	264.8	0.3814	0.77	3.436	1542	2.221
0.28	0.6275	281.7	0.4056	0.78	3.517	1578	2.273
0.29	0.6656	298.8	0.4302	0.79	3.598	1615	2.326
0.30	0.7044	316.2	0.4553	0.80	3.681	1652	2.379
0.31	0.7438	333.9	0.4808	0.81	3.765	1690	2.433
0.32	0.7840	351.9	0.5067	0.82	3.850	1728	2.488
0.33	0.8248	370.2	0.5331	0.83	3.935	1766	2.544
0.34	0.8664	388.9	0.5599	0.84	4.022	1805	2.600
0.35	0.9086	407.8	0.5873	0.85	4.110	1845	2.657
0.36	0.9516	427.1	0.6150	0.86	4.200	1885	2.714
0.37	0.9953	446.7	0.6433	0.87	4.290	1925	2.773
0.38	1.040	466.7	0.6720	0.88	4.381	1966	2.832
0.39	1.085	487.0	0.7012	0.89	4.474	2008	2.891
0.40	1.131	507.6	0.7309	0.90	4.567	2050	2.952
0.41	1.178	528.5	0.7611	0.91	4.662	2092	3.013
0.42	1.225	549.9	0.7918	0.92	4.758	2135	3.075
0.43	1.273	571.5	0.8230	0.93	4.855	2179	3.137
0.44	1.322	593.5	0.8547	0.94	4.953	2223	3.201
0.45	1.372	615.9	0.8869	0.95	5.052	2267	3.265
0.46	1.423	638.6	0.9196	0.96	5.152	2312	3.330
0.47	1.474	661.7	0.9529	0.97	5.254	2358	3.395
0.48	1.527	685.2	0.9867	0.98	5.356	2404	3.462
0.49	1.580	709.1	1.021	0.99	5.460	2451	3.529
0.50	1.634	733.3	1.056	1.00	5.565	2498	3.597

14

Table 14-11 (Continued)				Table 14-11 (Continued)			
Head (feet)	CFS	GPM	MGD	Head (feet)	CFS	GPM	MGD
1.01	5.671	2545	3.665	1.39	10.55	4735	6.819
1.02	5.778	2593	3.734	1.40	10.70	4803	6.916
1.03	5.886	2642	3.804	1.41	10.85	4871	7.014
1.04	5.996	2691	3.875	1.42	11.00	4939	7.112
1.05	6.106	2741	3.947	1.43	11.16	5008	7.211
1.06	6.218	2791	4.019	1.44	11.31	5077	7.311
1.07	6.331	2842	4.092	1.45	11.47	5146	7.411
1.08	6.445	2893	4.166	1.46	11.62	5216	7.512
1.09	6.561	2945	4.240	1.47	11.78	5287	7.613
1.10	6.677	2997	4.316	1.48	11.94	5358	7.715
1.11	6.795	3050	4.392	1.49	12.10	5429	7.818
1.12	6.913	3103	4.468	1.50	12.26	5501	7.921
1.13	7.033	3157	4.546	1.51	12.42	5573	8.025
1.14	7.154	3211	4.624	1.52	12.58	5646	8.130
1.15	7.277	3266	4.703	1.53	12.74	5718	8.235
1.16	7.400	3321	4.783	1.54	12.91	5792	8.341
1.17	7.525	3377	4.863	1.55	13.07	5866	8.447
1.18	7.650	3434	4.945	1.56	13.23	5940	8.554
1.19	7.777	3491	5.027	1.57	13.40	6014	8.661
1.20	7.905	3548	5.109	1.58	13.57	6089	8.769
1.21	8.034	3606	5.193	1.59	13.74	6165	8.877
1.22	8.165	3665	5.277	1.60	13.90	6240	8.986
1.23	8.296	3724	5.362	1.61	14.07	6316	9.095
1.24	8.429	3783	5.448	1.62	14.24	6393	9.205
1.25	8.562	3843	5.534	1.63	14.41	6469	9.316
1.26	8.697	3904	5.621	1.64	14.59	6546	9.427
1.27	8.833	3965	5.709	1.65	14.76	6624	9.538
1.28	8.970	4026	5.798	1.66	14.93	6701	9.650
1.29	9.109	4088	5.887	1.67	15.10	6779	9.762
1.30	9.248	4151	5.977	1.68	15.28	6858	9.875
1.31	9.388	4214	6.068	1.69	15.45	6936	9.988
1.32	9.530	4277	6.159	1.70	15.63	7015	10.10
1.33	9.672	4341	6.252	1.71	15.81	7094	10.22
1.34	9.816	4406	6.344	1.72	15.98	7174	10.33
1.35	9.961	4471	6.438	1.73	16.16	7253	10.45
1.36	10.11	4536	6.532	1.74	16.34	7333	10.56
1.37	10.25	4602	6.627	1.75	16.52	7414	10.68
1.38	10.40	4669	6.723				

14

The approximation formulas below fit the data in the table within 1% of full scale.

Formula: $CFS = 5.75 \, H^{1.9}$ $GPM = 2580.6 \, H^{1.9}$ $MGD = 3.72 \, H^{1.9}$ *Where:* H = head in feet

Table 14-12:
0.102 m Palmer-Bowlus Flume Discharge Table
with Head in Meters

Data in table from Plasti-Fab, Inc.

Table 14-12			Table 14-12 (Continued)		
Head (meters)	l/s	m³/hr	Head (meters)	l/s	m³/hr
0.005			0.045	1.229	4.424
0.010			0.050	1.510	5.437
0.015			0.055	1.823	6.563
0.020	0.2853	1.027	0.060	2.168	7.806
0.025	0.4189	1.508	0.065	2.539	9.139
0.030	0.5780	2.081	0.070	2.929	10.55
0.035	0.7651	2.754	0.075	3.336	12.01
0.040	0.9805	3.530			

The approximation formulas below fit the data in the table within 1% of full scale.

Formula: $l/s = 468.34\ H^{1.9}$ $m^3/hr = 1647.88\ H^{1.9}$ *Where:* H = head in meters

14

Table 14-13:
0.152 m Palmer-Bowlus Flume Discharge Table
with Head in Meters

Data in table from Plasti-Fab, Inc.

Table 14-13			Table 14-13 (Continued)		
Head (meters)	l/s	m³/hr	Head (meters)	l/s	m³/hr
0.005			0.060	2.719	9.787
0.010			0.065	3.165	11.39
0.015			0.070	3.650	13.14
0.020	0.3978	1.432	0.075	4.179	15.05
0.025	0.5808	2.091	0.080	4.748	17.09
0.030	0.7933	2.856	0.085	5.356	19.28
0.035	1.035	3.728	0.090	6.001	21.60
0.040	1.306	4.700	0.095	6.677	24.04
0.045	1.608	5.788	0.100	7.380	26.57
0.050	1.943	6.994	0.105	8.106	29.18
0.055	2.311	8.319			

The approximation formulas below fit the data in the table within 1% of full scale.

Formula: $l/s = 607.7\ H^{1.9}$ $m^3/hr = 1401.5\ H^{1.9}$ *Where:* H = head in meters

14

Table 14-14:
0.203 m Palmer-Bowlus Flume Discharge Table
with Head in Meters

Data in table from Plasti-Fab, Inc.

Head (meters)	l/s	m³/hr	Head (meters)	l/s	m³/hr
0.005			0.080	5.599	20.15
0.010			0.085	6.280	22.61
0.015			0.090	7.009	25.23
0.020			0.095	7.783	28.02
0.025	0.7419	2.671	0.100	8.606	30.98
0.030	1.007	3.626	0.105	9.476	34.11
0.035	1.306	4.703	0.110	10.39	37.40
0.040	1.637	5.893	0.115	11.35	40.85
0.045	2.003	7.209	0.120	12.35	44.45
0.050	2.402	8.649	0.125	13.38	48.17
0.055	2.836	10.21	0.130	14.45	52.02
0.060	3.309	11.91	0.135	15.55	55.98
0.065	3.819	13.75	0.140	16.67	60.01
0.070	4.368	15.73	0.145	17.81	64.12
0.075	4.963	17.87	0.150	18.97	68.29

The approximation formulas below fit the data in the table within 1% of full scale.

Formula: $l/s = 722.03 \, H^{1.9}$ $m^3/hr = 2599 \, H^{1.9}$ *Where:* H = head in meters

Table 14-15:
0.254 m Palmer-Bowlus Flume Discharge Table
with Head in Meters

Data in table from Plasti-Fab, Inc.

Table 14-15			Table 14-15 (Continued)		
Head (meters)	l/s	m³/hr	Head (meters)	l/s	m³/hr
0.005			0.095	8.816	31.74
0.010			0.100	9.713	34.97
0.015			0.105	10.66	38.39
0.020			0.110	11.67	42.01
0.025			0.115	12.73	45.83
0.030			0.120	13.85	49.85
0.035	1.582	5.696	0.125	15.01	54.05
0.040	1.973	7.103	0.130	16.24	58.46
0.045	2.400	8.641	0.135	17.51	63.05
0.050	2.862	10.30	0.140	18.84	67.82
0.055	3.358	12.09	0.145	20.21	72.75
0.060	3.893	14.02	0.150	21.62	77.84
0.065	4.466	16.08	0.155	23.07	83.06
0.070	5.077	18.28	0.160	24.56	88.41
0.075	5.733	20.64	0.165	26.07	93.87
0.080	6.432	23.15	0.170	27.62	99.42
0.085	7.177	25.84	0.175	29.18	105.0
0.090	7.972	28.70	0.180	30.76	110.7

The approximation formulas below fit the data in the table within 1% of full scale.

Formula: $l/s = 749.9\ H^{1.9}$ $m^3/hr = 2878\ H^{1.9}$ *Where:* H = head in meters

14

Table 14-16:
0.305 m Palmer-Bowlus Flume Discharge Table
with Head in Meters

Data in table from Plasti-Fab, Inc.

Table 14-16			Table 14-16 (Continued)		
Head (meters)	l/s	m³/hr	Head (meters)	l/s	m³/hr
0.005			0.115	14.30	51.48
0.010			0.120	15.48	55.74
0.015			0.125	16.72	60.20
0.020			0.130	18.02	64.87
0.025			0.135	19.37	69.75
0.030			0.140	20.78	74.83
0.035	1.829	6.585	0.145	22.26	80.12
0.040	2.286	8.229	0.150	23.78	85.62
0.045	2.787	10.03	0.155	25.37	91.33
0.050	3.330	11.99	0.160	27.01	97.25
0.055	3.912	14.08	0.165	28.71	103.4
0.060	4.538	16.34	0.170	30.46	109.7
0.065	5.203	18.73	0.175	32.26	116.2
0.070	5.908	21.27	0.180	34.11	122.8
0.075	6.658	23.97	0.185	36.01	129.6
0.080	7.449	26.82	0.190	37.95	136.6
0.085	8.284	29.82	0.195	39.93	143.7
0.090	9.166	33.00	0.200	41.94	151.0
0.095	10.09	36.33	0.205	43.98	158.3
0.100	11.07	39.85	0.210	46.05	165.8
0.105	12.09	43.54	0.215	48.14	173.3
0.110	13.17	47.41			

The approximation formulas below fit the data in the table within 1% of full scale.

Formula: $l/s = 922.75\ H^{1.9}$ $m^3/hr = 3214\ H^{1.9}$ *Where:* H = head in meters

14

Table 14-17:
0.381 m Palmer-Bowlus Flume Discharge Table
with Head in Meters

Data in table from Plasti-Fab, Inc.

Head (meters)	l/s	m³/hr	Head (meters)	l/s	m³/hr
0.005			0.145	25.43	91.55
0.010			0.150	27.09	97.51
0.015			0.155	28.81	103.7
0.020			0.160	30.59	110.1
0.025			0.165	32.44	116.8
0.030			0.170	34.36	123.7
0.035			0.175	36.34	130.8
0.040			0.180	38.38	138.2
0.045	3.364	12.11	0.185	40.50	145.8
0.050	4.009	14.43	0.190	42.68	153.6
0.055	4.700	16.92	0.195	44.92	161.7
0.060	5.442	19.59	0.200	47.23	170.0
0.065	6.230	22.43	0.205	49.60	178.6
0.070	7.062	25.42	0.210	52.03	187.3
0.075	7.945	28.60	0.215	54.52	196.3
0.080	8.872	31.94	0.220	57.07	205.4
0.085	9.845	35.44	0.225	59.67	214.8
0.090	10.87	39.12	0.230	62.31	224.3
0.095	11.93	42.96	0.235	65.01	234.0
0.100	13.05	46.98	0.240	67.74	243.9
0.105	14.22	51.18	0.245	70.51	253.9
0.110	15.43	55.55	0.250	73.32	264.0
0.115	16.70	60.11	0.255	76.16	274.2
0.120	18.01	64.85	0.260	79.02	284.5
0.125	19.38	69.78	0.265	81.91	294.9
0.130	20.81	74.92	0.270	84.82	305.3
0.135	22.29	80.25	0.275	87.75	315.9
0.140	23.83	85.78			

The approximation formulas below fit the data in the table within 1% of full scale.

Formula: $l/s = 1056.5 \, H^{1.9}$ $m^3/hr = 3671 \, H^{1.9}$ *Where:* H = head in meters

14

Table 14-18:
0.457 m Palmer-Bowlus Flume Discharge Table
with Head in Meters

Data in table from Plasti-Fab, Inc.

Head (meters)	l/s	m³/hr	Head (meters)	l/s	m³/hr
0.005			0.165	36.34	130.8
0.010			0.170	38.39	138.2
0.015			0.175	40.50	145.8
0.020			0.180	42.67	153.6
0.025			0.185	44.92	161.7
0.030			0.190	47.24	170.1
0.035			0.195	49.63	178.7
0.040			0.200	52.09	187.5
0.045			0.205	54.62	196.6
0.050	4.602	16.57	0.210	57.23	206.0
0.055	5.414	19.49	0.215	59.91	215.7
0.060	6.286	22.63	0.220	62.67	225.6
0.065	7.212	25.96	0.225	65.49	235.8
0.070	8.188	29.48	0.230	68.40	246.2
0.075	9.219	33.19	0.235	71.36	256.9
0.080	10.30	37.07	0.240	74.41	267.9
0.085	11.42	41.13	0.245	77.52	279.1
0.090	12.60	45.37	0.250	80.69	290.5
0.095	13.83	49.77	0.255	83.93	302.2
0.100	15.10	54.35	0.260	87.24	314.0
0.105	16.42	59.11	0.265	90.60	326.1
0.110	17.79	64.03	0.270	94.02	338.5
0.115	19.21	69.14	0.275	97.49	350.9
0.120	20.67	74.42	0.280	101.0	363.6
0.125	22.19	79.88	0.285	104.6	376.5
0.130	23.76	85.55	0.290	108.2	389.5
0.135	25.39	91.39	0.295	111.8	402.6
0.140	27.06	97.43	0.300	115.5	415.9
0.145	28.80	103.7	0.305	119.2	429.3
0.150	30.60	110.1	0.310	123.0	442.8
0.155	32.45	116.8	0.315	126.8	456.4
0.160	34.37	123.7	0.320	130.6	470.1

The approximation formulas below fit the data in the table within 1% of full scale.

Formula: $l/s = 1179.22\ H^{1.9}$ $m^3/hr = 4096\ H^{1.9}$ *Where:* H = head in meters

14

Table 14-19:
0.533 m Palmer-Bowlus Flume Discharge Table
with Head in Meters

Data in table from Plasti-Fab, Inc.

Table 14-19			Table 14-19 (Continued)		
Head (meters)	l/s	m³/hr	Head (meters)	l/s	m³/hr
0.005			0.195	54.65	196.7
0.010			0.200	57.28	206.2
0.015			0.205	59.97	215.9
0.020			0.210	62.73	225.8
0.025			0.215	65.57	236.1
0.030			0.220	68.49	246.6
0.035			0.225	71.47	257.3
0.040			0.230	74.54	268.3
0.045			0.235	77.67	279.6
0.050			0.240	80.89	291.2
0.055	6.318	22.75	0.245	84.18	303.1
0.060	7.299	26.28	0.250	87.55	315.2
0.065	8.332	29.99	0.255	90.99	327.6
0.070	9.416	33.90	0.260	94.51	340.2
0.075	10.56	38.00	0.265	98.10	353.2
0.080	11.75	42.29	0.270	101.8	366.4
0.085	12.99	46.76	0.275	105.5	379.9
0.090	14.29	51.43	0.280	109.3	393.6
0.095	15.63	56.28	0.285	113.2	407.6
0.100	17.04	61.33	0.290	117.2	421.9
0.105	18.49	66.58	0.295	121.2	436.4
0.110	20.00	72.01	0.300	125.3	451.2
0.115	21.57	77.64	0.305	129.5	466.1
0.120	23.19	83.47	0.310	133.7	481.4
0.125	24.86	89.49	0.315	138.0	496.8
0.130	26.59	95.73	0.320	142.4	512.5
0.135	28.38	102.2	0.325	146.8	528.4
0.140	30.23	108.8	0.330	151.2	544.5
0.145	32.13	115.7	0.335	155.8	560.7
0.150	34.10	122.7	0.340	160.3	577.2
0.155	36.12	130.0	0.345	165.0	593.8
0.160	38.21	137.6	0.350	169.6	610.6
0.165	40.36	145.3	0.355	174.3	627.6
0.170	42.58	153.3	0.360	179.1	644.6
0.175	44.86	161.5	0.365	183.8	661.8
0.180	47.20	169.9	0.370	188.7	679.2
0.185	49.62	178.6	0.375	193.5	696.6
0.190	52.10	187.6	0.380	198.4	714.1

14

The approximation formulas below fit the data in the table within 1% of full scale.

Formula: $l/s = 1285.16\ H^{1.9}$ $m^3/hr = 4489.2\ H^{1.9}$ *Where:* H = head in meters

Table 14-20:
0.610 m Palmer-Bowlus Flume Discharge Table
with Head in Meters

Data in table from Plasti-Fab, Inc.

Head (meters)	l/s	m³/hr	Head (meters)	l/s	m³/hr
0.005			0.220	74.46	268.1
0.010			0.225	77.61	279.4
0.015			0.230	80.83	291.0
0.020			0.235	84.12	302.8
0.025			0.240	87.50	315.0
0.030			0.245	90.96	327.4
0.035			0.250	94.49	340.2
0.040			0.255	98.11	353.2
0.045			0.260	101.8	366.5
0.050			0.265	105.6	380.1
0.055			0.270	109.4	394.0
0.060	8.097	29.15	0.275	113.4	408.2
0.065	9.241	33.27	0.280	117.4	422.7
0.070	10.45	37.61	0.285	121.5	437.5
0.075	11.72	42.19	0.290	125.7	452.5
0.080	13.05	46.98	0.295	130.0	467.9
0.085	14.44	51.98	0.300	134.3	483.6
0.090	15.89	57.21	0.305	138.8	499.6
0.095	17.40	62.63	0.310	143.3	515.9
0.100	18.96	68.27	0.315	147.9	532.4
0.105	20.59	74.12	0.320	152.6	549.2
0.110	22.27	80.16	0.325	157.3	566.4
0.115	24.01	86.42	0.330	162.2	583.8
0.120	25.80	92.88	0.335	167.1	601.4
0.125	27.65	99.54	0.340	172.0	619.4
0.130	29.56	106.4	0.345	177.1	637.5
0.135	31.53	113.5	0.350	182.2	656.0
0.140	33.55	120.8	0.355	187.4	674.7
0.145	35.63	128.3	0.360	192.7	693.6
0.150	37.77	136.0	0.365	198.0	712.7
0.155	39.97	143.9	0.370	203.4	732.1
0.160	42.23	152.0	0.375	208.8	751.7
0.165	44.56	160.4	0.380	214.3	771.5
0.170	46.94	169.0	0.385	219.9	791.5
0.175	49.39	177.8	0.390	225.5	811.7
0.180	51.90	186.8	0.395	231.1	832.0
0.185	54.48	196.1	0.400	236.8	852.5
0.190	57.13	205.7	0.405	242.6	873.2
0.195	59.84	215.4	0.410	248.3	894.0
0.200	62.62	225.4	0.415	254.2	914.9
0.205	65.47	235.7	0.420	260.0	936.0
0.210	68.39	246.2	0.425	265.9	957.2
0.215	71.39	257.0			

The approximation formulas below fit the data in the table within 1% of full scale.

Formula: $l/s = 1402.25 \, H^{1.9}$ $m^3/hr = 4864.7 \, H^{1.9}$ *Where:* H = head in meters

Table 14-21:
0.686 m Palmer-Bowlus Flume Discharge Table
with Head in Meters

Data in table from Plasti-Fab, Inc.

Head (meters)	l/s	m³/hr	Head (meters)	l/s	m³/hr
0.005			0.205	71.19	256.3
0.010			0.210	74.29	267.5
0.015			0.215	77.47	278.9
0.020			0.220	80.72	290.6
0.025			0.225	84.04	302.5
0.030			0.230	87.43	314.8
0.035			0.235	90.90	327.3
0.040			0.240	94.45	340.0
0.045			0.245	98.08	353.1
0.050			0.250	101.8	366.4
0.055			0.255	105.6	380.0
0.060			0.260	109.4	393.9
0.065	10.15	36.55	0.265	113.4	408.1
0.070	11.47	41.29	0.270	117.4	422.7
0.075	12.86	46.31	0.275	121.5	437.5
0.080	14.32	51.56	0.280	125.7	452.6
0.085	15.85	57.06	0.285	130.0	468.0
0.090	17.44	62.80	0.290	134.4	483.7
0.095	19.10	68.76	0.295	138.8	499.8
0.100	20.82	74.95	0.300	143.4	516.1
0.105	22.61	81.38	0.305	148.0	532.8
0.110	24.45	88.02	0.310	152.7	549.8
0.115	26.36	94.89	0.315	157.5	567.1
0.120	28.33	102.0	0.320	162.4	584.7
0.125	30.35	109.3	0.325	167.4	602.6
0.130	32.45	116.8	0.330	172.5	620.9
0.135	34.60	124.5	0.335	177.6	639.5
0.140	36.80	132.5	0.340	182.9	658.4
0.145	39.08	140.7	0.345	188.2	677.6
0.150	41.41	149.1	0.350	193.6	697.1
0.155	43.80	157.7	0.355	199.1	716.9
0.160	46.25	166.5	0.360	204.7	737.0
0.165	48.76	175.5	0.365	210.4	757.4
0.170	51.34	184.8	0.370	216.1	778.1
0.175	53.98	194.3	0.375	222.0	799.1
0.180	56.68	204.1	0.380	227.9	820.4
0.185	59.45	214.0	0.385	233.9	842.0
0.190	62.29	224.2	0.390	239.9	863.8
0.195	65.18	234.7	0.395	246.1	885.9
0.200	68.15	245.4	0.400	252.3	908.3

14

Table 14-21 (Continued)			Table 14-21 (Continued)		
Head (meters)	l/s	m³/hr	Head (meters)	l/s	m³/hr
0.405	258.6	930.9	0.455	324.7	1169
0.410	264.9	953.8	0.460	331.6	1194
0.415	271.3	976.8	0.465	338.5	1219
0.420	277.8	1000	0.470	345.5	1244
0.425	284.4	1024	0.475	352.5	1269
0.430	291.0	1047	0.480	359.6	1294
0.435	297.6	1071	0.485	366.6	1320
0.440	304.3	1096	0.490	373.7	1345
0.445	311.1	1120			
0.450	317.9	1144			

The approximation formulas below fit the data in the table within 1% of full scale.

Formula: $l/s = 1502.6\ H^{1.9}$ $m^3/hr = 5216.2\ H^{1.9}$ *Where:* H = head in meters

Table 14-22:
0.762 m Palmer-Bowlus Flume Discharge Table
with Head in Meters

Data in table from Plasti-Fab, Inc.

Head (meters)	l/s	m³/hr	Head (meters)	l/s	m³/hr
0.005			0.255	113.0	406.9
0.010			0.260	117.1	421.6
0.015			0.265	121.3	436.6
0.020			0.270	125.5	451.9
0.025			0.275	129.9	467.6
0.030			0.280	134.3	483.5
0.035			0.285	138.8	499.7
0.040			0.290	143.4	516.3
0.045			0.295	148.1	533.1
0.050			0.300	152.9	550.3
0.055			0.305	157.7	567.8
0.060			0.310	162.7	585.6
0.065			0.315	167.7	603.7
0.070			0.320	172.8	622.1
0.075	14.24	51.28	0.325	178.0	640.9
0.080	15.92	57.31	0.330	183.3	659.9
0.085	17.64	63.52	0.335	188.7	679.3
0.090	19.42	69.92	0.340	194.2	699.0
0.095	21.25	76.49	0.345	199.7	719.0
0.100	23.13	83.26	0.350	205.4	739.4
0.105	25.06	90.22	0.355	211.1	760.0
0.110	27.05	97.37	0.360	216.9	781.0
0.115	29.09	104.7	0.365	222.9	802.3
0.120	31.19	112.3	0.370	228.9	823.9
0.125	33.35	120.1	0.375	234.9	845.8
0.130	35.57	128.0	0.380	241.1	868.0
0.135	37.85	136.2	0.385	247.4	890.6
0.140	40.18	144.7	0.390	253.7	913.4
0.145	42.58	153.3	0.395	260.2	936.6
0.150	45.04	162.2	0.400	266.7	960.0
0.155	47.57	171.3	0.405	273.3	983.8
0.160	50.16	180.6	0.410	280.0	1008
0.165	52.82	190.1	0.415	286.7	1032
0.170	55.54	200.0	0.420	293.6	1057
0.175	58.34	210.0	0.425	300.5	1082
0.180	61.20	220.3	0.430	307.5	1107
0.185	64.13	230.9	0.435	314.6	1132
0.190	67.13	241.7	0.440	321.7	1158
0.195	70.20	252.7	0.445	329.0	1184
0.200	73.35	264.1	0.450	336.3	1211
0.205	76.57	275.7	0.455	343.6	1237
0.210	79.87	287.5	0.460	351.1	1264
0.215	83.24	299.7	0.465	358.6	1291
0.220	86.69	312.1	0.470	366.2	1318
0.225	90.21	324.8	0.475	373.9	1346
0.230	93.82	337.7	0.480	381.6	1374
0.235	97.49	351.0	0.485	389.4	1402
0.240	101.3	364.5	0.490	397.2	1430
0.245	105.1	378.4	0.495	405.1	1458
0.250	109.0	392.5	0.500	413.1	1487

14

Table 14-22 (Continued)			Table 14-22 (Continued)		
Head (meters)	l/s	m³/hr	Head (meters)	l/s	m³/hr
0.505	421.1	1516	0.525	453.6	1633
0.510	429.1	1545	0.530	461.9	1663
0.515	437.3	1574	0.535	470.2	1693
0.520	445.4	1604			

The approximation formulas below fit the data in the table within 1% of full scale.

Formula: $l/s = 1543 \, H^{1.9}$ $m^3/hr = 5556.28 \, H^{1.9}$ *Where:* H = head in meters

CHAPTER 15

Leopold-Lagco Flume Discharge Tables

Overview

This chapter contains discharge (head vs. flow rate) tables for Leopold-Lagco flumes. Note that all of the tabular data is for free flow.

Discharge tables for Leopold-Lagco flumes with head in feet

15-1:	4 in.	15-6:	15 in.
15-2:	6 in.	15-7:	18 in.
15-3:	8 in.	15-8:	21 in.
15-4:	10 in.	15-9:	24 in.
15-5:	12 in.	15-10:	30 in.

The discharges of the flumes are listed in three different units of measure:

CFS - cubic feet per second   GPM - gallons per minute
MGD - million gallons per day

Discharge tables for Leopold-Lagco flumes with head in meters

15-11:	0.102 m	15-16:	0.381 m
15-12:	0.152 m	15-17:	0.457 m
15-13:	0.203 m	15-18:	0.533 m
15-14:	0.254 m	15-19:	0.610 m
15-15:	0.305 m	15-20:	0.762 m

The discharges of the flumes are listed in two different units of measure:

l/s - liters per second m^3/hr - cubic meters per hour

The formulas used to develop each table are listed on the table.

Table 15-1:
4 in. Leopold-Lagco Flume Discharge Table with Head in Feet

Formula: $CFS = 0.8448\ H^{1.547}$
$GPM = 379.1\ H^{1.547}$
$MGD = 0.5462\ H^{1.547}$
Where: H = head in feet

Table 15-1				Table 15-1 (Continued)			
Head (feet)	CFS	GPM	MGD	Head (feet)	CFS	GPM	MGD
0.01	0.0007	0.3053	0.0004	0.13	0.0360	16.14	0.0233
0.02	0.0020	0.8922	0.0013	0.14	0.0403	18.11	0.0261
0.03	0.0037	1.671	0.0024	0.15	0.0449	20.14	0.0290
0.04	0.0058	2.607	0.0038	0.16	0.0496	22.26	0.0321
0.05	0.0082	3.682	0.0053	0.17	0.0545	24.45	0.0352
0.06	0.0109	4.882	0.0070	0.18	0.0595	26.71	0.0385
0.07	0.0138	6.196	0.0089	0.19	0.0647	29.04	0.0418
0.08	0.0170	7.618	0.0110	0.20	0.0701	31.44	0.0453
0.09	0.0204	9.140	0.0132	0.21	0.0755	33.90	0.0488
0.10	0.0240	10.76	0.0155	0.22	0.0812	36.43	0.0525
0.11	0.0278	12.47	0.0180	0.23	0.0870	39.03	0.0562
0.12	0.0318	14.26	0.0206	0.24	0.0929	41.68	0.0601

Table 15-2:
6 in. Leopold-Lagco Flume Discharge Table with Head in Feet

Formula: $CFS = 1.243\ H^{1.547}$
$GPM = 557.9\ H^{1.547}$
$MGD = 0.8038\ H^{1.547}$
Where: H = head in feet

Table 15-2				Table 15-2 (Continued)			
Head (feet)	CFS	GPM	MGD	Head (feet)	CFS	GPM	MGD
0.01	0.0010	0.4493	0.0006	0.19	0.0952	42.74	0.0616
0.02	0.0029	1.313	0.0019	0.20	0.1031	46.26	0.0667
0.03	0.0055	2.458	0.0035	0.21	0.1112	49.89	0.0719
0.04	0.0085	3.837	0.0055	0.22	0.1195	53.61	0.0772
0.05	0.0121	5.418	0.0078	0.23	0.1280	57.43	0.0827
0.06	0.0160	7.184	0.0104	0.24	0.1367	61.34	0.0884
0.07	0.0203	9.118	0.0131	0.25	0.1456	65.34	0.0941
0.08	0.0250	11.21	0.0162	0.26	0.1547	69.43	0.1000
0.09	0.0300	13.45	0.0194	0.27	0.1640	73.60	0.1060
0.10	0.0353	15.83	0.0228	0.28	0.1735	77.86	0.1122
0.11	0.0409	18.35	0.0264	0.29	0.1831	82.20	0.1184
0.12	0.0468	20.99	0.0302	0.30	0.1930	86.63	0.1248
0.13	0.0529	23.76	0.0342	0.31	0.2031	91.14	0.1313
0.14	0.0594	26.65	0.0384	0.32	0.2133	95.72	0.1379
0.15	0.0661	29.65	0.0427	0.33	0.2237	100.4	0.1446
0.16	0.0730	32.76	0.0472	0.34	0.2342	105.1	0.1515
0.17	0.0802	35.98	0.0518	0.35	0.2450	110.0	0.1584
0.18	0.0876	39.31	0.0566				

15

Table 15-3:
8 in. Leopold-Lagco Flume Discharge Table with Head in Feet

Formula: CFS $= 1.636 \, H^{1.547}$
GPM $= 733.9 \, H^{1.547}$
MGD $= 1.057 \, H^{1.547}$

Where: H = head in feet

Table 15-3				Table 15-3 (Continued)			
Head (feet)	CFS	GPM	MGD	Head (feet)	CFS	GPM	MGD
0.01	0.0013	0.5911	0.0009	0.24	0.1799	80.69	0.1162
0.02	0.0039	1.727	0.0025	0.25	0.1916	85.95	0.1238
0.03	0.0072	3.234	0.0047	0.26	0.2036	91.33	0.1315
0.04	0.0113	5.047	0.0073	0.27	0.2158	96.82	0.1394
0.05	0.0159	7.128	0.0103	0.28	0.2283	102.4	0.1475
0.06	0.0211	9.450	0.0136	0.29	0.2411	108.1	0.1557
0.07	0.0267	12.00	0.0173	0.30	0.2540	114.0	0.1641
0.08	0.0329	14.75	0.0212	0.31	0.2673	119.9	0.1727
0.09	0.0394	17.69	0.0255	0.32	0.2807	125.9	0.1814
0.10	0.0464	20.83	0.0300	0.33	0.2944	132.1	0.1902
0.11	0.0538	24.14	0.0348	0.34	0.3083	138.3	0.1992
0.12	0.0616	27.61	0.0398	0.35	0.3224	144.6	0.2083
0.13	0.0697	31.25	0.0450	0.36	0.3368	151.1	0.2176
0.14	0.0781	35.05	0.0505	0.37	0.3514	157.6	0.2270
0.15	0.0869	39.00	0.0562	0.38	0.3662	164.3	0.2366
0.16	0.0961	43.09	0.0621	0.39	0.3812	171.0	0.2463
0.17	0.1055	47.33	0.0682	0.40	0.3964	177.8	0.2561
0.18	0.1153	51.71	0.0745	0.41	0.4119	184.8	0.2661
0.19	0.1253	56.22	0.0810	0.42	0.4275	191.8	0.2762
0.20	0.1357	60.86	0.0877	0.43	0.4434	198.9	0.2865
0.21	0.1463	65.63	0.0945	0.44	0.4594	206.1	0.2968
0.22	0.1572	70.53	0.1016	0.45	0.4757	213.4	0.3073
0.23	0.1684	75.55	0.1088				

15

Table 15-4:
10 in. Leopold-Lagco Flume Discharge Table with Head in Feet

Formula: $CFS = 2.023\,H^{1.547}$
$GPM = 907.7\,H^{1.547}$
$MGD = 1.308\,H^{1.547}$
Where: H = head in feet

Table 15-4				Table 15-4 (Continued)			
Head (feet)	CFS	GPM	MGD	Head (feet)	CFS	GPM	MGD
0.01	0.0016	0.7310	0.0011	0.31	0.3305	148.3	0.2137
0.02	0.0048	2.136	0.0031	0.32	0.3471	155.7	0.2244
0.03	0.0089	4.000	0.0058	0.33	0.3640	163.3	0.2354
0.04	0.0139	6.242	0.0090	0.34	0.3812	171.1	0.2465
0.05	0.0196	8.816	0.0127	0.35	0.3987	178.9	0.2578
0.06	0.0260	11.69	0.0168	0.36	0.4165	186.9	0.2693
0.07	0.0331	14.84	0.0214	0.37	0.4345	195.0	0.2809
0.08	0.0407	18.24	0.0263	0.38	0.4528	203.2	0.2928
0.09	0.0488	21.89	0.0315	0.39	0.4714	211.5	0.3048
0.10	0.0574	25.76	0.0371	0.40	0.4902	220.0	0.3170
0.11	0.0665	29.85	0.0430	0.41	0.5093	228.5	0.3293
0.12	0.0761	34.15	0.0492	0.42	0.5286	237.2	0.3418
0.13	0.0862	38.66	0.0557	0.43	0.5482	246.0	0.3545
0.14	0.0966	43.35	0.0625	0.44	0.5681	254.9	0.3673
0.15	0.1075	48.23	0.0695	0.45	0.5882	263.9	0.3803
0.16	0.1188	53.30	0.0768	0.46	0.6085	273.0	0.3935
0.17	0.1305	58.54	0.0844	0.47	0.6291	282.3	0.4068
0.18	0.1425	63.95	0.0922	0.48	0.6499	291.6	0.4202
0.19	0.1550	69.53	0.1002	0.49	0.6710	301.1	0.4339
0.20	0.1678	75.27	0.1085	0.50	0.6923	310.6	0.4476
0.21	0.1809	81.17	0.1170	0.51	0.7138	320.3	0.4616
0.22	0.1944	87.23	0.1257	0.52	0.7356	330.1	0.4756
0.23	0.2083	93.44	0.1346	0.53	0.7576	339.9	0.4898
0.24	0.2224	99.80	0.1438	0.54	0.7798	349.9	0.5042
0.25	0.2369	106.3	0.1532	0.55	0.8023	360.0	0.5187
0.26	0.2517	113.0	0.1628	0.56	0.8250	370.2	0.5334
0.27	0.2669	119.7	0.1726	0.57	0.8479	380.4	0.5482
0.28	0.2823	126.7	0.1825	0.58	0.8710	390.8	0.5632
0.29	0.2981	133.7	0.1927	0.59	0.8943	401.3	0.5783
0.30	0.3141	140.9	0.2031	0.60	0.9179	411.9	0.5935

15

Table 15-5:
12 in. Leopold-Lagco Flume Discharge Table with Head in Feet

Formula: CFS $= 2.407\ H^{1.547}$
GPM $= 1080\ H^{1.547}$
MGD $= 1.556\ H^{1.547}$

Where: H = head in feet

Head (feet)	CFS	GPM	MGD	Head (feet)	CFS	GPM	MGD
0.01	0.0019	0.8698	0.0013	0.36	0.4955	222.3	0.3203
0.02	0.0057	2.542	0.0037	0.37	0.5170	232.0	0.3342
0.03	0.0106	4.759	0.0069	0.38	0.5388	241.7	0.3483
0.04	0.0166	7.427	0.0107	0.39	0.5609	251.7	0.3626
0.05	0.0234	10.49	0.0151	0.40	0.5833	261.7	0.3770
0.06	0.0310	13.91	0.0200	0.41	0.6060	271.9	0.3917
0.07	0.0393	17.65	0.0254	0.42	0.6290	282.2	0.4066
0.08	0.0484	21.70	0.0313	0.43	0.6523	292.7	0.4217
0.09	0.0580	26.04	0.0375	0.44	0.6759	303.3	0.4369
0.10	0.0683	30.65	0.0442	0.45	0.6998	314.0	0.4524
0.11	0.0792	35.52	0.0512	0.46	0.7240	324.9	0.4681
0.12	0.0906	40.64	0.0585	0.47	0.7485	335.9	0.4839
0.13	0.1025	45.99	0.0663	0.48	0.7733	347.0	0.4999
0.14	0.1150	51.58	0.0743	0.49	0.7984	358.2	0.5161
0.15	0.1279	57.39	0.0827	0.50	0.8237	369.6	0.5325
0.16	0.1413	63.42	0.0914	0.51	0.8494	381.1	0.5491
0.17	0.1552	69.65	0.1003	0.52	0.8753	392.7	0.5658
0.18	0.1696	76.09	0.1096	0.53	0.9014	404.5	0.5827
0.19	0.1844	82.73	0.1192	0.54	0.9279	416.3	0.5998
0.20	0.1996	89.56	0.1290	0.55	0.9546	428.3	0.6171
0.21	0.2153	96.58	0.1391	0.56	0.9816	440.4	0.6345
0.22	0.2313	103.8	0.1495	0.57	1.009	452.6	0.6522
0.23	0.2478	111.2	0.1602	0.58	1.036	465.0	0.6699
0.24	0.2646	118.7	0.1711	0.59	1.064	477.5	0.6879
0.25	0.2819	126.5	0.1822	0.60	1.092	490.0	0.7060
0.26	0.2995	134.4	0.1936	0.61	1.120	502.7	0.7243
0.27	0.3175	142.5	0.2053	0.62	1.149	515.5	0.7427
0.28	0.3359	150.7	0.2172	0.63	1.178	528.4	0.7614
0.29	0.3547	159.1	0.2293	0.64	1.207	541.5	0.7801
0.30	0.3738	167.7	0.2416	0.65	1.236	554.6	0.7991
0.31	0.3932	176.4	0.2542	0.66	1.266	567.9	0.8182
0.32	0.4130	185.3	0.2670	0.67	1.295	581.2	0.8374
0.33	0.4331	194.3	0.2800	0.68	1.325	594.7	0.8568
0.34	0.4536	203.5	0.2932	0.69	1.356	608.3	0.8764
0.35	0.4744	212.9	0.3067	0.70	1.386	622.0	0.8961

15

Table 15-6:
15 in. Leopold-Lagco Flume Discharge Table with Head in Feet

Formula: $CFS = 2.977\ H^{1.547}$
$GPM = 1336\ H^{1.547}$
$MGD = 1.925\ H^{1.547}$

Where: H = head in feet

Head (feet)	CFS	GPM	MGD	Head (feet)	CFS	GPM	MGD
0.01	0.0024	1.076	0.0016	0.46	0.8955	401.9	0.5791
0.02	0.0070	3.144	0.0045	0.47	0.9258	415.5	0.5986
0.03	0.0131	5.887	0.0085	0.48	0.9564	429.2	0.6185
0.04	0.0205	9.187	0.0132	0.49	0.9874	443.1	0.6385
0.05	0.0289	12.98	0.0187	0.50	1.019	457.2	0.6588
0.06	0.0383	17.20	0.0248	0.51	1.050	471.4	0.6793
0.07	0.0487	21.84	0.0315	0.52	1.083	485.8	0.7000
0.08	0.0598	26.85	0.0387	0.53	1.115	500.3	0.7209
0.09	0.0718	32.21	0.0464	0.54	1.148	515.0	0.7421
0.10	0.0845	37.91	0.0546	0.55	1.181	529.8	0.7634
0.11	0.0979	43.94	0.0633	0.56	1.214	544.8	0.7850
0.12	0.1120	50.27	0.0724	0.57	1.248	559.9	0.8068
0.13	0.1268	56.90	0.0820	0.58	1.282	575.2	0.8288
0.14	0.1422	63.81	0.0919	0.59	1.316	590.6	0.8510
0.15	0.1582	70.99	0.1023	0.60	1.351	606.2	0.8734
0.16	0.1748	78.45	0.1130	0.61	1.386	621.9	0.8961
0.17	0.1920	86.16	0.1241	0.62	1.421	637.7	0.9189
0.18	0.2097	94.13	0.1356	0.63	1.457	653.7	0.9419
0.19	0.2280	102.3	0.1475	0.64	1.493	669.8	0.9651
0.20	0.2469	110.8	0.1596	0.65	1.529	686.1	0.9886
0.21	0.2662	119.5	0.1721	0.66	1.565	702.5	1.012
0.22	0.2861	128.4	0.1850	0.67	1.602	719.0	1.036
0.23	0.3065	137.5	0.1982	0.68	1.639	735.7	1.060
0.24	0.3273	146.9	0.2116	0.69	1.677	752.5	1.084
0.25	0.3487	156.5	0.2254	0.70	1.715	769.4	1.109
0.26	0.3705	166.3	0.2395	0.71	1.753	786.5	1.133
0.27	0.3927	176.2	0.2540	0.72	1.791	803.7	1.158
0.28	0.4155	186.4	0.2686	0.73	1.830	821.0	1.183
0.29	0.4386	196.9	0.2836	0.74	1.868	838.5	1.208
0.30	0.4623	207.4	0.2989	0.75	1.908	856.1	1.234
0.31	0.4863	218.2	0.3145	0.76	1.947	873.8	1.259
0.32	0.5108	229.2	0.3303	0.77	1.987	891.7	1.285
0.33	0.5357	240.4	0.3464	0.78	2.027	909.7	1.311
0.34	0.5610	251.8	0.3628	0.79	2.067	927.8	1.337
0.35	0.5867	263.3	0.3794	0.80	2.108	946.0	1.363
0.36	0.6129	275.0	0.3963	0.81	2.149	964.3	1.389
0.37	0.6394	287.0	0.4135	0.82	2.190	982.8	1.416
0.38	0.6664	299.0	0.4309	0.83	2.231	1001	1.443
0.39	0.6937	311.3	0.4485	0.84	2.273	1020	1.470
0.40	0.7214	323.7	0.4665	0.85	2.315	1039	1.497
0.41	0.7495	336.3	0.4846	0.86	2.357	1058	1.524
0.42	0.7779	349.1	0.5030	0.87	2.400	1077	1.552
0.43	0.8068	362.1	0.5217	0.88	2.443	1096	1.580
0.44	0.8360	375.2	0.5406	0.89	2.486	1116	1.607
0.45	0.8656	388.4	0.5597	0.90	2.529	1135	1.635

15

Table 15-7:
18 in. Leopold-Lagco Flume Discharge Table with Head in Feet

Formula: $CFS = 3.542\,H^{1.547}$
$GPM = 1589\,H^{1.547}$
$MGD = 2.290\,H^{1.547}$

Where: H = head in feet

Head (feet)	CFS	GPM	MGD	Head (feet)	CFS	GPM	MGD
0.01	0.0029	1.280	0.0018	0.51	1.250	560.7	0.8081
0.02	0.0083	3.740	0.0054	0.52	1.288	577.8	0.8327
0.03	0.0156	7.002	0.0101	0.53	1.326	595.1	0.8576
0.04	0.0244	10.93	0.0157	0.54	1.365	612.5	0.8828
0.05	0.0344	15.43	0.0222	0.55	1.405	630.2	0.9082
0.06	0.0456	20.46	0.0295	0.56	1.444	648.0	0.9339
0.07	0.0579	25.97	0.0374	0.57	1.485	666.0	0.9598
0.08	0.0712	31.93	0.0460	0.58	1.525	684.1	0.9860
0.09	0.0854	38.31	0.0552	0.59	1.566	702.5	1.012
0.10	0.1005	45.09	0.0650	0.60	1.607	721.0	1.039
0.11	0.1165	52.26	0.0753	0.61	1.649	739.7	1.066
0.12	0.1333	59.79	0.0862	0.62	1.691	758.5	1.093
0.13	0.1508	67.67	0.0975	0.63	1.733	777.5	1.121
0.14	0.1692	75.89	0.1094	0.64	1.776	796.7	1.148
0.15	0.1882	84.44	0.1217	0.65	1.819	816.0	1.176
0.16	0.2080	93.30	0.1345	0.66	1.862	835.5	1.204
0.17	0.2284	102.5	0.1477	0.67	1.906	855.2	1.232
0.18	0.2495	112.0	0.1613	0.68	1.950	875.0	1.261
0.19	0.2713	121.7	0.1754	0.69	1.995	895.0	1.290
0.20	0.2937	131.8	0.1899	0.70	2.040	915.1	1.319
0.21	0.3168	142.1	0.2048	0.71	2.085	935.4	1.348
0.22	0.3404	152.7	0.2201	0.72	2.131	955.9	1.378
0.23	0.3646	163.6	0.2357	0.73	2.177	976.5	1.407
0.24	0.3894	174.7	0.2518	0.74	2.223	997.3	1.437
0.25	0.4148	186.1	0.2682	0.75	2.270	1018	1.467
0.26	0.4408	197.7	0.2850	0.76	2.317	1039	1.498
0.27	0.4673	209.6	0.3021	0.77	2.364	1061	1.528
0.28	0.4943	221.8	0.3196	0.78	2.412	1082	1.559
0.29	0.5219	234.1	0.3374	0.79	2.460	1103	1.590
0.30	0.5500	246.7	0.3556	0.80	2.508	1125	1.621
0.31	0.5786	259.6	0.3741	0.81	2.557	1147	1.653
0.32	0.6077	272.6	0.3929	0.82	2.606	1169	1.685
0.33	0.6374	285.9	0.4121	0.83	2.655	1191	1.717
0.34	0.6675	299.4	0.4316	0.84	2.705	1213	1.749
0.35	0.6981	313.2	0.4513	0.85	2.755	1236	1.781
0.36	0.7292	327.1	0.4714	0.86	2.805	1258	1.813
0.37	0.7608	341.3	0.4919	0.87	2.856	1281	1.846
0.38	0.7928	355.7	0.5126	0.88	2.906	1304	1.879
0.39	0.8253	370.3	0.5336	0.89	2.958	1327	1.912
0.40	0.8583	385.0	0.5549	0.90	3.009	1350	1.946
0.41	0.8917	400.0	0.5765	0.91	3.061	1373	1.979
0.42	0.9256	415.2	0.5984	0.92	3.113	1397	2.013
0.43	0.9599	430.6	0.6206	0.93	3.166	1420	2.047
0.44	0.9946	446.2	0.6431	0.94	3.219	1444	2.081
0.45	1.030	462.0	0.6658	0.95	3.272	1468	2.115
0.46	1.065	478.0	0.6888	0.96	3.325	1492	2.150
0.47	1.101	494.2	0.7121	0.97	3.379	1516	2.185
0.48	1.138	510.5	0.7357	0.98	3.433	1540	2.220
0.49	1.175	527.1	0.7596	0.99	3.487	1564	2.255
0.50	1.212	543.8	0.7837	1.00	3.542	1589	2.290

15

Table 15-7 (Continued)			
Head (feet)	CFS	GPM	MGD
1.01	3.597	1614	2.326
1.02	3.652	1638	2.361
1.03	3.708	1663	2.397

Table 15-7 (Continued)			
Head (feet)	CFS	GPM	MGD
1.04	3.764	1688	2.433
1.05	3.820	1714	2.470

15

Table 15-8:
21 in. Leopold-Lagco Flume Discharge Table with Head in Feet

Formula: CFS = 4.103 $H^{1.547}$
GPM = 1841 $H^{1.547}$
MGD = 2.652 $H^{1.547}$
Where: H = head in feet

Head (feet)	CFS	GPM	MGD	Head (feet)	CFS	GPM	MGD
0.01	0.0033	1.483	0.0021	0.51	1.448	649.6	0.9358
0.02	0.0097	4.333	0.0062	0.52	1.492	669.4	0.9643
0.03	0.0181	8.113	0.0117	0.53	1.537	689.5	0.9932
0.04	0.0282	12.66	0.0182	0.54	1.582	709.7	1.022
0.05	0.0398	17.88	0.0258	0.55	1.627	730.1	1.052
0.06	0.0528	23.71	0.0341	0.56	1.673	750.8	1.081
0.07	0.0671	30.09	0.0433	0.57	1.720	771.6	1.112
0.08	0.0824	36.99	0.0533	0.58	1.767	792.6	1.142
0.09	0.0989	44.39	0.0639	0.59	1.814	813.9	1.172
0.10	0.1164	52.25	0.0753	0.60	1.862	835.3	1.203
0.11	0.1349	60.55	0.0872	0.61	1.910	857.0	1.234
0.12	0.1544	69.27	0.0998	0.62	1.959	878.8	1.266
0.13	0.1747	78.40	0.1129	0.63	2.008	900.8	1.298
0.14	0.1960	87.93	0.1267	0.64	2.057	923.0	1.330
0.15	0.2180	97.83	0.1409	0.65	2.107	945.4	1.362
0.16	0.2409	108.1	0.1557	0.66	2.157	968.0	1.394
0.17	0.2646	118.7	0.1710	0.67	2.208	990.8	1.427
0.18	0.2891	129.7	0.1868	0.68	2.259	1014	1.460
0.19	0.3143	141.0	0.2031	0.69	2.311	1037	1.494
0.20	0.3402	152.7	0.2199	0.70	2.363	1060	1.527
0.21	0.3669	164.6	0.2372	0.71	2.415	1084	1.561
0.22	0.3943	176.9	0.2549	0.72	2.468	1108	1.595
0.23	0.4224	189.5	0.2730	0.73	2.522	1131	1.630
0.24	0.4511	202.4	0.2916	0.74	2.575	1155	1.664
0.25	0.4805	215.6	0.3106	0.75	2.629	1180	1.699
0.26	0.5106	229.1	0.3300	0.76	2.684	1204	1.735
0.27	0.5413	242.9	0.3499	0.77	2.738	1229	1.770
0.28	0.5726	256.9	0.3701	0.78	2.794	1253	1.806
0.29	0.6045	271.3	0.3908	0.79	2.849	1278	1.842
0.30	0.6371	285.9	0.4118	0.80	2.905	1304	1.878
0.31	0.6703	300.7	0.4332	0.81	2.962	1329	1.914
0.32	0.7040	315.9	0.4550	0.82	3.018	1354	1.951
0.33	0.7383	331.3	0.4772	0.83	3.075	1380	1.988
0.34	0.7732	346.9	0.4998	0.84	3.133	1406	2.025
0.35	0.8087	362.8	0.5227	0.85	3.191	1432	2.062
0.36	0.8447	379.0	0.5460	0.86	3.249	1458	2.100
0.37	0.8813	395.4	0.5696	0.87	3.308	1484	2.138
0.38	0.9184	412.1	0.5936	0.88	3.367	1511	2.176
0.39	0.9560	429.0	0.6179	0.89	3.426	1537	2.215
0.40	0.9942	446.1	0.6426	0.90	3.486	1564	2.253
0.41	1.033	463.5	0.6677	0.91	3.546	1591	2.292
0.42	1.072	481.1	0.6930	0.92	3.606	1618	2.331
0.43	1.112	498.9	0.7187	0.93	3.667	1645	2.370
0.44	1.152	517.0	0.7447	0.94	3.728	1673	2.410
0.45	1.193	535.3	0.7711	0.95	3.790	1701	2.450
0.46	1.234	553.8	0.7977	0.96	3.852	1728	2.490
0.47	1.276	572.5	0.8247	0.97	3.914	1756	2.530
0.48	1.318	591.5	0.8520	0.98	3.977	1784	2.570
0.49	1.361	610.6	0.8796	0.99	4.040	1813	2.611
0.50	1.404	630.0	0.9076	1.00	4.103	1841	2.652

15

Table 15-8 (Continued)					Table 15-8 (Continued)			
Head (feet)	CFS	GPM	MGD	Head (feet)	CFS	GPM	MGD
1.01	4.167	1870	2.693	1.14	5.025	2255	3.248
1.02	4.231	1898	2.735	1.15	5.093	2285	3.292
1.03	4.295	1927	2.776	1.16	5.162	2316	3.336
1.04	4.360	1956	2.818	1.17	5.231	2347	3.381
1.05	4.425	1985	2.860	1.18	5.300	2378	3.426
1.06	4.490	2015	2.902	1.19	5.370	2409	3.471
1.07	4.556	2044	2.945	1.20	5.440	2441	3.516
1.08	4.622	2074	2.987	1.21	5.510	2472	3.562
1.09	4.688	2104	3.030	1.22	5.581	2504	3.607
1.10	4.755	2133	3.073	1.23	5.652	2536	3.653
1.11	4.822	2164	3.117	1.24	5.723	2568	3.699
1.12	4.889	2194	3.160	1.25	5.795	2600	3.745
1.13	4.957	2224	3.204				

15

Table 15-9:
24 in. Leopold-Lagco Flume Discharge Table with Head in Feet

Formula: CFS $= 4.660\ H^{1.547}$
GPM $= 2091\ H^{1.547}$
MGD $= 3.012\ H^{1.547}$

Where: H = head in feet

Table 15-9				Table 15-9 (Continued)			
Head (feet)	CFS	GPM	MGD	Head (feet)	CFS	GPM	MGD
0.01	0.0038	1.684	0.0024	0.51	1.644	737.8	1.063
0.02	0.0110	4.921	0.0071	0.52	1.695	760.3	1.095
0.03	0.0205	9.214	0.0133	0.53	1.745	783.1	1.128
0.04	0.0320	14.38	0.0207	0.54	1.796	806.1	1.161
0.05	0.0453	20.31	0.0293	0.55	1.848	829.3	1.195
0.06	0.0600	26.92	0.0388	0.56	1.900	852.7	1.228
0.07	0.0762	34.18	0.0492	0.57	1.953	876.4	1.262
0.08	0.0936	42.02	0.0605	0.58	2.006	900.3	1.297
0.09	0.1124	50.42	0.0726	0.59	2.060	924.4	1.332
0.10	0.1322	59.34	0.0855	0.60	2.114	948.8	1.367
0.11	0.1533	68.77	0.0991	0.61	2.169	973.3	1.402
0.12	0.1753	78.68	0.1133	0.62	2.224	998.1	1.438
0.13	0.1985	89.05	0.1283	0.63	2.280	1023	1.474
0.14	0.2226	99.87	0.1439	0.64	2.336	1048	1.510
0.15	0.2476	111.1	0.1601	0.65	2.393	1074	1.547
0.16	0.2736	122.8	0.1769	0.66	2.450	1099	1.584
0.17	0.3005	134.9	0.1942	0.67	2.508	1125	1.621
0.18	0.3283	147.3	0.2122	0.68	2.566	1151	1.659
0.19	0.3570	160.2	0.2307	0.69	2.625	1178	1.697
0.20	0.3864	173.4	0.2498	0.70	2.684	1204	1.735
0.21	0.4167	187.0	0.2694	0.71	2.743	1231	1.773
0.22	0.4478	200.9	0.2895	0.72	2.803	1258	1.812
0.23	0.4797	215.3	0.3101	0.73	2.864	1285	1.851
0.24	0.5124	229.9	0.3312	0.74	2.925	1312	1.890
0.25	0.5458	244.9	0.3528	0.75	2.986	1340	1.930
0.26	0.5799	260.2	0.3748	0.76	3.048	1368	1.970
0.27	0.6148	275.9	0.3974	0.77	3.110	1396	2.010
0.28	0.6503	291.8	0.4203	0.78	3.173	1424	2.051
0.29	0.6866	308.1	0.4438	0.79	3.236	1452	2.092
0.30	0.7236	324.7	0.4677	0.80	3.300	1481	2.133
0.31	0.7612	341.6	0.4920	0.81	3.364	1509	2.174
0.32	0.7996	358.8	0.5168	0.82	3.428	1538	2.216
0.33	0.8385	376.3	0.5420	0.83	3.493	1567	2.258
0.34	0.8782	394.1	0.5676	0.84	3.558	1597	2.300
0.35	0.9185	412.1	0.5936	0.85	3.624	1626	2.342
0.36	0.9594	430.5	0.6201	0.86	3.690	1656	2.385
0.37	1.001	449.1	0.6469	0.87	3.757	1686	2.428
0.38	1.043	468.0	0.6742	0.88	3.824	1716	2.472
0.39	1.086	487.2	0.7018	0.89	3.891	1746	2.515
0.40	1.129	506.7	0.7299	0.90	3.959	1777	2.559
0.41	1.173	526.4	0.7583	0.91	4.027	1807	2.603
0.42	1.218	546.4	0.7871	0.92	4.096	1838	2.647
0.43	1.263	566.7	0.8163	0.93	4.165	1869	2.692
0.44	1.309	587.2	0.8458	0.94	4.235	1900	2.737
0.45	1.355	608.0	0.8757	0.95	4.305	1931	2.782
0.46	1.402	629.0	0.9060	0.96	4.375	1963	2.828
0.47	1.449	650.3	0.9367	0.97	4.446	1995	2.873
0.48	1.497	671.8	0.9677	0.98	4.517	2027	2.919
0.49	1.546	693.6	0.9991	0.99	4.588	2059	2.966
0.50	1.595	715.6	1.031	1.00	4.660	2091	3.012

15

Table 15-9 (Continued)			
Head (feet)	CFS	GPM	MGD
1.01	4.732	2123	3.059
1.02	4.805	2156	3.106
1.03	4.878	2189	3.153
1.04	4.951	2222	3.200
1.05	5.025	2255	3.248
1.06	5.100	2288	3.296
1.07	5.174	2322	3.344
1.08	5.249	2355	3.393
1.09	5.325	2389	3.442
1.10	5.400	2423	3.491
1.11	5.476	2457	3.540
1.12	5.553	2492	3.589
1.13	5.630	2526	3.639
1.14	5.707	2561	3.689
1.15	5.785	2596	3.739
1.16	5.863	2631	3.789
1.17	5.941	2666	3.840
1.18	6.020	2701	3.891
1.19	6.099	2737	3.942
1.20	6.178	2772	3.993

Table 15-9 (Continued)			
Head (feet)	CFS	GPM	MGD
1.21	6.258	2808	4.045
1.22	6.338	2844	4.097
1.23	6.419	2880	4.149
1.24	6.500	2917	4.201
1.25	6.581	2953	4.254
1.26	6.663	2990	4.307
1.27	6.745	3026	4.360
1.28	6.827	3063	4.413
1.29	6.910	3101	4.466
1.30	6.993	3138	4.520
1.31	7.076	3175	4.574
1.32	7.160	3213	4.628
1.33	7.244	3251	4.682
1.34	7.329	3288	4.737
1.35	7.413	3326	4.792
1.36	7.498	3365	4.847
1.37	7.584	3403	4.902
1.38	7.670	3441	4.957
1.39	7.756	3480	5.013
1.40	7.842	3519	5.069

15

Table 15-10:
30 in. Leopold-Lagco Flume Discharge Table with Head in Feet

Formula: CFS $= 5.764\ H^{1.547}$
            GPM $= 2586\ H^{1.547}$
            MGD $= 3.726\ H^{1.547}$
Where: H = head in feet

Table 15-10				Table 15-10 (Continued)			
Head (feet)	CFS	GPM	MGD	Head (feet)	CFS	GPM	MGD
0.01	0.0046	2.083	0.0030	0.51	2.034	912.5	1.315
0.02	0.0136	6.086	0.0088	0.52	2.096	940.3	1.355
0.03	0.0254	11.40	0.0164	0.53	2.159	968.5	1.395
0.04	0.0396	17.78	0.0256	0.54	2.222	996.9	1.436
0.05	0.0560	25.12	0.0362	0.55	2.286	1026	1.478
0.06	0.0742	33.30	0.0480	0.56	2.351	1055	1.519
0.07	0.0942	42.27	0.0609	0.57	2.416	1084	1.562
0.08	0.1158	51.96	0.0749	0.58	2.482	1113	1.604
0.09	0.1390	62.35	0.0898	0.59	2.548	1143	1.647
0.10	0.1636	73.39	0.1057	0.60	2.615	1173	1.691
0.11	0.1896	85.05	0.1225	0.61	2.683	1204	1.734
0.12	0.2169	97.30	0.1402	0.62	2.751	1234	1.779
0.13	0.2455	110.1	0.1587	0.63	2.820	1265	1.823
0.14	0.2753	123.5	0.1780	0.64	2.890	1297	1.868
0.15	0.3063	137.4	0.1980	0.65	2.960	1328	1.913
0.16	0.3385	151.8	0.2188	0.66	3.031	1360	1.959
0.17	0.3717	166.8	0.2403	0.67	3.102	1392	2.005
0.18	0.4061	182.2	0.2625	0.68	3.174	1424	2.052
0.19	0.4415	198.1	0.2854	0.69	3.247	1457	2.099
0.20	0.4780	214.4	0.3090	0.70	3.320	1489	2.146
0.21	0.5155	231.3	0.3332	0.71	3.393	1522	2.194
0.22	0.5539	248.5	0.3581	0.72	3.468	1556	2.241
0.23	0.5934	266.2	0.3836	0.73	3.542	1589	2.290
0.24	0.6337	284.3	0.4097	0.74	3.618	1623	2.339
0.25	0.6751	302.9	0.4364	0.75	3.694	1657	2.388
0.26	0.7173	321.8	0.4637	0.76	3.770	1691	2.437
0.27	0.7604	341.2	0.4915	0.77	3.847	1726	2.487
0.28	0.8044	360.9	0.5200	0.78	3.925	1761	2.537
0.29	0.8493	381.0	0.5490	0.79	4.003	1796	2.587
0.30	0.8950	401.5	0.5786	0.80	4.081	1831	2.638
0.31	0.9416	422.4	0.6087	0.81	4.161	1867	2.689
0.32	0.9890	443.7	0.6393	0.82	4.240	1902	2.741
0.33	1.037	465.3	0.6705	0.83	4.321	1938	2.793
0.34	1.086	487.3	0.7022	0.84	4.401	1975	2.845
0.35	1.136	509.7	0.7344	0.85	4.483	2011	2.898
0.36	1.187	532.4	0.7671	0.86	4.564	2048	2.951
0.37	1.238	555.4	0.8003	0.87	4.647	2085	3.004
0.38	1.290	578.8	0.8340	0.88	4.730	2122	3.057
0.39	1.343	602.6	0.8682	0.89	4.813	2159	3.111
0.40	1.397	626.6	0.9029	0.90	4.897	2197	3.166
0.41	1.451	651.0	0.9380	0.91	4.982	2235	3.220
0.42	1.506	675.8	0.9737	0.92	5.066	2273	3.275
0.43	1.562	700.8	1.010	0.93	5.152	2311	3.330
0.44	1.619	726.2	1.046	0.94	5.238	2350	3.386
0.45	1.676	751.9	1.083	0.95	5.324	2389	3.442
0.46	1.734	777.9	1.121	0.96	5.411	2428	3.498
0.47	1.793	804.2	1.159	0.97	5.499	2467	3.555
0.48	1.852	830.8	1.197	0.98	5.587	2506	3.611
0.49	1.912	857.8	1.236	0.99	5.675	2546	3.669
0.50	1.973	885.0	1.275	1.00	5.764	2586	3.726

15

Table 15-10 (Continued)				Table 15-10 (Continued)			
Head (feet)	CFS	GPM	MGD	Head (feet)	CFS	GPM	MGD
1.01	5.853	2626	3.784	1.39	9.593	4304	6.201
1.02	5.943	2666	3.842	1.40	9.700	4352	6.271
1.03	6.034	2707	3.900	1.41	9.808	4400	6.340
1.04	6.125	2748	3.959	1.42	9.915	4449	6.410
1.05	6.216	2789	4.018	1.43	10.02	4497	6.480
1.06	6.308	2830	4.077	1.44	10.13	4546	6.550
1.07	6.400	2871	4.137	1.45	10.24	4595	6.620
1.08	6.493	2913	4.197	1.46	10.35	4644	6.691
1.09	6.586	2955	4.257	1.47	10.46	4693	6.762
1.10	6.680	2997	4.318	1.48	10.57	4743	6.833
1.11	6.774	3039	4.379	1.49	10.68	4792	6.905
1.12	6.869	3082	4.440	1.50	10.79	4842	6.977
1.13	6.964	3124	4.501	1.51	10.90	4892	7.049
1.14	7.059	3167	4.563	1.52	11.02	4942	7.121
1.15	7.155	3210	4.625	1.53	11.13	4993	7.194
1.16	7.252	3253	4.688	1.54	11.24	5043	7.267
1.17	7.349	3297	4.750	1.55	11.35	5094	7.340
1.18	7.446	3341	4.813	1.56	11.47	5145	7.413
1.19	7.544	3385	4.877	1.57	11.58	5196	7.487
1.20	7.642	3429	4.940	1.58	11.70	5247	7.561
1.21	7.741	3473	5.004	1.59	11.81	5299	7.635
1.22	7.840	3517	5.068	1.60	11.93	5351	7.709
1.23	7.940	3562	5.132	1.61	12.04	5402	7.784
1.24	8.040	3607	5.197	1.62	12.16	5454	7.859
1.25	8.140	3652	5.262	1.63	12.27	5507	7.934
1.26	8.241	3697	5.327	1.64	12.39	5559	8.010
1.27	8.343	3743	5.393	1.65	12.51	5611	8.085
1.28	8.445	3789	5.459	1.66	12.62	5664	8.161
1.29	8.547	3835	5.525	1.67	12.74	5717	8.237
1.30	8.650	3881	5.591	1.68	12.86	5770	8.314
1.31	8.753	3927	5.658	1.69	12.98	5823	8.390
1.32	8.856	3973	5.725	1.70	13.10	5877	8.467
1.33	8.960	4020	5.792	1.71	13.22	5930	8.545
1.34	9.065	4067	5.860	1.72	13.34	5984	8.622
1.35	9.170	4114	5.927	1.73	13.46	6038	8.700
1.36	9.275	4161	5.996	1.74	13.58	6092	8.778
1.37	9.381	4209	6.064	1.75	13.70	6146	8.856
1.38	9.487	4256	6.132				

15

Table 15-11:
0.102 m Leopold-Lagco Flume Discharge Table
with Head in Meters

Formula: $l/s = 150.3\ H^{1.547}$
$m^3/hr = 541.2\ H^{1.547}$
Where: H = head in meters

Table 15-11			Table 15-11 (Continued)		
Head (meters)	l/s	m³/hr	Head (meters)	l/s	m³/hr
0.005	0.0414	0.1492	0.045	1.240	4.466
0.010	0.1210	0.4359	0.050	1.460	5.256
0.015	0.2267	0.8162	0.055	1.692	6.091
0.020	0.3537	1.274	0.060	1.935	6.969
0.025	0.4995	1.799	0.065	2.190	7.887
0.030	0.6623	2.385	0.070	2.457	8.846
0.035	0.8407	3.027	0.075	2.733	9.842
0.040	1.034	3.722			

Table 15-12:
0.152 m Leopold-Lagco Flume Discharge Table
with Head in Meters

Formula: $l/s = 221.3\ H^{1.547}$
$m^3/hr = 796.5\ H^{1.547}$
Where: H = head in meters

Table 15-12			Table 15-12 (Continued)		
Head (meters)	l/s	m³/hr	Head (meters)	l/s	m³/hr
0.005	0.0610	0.2195	0.060	2.850	10.26
0.010	0.1782	0.6415	0.065	3.225	11.61
0.015	0.3337	1.201	0.070	3.617	13.02
0.020	0.5208	1.874	0.075	4.024	14.48
0.025	0.7355	2.647	0.080	4.447	16.01
0.030	0.9752	3.510	0.085	4.884	17.58
0.035	1.238	4.455	0.090	5.336	19.20
0.040	1.522	5.477	0.095	5.801	20.88
0.045	1.826	6.572	0.100	6.280	22.60
0.050	2.149	7.736	0.105	6.773	24.38
0.055	2.491	8.965			

15

Table 15-13:
0.203 m Leopold-Lagco Flume Discharge Table
with Head in Meters

Formula: $l/s = 291.1\ H^{1.547}$
$m^3/hr = 1048\ H^{1.547}$
Where: H = head in meters

Table 15-13			Table 15-13 (Continued)		
Head (meters)	l/s	m³/hr	Head (meters)	l/s	m³/hr
0.005	0.0802	0.2888	0.075	5.294	19.06
0.010	0.2344	0.8440	0.080	5.850	21.06
0.015	0.4390	1.580	0.085	6.425	23.13
0.020	0.6851	2.466	0.090	7.019	25.27
0.025	0.9675	3.483	0.095	7.631	27.47
0.030	1.283	4.618	0.100	8.261	29.74
0.035	1.628	5.862	0.105	8.909	32.07
0.040	2.002	7.207	0.110	9.574	34.47
0.045	2.402	8.647	0.115	10.26	36.92
0.050	2.827	10.18	0.120	10.95	39.43
0.055	3.276	11.80	0.125	11.67	42.00
0.060	3.748	13.49	0.130	12.40	44.63
0.065	4.242	15.27	0.135	13.14	47.31
0.070	4.758	17.13			

Table 15-14:
0.254 m Leopold-Lagco Flume Discharge Table
with Head in Meters

Formula: $l/s = 360.0\ H^{1.547}$
$m^3/hr = 1296\ H^{1.547}$
Where: H = head in meters

Table 15-14			Table 15-14 (Continued)		
Head (meters)	l/s	m³/hr	Head (meters)	l/s	m³/hr
0.005	0.0992	0.3572	0.100	10.22	36.78
0.010	0.2899	1.044	0.105	11.02	39.66
0.015	0.5429	1.954	0.110	11.84	42.62
0.020	0.8472	3.050	0.115	12.68	45.66
0.025	1.197	4.307	0.120	13.55	48.76
0.030	1.586	5.711	0.125	14.43	51.94
0.035	2.014	7.249	0.130	15.33	55.19
0.040	2.476	8.912	0.135	16.25	58.51
0.045	2.970	10.69	0.140	17.19	61.90
0.050	3.496	12.59	0.145	18.15	65.35
0.055	4.052	14.59	0.150	19.13	68.87
0.060	4.636	16.69	0.155	20.13	72.45
0.065	5.247	18.89	0.160	21.14	76.10
0.070	5.884	21.18	0.165	22.17	79.81
0.075	6.547	23.57	0.170	23.22	83.58
0.080	7.234	26.04	0.175	24.28	87.41
0.085	7.945	28.60	0.180	25.36	91.31
0.090	8.680	31.25	0.185	26.46	95.26
0.095	9.437	33.97			

15

Table 15-15:
0.305 m Leopold-Lagco Flume Discharge Table
with Head in Meters

Formula: $l/s = 428.3 \ H^{1.547}$
$m^3/hr = 1542 \ H^{1.547}$
Where: H = head in meters

Table 15-15			Table 15-15 (Continued)		
Head (meters)	l/s	m³/hr	Head (meters)	l/s	m³/hr
0.005	0.1180	0.4250	0.115	15.09	54.32
0.010	0.3449	1.242	0.120	16.12	58.02
0.015	0.6459	2.325	0.125	17.17	61.80
0.020	1.008	3.629	0.130	18.24	65.67
0.025	1.424	5.125	0.135	19.34	69.62
0.030	1.887	6.795	0.140	20.46	73.65
0.035	2.396	8.625	0.145	21.60	77.75
0.040	2.945	10.60	0.150	22.76	81.94
0.045	3.534	12.72	0.155	23.94	86.20
0.050	4.160	14.98	0.160	25.15	90.54
0.055	4.820	17.36	0.165	26.38	94.96
0.060	5.515	19.86	0.170	27.62	99.45
0.065	6.242	22.47	0.175	28.89	104.0
0.070	7.000	25.20	0.180	30.18	108.6
0.075	7.789	28.04	0.185	31.48	113.3
0.080	8.607	30.99	0.190	32.81	118.1
0.085	9.453	34.03	0.195	34.15	123.0
0.090	10.33	37.18	0.200	35.52	127.9
0.095	11.23	40.42	0.205	36.90	132.9
0.100	12.15	43.76	0.210	38.30	137.9
0.105	13.11	47.19	0.215	39.72	143.0
0.110	14.09	50.71			

15

Table 15-16:
0.381 m Leopold-Lagco Flume Discharge Table
with Head in Meters

Formula: l/s = 529.8 H$^{1.547}$
           m^3/hr = 1907 H$^{1.547}$
Where: H = head in meters

Table 15-16			Table 15-16 (Continued)		
Head (meters)	l/s	m^3/hr	Head (meters)	l/s	m^3/hr
0.005	0.1460	0.5256	0.145	26.71	96.16
0.010	0.4267	1.536	0.150	28.15	101.3
0.015	0.7990	2.876	0.155	29.62	106.6
0.020	1.247	4.488	0.160	31.11	112.0
0.025	1.761	6.338	0.165	32.63	117.4
0.030	2.335	8.403	0.170	34.17	123.0
0.035	2.963	10.67	0.175	35.73	128.6
0.040	3.643	13.11	0.180	37.33	134.4
0.045	4.372	15.74	0.185	38.94	140.2
0.050	5.145	18.52	0.190	40.58	146.1
0.055	5.963	21.46	0.195	42.25	152.1
0.060	6.822	24.56	0.200	43.93	158.1
0.065	7.721	27.79	0.205	45.65	164.3
0.070	8.659	31.17	0.210	47.38	170.5
0.075	9.635	34.68	0.215	49.14	176.9
0.080	10.65	38.32	0.220	50.91	183.3
0.085	11.69	42.09	0.225	52.72	189.7
0.090	12.77	45.98	0.230	54.54	196.3
0.095	13.89	49.99	0.235	56.38	203.0
0.100	15.04	54.12	0.240	58.25	209.7
0.105	16.21	58.36	0.245	60.14	216.5
0.110	17.42	62.72	0.250	62.05	223.3
0.115	18.66	67.18	0.255	63.98	230.3
0.120	19.93	71.75	0.260	65.93	237.3
0.125	21.23	76.43	0.265	67.90	244.4
0.130	22.56	81.21	0.270	69.89	251.6
0.135	23.92	86.09	0.275	71.91	258.8
0.140	25.30	91.08			

15

Table 15-17:
0.457 m Leopold-Lagco Flume Discharge Table
with Head in Meters

Formula: $l/s = 630.4\ H^{1.547}$
$m^3/hr = 2269\ H^{1.547}$
Where: H = head in meters

Head (meters)	l/s	m³/hr	Head (meters)	l/s	m³/hr
0.005	0.1737	0.6254	0.165	38.82	139.7
0.010	0.5077	1.827	0.170	40.66	146.3
0.015	0.9507	3.422	0.175	42.52	153.0
0.020	1.484	5.340	0.180	44.41	159.9
0.025	2.095	7.541	0.185	46.34	166.8
0.030	2.778	9.999	0.190	48.29	173.8
0.035	3.526	12.69	0.195	50.27	180.9
0.040	4.335	15.60	0.200	52.28	188.2
0.045	5.202	18.72	0.205	54.31	195.5
0.050	6.122	22.04	0.210	56.38	202.9
0.055	7.095	25.54	0.215	58.47	210.4
0.060	8.117	29.22	0.220	60.58	218.1
0.065	9.187	33.07	0.225	62.73	225.8
0.070	10.30	37.09	0.230	64.89	233.6
0.075	11.46	41.26	0.235	67.09	241.5
0.080	12.67	45.59	0.240	69.31	249.5
0.085	13.91	50.08	0.245	71.56	257.6
0.090	15.20	54.71	0.250	73.83	265.7
0.095	16.53	59.48	0.255	76.13	274.0
0.100	17.89	64.39	0.260	78.45	282.4
0.105	19.29	69.44	0.265	80.79	290.8
0.110	20.73	74.62	0.270	83.16	299.3
0.115	22.21	79.93	0.275	85.56	308.0
0.120	23.72	85.37	0.280	87.98	316.7
0.125	25.27	90.94	0.285	90.42	325.4
0.130	26.85	96.63	0.290	92.89	334.3
0.135	28.46	102.4	0.295	95.37	343.3
0.140	30.11	108.4	0.300	97.89	352.3
0.145	31.79	114.4	0.305	100.4	361.4
0.150	33.50	120.6	0.310	103.0	370.7
0.155	35.24	126.8	0.315	105.6	379.9
0.160	37.02	133.2	0.320	108.2	389.3

15

Table 15-18:
0.533 m Leopold-Lagco Flume Discharge Table
with Head in Meters

Formula: l/s = 730.1 $H^{1.547}$
m^3/hr = 2628 $H^{1.547}$

Where: H = head in meters

Table 15-18			Table 15-18 (Continued)		
Head (meters)	l/s	m^3/hr	Head (meters)	l/s	m^3/hr
0.005	0.2012	0.7243	0.195	58.22	209.6
0.010	0.5880	2.117	0.200	60.54	217.9
0.015	1.101	3.963	0.205	62.90	226.4
0.020	1.718	6.185	0.210	65.29	235.0
0.025	2.427	8.735	0.215	67.71	243.7
0.030	3.217	11.58	0.220	70.16	252.6
0.035	4.084	14.70	0.225	72.65	261.5
0.040	5.021	18.07	0.230	75.16	270.5
0.045	6.024	21.68	0.235	77.70	279.7
0.050	7.091	25.52	0.240	80.27	288.9
0.055	8.217	29.58	0.245	82.87	298.3
0.060	9.401	33.84	0.250	85.51	307.8
0.065	10.64	38.30	0.255	88.17	317.4
0.070	11.93	42.95	0.260	90.85	327.0
0.075	13.28	47.79	0.265	93.57	336.8
0.080	14.67	52.81	0.270	96.32	346.7
0.085	16.11	58.00	0.275	99.09	356.7
0.090	17.60	63.36	0.280	101.9	366.8
0.095	19.14	68.89	0.285	104.7	376.9
0.100	20.72	74.58	0.290	107.6	387.2
0.105	22.34	80.43	0.295	110.5	397.6
0.110	24.01	86.43	0.300	113.4	408.1
0.115	25.72	92.58	0.305	116.3	418.6
0.120	27.47	98.88	0.310	119.3	429.3
0.125	29.26	105.3	0.315	122.3	440.1
0.130	31.09	111.9	0.320	125.3	450.9
0.135	32.96	118.6	0.325	128.3	461.9
0.140	34.87	125.5	0.330	131.4	472.9
0.145	36.81	132.5	0.335	134.5	484.0
0.150	38.80	139.6	0.340	137.6	495.2
0.155	40.82	146.9	0.345	140.7	506.6
0.160	42.87	154.3	0.350	143.9	518.0
0.165	44.96	161.8	0.355	147.1	529.5
0.170	47.09	169.5	0.360	150.3	541.0
0.175	49.25	177.3	0.365	153.5	552.7
0.180	51.44	185.2	0.370	156.8	564.5
0.185	53.67	193.2	0.375	160.1	576.3
0.190	55.93	201.3	0.380	163.4	588.2

15

Table 15-19:
0.610 m Leopold-Lagco Flume Discharge Table
with Head in Meters

Formula: $l/s = 829.2\ H^{1.547}$
$m^3/hr = 2985\ H^{1.547}$

Where: H = head in meters

Table 15-19			Table 15-19 (Continued)		
Head (meters)	l/s	m³/hr	Head (meters)	l/s	m³/hr
0.005	0.2285	0.8227	0.220	79.69	286.9
0.010	0.6678	2.404	0.225	82.51	297.0
0.015	1.250	4.502	0.230	85.36	307.3
0.020	1.951	7.025	0.235	88.25	317.7
0.025	2.756	9.921	0.240	91.17	328.2
0.030	3.654	13.15	0.245	94.12	338.8
0.035	4.638	16.70	0.250	97.11	349.6
0.040	5.702	20.53	0.255	100.1	360.5
0.045	6.842	24.63	0.260	103.2	371.5
0.050	8.053	28.99	0.265	106.3	382.6
0.055	9.333	33.60	0.270	109.4	393.8
0.060	10.68	38.44	0.275	112.5	405.1
0.065	12.08	43.50	0.280	115.7	416.6
0.070	13.55	48.79	0.285	118.9	428.1
0.075	15.08	54.28	0.290	122.2	439.8
0.080	16.66	59.98	0.295	125.5	451.6
0.085	18.30	65.88	0.300	128.8	463.5
0.090	19.99	71.97	0.305	132.1	475.5
0.095	21.74	78.25	0.310	135.5	487.6
0.100	23.53	84.71	0.315	138.8	499.8
0.105	25.38	91.35	0.320	142.3	512.2
0.110	27.27	98.17	0.325	145.7	524.6
0.115	29.21	105.2	0.330	149.2	537.1
0.120	31.20	112.3	0.335	152.7	549.8
0.125	33.23	119.6	0.340	156.3	562.5
0.130	35.31	127.1	0.345	159.8	575.4
0.135	37.44	134.8	0.350	163.4	588.3
0.140	39.60	142.6	0.355	167.1	601.4
0.145	41.81	150.5	0.360	170.7	614.5
0.150	44.06	158.6	0.365	174.4	627.8
0.155	46.36	166.9	0.370	178.1	641.1
0.160	48.69	175.3	0.375	181.8	654.6
0.165	51.06	183.8	0.380	185.6	668.1
0.170	53.48	192.5	0.385	189.4	681.8
0.175	55.93	201.3	0.390	193.2	695.5
0.180	58.42	210.3	0.395	197.1	709.4
0.185	60.95	219.4	0.400	200.9	723.3
0.190	63.52	228.7	0.405	204.8	737.4
0.195	66.12	238.0	0.410	208.8	751.5
0.200	68.76	247.5	0.415	212.7	765.7
0.205	71.44	257.2	0.420	216.7	780.0
0.210	74.15	266.9	0.425	220.7	794.4
0.215	76.90	276.8			

15

Table 15-20:
0.762 m Leopold-Lagco Flume Discharge Table
with Head in Meters

Formula: l/s = 1026 H$^{1.547}$
          m^3/hr = 3692 H$^{1.547}$
Where: H = head in meters

Table 15-20			Table 15-20 (Continued)		
Head (meters)	l/s	m^3/hr	Head (meters)	l/s	m^3/hr
0.005	0.2828	1.018	0.230	105.6	380.1
0.010	0.8263	2.973	0.235	109.2	392.9
0.015	1.547	5.568	0.240	112.8	405.9
0.020	2.415	8.689	0.245	116.5	419.1
0.025	3.410	12.27	0.250	120.2	432.4
0.030	4.521	16.27	0.255	123.9	445.8
0.035	5.739	20.65	0.260	127.7	459.4
0.040	7.056	25.39	0.265	131.5	473.2
0.045	8.466	30.46	0.270	135.4	487.1
0.050	9.964	35.86	0.275	139.2	501.1
0.055	11.55	41.55	0.280	143.2	515.2
0.060	13.21	47.54	0.285	147.2	529.5
0.065	14.95	53.81	0.290	151.2	544.0
0.070	16.77	60.34	0.295	155.2	558.6
0.075	18.66	67.14	0.300	159.3	573.3
0.080	20.62	74.19	0.305	163.4	588.1
0.085	22.64	81.48	0.310	167.6	603.1
0.090	24.74	89.02	0.315	171.8	618.2
0.095	26.90	96.78	0.320	176.0	633.5
0.100	29.12	104.8	0.325	180.3	648.9
0.105	31.40	113.0	0.330	184.6	664.4
0.110	33.74	121.4	0.335	189.0	680.0
0.115	36.14	130.1	0.340	193.4	695.8
0.120	38.60	138.9	0.345	197.8	711.7
0.125	41.12	148.0	0.350	202.2	727.7
0.130	43.69	157.2	0.355	206.7	743.8
0.135	46.32	166.7	0.360	211.2	760.1
0.140	49.00	176.3	0.365	215.8	776.5
0.145	51.73	186.2	0.370	220.4	793.0
0.150	54.52	196.2	0.375	225.0	809.6
0.155	57.36	206.4	0.380	229.7	826.4
0.160	60.24	216.8	0.385	234.3	843.3
0.165	63.18	227.4	0.390	239.1	860.3
0.170	66.17	238.1	0.395	243.8	877.4
0.175	69.20	249.0	0.400	248.6	894.6
0.180	72.29	260.1	0.405	253.4	912.0
0.185	75.42	271.4	0.410	258.3	929.5
0.190	78.59	282.8	0.415	263.2	947.1
0.195	81.81	294.4	0.420	268.1	964.8
0.200	85.08	306.2	0.425	273.1	982.6
0.205	88.40	318.1	0.430	278.1	1001
0.210	91.75	330.2	0.435	283.1	1019
0.215	95.15	342.4	0.440	288.1	1037
0.220	98.60	354.8	0.445	293.2	1055
0.225	102.1	367.4	0.450	298.3	1073

15

Table 15-20 (Continued)		
Head (meters)	l/s	m³/hr
0.455	303.5	1092
0.460	308.6	1111
0.465	313.8	1129
0.470	319.1	1148
0.475	324.3	1167
0.480	329.6	1186
0.485	335.0	1205
0.490	340.3	1225
0.495	345.7	1244

Table 15-20 (Continued)		
Head (meters)	l/s	m³/hr
0.500	351.1	1263
0.505	356.6	1283
0.510	362.0	1303
0.515	367.5	1323
0.520	373.1	1343
0.525	378.6	1363
0.530	384.2	1383
0.535	389.9	1403

15

15

CHAPTER
16
HS, H, and HL Flume Discharge Tables

Overview

This chapter contains discharge (head vs. flow rate) tables for HS, H, and HL Flumes. Note that all of the tabular data is for free flow.

Discharge tables for HS, H, and HL flumes with head in feet

16-1: 0.4 ft. HS	16-6: 0.75 ft. H	16-11: 3.0 ft. H
16-2: 0.6 ft. HS	16-7: 1.0 ft. H	16-12: 4.5 ft. H
16-3: 0.8 ft. HS	16-8: 1.5 ft. H	16-13: 4.0 ft. HL
16-4: 1.0 ft. HS	16-9: 2.0 ft. H	
16-5: 0.5 ft. H	16-10: 2.5 ft. H	

The discharges of the flumes are listed in three different units of measure:

CFS - cubic feet per second   GPM - gallons per minute
MGD - million gallons per day

Discharge tables for HS, H, and HL Flumes with head in meters

16-14: 0.122 m HS	16-19: 0.229 m H	16-24: 0.914 m H
16-15: 0.183 m HS	16-20: 0.305 m H	16-25: 1.37 m H
16-16: 0.244 m HS	16-21: 0.457 m H	16-26: 1.22 m HL
16-17: 0.305 m HS	16-22: 0.610 m H	
16-18: 0.152 m H	16-23: 0.762 m H	

The discharges of the flumes are listed in two different units of measure:

l/s - liters per second m^3/hr - cubic meters per hour

The source of data used to develop each table is the U.S.D.A. Handbook No. 224. The formulas in the H Flume tables are approximation formulas which fit data within 1% of full scale.

Table 16-1:
0.4 ft. HS Flume Discharge Table with Head in Feet

Source: U.S.D.A. Handbook No. 224

Table 16-1				Table 16-1 (Continued)			
Head (feet)	CFS	GPM	MGD	Head (feet)	CFS	GPM	MGD
0.01				0.21	0.0200	8.976	0.0129
0.02	0.0002	0.0718	0.0001	0.22	0.0221	9.918	0.0143
0.03	0.0004	0.1661	0.0002	0.23	0.0244	10.95	0.0158
0.04	0.0006	0.2872	0.0004	0.24	0.0268	12.03	0.0173
0.05	0.0010	0.4398	0.0006	0.25	0.0293	13.15	0.0189
0.06	0.0014	0.6328	0.0009	0.26	0.0320	14.36	0.0207
0.07	0.0019	0.8707	0.0013	0.27	0.0348	15.62	0.0225
0.08	0.0026	1.158	0.0017	0.28	0.0378	16.96	0.0244
0.09	0.0033	1.490	0.0021	0.29	0.0409	18.36	0.0264
0.10	0.0042	1.871	0.0027	0.30	0.0441	19.79	0.0285
0.11	0.0051	2.284	0.0033	0.31	0.0475	21.32	0.0307
0.12	0.0061	2.729	0.0039	0.32	0.0511	22.93	0.0330
0.13	0.0072	3.218	0.0046	0.33	0.0548	24.59	0.0354
0.14	0.0084	3.756	0.0054	0.34	0.0586	26.30	0.0379
0.15	0.0097	4.344	0.0063	0.35	0.0626	28.09	0.0405
0.16	0.0111	4.982	0.0072	0.36	0.0668	29.98	0.0432
0.17	0.0126	5.655	0.0081	0.37	0.0711	31.91	0.0460
0.18	0.0143	6.418	0.0092	0.38	0.0756	33.93	0.0489
0.19	0.0161	7.226	0.0104	0.39	0.0803	36.04	0.0519
0.20	0.0179	8.034	0.0116	0.40	0.0850	38.15	0.0549

16

Table 16-2:
0.6 ft. HS Flume Discharge Table with Head in Feet

Source: U.S.D.A. Handbook No. 224

Table 16-2				Table 16-2 (Continued)			
Head (feet)	CFS	GPM	MGD	Head (feet)	CFS	GPM	MGD
0.01				0.31	0.0524	23.52	0.0339
0.02	0.0002	0.1032	0.0001	0.32	0.0562	25.22	0.0363
0.03	0.0005	0.2379	0.0003	0.33	0.0601	26.97	0.0388
0.04	0.0009	0.4084	0.0006	0.34	0.0641	28.77	0.0414
0.05	0.0014	0.6193	0.0009	0.35	0.0683	30.65	0.0441
0.06	0.0019	0.8662	0.0012	0.36	0.0727	32.63	0.0470
0.07	0.0026	1.162	0.0017	0.37	0.0772	34.65	0.0499
0.08	0.0034	1.503	0.0022	0.38	0.0819	36.76	0.0529
0.09	0.0042	1.889	0.0027	0.39	0.0868	38.96	0.0561
0.10	0.0052	2.320	0.0033	0.40	0.0918	41.20	0.0593
0.11	0.0063	2.805	0.0040	0.41	0.0970	43.53	0.0627
0.12	0.0074	3.330	0.0048	0.42	0.1020	45.78	0.0659
0.13	0.0087	3.891	0.0056	0.43	0.1080	48.47	0.0698
0.14	0.0100	4.488	0.0065	0.44	0.1140	51.16	0.0737
0.15	0.0115	5.161	0.0074	0.45	0.1200	53.86	0.0776
0.16	0.0131	5.879	0.0085	0.46	0.1260	56.55	0.0814
0.17	0.0148	6.642	0.0096	0.47	0.1320	59.24	0.0853
0.18	0.0166	7.450	0.0107	0.48	0.1380	61.93	0.0892
0.19	0.0186	8.348	0.0120	0.49	0.1450	65.08	0.0937
0.20	0.0207	9.290	0.0134	0.50	0.1520	68.22	0.0982
0.21	0.0229	10.28	0.0148	0.51	0.1590	71.36	0.1028
0.22	0.0252	11.31	0.0163	0.52	0.1660	74.50	0.1073
0.23	0.0277	12.43	0.0179	0.53	0.1730	77.64	0.1118
0.24	0.0303	13.60	0.0196	0.54	0.1810	81.23	0.1170
0.25	0.0330	14.81	0.0213	0.55	0.1880	84.37	0.1215
0.26	0.0359	16.11	0.0232	0.56	0.1960	87.96	0.1267
0.27	0.0389	17.46	0.0251	0.57	0.2050	92.00	0.1325
0.28	0.0421	18.89	0.0272	0.58	0.2130	95.59	0.1377
0.29	0.0454	20.38	0.0293	0.59	0.2210	99.18	0.1428
0.30	0.0489	21.95	0.0316	0.60	0.2290	102.8	0.1480

16

Table 16-3:
0.8 ft. HS Flume Discharge Table with Head in Feet

Source: U.S.D.A. Handbook No. 224

Head (feet)	CFS	GPM	MGD	Head (feet)	CFS	GPM	MGD
0.01				0.41	0.1060	47.57	0.0685
0.02	0.0003	0.1346	0.0002	0.42	0.1110	49.82	0.0717
0.03	0.0007	0.3052	0.0004	0.43	0.1170	52.51	0.0756
0.04	0.0012	0.5206	0.0007	0.44	0.1230	55.20	0.0795
0.05	0.0017	0.7809	0.0011	0.45	0.1290	57.90	0.0834
0.06	0.0024	1.086	0.0016	0.46	0.1360	61.04	0.0879
0.07	0.0032	1.445	0.0021	0.47	0.1420	63.73	0.0918
0.08	0.0041	1.849	0.0027	0.48	0.1490	66.87	0.0963
0.09	0.0051	2.302	0.0033	0.49	0.1560	70.01	0.1008
0.10	0.0063	2.805	0.0040	0.50	0.1630	73.15	0.1053
0.11	0.0075	3.366	0.0048	0.51	0.1700	76.30	0.1099
0.12	0.0088	3.967	0.0057	0.52	0.1780	79.89	0.1150
0.13	0.0103	4.623	0.0067	0.53	0.1860	83.48	0.1202
0.14	0.0118	5.296	0.0076	0.54	0.1930	86.62	0.1247
0.15	0.0135	6.059	0.0087	0.55	0.2020	90.66	0.1306
0.16	0.0153	6.867	0.0099	0.56	0.2100	94.25	0.1357
0.17	0.0172	7.719	0.0111	0.57	0.2180	97.84	0.1409
0.18	0.0193	8.662	0.0125	0.58	0.2270	101.9	0.1467
0.19	0.0214	9.604	0.0138	0.59	0.2360	105.9	0.1525
0.20	0.0237	10.64	0.0153	0.60	0.2450	110.0	0.1583
0.21	0.0262	11.76	0.0169	0.61	0.2540	114.0	0.1642
0.22	0.0287	12.88	0.0185	0.62	0.2640	118.5	0.1706
0.23	0.0314	14.09	0.0203	0.63	0.2730	122.5	0.1764
0.24	0.0343	15.39	0.0222	0.64	0.2830	127.0	0.1829
0.25	0.0373	16.74	0.0241	0.65	0.2930	131.5	0.1894
0.26	0.0404	18.13	0.0261	0.66	0.3030	136.0	0.1958
0.27	0.0437	19.61	0.0282	0.67	0.3140	140.9	0.2029
0.28	0.0471	21.14	0.0304	0.68	0.3250	145.9	0.2100
0.29	0.0506	22.71	0.0327	0.69	0.3360	150.8	0.2172
0.30	0.0543	24.37	0.0351	0.70	0.3470	155.7	0.2243
0.31	0.0582	26.12	0.0376	0.71	0.3580	160.7	0.2314
0.32	0.0622	27.92	0.0402	0.72	0.3700	166.1	0.2391
0.33	0.0664	29.80	0.0429	0.73	0.3810	171.0	0.2462
0.34	0.0708	31.78	0.0458	0.74	0.3930	176.4	0.2540
0.35	0.0752	33.75	0.0486	0.75	0.4060	182.2	0.2624
0.36	0.0799	35.86	0.0516	0.76	0.4180	187.6	0.2702
0.37	0.0847	38.01	0.0547	0.77	0.4310	193.4	0.2786
0.38	0.0897	40.26	0.0580	0.78	0.4440	199.3	0.2870
0.39	0.0949	42.59	0.0613	0.79	0.4570	205.1	0.2954
0.40	0.1000	44.88	0.0646	0.80	0.4700	210.9	0.3038

16

Table 16-4:
1.0 ft. HS Flume Discharge Table with Head in Feet

Source: U.S.D.A. Handbook No. 224

Table 16-4				Table 16-4 (Continued)			
Head (feet)	CFS	GPM	MGD	Head (feet)	CFS	GPM	MGD
0.01				0.51	0.1830	82.13	0.1183
0.02	0.0004	0.1661	0.0002	0.52	0.1910	85.72	0.1234
0.03	0.0008	0.3725	0.0005	0.53	0.1990	89.31	0.1286
0.04	0.0014	0.6328	0.0009	0.54	0.2080	93.35	0.1344
0.05	0.0021	0.9380	0.0014	0.55	0.2160	96.94	0.1396
0.06	0.0029	1.302	0.0019	0.56	0.2250	101.0	0.1454
0.07	0.0038	1.723	0.0025	0.57	0.2330	104.6	0.1506
0.08	0.0049	2.195	0.0032	0.58	0.2430	109.1	0.1571
0.09	0.0061	2.720	0.0039	0.59	0.2520	113.1	0.1629
0.10	0.0074	3.303	0.0048	0.60	0.2610	117.1	0.1687
0.11	0.0088	3.958	0.0057	0.61	0.2710	121.6	0.1751
0.12	0.0103	4.623	0.0067	0.62	0.2810	126.1	0.1816
0.13	0.0120	5.386	0.0078	0.63	0.2910	130.6	0.1881
0.14	0.0137	6.149	0.0089	0.64	0.3010	135.1	0.1945
0.15	0.0157	7.046	0.0101	0.65	0.3120	140.0	0.2018
0.16	0.0177	7.944	0.0114	0.66	0.3220	144.5	0.2081
0.17	0.0198	8.886	0.0128	0.67	0.3330	149.5	0.2152
0.18	0.0221	9.918	0.0143	0.68	0.3440	154.4	0.2223
0.19	0.0245	11.00	0.0158	0.69	0.3550	159.3	0.2294
0.20	0.0270	12.12	0.0175	0.70	0.3670	164.7	0.2372
0.21	0.0297	13.33	0.0192	0.71	0.3790	170.1	0.2449
0.22	0.0325	14.59	0.0210	0.72	0.3910	175.5	0.2527
0.23	0.0355	15.93	0.0229	0.73	0.4030	180.9	0.2605
0.24	0.0386	17.32	0.0249	0.74	0.4160	186.7	0.2689
0.25	0.0418	18.76	0.0270	0.75	0.4280	192.1	0.2766
0.26	0.0452	20.29	0.0292	0.76	0.4410	197.9	0.2850
0.27	0.0488	21.90	0.0315	0.77	0.4540	203.8	0.2934
0.28	0.0525	23.56	0.0339	0.78	0.4680	210.0	0.3025
0.29	0.0563	25.27	0.0364	0.79	0.4810	215.9	0.3109
0.30	0.0603	27.06	0.0390	0.80	0.4950	222.2	0.3199
0.31	0.0645	28.95	0.0417	0.81	0.5090	228.4	0.3290
0.32	0.0688	30.88	0.0445	0.82	0.5240	235.2	0.3387
0.33	0.0733	32.90	0.0474	0.83	0.5380	241.5	0.3477
0.34	0.0779	34.96	0.0503	0.84	0.5530	248.2	0.3574
0.35	0.0827	37.12	0.0534	0.85	0.5680	254.9	0.3671
0.36	0.0877	39.36	0.0567	0.86	0.5830	261.7	0.3768
0.37	0.0929	41.69	0.0600	0.87	0.5990	268.8	0.3871
0.38	0.0981	44.03	0.0634	0.88	0.6140	275.6	0.3968
0.39	0.1040	46.68	0.0672	0.89	0.6300	282.7	0.4072
0.40	0.1090	48.92	0.0704	0.90	0.6460	289.9	0.4175
0.41	0.1150	51.61	0.0743	0.91	0.6630	297.6	0.4285
0.42	0.1210	54.30	0.0782	0.92	0.6800	305.2	0.4395
0.43	0.1270	57.00	0.0821	0.93	0.6970	312.8	0.4505
0.44	0.1340	60.14	0.0866	0.94	0.7140	320.4	0.4615
0.45	0.1400	62.83	0.0905	0.95	0.7310	328.1	0.4724
0.46	0.1470	65.97	0.0950	0.96	0.7490	336.2	0.4841
0.47	0.1540	69.12	0.0995	0.97	0.7670	344.2	0.4957
0.48	0.1610	72.26	0.1041	0.98	0.7850	352.3	0.5073
0.49	0.1680	75.40	0.1086	0.99	0.8030	360.4	0.5190
0.50	0.1760	78.99	0.1137	1.00	0.8210	368.5	0.5306

16

Table 16-5:
0.5 ft. H Flume Discharge Table with Head in Feet

Formula: CFS $= 1.71\ H^{2.31}$
GPM $= 767.4\ H^{2.31}$
MGD $= 1.12\ H^{2.31}$

Where: H = head in feet

Table 16-5				Table 16-5 (Continued)			
Head (feet)	CFS	GPM	MGD	Head (feet)	CFS	GPM	MGD
0.01				0.26	0.0767	34.42	0.0496
0.02	0.0004	0.1795	0.0003	0.27	0.0834	37.43	0.0539
0.03	0.0009	0.4039	0.0006	0.28	0.0905	40.62	0.0585
0.04	0.0016	0.7181	0.0010	0.29	0.0979	43.94	0.0633
0.05	0.0024	1.077	0.0016	0.30	0.1057	47.44	0.0683
0.06	0.0035	1.571	0.0023	0.31	0.1139	51.12	0.0736
0.07	0.0047	2.109	0.0030	0.32	0.1224	54.93	0.0791
0.08	0.0063	2.827	0.0041	0.33	0.1314	58.97	0.0849
0.09	0.0080	3.590	0.0052	0.34	0.1407	63.15	0.0909
0.10	0.0101	4.533	0.0065	0.35	0.1505	67.54	0.0973
0.11	0.0122	5.475	0.0079	0.36	0.1607	72.12	0.1039
0.12	0.0146	6.552	0.0094	0.37	0.1713	76.88	0.1107
0.13	0.0173	7.764	0.0112	0.38	0.1823	81.82	0.1178
0.14	0.0202	9.066	0.0131	0.39	0.1938	86.98	0.1253
0.15	0.0233	10.46	0.0151	0.40	0.2050	92.00	0.1325
0.16	0.0267	11.98	0.0173	0.41	0.2170	97.39	0.1402
0.17	0.0304	13.64	0.0196	0.42	0.2300	103.2	0.1486
0.18	0.0343	15.39	0.0222	0.43	0.2440	109.5	0.1577
0.19	0.0385	17.28	0.0249	0.44	0.2570	115.3	0.1661
0.20	0.0431	19.34	0.0279	0.45	0.2710	121.6	0.1751
0.21	0.0479	21.50	0.0310	0.46	0.2850	127.9	0.1842
0.22	0.0530	23.79	0.0343	0.47	0.3000	134.6	0.1939
0.23	0.0585	26.25	0.0378	0.48	0.3150	141.4	0.2036
0.24	0.0643	28.86	0.0416	0.49	0.3310	148.6	0.2139
0.25	0.0704	31.60	0.0455	0.50	0.3470	155.7	0.2243

16

Table 16-6:
0.75 ft. H Flume Discharge Table with Head in Feet

Formula: CFS $= 1.85\,H^{2.31}$
GPM $= 830.3\,H^{2.31}$
MGD $= 1.196\,H^{2.31}$

Where: H = head in feet

Table 16-6				Table 16-6 (Continued)			
Head (feet)	CFS	GPM	MGD	Head (feet)	CFS	GPM	MGD
0.01				0.39	0.2110	94.70	0.1364
0.02	0.0006	0.2693	0.0004	0.40	0.2240	100.5	0.1448
0.03	0.0013	0.5834	0.0008	0.41	0.2370	106.4	0.1532
0.04	0.0022	0.9874	0.0014	0.42	0.2500	112.2	0.1616
0.05	0.0032	1.436	0.0021	0.43	0.2630	118.0	0.1700
0.06	0.0046	2.064	0.0030	0.44	0.2770	124.3	0.1790
0.07	0.0061	2.738	0.0039	0.45	0.2910	130.6	0.1881
0.08	0.0080	3.590	0.0052	0.46	0.3060	137.3	0.1978
0.09	0.0101	4.533	0.0065	0.47	0.3210	144.1	0.2075
0.10	0.0126	5.655	0.0081	0.48	0.3370	151.2	0.2178
0.11	0.0151	6.777	0.0098	0.49	0.3530	158.4	0.2281
0.12	0.0179	8.034	0.0116	0.50	0.3700	166.1	0.2391
0.13	0.0210	9.425	0.0136	0.51	0.3880	174.1	0.2508
0.14	0.0242	10.86	0.0156	0.52	0.4060	182.2	0.2624
0.15	0.0278	12.48	0.0180	0.53	0.4240	190.3	0.2740
0.16	0.0317	14.23	0.0205	0.54	0.4430	198.8	0.2863
0.17	0.0358	16.07	0.0231	0.55	0.4620	207.3	0.2986
0.18	0.0403	18.09	0.0260	0.56	0.4820	216.3	0.3115
0.19	0.0451	20.24	0.0291	0.57	0.5020	225.3	0.3244
0.20	0.0501	22.48	0.0324	0.58	0.5230	234.7	0.3380
0.21	0.0555	24.91	0.0359	0.59	0.5440	244.1	0.3516
0.22	0.0612	27.47	0.0396	0.60	0.5660	254.0	0.3658
0.23	0.0672	30.16	0.0434	0.61	0.5880	263.9	0.3800
0.24	0.0735	32.99	0.0475	0.62	0.6110	274.2	0.3949
0.25	0.0802	35.99	0.0518	0.63	0.6350	285.0	0.4104
0.26	0.0872	39.14	0.0564	0.64	0.6590	295.8	0.4259
0.27	0.0946	42.46	0.0611	0.65	0.6830	306.5	0.4414
0.28	0.1023	45.91	0.0661	0.66	0.7080	317.8	0.4576
0.29	0.1104	49.55	0.0714	0.67	0.7340	329.4	0.4744
0.30	0.1190	53.41	0.0769	0.68	0.7600	341.1	0.4912
0.31	0.1280	57.45	0.0827	0.69	0.7860	352.8	0.5080
0.32	0.1370	61.49	0.0885	0.70	0.8130	364.9	0.5254
0.33	0.1460	65.52	0.0944	0.71	0.8410	377.4	0.5435
0.34	0.1560	70.01	0.1008	0.72	0.8690	390.0	0.5616
0.35	0.1670	74.95	0.1079	0.73	0.8980	403.0	0.5804
0.36	0.1770	79.44	0.1144	0.74	0.9270	416.0	0.5991
0.37	0.1880	84.37	0.1215	0.75	0.9570	429.5	0.6185
0.38	0.1990	89.31	0.1286				

16

Table 16-7:
1.0 ft. H Flume Discharge Table with Head in Feet

Formula: $\text{CFS} = 1.95\ H^{2.31}$
$\text{GPM} = 875.2\ H^{2.31}$
$\text{MGD} = 1.26\ H^{2.31}$

Where: H = head in feet

Table 16-7				Table 16-7 (Continued)			
Head (feet)	CFS	GPM	MGD	Head (feet)	CFS	GPM	MGD
0.01				0.51	0.4160	186.7	0.2689
0.02	0.0007	0.3142	0.0005	0.52	0.4340	194.8	0.2805
0.03	0.0017	0.7630	0.0011	0.53	0.4530	203.3	0.2928
0.04	0.0027	1.212	0.0017	0.54	0.4720	211.8	0.3051
0.05	0.0040	1.795	0.0026	0.55	0.4920	220.8	0.3180
0.06	0.0056	2.513	0.0036	0.56	0.5120	229.8	0.3309
0.07	0.0075	3.366	0.0048	0.57	0.5330	239.2	0.3445
0.08	0.0097	4.353	0.0063	0.58	0.5540	248.6	0.3581
0.09	0.0122	5.475	0.0079	0.59	0.5760	258.5	0.3723
0.10	0.0150	6.732	0.0097	0.60	0.5980	268.4	0.3865
0.11	0.0179	8.034	0.0116	0.61	0.6210	278.7	0.4014
0.12	0.0211	9.470	0.0136	0.62	0.6440	289.0	0.4162
0.13	0.0246	11.04	0.0159	0.63	0.6680	299.8	0.4317
0.14	0.0284	12.75	0.0184	0.64	0.6920	310.6	0.4472
0.15	0.0324	14.54	0.0209	0.65	0.7170	321.8	0.4634
0.16	0.0367	16.47	0.0237	0.66	0.7430	333.5	0.4802
0.17	0.0413	18.54	0.0267	0.67	0.7690	345.1	0.4970
0.18	0.0462	20.73	0.0299	0.68	0.7960	357.2	0.5145
0.19	0.0515	23.11	0.0333	0.69	0.8230	369.4	0.5319
0.20	0.0571	25.63	0.0369	0.70	0.8510	381.9	0.5500
0.21	0.0630	28.27	0.0407	0.71	0.8800	394.9	0.5687
0.22	0.0692	31.06	0.0447	0.72	0.9090	408.0	0.5875
0.23	0.0758	34.02	0.0490	0.73	0.9390	421.4	0.6069
0.24	0.0827	37.12	0.0534	0.74	0.9690	434.9	0.6263
0.25	0.0900	40.39	0.0582	0.75	1.000	448.8	0.6463
0.26	0.0976	43.80	0.0631	0.76	1.031	462.7	0.6663
0.27	0.1055	47.35	0.0682	0.77	1.063	477.1	0.6870
0.28	0.1138	51.07	0.0735	0.78	1.096	491.9	0.7083
0.29	0.1226	55.02	0.0792	0.79	1.129	506.7	0.7297
0.30	0.1320	59.24	0.0853	0.80	1.160	520.6	0.7497
0.31	0.1410	63.28	0.0911	0.81	1.200	538.6	0.7756
0.32	0.1510	67.77	0.0976	0.82	1.230	552.0	0.7949
0.33	0.1610	72.26	0.1041	0.83	1.270	570.0	0.8208
0.34	0.1720	77.19	0.1112	0.84	1.300	583.4	0.8402
0.35	0.1830	82.13	0.1183	0.85	1.340	601.4	0.8660
0.36	0.1940	87.07	0.1254	0.86	1.380	619.3	0.8919
0.37	0.2060	92.45	0.1331	0.87	1.410	632.8	0.9113
0.38	0.2180	97.84	0.1409	0.88	1.450	650.8	0.9371
0.39	0.2310	103.7	0.1493	0.89	1.490	668.7	0.9630
0.40	0.2440	109.5	0.1577	0.90	1.530	686.7	0.9888
0.41	0.2570	115.3	0.1661	0.91	1.570	704.6	1.015
0.42	0.2710	121.6	0.1751	0.92	1.610	722.6	1.041
0.43	0.2850	127.9	0.1842	0.93	1.660	745.0	1.073
0.44	0.3000	134.6	0.1939	0.94	1.700	763.0	1.099
0.45	0.3150	141.4	0.2036	0.95	1.740	780.9	1.125
0.46	0.3310	148.6	0.2139	0.96	1.780	798.9	1.150
0.47	0.3470	155.7	0.2243	0.97	1.830	821.3	1.183
0.48	0.3640	163.4	0.2353	0.98	1.870	839.3	1.209
0.49	0.3810	171.0	0.2462	0.99	1.920	861.7	1.241
0.50	0.3980	178.6	0.2572	1.00	1.970	884.1	1.273

16

Table 16-8:
1.5 ft. H Flume Discharge Table with Head in Feet

Formula: CFS $= 2.11\ H^{2.31}$
GPM $= 947\ H^{2.31}$
MGD $= 1.36\ H^{2.31}$

Where: H = head in feet

Table 16-8				Table 16-8 (Continued)			
Head (feet)	CFS	GPM	MGD	Head (feet)	CFS	GPM	MGD
0.01				0.51	0.4730	212.3	0.3057
0.02	0.0011	0.4937	0.0007	0.52	0.4930	221.3	0.3186
0.03	0.0023	1.032	0.0015	0.53	0.5140	230.7	0.3322
0.04	0.0039	1.750	0.0025	0.54	0.5350	240.1	0.3458
0.05	0.0057	2.558	0.0037	0.55	0.5570	250.0	0.3600
0.06	0.0078	3.501	0.0050	0.56	0.5790	259.9	0.3742
0.07	0.0103	4.623	0.0067	0.57	0.6010	269.7	0.3884
0.08	0.0131	5.879	0.0085	0.58	0.6240	280.1	0.4033
0.09	0.0164	7.360	0.0106	0.59	0.6480	290.8	0.4188
0.10	0.0200	8.976	0.0129	0.60	0.6720	301.6	0.4343
0.11	0.0237	10.64	0.0153	0.61	0.6970	312.8	0.4505
0.12	0.0276	12.39	0.0178	0.62	0.7220	324.0	0.4666
0.13	0.0319	14.32	0.0206	0.63	0.7470	335.3	0.4828
0.14	0.0365	16.38	0.0236	0.64	0.7730	346.9	0.4996
0.15	0.0414	18.58	0.0268	0.65	0.8000	359.0	0.5170
0.16	0.0467	20.96	0.0302	0.66	0.8270	371.2	0.5345
0.17	0.0523	23.47	0.0338	0.67	0.8550	383.7	0.5526
0.18	0.0582	26.12	0.0376	0.68	0.8830	396.3	0.5707
0.19	0.0645	28.95	0.0417	0.69	0.9120	409.3	0.5894
0.20	0.0711	31.91	0.0460	0.70	0.9420	422.8	0.6088
0.21	0.0780	35.01	0.0504	0.71	0.9720	436.2	0.6282
0.22	0.0854	38.33	0.0552	0.72	1.002	449.7	0.6476
0.23	0.0931	41.78	0.0602	0.73	1.033	463.6	0.6676
0.24	0.1011	45.37	0.0653	0.74	1.065	478.0	0.6883
0.25	0.1095	49.14	0.0708	0.75	1.097	492.3	0.7090
0.26	0.1183	53.09	0.0765	0.76	1.130	507.1	0.7303
0.27	0.1275	57.22	0.0824	0.77	1.163	522.0	0.7516
0.28	0.1371	61.53	0.0886	0.78	1.197	537.2	0.7736
0.29	0.1470	65.97	0.0950	0.79	1.231	552.5	0.7956
0.30	0.1570	70.46	0.1015	0.80	1.270	570.0	0.8208
0.31	0.1680	75.40	0.1086	0.81	1.300	583.4	0.8402
0.32	0.1790	80.34	0.1157	0.82	1.340	601.4	0.8660
0.33	0.1910	85.72	0.1234	0.83	1.380	619.3	0.8919
0.34	0.2030	91.11	0.1312	0.84	1.410	632.8	0.9113
0.35	0.2150	96.49	0.1390	0.85	1.450	650.8	0.9371
0.36	0.2280	102.3	0.1474	0.86	1.490	668.7	0.9630
0.37	0.2410	108.2	0.1558	0.87	1.530	686.7	0.9888
0.38	0.2550	114.4	0.1648	0.88	1.570	704.6	1.015
0.39	0.2690	120.7	0.1739	0.89	1.610	722.6	1.041
0.40	0.2830	127.0	0.1829	0.90	1.650	740.5	1.066
0.41	0.2980	133.7	0.1926	0.91	1.690	758.5	1.092
0.42	0.3140	140.9	0.2029	0.92	1.730	776.4	1.118
0.43	0.3300	148.1	0.2133	0.93	1.780	798.9	1.150
0.44	0.3460	155.3	0.2236	0.94	1.820	816.8	1.176
0.45	0.3630	162.9	0.2346	0.95	1.860	834.8	1.202
0.46	0.3800	170.5	0.2456	0.96	1.910	857.2	1.234
0.47	0.3980	178.6	0.2572	0.97	1.950	875.2	1.260
0.48	0.4160	186.7	0.2689	0.98	2.000	897.6	1.293
0.49	0.4350	195.2	0.2811	0.99	2.050	920.0	1.325
0.50	0.4540	203.8	0.2934	1.00	2.090	938.0	1.351

16

Table 16-8 (Continued)				Table 16-8 (Continued)			
Head (feet)	CFS	GPM	MGD	Head (feet)	CFS	GPM	MGD
1.01	2.140	960.4	1.383	1.26	3.590	1611	2.320
1.02	2.190	982.9	1.415	1.27	3.660	1643	2.365
1.03	2.240	1005	1.448	1.28	3.730	1674	2.411
1.04	2.300	1032	1.486	1.29	3.800	1705	2.456
1.05	2.350	1055	1.519	1.30	3.870	1737	2.501
1.06	2.400	1077	1.551	1.31	3.940	1768	2.546
1.07	2.450	1100	1.583	1.32	4.010	1800	2.592
1.08	2.500	1122	1.616	1.33	4.080	1831	2.637
1.09	2.560	1149	1.655	1.34	4.150	1863	2.682
1.10	2.610	1171	1.687	1.35	4.220	1894	2.727
1.11	2.670	1198	1.726	1.36	4.300	1930	2.779
1.12	2.730	1225	1.764	1.37	4.370	1961	2.824
1.13	2.780	1248	1.797	1.38	4.450	1997	2.876
1.14	2.840	1275	1.835	1.39	4.520	2029	2.921
1.15	2.900	1302	1.874	1.40	4.600	2064	2.973
1.16	2.960	1328	1.913	1.41	4.680	2100	3.025
1.17	3.020	1355	1.952	1.42	4.760	2136	3.076
1.18	3.080	1382	1.991	1.43	4.840	2172	3.128
1.19	3.140	1409	2.029	1.44	4.920	2208	3.180
1.20	3.200	1436	2.068	1.45	5.000	2244	3.232
1.21	3.270	1468	2.113	1.46	5.080	2280	3.283
1.22	3.330	1495	2.152	1.47	5.160	2316	3.335
1.23	3.390	1521	2.191	1.48	5.240	2352	3.387
1.24	3.460	1553	2.236	1.49	5.330	2392	3.445
1.25	3.520	1580	2.275	1.50	5.420	2432	3.503

16

Table 16-9:
2.0 ft. H Flume Discharge Table with Head in Feet

Formula: $CFS = 2.23\ H^{2.31}$
$GPM = 1000.8\ H^{2.31}$
$MGD = 1.44\ H^{2.31}$
Where: H = head in feet

Head (feet)	CFS	GPM	MGD	Head (feet)	CFS	GPM	MGD
0.01				0.51	0.5300	237.9	0.3425
0.02	0.0014	0.6283	0.0009	0.52	0.5520	247.7	0.3568
0.03	0.0031	1.391	0.0020	0.53	0.5740	257.6	0.3710
0.04	0.0050	2.244	0.0032	0.54	0.5970	267.9	0.3858
0.05	0.0073	3.276	0.0047	0.55	0.6200	278.3	0.4007
0.06	0.0100	4.488	0.0065	0.56	0.6440	289.0	0.4162
0.07	0.0130	5.834	0.0084	0.57	0.6680	299.8	0.4317
0.08	0.0166	7.450	0.0107	0.58	0.6930	311.0	0.4479
0.09	0.0205	9.200	0.0132	0.59	0.7190	322.7	0.4647
0.10	0.0248	11.13	0.0160	0.60	0.7450	334.4	0.4815
0.11	0.0293	13.15	0.0189	0.61	0.7710	346.0	0.4983
0.12	0.0341	15.30	0.0220	0.62	0.7980	358.1	0.5157
0.13	0.0392	17.59	0.0253	0.63	0.8260	370.7	0.5338
0.14	0.0447	20.06	0.0289	0.64	0.8540	383.3	0.5519
0.15	0.0505	22.66	0.0326	0.65	0.8820	395.8	0.5700
0.16	0.0567	25.45	0.0366	0.66	0.9110	408.9	0.5888
0.17	0.0632	28.36	0.0408	0.67	0.9410	422.3	0.6082
0.18	0.0701	31.46	0.0453	0.68	0.9710	435.8	0.6276
0.19	0.0774	34.74	0.0500	0.69	1.002	449.7	0.6476
0.20	0.0850	38.15	0.0549	0.70	1.030	462.3	0.6657
0.21	0.0930	41.74	0.0601	0.71	1.070	480.2	0.6915
0.22	0.1015	45.55	0.0656	0.72	1.100	493.7	0.7109
0.23	0.1103	49.50	0.0713	0.73	1.130	507.1	0.7303
0.24	0.1195	53.63	0.0772	0.74	1.160	520.6	0.7497
0.25	0.1290	57.90	0.0834	0.75	1.200	538.6	0.7756
0.26	0.1390	62.38	0.0898	0.76	1.230	552.0	0.7949
0.27	0.1494	67.05	0.0966	0.77	1.270	570.0	0.8208
0.28	0.1602	71.90	0.1035	0.78	1.300	583.4	0.8402
0.29	0.1714	76.92	0.1108	0.79	1.340	601.4	0.8660
0.30	0.1830	82.13	0.1183	0.80	1.380	619.3	0.8919
0.31	0.1950	87.52	0.1260	0.81	1.420	637.3	0.9177
0.32	0.2070	92.90	0.1338	0.82	1.460	655.2	0.9436
0.33	0.2200	98.74	0.1422	0.83	1.490	668.7	0.9630
0.34	0.2340	105.0	0.1512	0.84	1.530	686.7	0.9888
0.35	0.2480	111.3	0.1603	0.85	1.570	704.6	1.015
0.36	0.2620	117.6	0.1693	0.86	1.620	727.1	1.047
0.37	0.2760	123.9	0.1784	0.87	1.660	745.0	1.073
0.38	0.2910	130.6	0.1881	0.88	1.700	763.0	1.099
0.39	0.3070	137.8	0.1984	0.89	1.740	780.9	1.125
0.40	0.3230	145.0	0.2088	0.90	1.780	798.9	1.150
0.41	0.3390	152.1	0.2191	0.91	1.830	821.3	1.183
0.42	0.3560	159.8	0.2301	0.92	1.870	839.3	1.209
0.43	0.3740	167.9	0.2417	0.93	1.920	861.7	1.241
0.44	0.3920	175.9	0.2533	0.94	1.960	879.6	1.267
0.45	0.4100	184.0	0.2650	0.95	2.010	902.1	1.299
0.46	0.4290	192.5	0.2773	0.96	2.060	924.5	1.331
0.47	0.4480	201.1	0.2895	0.97	2.100	942.5	1.357
0.48	0.4680	210.0	0.3025	0.98	2.150	964.9	1.390
0.49	0.4880	219.0	0.3154	0.99	2.200	987.4	1.422
0.50	0.5090	228.4	0.3290	1.00	2.250	1010	1.454

16

Table 16-9 (Continued)				Table 16-9 (Continued)			
Head (feet)	CFS	GPM	MGD	Head (feet)	CFS	GPM	MGD
1.01	2.300	1032	1.486	1.51	5.740	2576	3.710
1.02	2.350	1055	1.519	1.52	5.830	2617	3.768
1.03	2.400	1077	1.551	1.53	5.920	2657	3.826
1.04	2.450	1100	1.583	1.54	6.010	2697	3.884
1.05	2.510	1126	1.622	1.55	6.110	2742	3.949
1.06	2.560	1149	1.655	1.56	6.200	2783	4.007
1.07	2.620	1176	1.693	1.57	6.290	2823	4.065
1.08	2.670	1198	1.726	1.58	6.380	2863	4.123
1.09	2.730	1225	1.764	1.59	6.480	2908	4.188
1.10	2.780	1248	1.797	1.60	6.580	2953	4.253
1.11	2.840	1275	1.835	1.61	6.670	2993	4.311
1.12	2.900	1302	1.874	1.62	6.770	3038	4.375
1.13	2.960	1328	1.913	1.63	6.870	3083	4.440
1.14	3.020	1355	1.952	1.64	6.970	3128	4.505
1.15	3.080	1382	1.991	1.65	7.070	3173	4.569
1.16	3.140	1409	2.029	1.66	7.170	3218	4.634
1.17	3.200	1436	2.068	1.67	7.270	3263	4.699
1.18	3.260	1463	2.107	1.68	7.370	3308	4.763
1.19	3.320	1490	2.146	1.69	7.470	3353	4.828
1.20	3.380	1517	2.184	1.70	7.580	3402	4.899
1.21	3.450	1548	2.230	1.71	7.680	3447	4.964
1.22	3.510	1575	2.269	1.72	7.790	3496	5.035
1.23	3.580	1607	2.314	1.73	7.900	3546	5.106
1.24	3.650	1638	2.359	1.74	8.000	3590	5.170
1.25	3.710	1665	2.398	1.75	8.110	3640	5.241
1.26	3.780	1696	2.443	1.76	8.220	3689	5.313
1.27	3.850	1728	2.488	1.77	8.330	3739	5.384
1.28	3.920	1759	2.533	1.78	8.440	3788	5.455
1.29	3.990	1791	2.579	1.79	8.560	3842	5.532
1.30	4.060	1822	2.624	1.80	8.670	3891	5.603
1.31	4.130	1854	2.669	1.81	8.780	3940	5.675
1.32	4.200	1885	2.714	1.82	8.900	3994	5.752
1.33	4.280	1921	2.766	1.83	9.010	4044	5.823
1.34	4.350	1952	2.811	1.84	9.130	4098	5.901
1.35	4.430	1988	2.863	1.85	9.240	4147	5.972
1.36	4.500	2020	2.908	1.86	9.360	4201	6.049
1.37	4.580	2056	2.960	1.87	9.480	4255	6.127
1.38	4.660	2091	3.012	1.88	9.600	4308	6.204
1.39	4.740	2127	3.063	1.89	9.720	4362	6.282
1.40	4.820	2163	3.115	1.90	9.850	4421	6.366
1.41	4.900	2199	3.167	1.91	9.970	4475	6.444
1.42	4.980	2235	3.219	1.92	10.09	4528	6.521
1.43	5.060	2271	3.270	1.93	10.21	4582	6.599
1.44	5.140	2307	3.322	1.94	10.34	4641	6.683
1.45	5.230	2347	3.380	1.95	10.47	4699	6.767
1.46	5.310	2383	3.432	1.96	10.60	4757	6.851
1.47	5.400	2424	3.490	1.97	10.72	4811	6.928
1.48	5.480	2459	3.542	1.98	10.85	4869	7.012
1.49	5.570	2500	3.600	1.99	10.98	4928	7.096
1.50	5.650	2536	3.652	2.00	11.10	4982	7.174

16

Table 16-10:
2.5 ft. H Flume Discharge Table with Head in Feet

Formula: $\text{CFS} = 2.33\ H^{2.31}$
$\text{GPM} = 1045.7\ H^{2.31}$
$\text{MGD} = 1.51\ H^{2.31}$

Where: H = head in feet

Table 16-10				Table 16-10 (Continued)			
Head (feet)	CFS	GPM	MGD	Head (feet)	CFS	GPM	MGD
0.01				0.51	0.5870	263.4	0.3794
0.02	0.0018	0.8078	0.0012	0.52	0.6110	274.2	0.3949
0.03	0.0038	1.705	0.0025	0.53	0.6350	285.0	0.4104
0.04	0.0061	2.738	0.0039	0.54	0.6590	295.8	0.4259
0.05	0.0089	3.994	0.0058	0.55	0.6840	307.0	0.4421
0.06	0.0121	5.430	0.0078	0.56	0.7100	318.6	0.4589
0.07	0.0158	7.091	0.0102	0.57	0.7360	330.3	0.4757
0.08	0.0200	8.976	0.0129	0.58	0.7630	342.4	0.4931
0.09	0.0247	11.09	0.0160	0.59	0.7900	354.6	0.5106
0.10	0.0298	13.37	0.0193	0.60	0.8180	367.1	0.5287
0.11	0.0350	15.71	0.0226	0.61	0.8460	379.7	0.5468
0.12	0.0406	18.22	0.0262	0.62	0.8750	392./	0.5655
0.13	0.0465	20.87	0.0301	0.63	0.9040	405.7	0.5843
0.14	0.0528	23.70	0.0341	0.64	0.9340	419.2	0.6036
0.15	0.0595	26.70	0.0385	0.65	0.9650	433.1	0.6237
0.16	0.0666	29.89	0.0430	0.66	0.9960	447.0	0.6437
0.17	0.0741	33.26	0.0479	0.67	1.027	460.9	0.6638
0.18	0.0820	36.80	0.0530	0.68	1.059	475.3	0.6844
0.19	0.0903	40.53	0.0584	0.69	1.092	490.1	0.7058
0.20	0.0990	44.43	0.0640	0.70	1.130	507.1	0.7303
0.21	0.1081	48.52	0.0699	0.71	1.160	520.6	0.7497
0.22	0.1176	52.78	0.0760	0.72	1.190	534.1	0.7691
0.23	0.1275	57.22	0.0824	0.73	1.230	552.0	0.7949
0.24	0.1379	61.89	0.0891	0.74	1.270	570.0	0.8208
0.25	0.1486	66.69	0.0960	0.75	1.300	583.4	0.8402
0.26	0.1597	71.67	0.1032	0.76	1.340	601.4	0.8660
0.27	0.1713	76.88	0.1107	0.77	1.380	619.3	0.8919
0.28	0.1834	82.31	0.1185	0.78	1.410	632.8	0.9113
0.29	0.1960	87.96	0.1267	0.79	1.450	650.8	0.9371
0.30	0.2090	93.80	0.1351	0.80	1.490	668.7	0.9630
0.31	0.2220	99.63	0.1435	0.81	1.530	686.7	0.9888
0.32	0.2360	105.9	0.1525	0.82	1.570	704.6	1.015
0.33	0.2500	112.2	0.1616	0.83	1.610	722.6	1.041
0.34	0.2650	118.9	0.1713	0.84	1.650	740.5	1.066
0.35	0.2800	125.7	0.1810	0.85	1.700	763.0	1.099
0.36	0.2960	132.8	0.1913	0.86	1.740	780.9	1.125
0.37	0.3120	140.0	0.2016	0.87	1.780	798.9	1.150
0.38	0.3280	147.2	0.2120	0.88	1.830	821.3	1.183
0.39	0.3450	154.8	0.2230	0.89	1.870	839.3	1.209
0.40	0.3630	162.9	0.2346	0.90	1.920	861.7	1.241
0.41	0.3810	171.0	0.2462	0.91	1.960	879.6	1.267
0.42	0.3990	179.1	0.2579	0.92	2.010	902.1	1.299
0.43	0.4180	187.6	0.2702	0.93	2.060	924.5	1.331
0.44	0.4370	196.1	0.2824	0.94	2.110	947.0	1.364
0.45	0.4570	205.1	0.2954	0.95	2.160	969.4	1.396
0.46	0.4780	214.5	0.3089	0.96	2.210	991.8	1.428
0.47	0.4990	224.0	0.3225	0.97	2.260	1014	1.461
0.48	0.5200	233.4	0.3361	0.98	2.310	1037	1.493
0.49	0.5420	243.2	0.3503	0.99	2.360	1059	1.525
0.50	0.5640	253.1	0.3645	1.00	2.410	1082	1.558

16

Table 16-10 (Continued)				Table 16-10 (Continued)			
Head (feet)	CFS	GPM	MGD	Head (feet)	CFS	GPM	MGD
1.01	2.460	1104	1.590	1.51	6.000	2693	3.878
1.02	2.510	1126	1.622	1.52	6.090	2733	3.936
1.03	2.570	1153	1.661	1.53	6.180	2774	3.994
1.04	2.620	1176	1.693	1.54	6.270	2814	4.052
1.05	2.680	1203	1.732	1.55	6.370	2859	4.117
1.06	2.740	1230	1.771	1.56	6.460	2899	4.175
1.07	2.790	1252	1.803	1.57	6.550	2940	4.233
1.08	2.850	1279	1.842	1.58	6.650	2985	4.298
1.09	2.910	1306	1.881	1.59	6.750	3029	4.363
1.10	2.970	1333	1.920	1.60	6.840	3070	4.421
1.11	3.030	1360	1.958	1.61	6.940	3115	4.485
1.12	3.090	1387	1.997	1.62	7.040	3160	4.550
1.13	3.150	1414	2.036	1.63	7.140	3204	4.615
1.14	3.210	1441	2.075	1.64	7.240	3249	4.679
1.15	3.270	1468	2.113	1.65	7.340	3294	4.744
1.16	3.330	1495	2.152	1.66	7.450	3344	4.815
1.17	3.400	1526	2.197	1.67	7.550	3388	4.880
1.18	3.460	1553	2.236	1.68	7.660	3438	4.951
1.19	3.530	1584	2.281	1.69	7.760	3483	5.015
1.20	3.590	1611	2.320	1.70	7.860	3528	5.080
1.21	3.660	1643	2.365	1.71	7.970	3577	5.151
1.22	3.730	1674	2.411	1.72	8.080	3626	5.222
1.23	3.800	1705	2.456	1.73	8.190	3676	5.293
1.24	3.860	1732	2.495	1.74	8.300	3725	5.364
1.25	3.930	1764	2.540	1.75	8.410	3774	5.435
1.26	4.000	1795	2.585	1.76	8.530	3828	5.513
1.27	4.070	1827	2.630	1.77	8.640	3878	5.584
1.28	4.150	1863	2.682	1.78	8.750	3927	5.655
1.29	4.220	1894	2.727	1.79	8.870	3981	5.733
1.30	4.290	1925	2.773	1.80	8.980	4030	5.804
1.31	4.370	1961	2.824	1.81	9.100	4084	5.881
1.32	4.440	1993	2.870	1.82	9.220	4138	5.959
1.33	4.520	2029	2.921	1.83	9.340	4192	6.036
1.34	4.590	2060	2.967	1.84	9.450	4241	6.108
1.35	4.670	2096	3.018	1.85	9.570	4295	6.185
1.36	4.750	2132	3.070	1.86	9.700	4353	6.269
1.37	4.820	2163	3.115	1.87	9.820	4407	6.347
1.38	4.900	2199	3.167	1.88	9.940	4461	6.424
1.39	4.980	2235	3.219	1.89	10.06	4515	6.502
1.40	5.060	2271	3.270	1.90	10.20	4578	6.592
1.41	5.150	2311	3.328	1.91	10.30	4623	6.657
1.42	5.230	2347	3.380	1.92	10.40	4668	6.722
1.43	5.310	2383	3.432	1.93	10.60	4757	6.851
1.44	5.390	2419	3.484	1.94	10.70	4802	6.915
1.45	5.480	2459	3.542	1.95	10.80	4847	6.980
1.46	5.560	2495	3.593	1.96	11.00	4937	7.109
1.47	5.650	2536	3.652	1.97	11.10	4982	7.174
1.48	5.740	2576	3.710	1.98	11.20	5027	7.239
1.49	5.820	2612	3.761	1.99	11.40	5116	7.368
1.50	5.910	2652	3.820	2.00	11.50	5161	7.432

16

Table 16-10 (Continued)					Table 16-10 (Continued)			
Head (feet)	CFS	GPM	MGD		Head (feet)	CFS	GPM	MGD
2.01	11.60	5206	7.497		2.26	15.30	6867	9.888
2.02	11.80	5296	7.626		2.27	15.50	6956	10.02
2.03	11.90	5341	7.691		2.28	15.60	7001	10.08
2.04	12.00	5386	7.756		2.29	15.80	7091	10.21
2.05	12.20	5475	7.885		2.30	16.00	7181	10.34
2.06	12.30	5520	7.949		2.31	16.10	7226	10.41
2.07	12.50	5610	8.079		2.32	16.30	7315	10.53
2.08	12.60	5655	8.143		2.33	16.40	7360	10.60
2.09	12.70	5700	8.208		2.34	16.60	7450	10.73
2.10	12.90	5790	8.337		2.35	16.80	7540	10.86
2.11	13.00	5834	8.402		2.36	17.00	7630	10.99
2.12	13.20	5924	8.531		2.37	17.10	7674	11.05
2.13	13.30	5969	8.596		2.38	17.30	7764	11.18
2.14	13.50	6059	8.725		2.39	17.50	7854	11.31
2.15	13.60	6104	8.790		2.40	17.60	7899	11.37
2.16	13.80	6193	8.919		2.41	17.80	7989	11.50
2.17	13.90	6238	8.984		2.42	18.00	8078	11.63
2.18	14.10	6328	9.113		2.43	18.20	8168	11.76
2.19	14.20	6373	9.177		2.44	18.30	8213	11.83
2.20	14.40	6463	9.307		2.45	18.50	8303	11.96
2.21	14.50	6508	9.371		2.46	18.70	8393	12.09
2.22	14.70	6597	9.501		2.47	18.90	8482	12.22
2.23	14.80	6642	9.565		2.48	19.10	8572	12.34
2.24	15.00	6732	9.695		2.49	19.20	8617	12.41
2.25	15.10	6777	9.759		2.50	19.40	8707	12.54

16

Table 16-11:
3.0 ft. H Flume Discharge Table with Head in Feet

Formula: CFS $= 2.41\ H^{2.31}$
GPM $= 1081.6\ H^{2.31}$
MGD $= 1.56\ H^{2.31}$
Where: H = head in feet

Table 16-11				Table 16-11 (Continued)			
Head (feet)	CFS	GPM	MGD	Head (feet)	CFS	GPM	MGD
0.01				0.51	0.6440	289.0	0.4162
0.02	0.0021	0.9425	0.0014	0.52	0.6690	300.2	0.4324
0.03	0.0045	2.020	0.0029	0.53	0.6950	311.9	0.4492
0.04	0.0073	3.276	0.0047	0.54	0.7210	323.6	0.4660
0.05	0.0105	4.712	0.0068	0.55	0.7480	335.7	0.4834
0.06	0.0143	6.418	0.0092	0.56	0.7750	347.8	0.5009
0.07	0.0186	8.348	0.0120	0.57	0.8030	360.4	0.5190
0.08	0.0234	10.50	0.0151	0.58	0.8320	373.4	0.5377
0.09	0.0288	12.93	0.0186	0.59	0.8610	386.4	0.5565
0.10	0.0347	15.57	0.0224	0.60	0.8900	399.4	0.5752
0.11	0.0407	18.27	0.0263	0.61	0.9200	412.9	0.5946
0.12	0.0471	21.14	0.0304	0.62	0.9510	426.8	0.6146
0.13	0.0538	24.15	0.0348	0.63	0.9820	440.7	0.6347
0.14	0.0610	27.38	0.0394	0.64	1.014	455.1	0.6553
0.15	0.0686	30.79	0.0443	0.65	1.047	469.9	0.6767
0.16	0.0766	34.38	0.0495	0.66	1.080	484.7	0.6980
0.17	0.0851	38.19	0.0550	0.67	1.113	499.5	0.7193
0.18	0.0939	42.14	0.0607	0.68	1.147	514.8	0.7413
0.19	0.1032	46.32	0.0667	0.69	1.182	530.5	0.7639
0.20	0.1130	50.71	0.0730	0.70	1.220	547.5	0.7885
0.21	0.1230	55.20	0.0795	0.71	1.250	561.0	0.8079
0.22	0.1340	60.14	0.0866	0.72	1.290	579.0	0.8337
0.23	0.1450	65.08	0.0937	0.73	1.330	596.9	0.8596
0.24	0.1560	70.01	0.1008	0.74	1.360	610.4	0.8790
0.25	0.1680	75.40	0.1086	0.75	1.400	628.3	0.9048
0.26	0.1800	80.78	0.1163	0.76	1.440	646.3	0.9307
0.27	0.1930	86.62	0.1247	0.77	1.480	664.2	0.9565
0.28	0.2070	92.90	0.1338	0.78	1.520	682.2	0.9824
0.29	0.2200	98.74	0.1422	0.79	1.560	700.1	1.008
0.30	0.2340	105.0	0.1512	0.80	1.600	718.1	1.034
0.31	0.2490	111.8	0.1609	0.81	1.650	740.5	1.066
0.32	0.2640	118.5	0.1706	0.82	1.690	758.5	1.092
0.33	0.2800	125.7	0.1810	0.83	1.730	776.4	1.118
0.34	0.2960	132.8	0.1913	0.84	1.780	798.9	1.150
0.35	0.3120	140.0	0.2016	0.85	1.820	816.8	1.176
0.36	0.3290	147.7	0.2126	0.86	1.860	834.8	1.202
0.37	0.3470	155.7	0.2243	0.87	1.910	857.2	1.234
0.38	0.3650	163.8	0.2359	0.88	1.960	879.6	1.267
0.39	0.3830	171.9	0.2475	0.89	2.000	897.6	1.293
0.40	0.4020	180.4	0.2598	0.90	2.050	920.0	1.325
0.41	0.4210	188.9	0.2721	0.91	2.100	942.5	1.357
0.42	0.4410	197.9	0.2850	0.92	2.150	964.9	1.390
0.43	0.4620	207.3	0.2986	0.93	2.200	987.4	1.422
0.44	0.4830	216.8	0.3122	0.94	2.250	1010	1.454
0.45	0.5040	226.2	0.3257	0.95	2.300	1032	1.486
0.46	0.5260	236.1	0.3400	0.96	2.350	1055	1.519
0.47	0.5490	246.4	0.3548	0.97	2.410	1082	1.558
0.48	0.5720	256.7	0.3697	0.98	2.460	1104	1.590
0.49	0.5960	267.5	0.3852	0.99	2.510	1126	1.622
0.50	0.6200	278.3	0.4007	1.00	2.570	1153	1.661

16

Table 16-11 (Continued)

Head (feet)	CFS	GPM	MGD	Head (feet)	CFS	GPM	MGD
1.01	2.620	1176	1.693	1.51	6.300	2827	4.072
1.02	2.680	1203	1.732	1.52	6.390	2868	4.130
1.03	2.730	1225	1.764	1.53	6.480	2908	4.188
1.04	2.790	1252	1.803	1.54	6.580	2953	4.253
1.05	2.850	1279	1.842	1.55	6.670	2993	4.311
1.06	2.910	1306	1.881	1.56	6.770	3038	4.375
1.07	2.970	1333	1.920	1.57	6.870	3083	4.440
1.08	3.030	1360	1.958	1.58	6.960	3124	4.498
1.09	3.090	1387	1.997	1.59	7.060	3169	4.563
1.10	3.150	1414	2.036	1.60	7.160	3213	4.628
1.11	3.210	1441	2.075	1.61	7.260	3258	4.692
1.12	3.270	1468	2.113	1.62	7.360	3303	4.757
1.13	3.340	1499	2.159	1.63	7.470	3353	4.828
1.14	3.400	1526	2.197	1.64	7.570	3397	4.892
1.15	3.460	1553	2.236	1.65	7.670	3442	4.957
1.16	3.530	1584	2.281	1.66	7.780	3492	5.028
1.17	3.600	1616	2.327	1.67	7.880	3537	5.093
1.18	3.660	1643	2.365	1.68	7.990	3586	5.164
1.19	3.730	1674	2.411	1.69	8.100	3635	5.235
1.20	3.800	1705	2.456	1.70	8.200	3680	5.300
1.21	3.870	1737	2.501	1.71	8.310	3730	5.371
1.22	3.940	1768	2.546	1.72	8.420	3779	5.442
1.23	4.010	1800	2.592	1.73	8.530	3828	5.513
1.24	4.080	1831	2.637	1.74	8.640	3878	5.584
1.25	4.150	1863	2.682	1.75	8.750	3927	5.655
1.26	4.230	1898	2.734	1.76	8.870	3981	5.733
1.27	4.300	1930	2.779	1.77	8.980	4030	5.804
1.28	4.370	1961	2.824	1.78	9.100	4084	5.881
1.29	4.450	1997	2.876	1.79	9.210	4133	5.952
1.30	4.530	2033	2.928	1.80	9.330	4187	6.030
1.31	4.600	2064	2.973	1.81	9.450	4241	6.108
1.32	4.680	2100	3.025	1.82	9.560	4291	6.179
1.33	4.760	2136	3.076	1.83	9.680	4344	6.256
1.34	4.840	2172	3.128	1.84	9.800	4398	6.334
1.35	4.920	2208	3.180	1.85	9.920	4452	6.411
1.36	5.000	2244	3.232	1.86	10.05	4510	6.495
1.37	5.080	2280	3.283	1.87	10.17	4564	6.573
1.38	5.160	2316	3.335	1.88	10.29	4618	6.650
1.39	5.240	2352	3.387	1.89	10.41	4672	6.728
1.40	5.330	2392	3.445	1.90	10.50	4712	6.786
1.41	5.410	2428	3.496	1.91	10.70	4802	6.915
1.42	5.500	2468	3.555	1.92	10.80	4847	6.980
1.43	5.580	2504	3.606	1.93	10.90	4892	7.045
1.44	5.670	2545	3.665	1.94	11.00	4937	7.109
1.45	5.760	2585	3.723	1.95	11.20	5027	7.239
1.46	5.840	2621	3.774	1.96	11.30	5071	7.303
1.47	5.930	2661	3.833	1.97	11.40	5116	7.368
1.48	6.020	2702	3.891	1.98	11.60	5206	7.497
1.49	6.110	2742	3.949	1.99	11.70	5251	7.562
1.50	6.200	2783	4.007	2.00	11.90	5341	7.691

16

| Table 16-11 (Continued) | | | |

Head (feet)	CFS	GPM	MGD	Head (feet)	CFS	GPM	MGD
2.01	12.00	5386	7.756	2.51	20.10	9021	12.99
2.02	12.10	5430	7.820	2.52	20.30	9111	13.12
2.03	12.30	5520	7.949	2.53	20.50	9200	13.25
2.04	12.40	5565	8.014	2.54	20.70	9290	13.38
2.05	12.60	5655	8.143	2.55	20.90	9380	13.51
2.06	12.70	5700	8.208	2.56	21.10	9470	13.64
2.07	12.80	5745	8.273	2.57	21.30	9559	13.77
2.08	13.00	5834	8.402	2.58	21.50	9649	13.90
2.09	13.10	5879	8.467	2.59	21.70	9739	14.02
2.10	13.30	5969	8.596	2.60	21.90	9829	14.15
2.11	13.40	6014	8.660	2.61	22.10	9918	14.28
2.12	13.60	6104	8.790	2.62	22.30	10,010	14.41
2.13	13.70	6149	8.854	2.63	22.50	10,100	14.54
2.14	13.90	6238	8.984	2.64	22.70	10,190	14.67
2.15	14.00	6283	9.048	2.65	22.90	10,280	14.80
2.16	14.20	6373	9.177	2.66	23.10	10,370	14.93
2.17	14.30	6418	9.242	2.67	23.30	10,460	15.06
2.18	14.50	6508	9.371	2.68	23.50	10,550	15.19
2.19	14.60	6552	9.436	2.69	23.70	10,640	15.32
2.20	14.80	6642	9.565	2.70	23.90	10,730	15.45
2.21	14.90	6687	9.630	2.71	24.10	10,820	15.58
2.22	15.10	6777	9.759	2.72	24.30	10,910	15.71
2.23	15.30	6867	9.888	2.73	24.50	11,000	15.83
2.24	15.40	6912	9.953	2.74	24.70	11,090	15.96
2.25	15.60	7001	10.08	2.75	24.90	11,180	16.09
2.26	15.70	7046	10.15	2.76	25.20	11,310	16.29
2.27	15.90	7136	10.28	2.77	25.40	11,400	16.42
2.28	16.10	7226	10.41	2.78	25.60	11,490	16.55
2.29	16.20	7271	10.47	2.79	25.80	11,580	16.67
2.30	16.40	7360	10.60	2.80	26.00	11,670	16.80
2.31	16.60	7450	10.73	2.81	26.20	11,760	16.93
2.32	16.70	7495	10.79	2.82	26.50	11,890	17.13
2.33	16.90	7585	10.92	2.83	26.70	11,980	17.26
2.34	17.10	7674	11.05	2.84	26.90	12,070	17.39
2.35	17.20	7719	11.12	2.85	27.10	12,160	17.51
2.36	17.40	7809	11.25	2.86	27.40	12,300	17.71
2.37	17.60	7899	11.37	2.87	27.60	12,390	17.84
2.38	17.80	7989	11.50	2.88	27.80	12,480	17.97
2.39	17.90	8034	11.57	2.89	28.00	12,570	18.10
2.40	18.10	8123	11.70	2.90	28.30	12,700	18.29
2.41	18.30	8213	11.83	2.91	28.50	12,790	18.42
2.42	18.50	8303	11.96	2.92	28.70	12,880	18.55
2.43	18.70	8393	12.09	2.93	28.90	12,970	18.68
2.44	18.80	8437	12.15	2.94	29.20	13,100	18.87
2.45	19.00	8527	12.28	2.95	29.40	13,190	19.00
2.46	19.20	8617	12.41	2.96	29.70	13,330	19.20
2.47	19.40	8707	12.54	2.97	29.90	13,420	19.32
2.48	19.60	8796	12.67	2.98	30.10	13,510	19.45
2.49	19.80	8886	12.80	2.99	30.40	13,640	19.65
2.50	19.90	8931	12.86	3.00	30.70	13,780	19.84

16

Table 16-12:
4.5 ft. H Flume Discharge Table with Head in Feet

Formula: $CFS = 2.6 \, H^{2.31}$
$GPM = 1166.9 \, H^{2.31}$
$MGD = 1.68 \, H^{2.31}$

Where: H = head in feet

Table 16-12				Table 16-12 (Continued)			
Head (feet)	CFS	GPM	MGD	Head (feet)	CFS	GPM	MGD
0.01				0.51	0.8150	365.8	0.5267
0.02	0.0031	1.391	0.0020	0.52	0.8450	379.2	0.5461
0.03	0.0066	2.962	0.0043	0.53	0.8760	393.1	0.5662
0.04	0.0106	4.757	0.0069	0.54	0.9070	407.1	0.5862
0.05	0.0154	6.912	0.0100	0.55	0.9390	421.4	0.6069
0.06	0.0208	9.335	0.0134	0.56	0.9720	436.2	0.6282
0.07	0.0269	12.07	0.0174	0.57	1.005	451.0	0.6495
0.08	0.0337	15.12	0.0218	0.58	1.039	466.3	0.6715
0.09	0.0413	18.54	0.0267	0.59	1.073	481.6	0.6935
0.10	0.0496	22.26	0.0321	0.60	1.110	498.2	0.7174
0.11	0.0578	25.94	0.0374	0.61	1.140	511.6	0.7368
0.12	0.0666	29.89	0.0430	0.62	1.180	529.6	0.7626
0.13	0.0758	34.02	0.0490	0.63	1.122	503.6	0.7251
0.14	0.0855	38.37	0.0553	0.64	1.250	561.0	0.8079
0.15	0.0959	43.04	0.0620	0.65	1.290	579.0	0.8337
0.16	0.1067	47.89	0.0690	0.66	1.330	596.9	0.8596
0.17	0.1180	52.96	0.0763	0.67	1.380	619.3	0.8919
0.18	0.1298	58.25	0.0839	0.68	1.410	632.8	0.9113
0.19	0.1420	63.73	0.0918	0.69	1.450	650.8	0.9371
0.20	0.1550	69.56	0.1002	0.70	1.490	668.7	0.9630
0.21	0.1680	75.40	0.1086	0.71	1.530	686.7	0.9888
0.22	0.1820	81.68	0.1176	0.72	1.580	709.1	1.021
0.23	0.1960	87.96	0.1267	0.73	1.620	727.1	1.047
0.24	0.2110	94.70	0.1364	0.74	1.660	745.0	1.073
0.25	0.2260	101.4	0.1461	0.75	1.710	767.4	1.105
0.26	0.2420	108.6	0.1564	0.76	1.750	785.4	1.131
0.27	0.2590	116.2	0.1674	0.77	1.800	807.8	1.163
0.28	0.2760	123.9	0.1784	0.78	1.840	825.8	1.189
0.29	0.2930	131.5	0.1894	0.79	1.890	848.2	1.222
0.30	0.3110	139.6	0.2010	0.80	1.940	870.7	1.254
0.31	0.3300	148.1	0.2133	0.81	1.990	893.1	1.286
0.32	0.3490	156.6	0.2256	0.82	2.040	915.6	1.318
0.33	0.3680	165.2	0.2378	0.83	2.090	938.0	1.351
0.34	0.3880	174.1	0.2508	0.84	2.140	960.4	1.383
0.35	0.4090	183.6	0.2643	0.85	2.190	982.9	1.415
0.36	0.4300	193.0	0.2779	0.86	2.240	1005	1.448
0.37	0.4520	202.9	0.2921	0.87	2.290	1028	1.480
0.38	0.4740	212.7	0.3063	0.88	2.350	1055	1.519
0.39	0.4970	223.1	0.3212	0.89	2.400	1077	1.551
0.40	0.5200	233.4	0.3361	0.90	2.450	1100	1.583
0.41	0.5440	244.1	0.3516	0.91	2.510	1126	1.622
0.42	0.5690	255.4	0.3677	0.92	2.560	1149	1.655
0.43	0.5940	266.6	0.3839	0.93	2.620	1176	1.693
0.44	0.6200	278.3	0.4007	0.94	2.680	1203	1.732
0.45	0.6460	289.9	0.4175	0.95	2.740	1230	1.771
0.46	0.6730	302.0	0.4350	0.96	2.790	1252	1.803
0.47	0.7000	314.2	0.4524	0.97	2.850	1279	1.842
0.48	0.7280	326.7	0.4705	0.98	2.910	1306	1.881
0.49	0.7560	339.3	0.4886	0.99	2.980	1337	1.926
0.50	0.7850	352.3	0.5073	1.00	3.040	1364	1.965

16

Table 16-12 (Continued)					Table 16-12 (Continued)			
Head (feet)	CFS	GPM	MGD		Head (feet)	CFS	GPM	MGD
1.01	3.100	1391	2.004		1.51	7.170	3218	4.634
1.02	3.160	1418	2.042		1.52	7.270	3263	4.699
1.03	3.220	1445	2.081		1.53	7.370	3308	4.763
1.04	3.290	1477	2.126		1.54	7.480	3357	4.834
1.05	3.350	1503	2.165		1.55	7.590	3406	4.905
1.06	3.420	1535	2.210		1.56	7.690	3451	4.970
1.07	3.490	1566	2.256		1.57	7.800	3501	5.041
1.08	3.550	1593	2.294		1.58	7.900	3546	5.106
1.09	3.620	1625	2.340		1.59	8.010	3595	5.177
1.10	3.690	1656	2.385		1.60	8.120	3644	5.248
1.11	3.760	1687	2.430		1.61	8.230	3694	5.319
1.12	3.830	1719	2.475		1.62	8.340	3743	5.390
1.13	3.900	1750	2.521		1.63	8.450	3792	5.461
1.14	3.970	1782	2.566		1.64	8.560	3842	5.532
1.15	4.040	1813	2.611		1.65	8.680	3896	5.610
1.16	4.120	1849	2.663		1.66	8.790	3945	5.681
1.17	4.190	1880	2.708		1.67	8.900	3994	5.752
1.18	4.270	1916	2.760		1.68	9.020	4048	5.830
1.19	4.340	1948	2.805		1.69	9.140	4102	5.907
1.20	4.420	1984	2.857		1.70	9.250	4151	5.978
1.21	4.500	2020	2.908		1.71	9.370	4205	6.056
1.22	4.580	2056	2.960		1.72	9.490	4259	6.133
1.23	4.650	2087	3.005		1.73	9.610	4313	6.211
1.24	4.730	2123	3.057		1.74	9.730	4367	6.288
1.25	4.810	2159	3.109		1.75	9.850	4421	6.366
1.26	4.890	2195	3.160		1.76	9.980	4479	6.450
1.27	4.980	2235	3.219		1.77	10.10	4533	6.528
1.28	5.060	2271	3.270		1.78	10.22	4587	6.605
1.29	5.140	2307	3.322		1.79	10.35	4645	6.689
1.30	5.220	2343	3.374		1.80	10.50	4712	6.786
1.31	5.310	2383	3.432		1.81	10.60	4757	6.851
1.32	5.390	2419	3.484		1.82	10.70	4802	6.915
1.33	5.480	2459	3.542		1.83	10.80	4847	6.980
1.34	5.570	2500	3.600		1.84	11.00	4937	7.109
1.35	5.660	2540	3.658		1.85	11.10	4982	7.174
1.36	5.740	2576	3.710		1.86	11.20	5027	7.239
1.37	5.830	2617	3.768		1.87	11.40	5116	7.368
1.38	5.920	2657	3.826		1.88	11.50	5161	7.432
1.39	6.020	2702	3.891		1.89	11.60	5206	7.497
1.40	6.110	2742	3.949		1.90	11.80	5296	7.626
1.41	6.200	2783	4.007		1.91	11.90	5341	7.691
1.42	6.290	2823	4.065		1.92	12.00	5386	7.756
1.43	6.390	2868	4.130		1.93	12.20	5475	7.885
1.44	6.480	2908	4.188		1.94	12.30	5520	7.949
1.45	6.580	2953	4.253		1.95	12.50	5610	8.079
1.46	6.680	2998	4.317		1.96	12.60	5655	8.143
1.47	6.770	3038	4.375		1.97	12.80	5745	8.273
1.48	6.870	3083	4.440		1.98	12.90	5790	8.337
1.49	6.970	3128	4.505		1.99	13.00	5834	8.402
1.50	7.070	3173	4.569		2.00	13.20	5924	8.531

16

Table 16-12 (Continued)				Table 16-12 (Continued)			
Head (feet)	CFS	GPM	MGD	Head (feet)	CFS	GPM	MGD
2.01	13.30	5969	8.596	2.51	21.80	9784	14.09
2.02	13.50	6059	8.725	2.52	22.00	9874	14.22
2.03	13.60	6104	8.790	2.53	22.20	9963	14.35
2.04	13.70	6149	8.854	2.54	22.40	10,050	14.48
2.05	13.90	6238	8.984	2.55	22.60	10,140	14.61
2.06	14.10	6328	9.113	2.56	22.80	10,230	14.74
2.07	14.20	6373	9.177	2.57	23.00	10,320	14.86
2.08	14.40	6463	9.307	2.58	23.20	10,410	14.99
2.09	14.50	6508	9.371	2.59	23.40	10,500	15.12
2.10	14.70	6597	9.501	2.60	23.60	10,590	15.25
2.11	14.80	6642	9.565	2.61	23.80	10,680	15.38
2.12	15.00	6732	9.695	2.62	24.00	10,770	15.51
2.13	15.20	6822	9.824	2.63	24.20	10,860	15.64
2.14	15.30	6867	9.888	2.64	24.40	10,950	15.77
2.15	15.50	6956	10.02	2.65	24.60	11,040	15.90
2.16	15.60	7001	10.08	2.66	24.90	11,180	16.09
2.17	15.80	7091	10.21	2.67	25.10	11,260	16.22
2.18	15.90	7136	10.28	2.68	25.30	11,350	16.35
2.19	16.10	7226	10.41	2.69	25.50	11,440	16.48
2.20	16.30	7315	10.53	2.70	25.70	11,530	16.61
2.21	16.40	7360	10.60	2.71	25.90	11,620	16.74
2.22	16.60	7450	10.73	2.72	26.10	11,710	16.87
2.23	16.80	7540	10.86	2.73	26.40	11,850	17.06
2.24	16.90	7585	10.92	2.74	26.60	11,940	17.19
2.25	17.10	7674	11.05	2.75	26.80	12,030	17.32
2.26	17.30	7764	11.18	2.76	27.00	12,120	17.45
2.27	17.40	7809	11.25	2.77	27.20	12,210	17.58
2.28	17.60	7899	11.37	2.78	27.40	12,300	17.71
2.29	17.80	7989	11.50	2.79	27.70	12,430	17.90
2.30	18.00	8078	11.63	2.80	27.90	12,520	18.03
2.31	18.10	8123	11.70	2.81	28.10	12,610	18.16
2.32	18.30	8213	11.83	2.82	28.40	12,750	18.35
2.33	18.50	8303	11.96	2.83	28.60	12,840	18.48
2.34	18.70	8393	12.09	2.84	28.80	12,930	18.61
2.35	18.80	8437	12.15	2.85	29.00	13,020	18.74
2.36	19.00	8527	12.28	2.86	29.30	13,150	18.94
2.37	19.20	8617	12.41	2.87	29.50	13,240	19.07
2.38	19.40	8707	12.54	2.88	29.70	13,330	19.20
2.39	19.60	8796	12.67	2.89	30.00	13,460	19.39
2.40	19.70	8841	12.73	2.90	30.20	13,550	19.52
2.41	19.90	8931	12.86	2.91	30.40	13,640	19.65
2.42	20.10	9021	12.99	2.92	30.70	13,780	19.84
2.43	20.30	9111	13.12	2.93	30.90	13,870	19.97
2.44	20.50	9200	13.25	2.94	31.20	14,000	20.16
2.45	20.70	9290	13.38	2.95	31.40	14,090	20.29
2.46	20.90	9380	13.51	2.96	31.70	14,230	20.49
2.47	21.00	9425	13.57	2.97	31.90	14,320	20.62
2.48	21.20	9515	13.70	2.98	32.20	14,450	20.81
2.49	21.40	9604	13.83	2.99	32.40	14,540	20.94
2.50	21.60	9694	13.96	3.00	32.70	14,680	21.13

16

Table 16-12 (Continued)				Table 16-12 (Continued)			
Head (feet)	CFS	GPM	MGD	Head (feet)	CFS	GPM	MGD
3.01	32.90	14,770	21.26	3.51	47.10	21,140	30.44
3.02	33.20	14,900	21.46	3.52	47.40	21,270	30.63
3.03	33.40	14,990	21.59	3.53	47.70	21,410	30.83
3.04	33.70	15,120	21.78	3.54	48.00	21,540	31.02
3.05	33.90	15,210	21.91	3.55	48.30	21,680	31.22
3.06	34.20	15,350	22.10	3.56	48.60	21,810	31.41
3.07	34.40	15,440	22.23	3.57	49.00	21,990	31.67
3.08	34.70	15,570	22.43	3.58	49.30	22,130	31.86
3.09	35.00	15,710	22.62	3.59	49.60	22,260	32.06
3.10	35.20	15,800	22.75	3.60	49.90	22,400	32.25
3.11	35.50	15,930	22.94	3.61	50.30	22,570	32.51
3.12	35.80	16,070	23.14	3.62	50.60	22,710	32.70
3.13	36.00	16,160	23.27	3.63	50.90	22,840	32.90
3.14	36.30	16,290	23.46	3.64	51.20	22,980	33.09
3.15	36.60	16,430	23.65	3.65	51.60	23,160	33.35
3.16	36.80	16,520	23.78	3.66	51.90	23,290	33.54
3.17	37.10	16,650	23.98	3.67	52.20	23,430	33.74
3.18	37.40	16,790	24.17	3.68	52.60	23,610	34.00
3.19	37.70	16,920	24.37	3.69	52.90	23,740	34.19
3.20	37.90	17,010	24.49	3.70	53.20	23,880	34.38
3.21	38.20	17,140	24.69	3.71	53.60	24,060	34.64
3.22	38.50	17,280	24.88	3.72	53.90	24,190	34.84
3.23	38.80	17,410	25.08	3.73	54.30	24,370	35.09
3.24	39.00	17,500	25.21	3.74	54.60	24,500	35.29
3.25	39.30	17,640	25.40	3.75	54.90	24,640	35.48
3.26	39.60	17,770	25.59	3.76	55.30	24,820	35.74
3.27	39.90	17,910	25.79	3.77	55.60	24,950	35.93
3.28	40.20	18,040	25.98	3.78	56.00	25,130	36.19
3.29	40.50	18,180	26.18	3.79	56.30	25,270	36.39
3.30	40.80	18,310	26.37	3.80	56.70	25,450	36.65
3.31	41.20	18,490	26.63	3.81	57.00	25,580	36.84
3.32	41.30	18,540	26.69	3.82	57.40	25,760	37.10
3.33	41.60	18,670	26.89	3.83	57.70	25,900	37.29
3.34	41.90	18,800	27.08	3.84	58.10	26,080	37.55
3.35	42.20	18,940	27.27	3.85	58.40	26,210	37.74
3.36	42.50	19,070	27.47	3.86	58.80	26,390	38.00
3.37	42.80	19,210	27.66	3.87	59.20	26,570	38.26
3.38	43.10	19,340	27.86	3.88	59.50	26,700	38.45
3.39	43.40	19,480	28.05	3.89	59.90	26,880	38.71
3.40	43.70	19,610	28.24	3.90	60.20	27,020	38.91
3.41	44.00	19,750	28.44	3.91	60.60	27,200	39.17
3.42	44.30	19,880	28.63	3.92	61.00	27,380	39.42
3.43	44.60	20,020	28.82	3.93	61.30	27,510	39.62
3.44	44.90	20,150	29.02	3.94	61.70	27,690	39.88
3.45	45.20	20,290	29.21	3.95	62.10	27,870	40.14
3.46	45.50	20,420	29.41	3.96	62.40	28,010	40.33
3.47	45.80	20,560	29.60	3.97	62.80	28,180	40.59
3.48	46.10	20,690	29.79	3.98	63.20	28,360	40.85
3.49	46.40	20,820	29.99	3.99	63.60	28,540	41.10
3.50	46.80	21,000	30.25	4.00	63.90	28,680	41.30

16

Table 16-12 (Continued)				Table 16-12 (Continued)			
Head (feet)	CFS	GPM	MGD	Head (feet)	CFS	GPM	MGD
4.01	64.30	28,860	41.56	4.26	74.20	33,300	47.96
4.02	64.70	29,040	41.82	4.27	74.60	33,480	48.21
4.03	65.10	29,220	42.07	4.28	75.00	33,660	48.47
4.04	65.40	29,350	42.27	4.29	75.40	33,840	48.73
4.05	65.80	29,530	42.53	4.30	75.80	34,020	48.99
4.06	66.20	29,710	42.79	4.31	76.20	34,200	49.25
4.07	66.60	29,890	43.04	4.32	76.60	34,380	49.51
4.08	67.00	30,070	43.30	4.33	77.10	34,600	49.83
4.09	67.40	30,250	43.56	4.34	77.50	34,780	50.09
4.10	67.80	30,430	43.82	4.35	77.90	34,960	50.35
4.11	68.20	30,610	44.08	4.36	78.30	35,140	50.61
4.12	68.50	30,740	44.27	4.37	78.80	35,370	50.93
4.13	68.90	30,920	44.53	4.38	79.20	35,540	51.19
4.14	69.30	31,100	44.79	4.39	79.60	35,720	51.45
4.15	69.70	31,280	45.05	4.40	80.00	35,900	51.70
4.16	70.10	31,460	45.31	4.41	80.50	36,130	52.03
4.17	70.50	31,640	45.56	4.42	80.90	36,310	52.29
4.18	70.90	31,820	45.82	4.43	81.30	36,490	52.54
4.19	71.30	32,000	46.08	4.44	81.80	36,710	52.87
4.20	71.70	32,180	46.34	4.45	82.20	36,890	53.13
4.21	72.10	32,360	46.60	4.46	82.60	37,070	53.38
4.22	72.50	32,540	46.86	4.47	83.10	37,300	53.71
4.23	72.90	32,720	47.12	4.48	83.50	37,470	53.97
4.24	73.30	32,900	47.37	4.49	84.00	37,700	54.29
4.25	73.80	33,120	47.70	4.50	84.50	37,920	54.61

16

Table 16-13:
4.0 ft. HL Flume Discharge Table with Head in Feet

Source: U.S.D.A. Handbook No. 224

Table 16-13				Table 16-13 (Continued)			
Head (feet)	CFS	GPM	MGD	Head (feet)	CFS	GPM	MGD
0.01				0.51	1.480	664.2	0.9565
0.02	0.0050	2.244	0.0032	0.52	1.530	686.7	0.9888
0.03	0.0120	5.386	0.0078	0.53	1.590	713.6	1.028
0.04	0.0200	8.976	0.0129	0.54	1.640	736.0	1.060
0.05	0.0290	13.02	0.0187	0.55	1.700	763.0	1.099
0.06	0.0390	17.50	0.0252	0.56	1.760	789.9	1.137
0.07	0.0500	22.44	0.0323	0.57	1.820	816.8	1.176
0.08	0.0620	27.83	0.0401	0.58	1.880	843.7	1.215
0.09	0.0750	33.66	0.0485	0.59	1.940	870.7	1.254
0.10	0.0890	39.94	0.0575	0.60	2.010	902.1	1.299
0.11	0.1030	46.23	0.0666	0.61	2.070	929.0	1.338
0.12	0.1190	53.41	0.0769	0.62	2.140	960.4	1.383
0.13	0.1350	60.59	0.0873	0.63	2.210	991.8	1.428
0.14	0.1520	68.22	0.0982	0.64	2.280	1023	1.474
0.15	0.1700	76.30	0.1099	0.65	2.350	1055	1.519
0.16	0.1900	85.27	0.1228	0.66	2.420	1086	1.564
0.17	0.2110	94.70	0.1364	0.67	2.490	1118	1.609
0.18	0.2320	104.1	0.1499	0.68	2.560	1149	1.655
0.19	0.2550	114.4	0.1648	0.69	2.640	1185	1.706
0.20	0.2780	124.8	0.1797	0.70	2.710	1216	1.751
0.21	0.3020	135.5	0.1952	0.71	2.790	1252	1.803
0.22	0.3270	146.8	0.2113	0.72	2.870	1288	1.855
0.23	0.3520	158.0	0.2275	0.73	2.950	1324	1.907
0.24	0.3780	169.6	0.2443	0.74	3.030	1360	1.958
0.25	0.4050	181.8	0.2618	0.75	3.110	1396	2.010
0.26	0.4340	194.8	0.2805	0.76	3.190	1432	2.062
0.27	0.4650	208.7	0.3005	0.77	3.280	1472	2.120
0.28	0.4970	223.1	0.3212	0.78	3.360	1508	2.172
0.29	0.5300	237.9	0.3425	0.79	3.440	1544	2.223
0.30	0.5650	253.6	0.3652	0.80	3.530	1584	2.281
0.31	0.6000	269.3	0.3878	0.81	3.610	1620	2.333
0.32	0.6350	285.0	0.4104	0.82	3.700	1661	2.391
0.33	0.6700	300.7	0.4330	0.83	3.790	1701	2.449
0.34	0.7050	316.4	0.4556	0.84	3.880	1741	2.508
0.35	0.7400	332.1	0.4783	0.85	3.980	1786	2.572
0.36	0.7800	350.1	0.5041	0.86	4.080	1831	2.637
0.37	0.8200	368.0	0.5300	0.87	4.180	1876	2.702
0.38	0.8600	386.0	0.5558	0.88	4.280	1921	2.766
0.39	0.9000	403.9	0.5817	0.89	4.380	1966	2.831
0.40	0.9400	421.9	0.6075	0.90	4.480	2011	2.895
0.41	0.9820	440.7	0.6347	0.91	4.580	2056	2.960
0.42	1.030	462.3	0.6657	0.92	4.680	2100	3.025
0.43	1.080	484.7	0.6980	0.93	4.790	2150	3.096
0.44	1.120	502.7	0.7239	0.94	4.900	2199	3.167
0.45	1.170	525.1	0.7562	0.95	5.010	2248	3.238
0.46	1.220	547.5	0.7885	0.96	5.120	2298	3.309
0.47	1.270	570.0	0.8208	0.97	5.230	2347	3.380
0.48	1.320	592.4	0.8531	0.98	5.340	2397	3.451
0.49	1.370	614.9	0.8854	0.99	5.450	2446	3.522
0.50	1.420	637.3	0.9177	1.00	5.560	2495	3.593

16

Table 16-13 (Continued)					Table 16-13 (Continued)			
Head (feet)	CFS	GPM	MGD		Head (feet)	CFS	GPM	MGD
1.01	5.680	2549	3.671		1.51	13.20	5924	8.531
1.02	5.800	2603	3.749		1.52	13.30	5969	8.596
1.03	5.920	2657	3.826		1.53	13.50	6059	8.725
1.04	6.040	2711	3.904		1.54	13.70	6149	8.854
1.05	6.160	2765	3.981		1.55	13.90	6238	8.984
1.06	6.280	2818	4.059		1.56	14.10	6328	9.113
1.07	6.400	2872	4.136		1.57	14.30	6418	9.242
1.08	6.520	2926	4.214		1.58	14.50	6508	9.371
1.09	6.640	2980	4.291		1.59	14.70	6597	9.501
1.10	6.760	3034	4.369		1.60	14.90	6687	9.630
1.11	6.890	3092	4.453		1.61	15.10	6777	9.759
1.12	7.020	3151	4.537		1.62	15.30	6867	9.888
1.13	7.150	3209	4.621		1.63	15.50	6956	10.02
1.14	7.280	3267	4.705		1.64	15.70	7046	10.15
1.15	7.410	3326	4.789		1.65	15.90	7136	10.28
1.16	7.540	3384	4.873		1.66	16.20	7271	10.47
1.17	7.670	3442	4.957		1.67	16.40	7360	10.60
1.18	7.800	3501	5.041		1.68	16.60	7450	10.73
1.19	7.930	3559	5.125		1.69	16.80	7540	10.86
1.20	8.060	3617	5.209		1.70	17.00	7630	10.99
1.21	8.200	3680	5.300		1.71	17.20	7719	11.12
1.22	8.350	3747	5.397		1.72	17.40	7809	11.25
1.23	8.500	3815	5.494		1.73	17.60	7899	11.37
1.24	8.650	3882	5.590		1.74	17.80	7989	11.50
1.25	8.800	3949	5.687		1.75	18.10	8123	11.70
1.26	8.950	4017	5.784		1.76	18.30	8213	11.83
1.27	9.100	4084	5.881		1.77	18.50	8303	11.96
1.28	9.250	4151	5.978		1.78	18.70	8393	12.09
1.29	9.400	4219	6.075		1.79	19.00	8527	12.28
1.30	9.550	4286	6.172		1.80	19.20	8617	12.41
1.31	9.700	4353	6.269		1.81	19.40	8707	12.54
1.32	9.900	4443	6.398		1.82	19.70	8841	12.73
1.33	10.10	4533	6.528		1.83	19.90	8931	12.86
1.34	10.20	4578	6.592		1.84	20.20	9066	13.06
1.35	10.40	4668	6.722		1.85	20.40	9156	13.18
1.36	10.50	4712	6.786		1.86	20.60	9245	13.31
1.37	10.70	4802	6.915		1.87	20.90	9380	13.51
1.38	10.80	4847	6.980		1.88	21.20	9515	13.70
1.39	11.00	4937	7.109		1.89	21.40	9604	13.83
1.40	11.20	5027	7.239		1.90	21.70	9739	14.02
1.41	11.40	5116	7.368		1.91	21.90	9829	14.15
1.42	11.60	5206	7.497		1.92	22.10	9918	14.28
1.43	11.70	5251	7.562		1.93	22.40	10,050	14.48
1.44	11.90	5341	7.691		1.94	22.70	10,190	14.67
1.45	12.10	5430	7.820		1.95	23.00	10,320	14.86
1.46	12.30	5520	7.949		1.96	23.20	10,410	14.99
1.47	12.40	5565	8.014		1.97	23.40	10,500	15.12
1.48	12.60	5655	8.143		1.98	23.70	10,640	15.32
1.49	12.80	5745	8.273		1.99	24.00	10,770	15.51
1.50	13.00	5834	8.402		2.00	24.30	10,910	15.71

16

Table 16-13 (Continued)				Table 16-13 (Continued)			
Head (feet)	CFS	GPM	MGD	Head (feet)	CFS	GPM	MGD
2.01	24.50	11,000	15.83	2.51	40.30	18,090	26.05
2.02	24.80	11,130	16.03	2.52	40.60	18,220	26.24
2.03	25.00	11,220	16.16	2.53	41.00	18,400	26.50
2.04	25.30	11,350	16.35	2.54	41.40	18,580	26.76
2.05	25.60	11,490	16.55	2.55	41.70	18,710	26.95
2.06	25.80	11,580	16.67	2.56	42.10	18,890	27.21
2.07	26.10	11,710	16.87	2.57	42.40	19,030	27.40
2.08	26.40	11,850	17.06	2.58	42.80	19,210	27.66
2.09	26.70	11,980	17.26	2.59	43.20	19,390	27.92
2.10	27.00	12,120	17.45	2.60	43.60	19,570	28.18
2.11	27.30	12,250	17.64	2.61	43.90	19,700	28.37
2.12	27.60	12,390	17.84	2.62	44.30	19,880	28.63
2.13	27.90	12,520	18.03	2.63	44.70	20,060	28.89
2.14	28.20	12,660	18.23	2.64	45.10	20,240	29.15
2.15	28.50	12,790	18.42	2.65	45.50	20,420	29.41
2.16	28.80	12,930	18.61	2.66	45.80	20,560	29.60
2.17	29.10	13,060	18.81	2.67	46.20	20,730	29.86
2.18	29.40	13,190	19.00	2.68	46.60	20,910	30.12
2.19	29.70	13,330	19.20	2.69	47.10	21,140	30.44
2.20	30.00	13,460	19.39	2.70	47.50	21,320	30.70
2.21	30.30	13,600	19.58	2.71	47.90	21,500	30.96
2.22	30.60	13,730	19.78	2.72	48.20	21,630	31.15
2.23	30.90	13,870	19.97	2.73	48.60	21,810	31.41
2.24	31.20	14,000	20.16	2.74	49.00	21,990	31.67
2.25	31.50	14,140	20.36	2.75	49.40	22,170	31.93
2.26	31.90	14,320	20.62	2.76	49.80	22,350	32.19
2.27	32.20	14,450	20.81	2.77	50.20	22,530	32.44
2.28	32.50	14,590	21.00	2.78	50.70	22,750	32.77
2.29	32.80	14,720	21.20	2.79	51.10	22,930	33.03
2.30	33.10	14,860	21.39	2.80	51.60	23,160	33.35
2.31	33.50	15,030	21.65	2.81	52.00	23,340	33.61
2.32	33.80	15,170	21.84	2.82	52.40	23,520	33.87
2.33	34.10	15,300	22.04	2.83	52.80	23,700	34.12
2.34	34.50	15,480	22.30	2.84	53.30	23,920	34.45
2.35	34.80	15,620	22.49	2.85	53.70	24,100	34.71
2.36	35.10	15,750	22.69	2.86	54.10	24,280	34.96
2.37	35.40	15,890	22.88	2.87	54.50	24,460	35.22
2.38	35.80	16,070	23.14	2.88	54.90	24,640	35.48
2.39	36.10	16,200	23.33	2.89	55.40	24,860	35.81
2.40	36.50	16,380	23.59	2.90	55.90	25,090	36.13
2.41	36.80	16,520	23.78	2.91	56.30	25,270	36.39
2.42	37.10	16,650	23.98	2.92	56.70	25,450	36.65
2.43	37.40	16,790	24.17	2.93	57.20	25,670	36.97
2.44	37.80	16,960	24.43	2.94	57.60	25,850	37.23
2.45	38.20	17,140	24.69	2.95	58.10	26,080	37.55
2.46	38.50	17,280	24.88	2.96	58.60	26,300	37.87
2.47	38.80	17,410	25.08	2.97	59.10	26,520	38.20
2.48	39.10	17,550	25.27	2.98	59.50	26,700	38.45
2.49	39.50	17,730	25.53	2.99	59.90	26,880	38.71
2.50	39.90	17,910	25.79	3.00	60.30	27,060	38.97

16

Table 16-13 (Continued)				Table 16-13 (Continued)			
Head (feet)	CFS	GPM	MGD	Head (feet)	CFS	GPM	MGD
3.01	60.80	27,290	39.30	3.51	86.50	38,820	55.90
3.02	61.30	27,510	39.62	3.52	87.10	39,090	56.29
3.03	61.80	27,740	39.94	3.53	87.70	39,360	56.68
3.04	62.30	27,960	40.26	3.54	88.30	39,630	57.07
3.05	62.80	28,180	40.59	3.55	88.90	39,900	57.46
3.06	63.20	28,360	40.85	3.56	89.50	40,170	57.84
3.07	63.70	28,590	41.17	3.57	90.10	40,440	58.23
3.08	64.10	28,770	41.43	3.58	90.70	40,710	58.62
3.09	64.60	28,990	41.75	3.59	91.30	40,980	59.01
3.10	65.10	29,220	42.07	3.60	91.90	41,240	59.39
3.11	65.60	29,440	42.40	3.61	92.50	41,510	59.78
3.12	66.10	29,670	42.72	3.62	93.10	41,780	60.17
3.13	66.60	29,890	43.04	3.63	93.70	42,050	60.56
3.14	67.10	30,110	43.37	3.64	94.30	42,320	60.95
3.15	67.50	30,290	43.63	3.65	94.90	42,590	61.33
3.16	68.00	30,520	43.95	3.66	95.50	42,860	61.72
3.17	68.50	30,740	44.27	3.67	96.10	43,130	62.11
3.18	69.00	30,970	44.59	3.68	96.70	43,400	62.50
3.19	69.50	31,190	44.92	3.69	97.40	43,710	62.95
3.20	70.00	31,420	45.24	3.70	98.00	43,980	63.34
3.21	70.50	31,640	45.56	3.71	98.60	44,250	63.73
3.22	71.00	31,860	45.89	3.72	99.20	44,520	64.11
3.23	71.50	32,090	46.21	3.73	99.80	44,790	64.50
3.24	72.00	32,310	46.53	3.74	100.4	45,080	64.91
3.25	72.50	32,540	46.86	3.75	101.1	45,360	65.33
3.26	73.00	32,760	47.18	3.76	101.7	45,650	65.74
3.27	73.50	32,990	47.50	3.77	102.4	45,940	66.16
3.28	74.00	33,210	47.83	3.78	103.0	46,230	66.57
3.29	74.50	33,440	48.15	3.79	103.6	46,510	66.98
3.30	75.00	33,660	48.47	3.80	104.3	46,800	67.40
3.31	75.50	33,880	48.80	3.81	104.9	47,090	67.81
3.32	76.00	34,110	49.12	3.82	105.6	47,380	68.22
3.33	76.50	34,330	49.44	3.83	106.2	47,660	68.64
3.34	77.00	34,560	49.77	3.84	106.8	47,950	69.05
3.35	77.60	34,830	50.15	3.85	107.5	48,240	69.46
3.36	78.20	35,100	50.54	3.86	108.1	48,520	69.88
3.37	78.70	35,320	50.86	3.87	108.8	48,810	70.29
3.38	79.30	35,590	51.25	3.88	109.4	49,100	70.71
3.39	79.90	35,860	51.64	3.89	110.0	49,390	71.12
3.40	80.50	36,130	52.03	3.90	110.7	49,670	71.53
3.41	80.90	36,310	52.29	3.91	111.3	49,960	71.95
3.42	81.50	36,580	52.67	3.92	112.0	50,250	72.36
3.43	82.00	36,800	53.00	3.93	112.6	50,530	72.77
3.44	82.60	37,070	53.38	3.94	113.2	50,820	73.19
3.45	83.10	37,300	53.71	3.95	113.9	51,110	73.60
3.46	83.60	37,520	54.03	3.96	114.5	51,400	74.01
3.47	84.20	37,790	54.42	3.97	115.2	51,680	74.43
3.48	84.80	38,060	54.81	3.98	115.8	51,970	74.84
3.49	85.30	38,280	55.13	3.99	116.4	52,260	75.26
3.50	85.90	38,550	55.52	4.00	117.1	52,550	75.67

16

Table 16-14:
0.122 m HS Flume Discharge Table with Head in Meters

Source for data in table: U.S.D.A. Handbook No. 224

Table 16-14			Table 16-14 (Continued)		
Head (meters)	l/s	m³/hr	Head (meters)	l/s	m³/hr
0.005	0.0037	0.0134	0.065	0.5854	2.108
0.010	0.0126	0.0454	0.070	0.6884	2.478
0.015	0.0270	0.0971	0.075	0.8015	2.885
0.020	0.0483	0.1740	0.080	0.9253	3.331
0.025	0.0773	0.2781	0.085	1.060	3.817
0.030	0.1142	0.4113	0.090	1.205	4.339
0.035	0.1576	0.5674	0.095	1.362	4.901
0.040	0.2071	0.7457	0.100	1.531	5.512
0.045	0.2652	0.9548	0.105	1.709	6.154
0.050	0.3313	1.193	0.110	1.902	6.845
0.055	0.4070	1.465	0.115	2.105	7.579
0.060	0.4906	1.766	0.120	2.322	8.359

The approximation formulas below fit the data in the table within 1% of full scale.

Formula: $l/s = 310\ H^{2.31}$ $m^3/hr = 1135\ H^{2.31}$ *Where:* H = head in meters

Table 16-15:
0.183 m HS Flume Discharge Table with Head in Meters

Source for data in table: U.S.D.A. Handbook No. 224

Table 16-15			Table 16-15 (Continued)		
Head (meters)	l/s	m³/hr	Head (meters)	l/s	m³/hr
0.005	0.0053	0.0190	0.095	1.501	5.404
0.010	0.0180	0.0649	0.100	1.680	6.048
0.015	0.0380	0.1369	0.105	1.868	6.724
0.020	0.0651	0.2344	0.110	2.069	7.449
0.025	0.0997	0.3591	0.115	2.282	8.216
0.030	0.1421	0.5114	0.120	2.509	9.033
0.035	0.1929	0.6945	0.125	2.747	9.889
0.040	0.2501	0.9002	0.130	2.997	10.79
0.045	0.3155	1.136	0.135	3.276	11.79
0.050	0.3902	1.405	0.140	3.555	12.80
0.055	0.4724	1.701	0.145	3.833	13.80
0.060	0.5672	2.042	0.150	4.146	14.93
0.065	0.6694	2.410	0.155	4.471	16.10
0.070	0.7816	2.814	0.160	4.796	17.27
0.075	0.9040	3.254	0.165	5.150	18.54
0.080	1.037	3.733	0.170	5.496	19.79
0.085	1.181	4.253	0.175	5.896	21.23
0.090	1.337	4.814	0.180	6.268	22.56

The approximation formulas below fit the data in the table within 1% of full scale.

Formula: $l/s = 341\ H^{2.31}$ $m^3/hr = 1210\ H^{2.31}$ *Where:* H = head in meters

16

Table 16-16:
0.244 m HS Flume Discharge Table with Head in Meters

Source for data in table: U.S.D.A. Handbook No. 224

Table 16-16			Table 16-16 (Continued)		
Head (meters)	l/s	m³/hr	Head (meters)	l/s	m³/hr
0.005	0.0070	0.0251	0.125	3.002	10.81
0.010	0.0231	0.0830	0.130	3.252	11.71
0.015	0.0480	0.1727	0.135	3.531	12.71
0.020	0.0812	0.2924	0.140	3.836	13.81
0.025	0.1224	0.4406	0.145	4.132	14.88
0.030	0.1719	0.6189	0.150	4.458	16.05
0.035	0.2306	0.8302	0.155	4.783	17.22
0.040	0.2968	1.068	0.160	5.150	18.54
0.045	0.3708	1.335	0.165	5.496	19.79
0.050	0.4548	1.637	0.170	5.893	21.21
0.055	0.5490	1.976	0.175	6.276	22.59
0.060	0.6503	2.341	0.180	6.694	24.10
0.065	0.7646	2.753	0.185	7.112	25.60
0.070	0.8862	3.190	0.190	7.558	27.21
0.075	1.022	3.680	0.195	8.003	28.81
0.080	1.167	4.200	0.200	8.468	30.48
0.085	1.322	4.760	0.205	8.967	32.28
0.090	1.487	5.355	0.210	9.478	34.12
0.095	1.666	5.999	0.215	9.989	35.96
0.100	1.857	6.684	0.220	10.53	37.90
0.105	2.060	7.416	0.225	11.06	39.82
0.110	2.274	8.185	0.230	11.65	41.93
0.115	2.501	9.002	0.235	12.24	44.05
0.120	2.740	9.862	0.240	12.84	46.22

The approximation formulas below fit the data in the table within 1% of full scale.

Formula: $l/s = 375\ H^{2.31}$ $m^3/hr = 1250\ H^{2.31}$ *Where:* H = head in meters

16

Table 16-17:
0.305 m HS Flume Discharge Table with Head in Meters

Source for data in table: U.S.D.A. Handbook No. 224

Table 16-17			Table 16-17 (Continued)		
Head (meters)	l/s	m³/hr	Head (meters)	l/s	m³/hr
0.005	0.0085	0.0307	0.155	5.151	18.54
0.010	0.0281	0.1012	0.160	5.518	19.86
0.015	0.0576	0.2075	0.165	5.918	21.30
0.020	0.0970	0.3493	0.170	6.311	22.72
0.025	0.1451	0.5224	0.175	6.712	24.16
0.030	0.2025	0.7292	0.180	7.147	25.73
0.035	0.2699	0.9716	0.185	7.584	27.30
0.040	0.3456	1.244	0.190	8.049	28.97
0.045	0.4310	1.552	0.195	8.513	30.65
0.050	0.5251	1.890	0.200	9.006	32.42
0.055	0.6286	2.263	0.205	9.505	34.22
0.060	0.7420	2.671	0.210	10.02	36.06
0.065	0.8665	3.119	0.215	10.57	38.05
0.070	1.002	3.607	0.220	11.13	40.06
0.075	1.148	4.131	0.225	11.71	42.15
0.080	1.305	4.696	0.230	12.28	44.22
0.085	1.474	5.307	0.235	12.89	46.40
0.090	1.653	5.952	0.240	13.52	48.67
0.095	1.846	6.646	0.245	14.16	50.98
0.100	2.050	7.381	0.250	14.84	53.42
0.105	2.266	8.157	0.255	15.51	55.83
0.110	2.495	8.984	0.260	16.20	58.34
0.115	2.737	9.853	0.265	16.93	60.94
0.120	2.996	10.79	0.270	17.64	63.51
0.125	3.257	11.72	0.275	18.39	66.21
0.130	3.535	12.73	0.280	19.18	69.05
0.135	3.842	13.83	0.285	19.97	71.89
0.140	4.147	14.93	0.290	20.76	74.75
0.145	4.472	16.10	0.295	21.60	77.76
0.150	4.803	17.29	0.300	22.44	80.77

The approximation formulas below fit the data in the table within 1% of full scale.

Formula: $l/s = 400\ H^{2.31}$ $m^3/hr = 1303\ H^{2.31}$ *Where:* H = head in meters

16

Table 16-18:
0.152 m H Flume Discharge Table with Head in Meters

Source for data in table: U.S.D.A. Handbook No. 224

Table 16-18			Table 16-18 (Continued)		
Head (meters)	l/s	m³/hr	Head (meters)	l/s	m³/hr
0.005	0.0093	0.0334	0.080	2.218	7.984
0.010	0.0310	0.1117	0.085	2.539	9.140
0.015	0.0662	0.2382	0.090	2.887	10.39
0.020	0.1182	0.4253	0.095	3.264	11.75
0.025	0.1880	0.6770	0.100	3.670	13.21
0.030	0.2765	0.9955	0.105	4.107	14.78
0.035	0.3781	1.361	0.110	4.575	16.47
0.040	0.4998	1.799	0.115	5.076	18.27
0.045	0.6388	2.300	0.120	5.603	20.17
0.050	0.7981	2.873	0.125	6.145	22.12
0.055	0.9761	3.514	0.130	6.767	24.36
0.060	1.179	4.244	0.135	7.389	26.60
0.065	1.403	5.050	0.140	8.039	28.94
0.070	1.650	5.942	0.145	8.734	31.44
0.075	1.925	6.929	0.150	9.465	34.07

The approximation formulas below fit the data in the table within 1% of full scale.

Formula: $l/s = 775\ H^{2.31}$ $m^3/hr = 2750\ H^{2.31}$ *Where:* H = head in meters

16

Table 16-19:
0.229 m H Flume Discharge Table with Head in Meters

Source for data in table: U.S.D.A. Handbook No. 224

Table 16-19			Table 16-19 (Continued)		
Head (meters)	l/s	m³/hr	Head (meters)	l/s	m³/hr
0.005	0.0139	0.0502	0.120	6.108	21.99
0.010	0.0440	0.1582	0.125	6.712	24.16
0.015	0.0884	0.3181	0.130	7.316	26.34
0.020	0.1541	0.5546	0.135	7.956	28.64
0.025	0.2385	0.8584	0.140	8.632	31.07
0.030	0.3455	1.244	0.145	9.344	33.64
0.035	0.4657	1.676	0.150	10.09	36.34
0.040	0.6056	2.180	0.155	10.91	39.26
0.045	0.7628	2.746	0.160	11.74	42.27
0.050	0.9442	3.399	0.165	12.61	45.40
0.055	1.147	4.128	0.170	13.51	48.65
0.060	1.374	4.945	0.175	14.45	52.04
0.065	1.623	5.844	0.180	15.43	55.55
0.070	1.896	6.827	0.185	16.45	59.23
0.075	2.195	7.903	0.190	17.52	63.08
0.080	2.520	9.071	0.195	18.64	67.09
0.085	2.871	10.34	0.200	19.77	71.16
0.090	3.253	11.71	0.205	20.96	75.47
0.095	3.666	13.20	0.210	22.17	79.82
0.100	4.084	14.70	0.215	23.44	84.37
0.105	4.555	16.40	0.220	24.74	89.07
0.110	5.038	18.14	0.225	26.09	93.92
0.115	5.548	19.97			

The approximation formulas below fit the data in the table within 1% of full scale.

Formula: $l/s = 843\ H^{2.31}$ $m^3/hr = 2968\ H^{2.31}$ *Where:* H = head in meters

Table 16-20:
0.305 m H Flume Discharge Table with Head in Meters

Source for data in table: U.S.D.A. Handbook No. 224

Table 16-20			Table 16-20 (Continued)		
Head (meters)	l/s	m³/hr	Head (meters)	l/s	m³/hr
0.005	0.0157	0.0567	0.155	11.70	42.12
0.010	0.0561	0.2019	0.160	12.55	45.18
0.015	0.1103	0.3972	0.165	13.44	48.37
0.020	0.1887	0.6794	0.170	14.36	51.71
0.025	0.2889	1.040	0.175	15.33	55.20
0.030	0.4121	1.484	0.180	16.34	58.81
0.035	0.5504	1.982	0.185	17.38	62.56
0.040	0.7096	2.555	0.190	18.46	66.44
0.045	0.8904	3.205	0.195	19.57	70.45
0.050	1.091	3.929	0.200	20.75	74.69
0.055	1.314	4.732	0.205	21.96	79.06
0.060	1.566	5.639	0.210	23.22	83.58
0.065	1.840	6.625	0.215	24.53	88.30
0.070	2.139	7.701	0.220	25.88	93.16
0.075	2.466	8.878	0.225	27.27	98.18
0.080	2.818	10.14	0.230	28.71	103.3
0.085	3.195	11.50	0.235	30.18	108.6
0.090	3.610	13.00	0.240	31.71	114.2
0.095	4.038	14.54	0.245	33.26	119.7
0.100	4.503	16.21	0.250	34.83	125.4
0.105	5.008	18.03	0.255	36.51	131.4
0.110	5.521	19.88	0.260	38.27	137.8
0.115	6.079	21.88	0.265	39.86	143.5
0.120	6.674	24.03	0.270	41.70	150.1
0.125	7.278	26.20	0.275	43.56	156.8
0.130	7.928	28.54	0.280	45.41	163.5
0.135	8.615	31.01	0.285	47.55	171.2
0.140	9.338	33.62	0.290	49.41	177.9
0.145	10.10	36.35	0.295	51.49	185.3
0.150	10.89	39.19	0.300	53.52	192.7

The approximation formulas below fit the data in the table within 1% of full scale.

Formula: $l/s = 863.7 \, H^{2.31}$ $m^3/hr = 3109 \, H^{2.31}$ *Where:* H = head in meters

16

Table 16-21:
0.457 m H Flume Discharge Table with Head in Meters

Source for data in table: U.S.D.A. Handbook No. 224

Head (meters)	l/s	m³/hr	Head (meters)	l/s	m³/hr
0.005	0.0250	0.0901	0.235	33.01	118.8
0.010	0.0778	0.2802	0.240	34.59	124.5
0.015	0.1573	0.5664	0.245	36.27	130.6
0.020	0.2605	0.9380	0.250	37.95	136.6
0.025	0.3897	1.403	0.255	39.63	142.7
0.030	0.5501	1.980	0.260	41.38	149.0
0.035	0.7242	2.607	0.265	43.24	155.7
0.040	0.9190	3.309	0.270	45.10	162.3
0.045	1.139	4.101	0.275	46.95	169.0
0.050	1.386	4.990	0.280	48.81	175.7
0.055	1.655	5.959	0.285	50.95	183.4
0.060	1.954	7.033	0.290	52.85	190.2
0.065	2.276	8.194	0.295	54.95	197.8
0.070	2.628	9.460	0.300	57.21	205.9
0.075	3.006	10.82	0.305	59.25	213.3
0.080	3.413	12.29	0.310	61.57	221.6
0.085	3.850	13.86	0.315	63.98	230.3
0.090	4.310	15.52	0.320	66.50	239.4
0.095	4.808	17.31	0.325	68.82	247.7
0.100	5.341	19.23	0.330	71.21	256.3
0.105	5.898	21.23	0.335	73.75	265.5
0.110	6.486	23.35	0.340	76.50	275.4
0.115	7.111	25.60	0.345	79.00	284.4
0.120	7.761	27.94	0.350	81.79	294.4
0.125	8.439	30.38	0.355	84.57	304.5
0.130	9.182	33.06	0.360	87.36	314.5
0.135	9.934	35.76	0.365	90.15	324.5
0.140	10.72	38.60	0.370	93.22	335.6
0.145	11.56	41.60	0.375	96.00	345.6
0.150	12.43	44.74	0.380	99.07	356.7
0.155	13.31	47.91	0.385	102.2	368.0
0.160	14.25	51.29	0.390	105.5	379.7
0.165	15.23	54.81	0.395	108.7	391.4
0.170	16.25	58.49	0.400	112.0	403.1
0.175	17.28	62.21	0.405	115.2	414.8
0.180	18.38	66.16	0.410	118.5	426.5
0.185	19.51	70.24	0.415	122.0	439.2
0.190	20.67	74.42	0.420	125.5	451.7
0.195	21.86	78.70	0.425	128.9	464.1
0.200	23.11	83.21	0.430	132.6	477.5
0.205	24.40	87.85	0.435	136.3	490.8
0.210	25.73	92.63	0.440	140.1	504.2
0.215	27.12	97.63	0.445	143.8	517.6
0.220	28.52	102.7	0.450	147.5	531.0
0.225	29.98	107.9	0.455	151.6	545.6
0.230	31.48	113.3			

The approximation formulas below fit the data in the table within 1% of full scale.

Formula: $l/s = 970\ H^{2.31}$ $m^3/hr = 3410\ H^{2.31}$ *Where:* H = head in meters

Table 16-22:
0.610 m H Flume Discharge Table with Head in Meters

Source for data in table: U.S.D.A. Handbook No. 224

Table 16-22			Table 16-22 (Continued)		
Head (meters)	l/s	m³/hr	Head (meters)	l/s	m³/hr
0.005	0.0325	0.1170	0.255	42.92	154.5
0.010	0.1029	0.3703	0.260	44.86	161.5
0.015	0.2015	0.7255	0.265	46.92	168.9
0.020	0.3308	1.191	0.270	48.78	175.6
0.025	0.4922	1.772	0.275	50.69	182.5
0.030	0.6829	2.458	0.280	52.78	190.0
0.035	0.8950	3.222	0.285	54.92	197.7
0.040	1.129	4.064	0.290	57.09	205.5
0.045	1.391	5.007	0.295	59.20	213.1
0.050	1.679	6.046	0.300	61.45	221.2
0.055	1.994	7.177	0.305	63.78	229.6
0.060	2.338	8.418	0.310	66.10	238.0
0.065	2.711	9.759	0.315	68.42	246.3
0.070	3.114	11.21	0.320	71.02	255.7
0.075	3.546	12.76	0.325	73.52	264.7
0.080	4.007	14.43	0.330	76.02	273.7
0.085	4.500	16.20	0.335	78.56	282.8
0.090	5.025	18.09	0.340	81.31	292.7
0.095	5.577	20.08	0.345	84.10	302.8
0.100	6.157	22.16	0.350	86.89	312.8
0.105	6.801	24.48	0.355	89.67	322.8
0.110	7.452	26.83	0.360	92.46	332.9
0.115	8.122	29.24	0.365	95.25	342.9
0.120	8.857	31.89	0.370	98.32	353.9
0.125	9.600	34.56	0.375	101.4	365.0
0.130	10.41	37.47	0.380	104.5	376.0
0.135	11.24	40.48	0.385	107.6	387.4
0.140	12.11	43.58	0.390	110.9	399.1
0.145	13.00	46.82	0.395	114.1	410.8
0.150	13.94	50.18	0.400	117.4	422.5
0.155	14.91	53.69	0.405	120.8	435.0
0.160	15.93	57.35	0.410	124.3	447.4
0.165	16.99	61.15	0.415	127.7	459.8
0.170	18.07	65.07	0.420	131.4	473.1
0.175	19.20	69.12	0.425	135.1	486.5
0.180	20.39	73.41	0.430	138.9	499.9
0.185	21.60	77.76	0.435	142.6	513.3
0.190	22.85	82.27	0.440	146.4	527.0
0.195	24.15	86.95	0.445	150.3	541.0
0.200	25.47	91.70	0.450	154.3	555.4
0.205	26.85	96.67	0.455	158.3	569.8
0.210	28.27	101.8	0.460	162.3	584.1
0.215	29.76	107.1	0.465	166.4	599.2
0.220	31.29	112.6	0.470	170.7	614.4
0.225	32.68	117.7	0.475	175.1	630.3
0.230	34.36	123.7	0.480	179.3	645.3
0.235	36.03	129.7	0.485	183.7	661.5
0.240	37.63	135.5	0.490	188.2	677.5
0.245	39.49	142.2	0.495	192.7	693.9
0.250	41.35	148.8	0.500	197.4	710.6

16

Table 16-22 (Continued)				Table 16-22 (Continued)		
Head (meters)	l/s	m³/hr		Head (meters)	l/s	m³/hr
0.505	202.0	727.3		0.560	257.5	926.9
0.510	206.7	744.0		0.565	262.8	946.0
0.515	211.3	760.8		0.570	268.3	966.0
0.520	216.3	778.5		0.575	273.9	986.1
0.525	221.2	796.4		0.580	279.8	1007
0.530	226.1	814.0		0.585	285.3	1027
0.535	231.2	832.2		0.590	291.1	1048
0.540	236.3	850.6		0.595	297.1	1070
0.545	241.6	869.8		0.600	302.9	1090
0.550	246.8	888.4		0.605	308.9	1112
0.555	252.2	907.8				

The approximation formulas below fit the data in the table within 1% of full scale.

Formula: $l/s = 1025\ H^{2.31}$ $m^3/hr = 3523.7\ H^{2.31}$ *Where:* H = head in meters

16

Table 16-23:
0.762 m H Flume Discharge Table with Head in Meters

Source for data in table: U.S.D.A. Handbook No. 224

Table 16-23			Table 16-23 (Continued)		
Head (meters)	l/s	m³/hr	Head (meters)	l/s	m³/hr
0.005	0.0418	0.1505	0.255	46.32	166.8
0.010	0.1259	0.4531	0.260	48.46	174.5
0.015	0.2457	0.8845	0.265	50.32	181.1
0.020	0.4014	1.445	0.270	52.46	188.9
0.025	0.5930	2.135	0.275	54.60	196.6
0.030	0.8208	2.955	0.280	56.70	204.1
0.035	1.067	3.842	0.285	59.02	212.5
0.040	1.338	4.818	0.290	61.34	220.8
0.045	1.640	5.902	0.295	63.66	229.2
0.050	1.971	7.096	0.300	65.99	237.5
0.055	2.332	8.394	0.305	68.31	245.9
0.060	2.725	9.809	0.310	70.63	254.3
0.065	3.147	11.33	0.315	73.24	263.6
0.070	3.600	12.96	0.320	75.83	273.0
0.075	4.087	14.71	0.325	78.45	282.4
0.080	4.602	16.57	0.330	81.12	292.0
0.085	5.153	18.55	0.335	83.91	302.1
0.090	5.742	20.67	0.340	86.69	312.1
0.095	6.350	22.86	0.345	89.48	322.1
0.100	7.001	25.20	0.350	92.27	332.2
0.105	7.692	27.69	0.355	95.18	342.6
0.110	8.419	30.31	0.360	98.15	353.3
0.115	9.162	32.98	0.365	101.2	364.3
0.120	9.954	35.83	0.370	104.4	375.7
0.125	10.79	38.84	0.375	107.6	387.4
0.130	11.64	41.92	0.380	110.6	398.1
0.135	12.53	45.12	0.385	113.8	409.8
0.140	13.49	48.56	0.390	117.3	422.4
0.145	14.46	52.07	0.395	120.6	434.2
0.150	15.47	55.71	0.400	124.2	447.0
0.155	16.52	59.47	0.405	127.6	459.5
0.160	17.63	63.47	0.410	131.1	471.9
0.165	18.75	67.49	0.415	134.8	485.1
0.170	19.93	71.75	0.420	138.2	497.6
0.175	21.15	76.14	0.425	141.9	511.0
0.180	22.40	80.66	0.430	145.9	525.4
0.185	23.70	85.34	0.435	149.7	538.8
0.190	25.04	90.15	0.440	153.5	552.5
0.195	26.42	95.10	0.445	157.4	566.5
0.200	27.86	100.3	0.450	161.5	581.5
0.205	29.30	105.5	0.455	165.4	595.6
0.210	30.81	110.9	0.460	169.6	610.6
0.215	32.44	116.8	0.465	173.8	625.7
0.220	33.88	122.0	0.470	178.0	640.9
0.225	35.74	128.7	0.475	182.4	656.8
0.230	37.31	134.3	0.480	186.7	672.3
0.235	39.15	140.9	0.485	191.4	688.9
0.240	40.75	146.7	0.490	195.7	704.7
0.245	42.60	153.4	0.495	200.4	721.4
0.250	44.46	160.1	0.500	205.0	738.1

16

Table 16-23 (Continued)			Table 16-23 (Continued)		
Head (meters)	l/s	m³/hr	Head (meters)	l/s	m³/hr
0.505	209.9	755.5	0.635	357.6	1287
0.510	214.7	772.9	0.640	364.9	1314
0.515	219.5	790.3	0.645	371.3	1337
0.520	224.3	807.6	0.650	377.8	1360
0.525	229.4	826.0	0.655	384.7	1385
0.530	234.6	844.4	0.660	392.2	1412
0.535	239.8	863.3	0.665	399.7	1439
0.540	245.1	882.2	0.670	406.4	1463
0.545	250.4	901.4	0.675	412.9	1486
0.550	255.7	920.4	0.680	419.4	1510
0.555	261.2	940.5	0.685	426.7	1536
0.560	266.6	959.9	0.690	435.1	1566
0.565	272.2	979.9	0.695	441.7	1590
0.570	278.0	1001	0.700	450.9	1623
0.575	283.5	1021	0.705	457.3	1646
0.580	289.5	1042	0.710	464.1	1671
0.585	294.2	1059	0.715	473.1	1703
0.590	301.7	1086	0.720	481.9	1735
0.595	306.8	1104	0.725	488.8	1760
0.600	313.8	1130	0.730	496.8	1789
0.605	319.7	1151	0.735	504.5	1816
0.610	325.9	1173	0.740	513.8	1850
0.615	332.6	1197	0.745	520.3	1873
0.620	338.0	1217	0.750	529.6	1907
0.625	345.5	1244	0.755	538.9	1940
0.630	352.0	1267	0.760	545.3	1963

The approximation formulas below fit the data in the table within 1% of full scale.

Formula: $l/s = 1045\ H^{2.31}$ $m^3/hr = 3780\ H^{2.31}$ *Where:* H = head in meters

16

Table 16-24:
0.914 m H Flume Discharge Table with Head in Meters

Source for data in table: U.S.D.A. Handbook No. 224

Table 16-24			Table 16-24 (Continued)		
Head (meters)	l/s	m³/hr	Head (meters)	l/s	m³/hr
0.005	0.0483	0.1737	0.255	49.90	179.6
0.010	0.1496	0.5387	0.260	51.86	186.7
0.015	0.2901	1.044	0.265	53.98	194.3
0.020	0.4732	1.703	0.270	56.14	202.1
0.025	0.6933	2.496	0.275	58.34	210.0
0.030	0.9560	3.441	0.280	60.66	218.4
0.035	1.240	4.463	0.285	62.98	226.7
0.040	1.548	5.573	0.290	65.31	235.1
0.045	1.891	6.808	0.295	67.84	244.2
0.050	2.266	8.156	0.300	70.23	252.8
0.055	2.670	9.611	0.305	72.84	262.2
0.060	3.111	11.20	0.310	75.35	271.3
0.065	3.583	12.90	0.315	77.86	280.3
0.070	4.094	14.74	0.320	80.64	290.3
0.075	4.622	16.64	0.325	83.43	300.4
0.080	5.186	18.67	0.330	86.22	310.4
0.085	5.815	20.93	0.335	89.00	320.4
0.090	6.437	23.17	0.340	91.79	330.4
0.095	7.120	25.63	0.345	94.86	341.5
0.100	7.839	28.22	0.350	97.65	351.5
0.105	8.582	30.90	0.355	100.8	363.0
0.110	9.358	33.69	0.360	103.8	373.7
0.115	10.19	36.70	0.365	107.1	385.4
0.120	11.04	39.74	0.370	110.3	397.1
0.125	11.92	42.92	0.375	113.6	408.8
0.130	12.87	46.33	0.380	116.8	420.5
0.135	13.85	49.84	0.385	120.3	433.3
0.140	14.85	53.45	0.390	123.6	445.0
0.145	15.91	57.28	0.395	127.3	458.3
0.150	17.01	61.25	0.400	130.7	470.6
0.155	18.13	65.27	0.405	134.4	484.0
0.160	19.30	69.48	0.410	138.2	497.4
0.165	20.51	73.84	0.415	141.9	510.7
0.170	21.76	78.35	0.420	145.6	524.1
0.175	23.07	83.05	0.425	149.4	537.9
0.180	24.42	87.90	0.430	153.3	551.9
0.185	25.78	92.82	0.435	157.3	566.3
0.190	27.21	97.97	0.440	161.4	581.0
0.195	28.68	103.2	0.445	165.3	595.1
0.200	30.21	108.8	0.450	169.5	610.1
0.205	31.75	114.3	0.455	173.6	625.1
0.210	33.36	120.1	0.460	178.1	641.1
0.215	34.99	126.0	0.465	182.3	656.2
0.220	36.71	132.2	0.470	186.8	672.3
0.225	38.35	138.0	0.475	191.2	688.2
0.230	40.15	144.5	0.480	195.7	704.4
0.235	42.00	151.2	0.485	200.2	720.6
0.240	43.86	157.9	0.490	204.8	737.3
0.245	45.82	165.0	0.495	209.6	754.4
0.250	47.86	172.3	0.500	214.4	771.8

16

Table 16-24 (Continued)			Table 16-24 (Continued)		
Head (meters)	l/s	m³/hr	Head (meters)	l/s	m³/hr
0.505	219.2	789.1	0.710	477.9	1721
0.510	224.0	806.5	0.715	485.7	1749
0.515	229.1	824.9	0.720	493.7	1777
0.520	234.0	842.3	0.725	503.0	1811
0.525	239.1	860.7	0.730	509.4	1834
0.530	244.2	879.1	0.735	518.7	1867
0.535	249.4	898.0	0.740	528.0	1901
0.540	254.7	917.0	0.745	534.5	1924
0.545	260.1	936.3	0.750	543.7	1957
0.550	265.6	956.1	0.755	553.0	1991
0.555	270.9	975.2	0.760	561.5	2022
0.560	276.4	995.2	0.765	568.8	2048
0.565	282.1	1016	0.770	578.1	2081
0.570	287.9	1036	0.775	587.4	2114
0.575	293.5	1056	0.780	596.6	2148
0.580	298.7	1075	0.785	605.9	2181
0.585	305.5	1100	0.790	615.2	2215
0.590	310.2	1117	0.795	624.5	2248
0.595	317.6	1143	0.800	633.8	2282
0.600	322.3	1160	0.805	643.1	2315
0.605	329.8	1187	0.810	652.4	2349
0.610	337.2	1214	0.815	661.7	2382
0.615	341.9	1231	0.820	671.0	2415
0.620	349.4	1258	0.825	680.2	2449
0.625	356.8	1285	0.830	689.5	2482
0.630	361.5	1301	0.835	698.8	2516
0.635	369.0	1328	0.840	709.6	2555
0.640	376.2	1354	0.845	720.2	2593
0.645	382.7	1378	0.850	729.5	2626
0.650	389.1	1401	0.855	738.8	2660
0.655	396.0	1426	0.860	750.9	2703
0.660	403.5	1453	0.865	760.2	2737
0.665	411.0	1480	0.870	770.5	2774
0.670	417.8	1504	0.875	781.6	2814
0.675	424.2	1527	0.880	790.9	2847
0.680	433.4	1560	0.885	803.0	2891
0.685	440.0	1584	0.890	812.3	2924
0.690	446.4	1607	0.895	823.2	2964
0.695	455.7	1641	0.900	834.3	3004
0.700	462.2	1664	0.905	845.9	3045
0.705	470.8	1695	0.910	856.5	3083

The approximation formulas below fit the data in the table within 1% of full scale.

Formula: $l/s = 1064.98\ H^{2.31}$ $m^3/hr = 3900\ H^{2.31}$ *Where:* H = head in meters

16

Table 16-25:
1.37 m H Flume Discharge Table with Head in Meters

Source for data in table: U.S.D.A. Handbook No. 224

Table 16-25			Table 16-25 (Continued)		
Head (meters)	l/s	m³/hr	Head (meters)	l/s	m³/hr
0.005	0.0715	0.2573	0.255	60.10	216.3
0.010	0.2186	0.7871	0.260	62.42	224.7
0.015	0.4253	1.531	0.265	64.74	233.1
0.020	0.6858	2.469	0.270	67.34	242.4
0.025	0.9974	3.591	0.275	69.72	251.0
0.030	1.367	4.921	0.280	72.27	260.2
0.035	1.757	6.323	0.285	75.01	270.1
0.040	2.180	7.847	0.290	77.77	280.0
0.045	2.645	9.523	0.295	80.30	289.1
0.050	3.150	11.34	0.300	83.20	299.5
0.055	3.690	13.28	0.305	86.16	310.2
0.060	4.272	15.38	0.310	88.95	320.2
0.065	4.885	17.58	0.315	91.82	330.6
0.070	5.535	19.93	0.320	94.80	341.3
0.075	6.230	22.43	0.325	98.04	353.0
0.080	6.969	25.09	0.330	101.0	363.6
0.085	7.759	27.93	0.335	104.3	375.3
0.090	8.563	30.83	0.340	107.5	387.1
0.095	9.432	33.95	0.345	110.8	398.8
0.100	10.31	37.13	0.350	114.0	410.5
0.105	11.25	40.50	0.355	117.6	423.2
0.110	12.23	44.02	0.360	121.1	435.9
0.115	13.25	47.70	0.365	124.5	448.3
0.120	14.31	51.51	0.370	128.3	461.7
0.125	15.41	55.46	0.375	131.7	474.1
0.130	16.57	59.64	0.380	135.4	487.5
0.135	17.76	63.95	0.385	139.2	501.1
0.140	19.00	68.39	0.390	143.1	515.2
0.145	20.27	72.97	0.395	146.8	528.6
0.150	21.57	77.67	0.400	150.8	543.0
0.155	22.94	82.60	0.405	154.8	557.2
0.160	24.35	87.67	0.410	159.0	572.3
0.165	25.79	92.86	0.415	162.9	586.3
0.170	27.30	98.29	0.420	167.0	601.4
0.175	28.85	103.8	0.425	171.5	617.4
0.180	30.43	109.5	0.430	175.7	632.5
0.185	32.01	115.2	0.435	180.1	648.2
0.190	32.89	118.4	0.440	184.4	663.9
0.195	35.26	126.9	0.445	189.1	680.6
0.200	37.21	134.0	0.450	193.4	696.3
0.205	39.29	141.4	0.455	198.1	713.1
0.210	40.93	147.3	0.460	202.7	729.8
0.215	42.79	154.0	0.465	207.4	746.5
0.220	44.93	161.7	0.470	212.3	764.4
0.225	46.78	168.4	0.475	217.2	782.0
0.230	48.93	176.1	0.480	222.1	799.7
0.235	51.07	183.8	0.485	227.1	817.5
0.240	53.13	191.3	0.490	232.2	835.9
0.245	55.45	199.6	0.495	237.3	854.3
0.250	57.77	208.0	0.500	242.4	872.7

16

Table 16-25 (Continued)				Table 16-25 (Continued)		
Head (meters)	l/s	m³/hr		Head (meters)	l/s	m³/hr
0.505	247.8	892.1		0.755	598.3	2154
0.510	253.0	910.8		0.760	607.6	2187
0.515	258.6	930.9		0.765	616.9	2221
0.520	263.9	949.9		0.770	626.2	2254
0.525	269.4	970.0		0.775	635.5	2288
0.530	275.0	990.0		0.780	644.8	2321
0.535	280.7	1011		0.785	654.1	2355
0.540	286.4	1031		0.790	663.4	2388
0.545	292.2	1052		0.795	672.7	2422
0.550	298.5	1075		0.800	681.9	2455
0.555	303.1	1091		0.805	691.2	2488
0.560	309.7	1115		0.810	702.4	2529
0.565	315.3	1135		0.815	712.6	2566
0.570	322.6	1161		0.820	721.9	2599
0.575	327.4	1179		0.825	731.2	2632
0.580	334.9	1205		0.830	741.2	2668
0.585	339.5	1222		0.835	752.6	2709
0.590	347.0	1249		0.840	761.9	2743
0.595	354.5	1276		0.845	771.2	2776
0.600	361.4	1301		0.850	782.8	2818
0.605	366.6	1320		0.855	792.6	2853
0.610	374.1	1347		0.860	804.7	2897
0.615	380.7	1371		0.865	814.0	2931
0.620	386.2	1390		0.870	824.3	2968
0.625	393.6	1417		0.875	835.4	3008
0.630	401.1	1444		0.880	846.5	3048
0.635	408.6	1471		0.885	856.8	3085
0.640	415.9	1497		0.890	868.7	3127
0.645	422.3	1520		0.895	879.8	3167
0.650	431.0	1552		0.900	890.9	3207
0.655	438.1	1577		0.905	902.5	3249
0.660	444.5	1600		0.910	914.6	3293
0.665	451.0	1623		0.915	926.7	3336
0.670	460.3	1657		0.920	938.2	3377
0.675	466.7	1680		0.925	949.3	3417
0.680	475.9	1713		0.930	960.4	3457
0.685	482.5	1737		0.935	972.4	3501
0.690	490.8	1767		0.940	985.4	3548
0.695	498.2	1794		0.945	996.6	3588
0.700	507.5	1827		0.950	1010	3638
0.705	514.0	1850		0.955	1022	3678
0.710	523.2	1884		0.960	1035	3728
0.715	531.1	1912		0.965	1047	3768
0.720	539.0	1940		0.970	1061	3818
0.725	548.3	1974		0.975	1072	3860
0.730	556.3	2003		0.980	1086	3908
0.735	564.0	2030		0.985	1099	3957
0.740	573.3	2064		0.990	1111	3998
0.745	582.6	2097		0.995	1125	4048
0.750	591.9	2131		1.000	1138	4098

16

Table 16-25 (Continued)			Table 16-25 (Continued)		
Head (meters)	l/s	m³/hr	Head (meters)	l/s	m³/hr
1.005	1152	4149	1.190	1708	6151
1.010	1168	4203	1.195	1727	6217
1.015	1177	4239	1.200	1743	6274
1.020	1191	4289	1.205	1761	6339
1.025	1205	4339	1.210	1777	6398
1.030	1219	4389	1.215	1796	6465
1.035	1233	4439	1.220	1811	6521
1.040	1247	4490	1.225	1830	6588
1.045	1261	4540	1.230	1847	6651
1.050	1275	4590	1.235	1864	6712
1.055	1289	4640	1.240	1883	6779
1.060	1303	4690	1.245	1902	6845
1.065	1318	4744	1.250	1920	6912
1.070	1334	4801	1.255	1937	6973
1.075	1347	4851	1.260	1954	7036
1.080	1361	4901	1.265	1973	7103
1.085	1375	4951	1.270	1992	7170
1.090	1392	5012	1.275	2010	7237
1.095	1406	5062	1.280	2029	7303
1.100	1422	5120	1.285	2047	7370
1.105	1437	5172	1.290	2066	7437
1.110	1451	5223	1.295	2087	7512
1.115	1467	5283	1.300	2106	7581
1.120	1482	5337	1.305	2124	7648
1.125	1498	5393	1.310	2143	7715
1.130	1514	5450	1.315	2162	7782
1.135	1530	5507	1.320	2183	7858
1.140	1546	5564	1.325	2202	7926
1.145	1561	5620	1.330	2221	7995
1.150	1577	5677	1.335	2242	8070
1.155	1593	5735	1.340	2260	8137
1.160	1610	5795	1.345	2282	8214
1.165	1627	5856	1.350	2300	8281
1.170	1643	5914	1.355	2322	8358
1.175	1658	5970	1.360	2340	8425
1.180	1677	6037	1.365	2362	8502
1.185	1693	6094	1.370	2384	8582

16

Table 16-26:
1.22 m HL Flume Discharge Table with Head in Feet

Source: U.S.D.A. Handbook No. 224

Table 16-26			Table 16-26 (Continued)		
Head (meters)	l/s	m³/hr	Head (meters)	l/s	m³/hr
0.005	0.1161	0.4180	0.255	109.0	392.3
0.010	0.4033	1.452	0.260	113.5	408.6
0.015	0.8009	2.883	0.265	118.2	425.3
0.020	1.279	4.604	0.270	122.8	442.1
0.025	1.829	6.586	0.275	127.4	458.8
0.030	2.457	8.845	0.280	132.1	475.5
0.035	3.134	11.28	0.285	137.1	493.7
0.040	3.881	13.97	0.290	142.3	512.1
0.045	4.692	16.89	0.295	147.4	530.5
0.050	5.619	20.23	0.300	152.5	548.9
0.055	6.596	23.75	0.305	157.6	567.3
0.060	7.665	27.59	0.310	163.2	587.4
0.065	8.779	31.61	0.315	168.7	607.5
0.070	9.940	35.79	0.320	174.3	627.5
0.075	11.16	40.19	0.325	179.9	647.6
0.080	12.50	45.01	0.330	185.5	667.7
0.085	13.97	50.28	0.335	191.0	687.7
0.090	15.53	55.89	0.340	197.0	709.3
0.095	17.15	61.74	0.345	203.1	731.1
0.100	18.78	67.59	0.350	209.1	752.8
0.105	20.40	73.45	0.355	215.2	774.5
0.110	22.18	79.85	0.360	221.2	796.3
0.115	24.04	86.54	0.365	227.2	818.0
0.120	25.90	93.22	0.370	233.8	841.5
0.125	27.81	100.1	0.375	240.7	866.6
0.130	30.08	108.3	0.380	247.7	891.7
0.135	32.11	115.6	0.385	254.7	916.8
0.140	34.44	124.0	0.390	261.6	941.8
0.145	36.76	132.3	0.395	268.6	966.9
0.150	39.08	140.7	0.400	275.8	993.0
0.155	41.64	149.9	0.405	285.1	1026
0.160	44.15	158.9	0.410	291.6	1050
0.165	46.65	167.9	0.415	298.0	1073
0.170	49.44	178.0	0.420	305.2	1099
0.175	52.22	188.0	0.425	313.8	1130
0.180	55.02	198.1	0.430	323.1	1163
0.185	58.08	209.1	0.435	330.4	1190
0.190	61.24	220.5	0.440	338.8	1220
0.195	64.49	232.2	0.445	348.1	1253
0.200	67.74	243.9	0.450	354.6	1276
0.205	70.99	255.6	0.455	363.9	1310
0.210	74.49	268.2	0.460	373.1	1343
0.215	77.93	280.5	0.465	379.6	1367
0.220	81.64	293.9	0.470	388.9	1400
0.225	85.36	307.3	0.475	398.2	1433
0.230	89.07	320.7	0.480	407.5	1467
0.235	93.07	335.1	0.485	416.8	1500
0.240	96.79	348.4	0.490	426.0	1534
0.245	100.8	362.8	0.495	435.3	1567
0.250	104.8	377.2	0.500	444.6	1601

Table 16-26 (Continued)			Table 16-26 (Continued)		
Head (meters)	l/s	m³/hr	Head (meters)	l/s	m³/hr
0.505	455.7	1641	0.755	1104	3975
0.510	466.0	1678	0.760	1122	4039
0.515	475.3	1711	0.765	1140	4105
0.520	484.6	1745	0.770	1156	4162
0.525	493.9	1778	0.775	1174	4227
0.530	503.2	1811	0.780	1190	4286
0.535	515.3	1855	0.785	1206	4342
0.540	524.6	1889	0.790	1225	4409
0.545	536.0	1930	0.795	1241	4468
0.550	546.0	1966	0.800	1259	4533
0.555	558.1	2009	0.805	1278	4600
0.560	569.3	2050	0.810	1294	4660
0.565	579.5	2086	0.815	1312	4723
0.570	591.5	2130	0.820	1333	4800
0.575	603.8	2174	0.825	1352	4867
0.580	615.9	2217	0.830	1368	4924
0.585	625.2	2251	0.835	1386	4991
0.590	638.8	2300	0.840	1405	5058
0.595	652.3	2348	0.845	1424	5126
0.600	661.6	2382	0.850	1445	5202
0.605	674.9	2430	0.855	1466	5279
0.610	688.6	2479	0.860	1485	5346
0.615	700.0	2520	0.865	1505	5420
0.620	711.1	2560	0.870	1525	5490
0.625	725.0	2610	0.875	1543	5556
0.630	736.1	2650	0.880	1564	5630
0.635	750.0	2700	0.885	1586	5711
0.640	764.0	2750	0.890	1605	5777
0.645	777.9	2800	0.895	1626	5854
0.650	791.8	2851	0.900	1648	5934
0.655	805.8	2901	0.905	1671	6017
0.660	819.7	2951	0.910	1690	6086
0.665	833.6	3001	0.915	1709	6154
0.670	847.6	3051	0.920	1733	6237
0.675	861.5	3101	0.925	1756	6321
0.680	875.4	3152	0.930	1779	6404
0.685	889.4	3202	0.935	1799	6478
0.690	906.1	3262	0.940	1820	6551
0.695	920.1	3312	0.945	1843	6635
0.700	934.0	3362	0.950	1866	6719
0.705	950.8	3423	0.955	1890	6802
0.710	964.7	3473	0.960	1910	6877
0.715	981.5	3533	0.965	1933	6959
0.720	995.4	3583	0.970	1956	7043
0.725	1012	3642	0.975	1980	7126
0.730	1027	3698	0.980	2003	7210
0.735	1043	3754	0.985	2026	7294
0.740	1057	3804	0.990	2049	7377
0.745	1075	3868	0.995	2072	7461
0.750	1090	3925	1.000	2096	7544

16

Table 16-26 (Continued)			Table 16-26 (Continued)		
Head (meters)	l/s	m³/hr	Head (meters)	l/s	m³/hr
1.005	2119	7628	1.115	2700	9719
1.010	2142	7712	1.120	2728	9820
1.015	2165	7795	1.125	2758	9930
1.020	2190	7885	1.130	2786	10,030
1.025	2217	7983	1.135	2814	10,130
1.030	2243	8075	1.140	2843	10,230
1.035	2271	8175	1.145	2873	10,340
1.040	2293	8255	1.150	2902	10,450
1.045	2319	8348	1.155	2932	10,560
1.050	2345	8442	1.160	2962	10,660
1.055	2368	8526	1.165	2992	10,770
1.060	2396	8626	1.170	3021	10,880
1.065	2421	8716	1.175	3051	10,980
1.070	2449	8816	1.180	3081	11,090
1.075	2477	8917	1.185	3111	11,200
1.080	2505	9017	1.190	3140	11,300
1.085	2533	9117	1.195	3170	11,410
1.090	2560	9218	1.200	3200	11,520
1.095	2588	9318	1.205	3229	11,630
1.100	2616	9418	1.210	3259	11,730
1.105	2644	9519	1.215	3289	11,840
1.110	2672	9619			

16

CHAPTER
17
Trapezoidal Flume Discharge Tables

Overview

This chapter contains discharge (head vs. flow rate) tables for trapezoidal flumes (manufactured by Plasti-Fab, Inc.). Note that all of the tabular data is for free flow. [1]

Discharge tables for trapezoidal flumes with head in feet

17-1: Large 60° V Trapezoidal Flume
17-2: Extra Large 60° V Trapezoidal Flume
17-3: 2 in. 45° WSC Trapezoidal Flume
17-4: 12 in. 45° SRCRC Trapezoidal Flume

The discharges of the flumes are listed in three different units of measure:
CFS - cubic feet per second   GPM - gallons per minute
MGD - million gallons per day

Discharge tables for trapezoidal flumes with head in meters

17-5: Large 60° V Trapezoidal Flume
17-6: Extra Large 60° V Trapezoidal Flume
17-7: 2 in. 45° WSC Trapezoidal Flume
17-8: 12 in. 45° SRCRC Trapezoidal Flume

The discharges of the flumes are listed in two different units of measure:
l/s - liters per second m^3/hr - cubic meters per hour

The data in the tables are provided by Plasti-Fab, Inc. The formulas that follow each table are approximation formulas which fit the data within 1% of full scale.

---

1. All trapezoidal flume data, © Copyright Plasti-Fab, Inc., Taulatin, Oregon

Table 17-1:
Large 60° V Trapezoidal Flume Discharge Table
with Head in Feet

Data in table from Plasti-Fab, Inc.

Head (feet)	CFS	GPM	MGD	Head (feet)	CFS	GPM	MGD
0.01				0.29	0.0636	28.53	0.0411
0.02				0.30	0.0694	31.14	0.0449
0.03				0.31	0.0755	33.89	0.0488
0.04	0.0004	0.1721	0.0002	0.32	0.0820	36.78	0.0530
0.05	0.0007	0.3060	0.0004	0.33	0.0887	39.82	0.0574
0.06	0.0011	0.4898	0.0007	0.34	0.0958	43.01	0.0620
0.07	0.0016	0.7290	0.0011	0.35	0.1033	46.35	0.0668
0.08	0.0023	1.029	0.0015	0.36	0.1111	49.84	0.0718
0.09	0.0031	1.394	0.0020	0.37	0.1192	53.50	0.0771
0.10	0.0041	1.830	0.0026	0.38	0.1277	57.31	0.0825
0.11	0.0052	2.340	0.0034	0.39	0.1365	61.28	0.0883
0.12	0.0065	2.929	0.0042	0.40	0.1458	65.41	0.0942
0.13	0.0080	3.600	0.0052	0.41	0.1554	69.72	0.1004
0.14	0.0097	4.359	0.0063	0.42	0.1653	74.19	0.1069
0.15	0.0116	5.208	0.0075	0.43	0.1757	78.83	0.1136
0.16	0.0137	6.152	0.0089	0.44	0.1864	83.65	0.1205
0.17	0.0160	7.193	0.0104	0.45	0.1975	88.64	0.1277
0.18	0.0186	8.336	0.0120	0.46	0.2090	93.82	0.1351
0.19	0.0214	9.584	0.0138	0.47	0.2210	99.17	0.1428
0.20	0.0244	10.94	0.0158	0.48	0.2333	104.7	0.1508
0.21	0.0276	12.41	0.0179	0.49	0.2461	110.4	0.1591
0.22	0.0312	13.99	0.0202	0.50	0.2592	116.3	0.1676
0.23	0.0350	15.69	0.0226	0.51	0.2728	122.4	0.1764
0.24	0.0390	17.51	0.0252	0.52	0.2868	128.7	0.1854
0.25	0.0434	19.46	0.0280	0.53	0.3013	135.2	0.1948
0.26	0.0480	21.53	0.0310	0.54	0.3162	141.9	0.2044
0.27	0.0529	23.73	0.0342	0.55	0.3315	148.8	0.2143
0.28	0.0581	26.06	0.0375	0.56	0.3473	155.8	0.2245

The approximation formulas below fit the data in the table within 1% of full scale.

Formula: CFS = $1.55\ H^{2.58}$ GPM = $695.64\ H^{2.58}$ MGD= $1.002\ H^{2.58}$ *Where:* H = head in feet

17

Table 17-2:
Extra Large 60° V Trapezoidal Flume Discharge Table
with Head in Feet

Data in table from Plasti-Fab, Inc.

Head (feet)	CFS	GPM	MGD	Head (feet)	CFS	GPM	MGD
0.01				0.51	0.2623	117.7	0.1695
0.02				0.52	0.2761	123.9	0.1784
0.03				0.53	0.2903	130.3	0.1875
0.04				0.54	0.3050	136.9	0.1970
0.05				0.55	0.3201	143.7	0.2068
0.06	0.0009	0.4175	0.0006	0.56	0.3357	150.6	0.2168
0.07	0.0014	0.6268	0.0009	0.57	0.3517	157.8	0.2272
0.08	0.0020	0.8913	0.0013	0.58	0.3682	165.2	0.2379
0.09	0.0027	1.216	0.0018	0.59	0.3852	172.9	0.2488
0.10	0.0036	1.605	0.0023	0.60	0.4026	180.7	0.2601
0.11	0.0046	2.064	0.0030	0.61	0.4206	188.7	0.2717
0.12	0.0058	2.596	0.0037	0.62	0.4390	197.0	0.2836
0.13	0.0071	3.205	0.0046	0.63	0.4579	205.5	0.2958
0.14	0.0087	3.897	0.0056	0.64	0.4773	214.2	0.3083
0.15	0.0104	4.674	0.0067	0.65	0.4972	223.1	0.3212
0.16	0.0123	5.541	0.0080	0.66	0.5176	232.3	0.3344
0.17	0.0145	6.502	0.0094	0.67	0.5386	241.7	0.3479
0.18	0.0168	7.559	0.0109	0.68	0.5600	251.3	0.3618
0.19	0.0194	8.717	0.0125	0.69	0.5820	261.2	0.3760
0.20	0.0222	9.979	0.0144	0.70	0.6045	271.3	0.3905
0.21	0.0253	11.35	0.0163	0.71	0.6275	281.6	0.4054
0.22	0.0286	12.83	0.0185	0.72	0.6511	292.2	0.4206
0.23	0.0321	14.43	0.0208	0.73	0.6752	303.0	0.4362
0.24	0.0360	16.14	0.0232	0.74	0.6999	314.1	0.4521
0.25	0.0400	17.97	0.0259	0.75	0.7251	325.4	0.4684
0.26	0.0444	19.93	0.0287	0.76	0.7509	337.0	0.4851
0.27	0.0491	22.01	0.0317	0.77	0.7772	348.8	0.5021
0.28	0.0540	24.23	0.0349	0.78	0.8041	360.8	0.5194
0.29	0.0592	26.58	0.0383	0.79	0.8315	373.2	0.5372
0.30	0.0648	29.06	0.0418	0.80	0.8596	385.8	0.5553
0.31	0.0706	31.69	0.0456	0.81	0.8882	398.6	0.5738
0.32	0.0768	34.45	0.0496	0.82	0.9174	411.7	0.5926
0.33	0.0833	37.36	0.0538	0.83	0.9472	425.1	0.6119
0.34	0.0901	40.42	0.0582	0.84	0.9776	438.7	0.6315
0.35	0.0972	43.63	0.0628	0.85	1.009	452.6	0.6515
0.36	0.1047	47.00	0.0677	0.86	1.040	466.8	0.6719
0.37	0.1126	50.52	0.0727	0.87	1.072	481.2	0.6927
0.38	0.1208	54.20	0.0780	0.88	1.105	495.9	0.7139
0.39	0.1293	58.04	0.0835	0.89	1.139	510.9	0.7355
0.40	0.1383	62.05	0.0893	0.90	1.173	526.2	0.7575
0.41	0.1476	66.22	0.0953	0.91	1.207	541.8	0.7799
0.42	0.1572	70.56	0.1016	0.92	1.243	557.6	0.8027
0.43	0.1673	75.08	0.1081	0.93	1.278	573.7	0.8259
0.44	0.1777	79.77	0.1148	0.94	1.315	590.1	0.8495
0.45	0.1886	84.64	0.1218	0.95	1.352	606.8	0.8735
0.46	0.1998	89.69	0.1291	0.96	1.390	623.8	0.8980
0.47	0.2115	94.92	0.1366	0.97	1.429	641.1	0.9228
0.48	0.2236	100.3	0.1444	0.98	1.468	658.7	0.9481
0.49	0.2361	105.9	0.1525	0.99	1.508	676.5	0.9739
0.50	0.2490	111.7	0.1608	1.00	1.548	694.7	1.000

The approximation formulas below fit the data in the table within 1% of full scale.

Formula: $CFS = 1.55\ H^{2.63}$ $GPM = 695.64\ H^{2.63}$ $MGD = 1.002\ H^{2.63}$ *Where:* H = head in feet

17

Table 17-3:
2 in. 45° WSC Trapezoidal Flume Discharge Table with Head in Feet

Data in table from Plasti-Fab, Inc.

Head (feet)	CFS	GPM	MGD	Head (feet)	CFS	GPM	MGD
0.01				0.43	0.4690	210.5	0.3031
0.02				0.44	0.4940	221.7	0.3193
0.03				0.45	0.5199	233.3	0.3360
0.04				0.46	0.5465	245.3	0.3532
0.05				0.47	0.5739	257.6	0.3709
0.06				0.48	0.6022	270.3	0.3892
0.07				0.49	0.6313	283.3	0.4080
0.08				0.50	0.6612	296.8	0.4273
0.09				0.51	0.6920	310.6	0.4473
0.10				0.52	0.7237	324.8	0.4677
0.11	0.0277	12.42	0.0179	0.53	0.7562	339.4	0.4887
0.12	0.0328	14.71	0.0212	0.54	0.7896	354.4	0.5103
0.13	0.0383	17.20	0.0248	0.55	0.8239	369.8	0.5325
0.14	0.0443	19.89	0.0287	0.56	0.8591	385.6	0.5553
0.15	0.0508	22.80	0.0328	0.57	0.8953	401.8	0.5786
0.16	0.0577	25.91	0.0373	0.58	0.9323	418.5	0.6026
0.17	0.0652	29.25	0.0421	0.59	0.9703	435.5	0.6271
0.18	0.0731	32.82	0.0473	0.60	1.009	452.9	0.6522
0.19	0.0816	36.61	0.0527	0.61	1.049	470.8	0.6780
0.20	0.0906	40.64	0.0585	0.62	1.090	489.1	0.7044
0.21	0.1001	44.92	0.0647	0.63	1.132	507.9	0.7313
0.22	0.1102	49.44	0.0712	0.64	1.174	527.1	0.7590
0.23	0.1208	54.21	0.0781	0.65	1.218	546.7	0.7872
0.24	0.1320	59.25	0.0853	0.66	1.263	566.7	0.8161
0.25	0.1438	64.54	0.0929	0.67	1.308	587.2	0.8456
0.26	0.1562	70.11	0.1010	0.68	1.355	608.2	0.8758
0.27	0.1692	75.94	0.1094	0.69	1.403	629.6	0.9066
0.28	0.1828	82.06	0.1182	0.70	1.451	651.4	0.9380
0.29	0.1971	88.46	0.1274	0.71	1.501	673.7	0.9702
0.30	0.2120	95.15	0.1370	0.72	1.552	696.5	1.003
0.31	0.2275	102.1	0.1471	0.73	1.604	719.8	1.036
0.32	0.2438	109.4	0.1575	0.74	1.656	743.5	1.071
0.33	0.2607	117.0	0.1685	0.75	1.710	767.6	1.105
0.34	0.2782	124.9	0.1798	0.76	1.765	792.3	1.141
0.35	0.2965	133.1	0.1916	0.77	1.821	817.4	1.177
0.36	0.3155	141.6	0.2039	0.78	1.878	843.1	1.214
0.37	0.3352	150.4	0.2166	0.79	1.937	869.2	1.252
0.38	0.3556	159.6	0.2298	0.80	1.996	895.7	1.290
0.39	0.3768	169.1	0.2435	0.81	2.056	922.8	1.329
0.40	0.3987	178.9	0.2577	0.82	2.118	950.4	1.369
0.41	0.4214	189.1	0.2723	0.83	2.180	978.5	1.409
0.42	0.4448	199.6	0.2875				

The approximation formulas below fit the data in the table within 1% of full scale.

Formula: $CFS = 3.32\, H^{2.32}$ $GPM = 1490\, H^{2.32}$ $MGD = 2.146\, H^{2.32}$ *Where:* H = head in feet

Table 17-4:
12 in. 45° SRCRC Trapezoidal Flume Discharge Table with Head in Feet

Data in table from Plasti-Fab, Inc.

Table 17-4				Table 17-4 (Continued)			
Head (feet)	CFS	GPM	MGD	Head (feet)	CFS	GPM	MGD
0.01				0.51	0.8794	394.7	0.5674
0.02				0.52	0.9161	411.2	0.5910
0.03				0.53	0.9536	428.0	0.6152
0.04				0.54	0.9921	445.3	0.6401
0.05				0.55	1.032	463.0	0.6655
0.06				0.56	1.072	481.2	0.6916
0.07				0.57	1.113	499.7	0.7183
0.08				0.58	1.156	518.8	0.7457
0.09				0.59	1.199	538.2	0.7736
0.10				0.60	1.244	558.1	0.8023
0.11				0.61	1.289	578.5	0.8315
0.12				0.62	1.335	599.3	0.8614
0.13				0.63	1.383	620.5	0.8920
0.14				0.64	1.431	642.3	0.9232
0.15				0.65	1.480	664.4	0.9551
0.16	*0.1234*	*55.38*	*0.0798*	0.66	1.531	687.1	0.9876
0.17	*0.1327*	*59.54*	*0.0856*	0.67	1.582	710.2	1.021
0.18	*0.1425*	*63.96*	*0.0919*	0.68	1.635	733.8	1.055
0.19	*0.1530*	*68.67*	*0.0987*	0.69	1.689	757.8	1.089
0.20	0.1641	73.67	0.1059	0.70	1.743	782.4	1.125
0.21	0.1759	78.95	0.1135	0.71	1.799	807.4	1.161
0.22	0.1883	84.53	0.1215	0.72	1.856	832.9	1.197
0.23	0.2014	90.41	0.1300	0.73	1.914	858.9	1.235
0.24	0.2152	96.60	0.1389	0.74	1.973	885.4	1.273
0.25	0.2297	103.1	0.1482	0.75	2.033	912.3	1.311
0.26	0.2449	109.9	0.1580	0.76	2.094	939.8	1.351
0.27	0.2607	117.0	0.1682	0.77	2.156	967.7	1.391
0.28	0.2773	124.5	0.1789	0.78	2.220	996.2	1.432
0.29	0.2947	132.3	0.1901	0.79	2.284	1025	1.474
0.30	0.3127	140.4	0.2018	0.80	2.350	1055	1.516
0.31	0.3316	148.8	0.2139	0.81	2.417	1085	1.559
0.32	0.3511	157.6	0.2265	0.82	2.485	1115	1.603
0.33	0.3715	166.7	0.2397	0.83	2.554	1146	1.648
0.34	0.3926	176.2	0.2533	0.84	2.624	1178	1.693
0.35	0.4145	186.1	0.2674	0.85	2.695	1210	1.739
0.36	0.4372	196.3	0.2821	0.86	2.768	1242	1.786
0.37	0.4608	206.8	0.2973	0.87	2.842	1275	1.833
0.38	0.4851	217.7	0.3130	0.88	2.917	1309	1.882
0.39	0.5103	229.0	0.3292	0.89	2.993	1343	1.931
0.40	0.5362	240.7	0.3460	0.90	3.070	1378	1.981
0.41	0.5631	252.7	0.3633	0.91	3.149	1413	2.031
0.42	0.5907	265.1	0.3811	0.92	3.228	1449	2.083
0.43	0.6193	278.0	0.3995	0.93	3.309	1485	2.135
0.44	0.6487	291.1	0.4185	0.94	3.391	1522	2.188
0.45	0.6789	304.7	0.4380	0.95	3.475	1560	2.242
0.46	0.7101	318.7	0.4581	0.96	3.559	1598	2.296
0.47	0.7422	333.1	0.4788	0.97	3.645	1636	2.352
0.48	0.7751	347.9	0.5001	0.98	3.732	1675	2.408
0.49	0.8090	363.1	0.5219	0.99	3.820	1715	2.465
0.50	0.8437	378.7	0.5443	1.00	3.910	1755	2.523

17

Table 17-4 (Continued)					Table 17-4 (Continued)			
Head (feet)	CFS	GPM	MGD		Head (feet)	CFS	GPM	MGD
1.01	4.001	1796	2.581		1.12	5.085	2282	3.280
1.02	4.093	1837	2.641		1.13	5.191	2330	3.349
1.03	4.186	1879	2.701		1.14	5.299	2378	3.419
1.04	4.281	1921	2.762		1.15	5.408	2427	3.489
1.05	4.377	1965	2.824		1.16	5.518	2477	3.560
1.06	4.474	2008	2.887		1.17	5.630	2527	3.632
1.07	4.573	2052	2.950		1.18	5.743	2578	3.705
1.08	4.672	2097	3.014		1.19	5.858	2629	3.779
1.09	4.774	2143	3.080		1.20	5.973	2681	3.854
1.10	4.876	2188	3.146		1.21	6.091	2734	3.929
1.11	4.980	2235	3.213					

The approximation formulas below fit the data in the table within 1% of full scale.

Formula: CFS $= 3.93\ H^{2.29}$ GPM $= 1764\ H^{2.29}$ MGD $= 2.54\ H^{2.29}$ *Where:* H = head in feet

17

Table 17-5:
Large 60° V Trapezoidal Flume Discharge Table with
Head in Meters

Data in table from Plasti-Fab, Inc.

Table 17-5			Table 17-5 (Continued)		
Head (meters)	l/s	m³/hr	Head (meters)	l/s	m³/hr
0.005			0.090	1.886	6.790
0.010	0.0065	0.0234	0.095	2.169	7.807
0.015	0.0185	0.0667	0.100	2.475	8.911
0.020	0.0389	0.1402	0.105	2.807	10.11
0.025	0.0692	0.2492	0.110	3.165	11.40
0.030	0.1108	0.3989	0.115	3.550	12.78
0.035	0.1649	0.5938	0.120	3.962	14.26
0.040	0.2328	0.8380	0.125	4.402	15.85
0.045	0.3154	1.136	0.130	4.871	17.54
0.050	0.4140	1.490	0.135	5.369	19.33
0.055	0.5294	1.906	0.140	5.897	21.23
0.060	0.6626	2.385	0.145	6.456	23.24
0.065	0.8146	2.933	0.150	7.046	25.37
0.070	0.9863	3.551	0.155	7.668	27.61
0.075	1.178	4.242	0.160	8.323	29.96
0.080	1.392	5.011	0.165	9.010	32.44
0.085	1.628	5.859	0.170	9.732	35.03

The approximation formulas below fit the data in the table within 1% of full scale.

Formula: $l/s = 942.8\ H^{2.58}$ $m^3/hr = 3394\ H^{2.58}$ *Where:* H = head in meters

17

Table 17-6:
Extra Large 60° V Trapezoidal Flume Discharge Table with Head in Meters

Data in table from Plasti-Fab, Inc.

Head (meters)	l/s	m³/hr	Head (meters)	l/s	m³/hr
0.005			0.160	8.017	28.86
0.010	0.0054	0.0193	0.165	8.694	31.30
0.015	0.0156	0.0562	0.170	9.406	33.86
0.020	0.0334	0.1201	0.175	10.15	36.55
0.025	0.0601	0.2163	0.180	10.94	39.37
0.030	0.0971	0.3497	0.185	11.75	42.32
0.035	0.1458	0.5250	0.190	12.61	45.40
0.040	0.2074	0.7466	0.195	13.50	48.62
0.045	0.2829	1.018	0.200	14.44	51.97
0.050	0.3735	1.345	0.205	15.41	55.47
0.055	0.4802	1.729	0.210	16.42	59.11
0.060	0.6040	2.174	0.215	17.47	62.89
0.065	0.7458	2.685	0.220	18.56	66.82
0.070	0.9068	3.264	0.225	19.69	70.90
0.075	1.088	3.916	0.230	20.87	75.13
0.080	1.289	4.642	0.235	22.09	79.51
0.085	1.513	5.446	0.240	23.35	84.05
0.090	1.759	6.332	0.245	24.65	88.74
0.095	2.028	7.302	0.250	26.00	93.60
0.100	2.322	8.359	0.255	27.39	98.61
0.105	2.641	9.507	0.260	28.83	103.8
0.110	2.985	10.75	0.265	30.32	109.1
0.115	3.356	12.08	0.270	31.85	114.6
0.120	3.755	13.52	0.275	33.43	120.3
0.125	4.182	15.05	0.280	35.05	126.2
0.130	4.637	16.69	0.285	36.73	132.2
0.135	5.122	18.44	0.290	38.45	138.4
0.140	5.638	20.30	0.295	40.22	144.8
0.145	6.184	22.26	0.300	42.04	151.4
0.150	6.762	24.34	0.305	43.92	158.1
0.155	7.373	26.54			

The approximation formulas below fit the data in the table within 1% of full scale.

Formula: $l/s = 1001.3\ H^{2.63}$ $m^3/hr = 3604.6\ H^{2.63}$ *Where:* H = head in meters

17

Table 17-7:
2 in. 45° WSC Trapezoidal Flume Discharge Table with
Head in Meters

Data in table from Plasti-Fab, Inc.

Head (meters)	l/s	m³/hr	Head (meters)	l/s	m³/hr
0.005			0.130	13.27	47.79
0.010			0.135	14.71	52.97
0.015			0.140	16.24	58.48
0.020			0.145	17.04	61.36
0.025			0.150	18.71	67.38
0.030	0.783	2.821	0.155	20.48	73.74
0.035	0.928	3.340	0.160	21.40	77.06
0.040	1.084	3.905	0.165	23.32	83.96
0.045	1.437	5.176	0.170	25.34	91.23
0.050	1.844	6.641	0.175	26.38	95.00
0.055	2.069	7.450	0.180	28.56	102.8
0.060	2.563	9.227	0.185	30.84	111.1
0.065	3.117	11.22	0.190	32.02	115.3
0.070	3.418	12.31	0.195	34.47	124.1
0.075	4.070	14.65	0.200	37.02	133.3
0.080	4.788	17.24	0.205	38.35	138.1
0.085	5.174	18.63	0.210	41.07	147.9
0.090	5.999	21.60	0.215	43.92	158.1
0.095	6.898	24.84	0.220	45.38	163.4
0.100	7.376	26.56	0.225	48.40	174.3
0.105	8.391	30.21	0.230	51.54	185.6
0.110	9.486	34.15	0.235	53.16	191.4
0.115	10.06	36.24	0.240	56.48	203.4
0.120	11.28	40.63	0.245	59.93	215.8
0.125	12.59	45.33	0.250	61.69	222.1

The approximation formulas below fit the data in the table within 1% of full scale.

Formula: $l/s = 1476.6 \, H^{2.32}$ $m^3/hr = 5315.8 \, H^{2.32}$ *Where:* H = head in meters

17

Table 17-8:
12 in. 45° SRCRC Trapezoidal Flume Discharge Table with Head in Meters

Data in table from Plasti-Fab, Inc.

Table 17-8			Table 17-8 (Continued)		
Head (meters)	l/s	m³/hr	Head (meters)	l/s	m³/hr
0.005			0.205	45.13	162.5
0.010			0.210	47.59	171.4
0.015			0.215	50.14	180.6
0.020			0.220	52.77	190.0
0.025			0.225	55.48	199.8
0.030			0.230	58.27	209.9
0.035			0.235	61.15	220.2
0.040			0.240	64.11	230.9
0.045			0.245	67.16	241.9
0.050			0.250	70.30	253.2
0.055			0.255	73.52	264.8
0.060	4.548	16.38	0.260	76.83	276.7
0.065	5.094	18.35	0.265	80.23	288.9
0.070	5.691	20.49	0.270	83.72	301.5
0.075	6.339	22.83	0.275	87.30	314.4
0.080	7.041	25.36	0.280	90.97	327.6
0.085	7.796	28.08	0.285	94.73	341.2
0.090	8.607	31.00	0.290	98.59	355.1
0.095	9.475	34.13	0.295	102.5	369.3
0.100	10.40	37.46	0.300	106.6	383.9
0.105	11.39	41.01	0.305	110.7	398.8
0.110	12.43	44.77	0.310	115.0	414.0
0.115	13.54	48.76	0.315	119.3	429.6
0.120	14.71	52.96	0.320	123.7	445.6
0.125	15.94	57.40	0.325	128.2	461.9
0.130	17.23	62.07	0.330	132.9	478.5
0.135	18.60	66.98	0.335	137.6	495.5
0.140	20.03	72.13	0.340	142.4	512.9
0.145	21.52	77.52	0.345	147.3	530.7
0.150	23.09	83.16	0.350	152.4	548.8
0.155	24.72	89.05	0.355	157.5	567.2
0.160	26.43	95.20	0.360	162.7	586.1
0.165	28.21	101.6	0.365	168.1	605.3
0.170	30.06	108.3	0.370	173.5	624.9
0.175	31.98	115.2	0.375	179.0	644.8
0.180	33.98	122.4	0.380	184.7	665.2
0.185	36.06	129.9	0.385	190.5	685.9
0.190	38.21	137.6	0.390	196.3	707.0
0.195	40.44	145.6	0.395	202.3	728.5
0.200	42.74	153.9			

17

The approximation formulas below fit the data in the table within 1% of full scale.

Formula: $l/s = 1685.9\ H^{2.29}$ $m^3/hr = 6069.3\ H^{2.29}$ *Where:* H = head in meters

CHAPTER

18

Isco Flow Metering Inserts Discharge Tables

Overview

This chapter contains discharge (head vs. flow rate) tables for Isco Flow Metering Inserts (manufactured by Teledyne Isco, Inc.). Note that all of the tabular data is for free flow. [1]

Discharge tables for Flow Metering Inserts with head in feet

18-1: 6 in. V-notch Weir	18-9: 6 in. Round Orifice
18-2: 8 in. V-notch Weir	18-10: 8 in. Round Orifice
18-3: 10 in.V-notch Weir	18-11: 10 in. Round Orifice
18-4: 12 in. V-notch Weir	18-12: 12 in. Round Orifice

The discharges of the inserts are listed in three different units of measure:
CFS - cubic feet per second   GPM - gallons per minute
MGD - million gallons per day

Discharge tables for Flow Metering Inserts with head in meters

18-5: 0.152 m V-notch Weir	18-13: 0.152 m Round Orifice
18-6: 0.203 m V-notch Weir	18-14: 0.203 m Round Orifice
18-7: 0.254 m V-notch Weir	18-15: 0.254 m Round Orifice
18-8: 0.305 m V-notch Weir	18-16: 0.305 m Round Orifice

The discharges of the inserts are listed in two different units of measure:
l/s - liters per second m^3/hr - cubic meters per hour

The source of data used to develop each table is listed on the table.

---

1. All flow metering insert data, © Copyright Teledyne Isco, Inc., Lincoln, NE

Table 18-1:
6 in. Isco Flow Metering Insert with V-notch Weir Discharge Table with Head in Feet

Manufactured by Teledyne Isco, Inc. (Data from Teledyne Isco, Inc.)

Table 18-1				Table 18-1 (Continued)			
Head (feet)	CFS	GPM	MGD	Head (feet)	CFS	GPM	MGD
0.01	0	0	0	0.51	0.09069	40.71	0.05862
0.02	0	0	0	0.52	0.09272	41.62	0.05993
0.03	0	0	0	0.53	0.09469	42.50	0.06120
0.04	0	0	0	0.54	0.09660	43.36	0.06243
0.05	0	0	0	0.55	0.09845	44.19	0.06363
0.06	0	0	0	0.56	0.10025	44.99	0.06479
0.07	0	0	0	0.57	0.10200	45.78	0.06593
0.08	0	0	0	0.58	0.10371	46.55	0.06703
0.09	0	0	0	0.59	0.10538	47.30	0.06811
0.1	0	0	0	0.60	0.10701	48.03	0.06916
0.11	0	0	0	0.61	0.10861	48.75	0.07019
0.12	0	0	0	0.62	0.11017	49.45	0.07120
0.13	0.00001	0.01	0.00001	0.63	0.11170	50.13	0.07219
0.14	0.00011	0.05	0.00007	0.64	0.11320	50.81	0.07316
0.15	0.00031	0.14	0.00020	0.65	0.11467	51.47	0.07411
0.16	0.00062	0.28	0.00040	0.66	0.11611	52.12	0.07505
0.17	0.00105	0.47	0.00068	0.67	0.11754	52.75	0.07596
0.18	0.00162	0.73	0.00105	0.68	0.11893	53.38	0.07687
0.19	0.00232	1.04	0.00150	0.69	0.12031	54.00	0.07776
0.20	0.00317	1.43	0.00205	0.70	0.12167	54.61	0.07863
0.21	0.00419	1.88	0.00271	0.71	0.12300	55.21	0.07950
0.22	0.00537	2.41	0.00347	0.72	0.12432	55.80	0.08035
0.23	0.00673	3.02	0.00435	0.73	0.12562	56.38	0.08119
0.24	0.00828	3.71	0.00535	0.74	0.12691	56.96	0.08202
0.25	0.01002	4.50	0.00648	0.75	0.12818	57.53	0.08284
0.26	0.01199	5.38	0.00775	0.76	0.12943	58.09	0.08365
0.27	0.01417	6.36	0.00916	0.77	0.13067	58.65	0.08445
0.28	0.01658	7.44	0.01072	0.78	0.13190	59.20	0.08525
0.29	0.01925	8.64	0.01244	0.79	0.13311	59.74	0.08603
0.30	0.02216	9.95	0.01432	0.80	0.13432	60.28	0.08681
0.31	0.02535	11.38	0.01639	0.81	0.13551	60.82	0.08758
0.32	0.02882	12.94	0.01863	0.82	0.13669	61.35	0.08834
0.33	0.03322	14.91	0.02147	0.83	0.13786	61.87	0.08910
0.34	0.03824	17.16	0.02471	0.84	0.13902	62.40	0.08985
0.35	0.04291	19.26	0.02773	0.85	0.14017	62.91	0.09059
0.36	0.04727	21.22	0.03055	0.86	0.14131	63.42	0.09133
0.37	0.05136	23.05	0.03319	0.87	0.14244	63.93	0.09206
0.38	0.05519	24.77	0.03567	0.88	0.14357	64.44	0.09279
0.39	0.05880	26.39	0.03800	0.89	0.14469	64.94	0.09351
0.40	0.06221	27.92	0.04021	0.90	0.14580	65.44	0.09423
0.41	0.06544	29.37	0.04230	0.91	0.14690	65.93	0.09495
0.42	0.06851	30.75	0.04428	0.92	0.14800	66.43	0.09565
0.43	0.07142	32.06	0.04616	0.93	0.14909	66.92	0.09636
0.44	0.07420	33.30	0.04796	0.94	0.15017	67.40	0.09706
0.45	0.07685	34.49	0.04967	0.95	0.15125	67.89	0.09776
0.46	0.07939	35.63	0.05131	0.96	0.15232	68.37	0.09845
0.47	0.08183	36.73	0.05289	0.97	0.15339	68.85	0.09914
0.48	0.08417	37.78	0.05440	0.98	0.15445	69.32	0.09982
0.49	0.08642	38.79	0.05586	0.99	0.15551	69.80	0.10051
0.50	0.08860	39.76	0.05726	1.00	0.15656	70.27	0.10119

18

Table 18-1 (Continued)				Table 18-1 (Continued)			
Head (feet)	CFS	GPM	MGD	Head (feet)	CFS	GPM	MGD
1.01	0.15760	70.74	0.10186	1.26	0.18267	81.99	0.11807
1.02	0.15865	71.21	0.10254	1.27	0.18365	82.43	0.11869
1.03	0.15969	71.67	0.10321	1.28	0.18461	82.86	0.11932
1.04	0.16072	72.14	0.10388	1.29	0.18558	83.29	0.11994
1.05	0.16175	72.60	0.10454	1.30	0.18655	83.73	0.12057
1.06	0.16278	73.06	0.10520	1.31	0.18751	84.16	0.12119
1.07	0.16380	73.52	0.10587	1.32	0.18847	84.59	0.12181
1.08	0.16482	73.97	0.10652	1.33	0.18943	85.02	0.12243
1.09	0.16583	74.43	0.10718	1.34	0.19039	85.45	0.12305
1.10	0.16684	74.89	0.10783	1.35	0.19135	85.88	0.12367
1.11	0.16785	75.34	0.10849	1.36	0.19231	86.31	0.12429
1.12	0.16886	75.79	0.10914	1.37	0.19326	86.74	0.12491
1.13	0.16986	76.24	0.10979	1.38	0.19422	87.17	0.12553
1.14	0.17086	76.69	0.11043	1.39	0.19517	87.60	0.12614
1.15	0.17186	77.14	0.11108	1.40	0.19612	88.02	0.12676
1.16	0.17286	77.58	0.11172	1.41	0.19707	88.45	0.12737
1.17	0.17385	78.03	0.11236	1.42	0.19802	88.88	0.12798
1.18	0.17484	78.47	0.11300	1.43	0.19897	89.30	0.12860
1.19	0.17582	78.92	0.11364	1.44	0.19991	89.73	0.12921
1.20	0.17681	79.36	0.11427	1.45	0.20086	90.15	0.12982
1.21	0.17779	79.80	0.11491	1.46	0.20180	90.58	0.13043
1.22	0.17877	80.24	0.11554	1.47	0.20275	91.00	0.13104
1.23	0.17975	80.68	0.11618	1.48	0.20369	91.42	0.13165
1.24	0.18073	81.12	0.11681	1.49	0.20463	91.84	0.13226
1.25	0.18170	81.55	0.11744	1.50	0.20557	92.27	0.13286

18

Table 18-2:
8 in. Isco Flow Metering Insert with V-notch Weir Discharge Table with Head in Feet

Manufactured by Teledyne Isco, Inc. (Data from Teledyne Isco, Inc.)

Table 18-2				Table 18-2 (Continued)			
Head (feet)	CFS	GPM	MGD	Head (feet)	CFS	GPM	MGD
0.01	0	0	0	0.51	0.10987	49.31	0.07101
0.02	0	0	0	0.52	0.11572	51.94	0.07479
0.03	0	0	0	0.53	0.12131	54.45	0.07841
0.04	0	0	0	0.54	0.12669	56.86	0.08188
0.05	0	0	0	0.55	0.13185	59.18	0.08522
0.06	0	0	0	0.56	0.13681	61.41	0.08842
0.07	0	0	0	0.57	0.14160	63.55	0.09152
0.08	0	0	0	0.58	0.14621	65.63	0.09450
0.09	0	0	0	0.59	0.15067	67.63	0.09738
0.10	0	0	0	0.60	0.15498	69.56	0.10017
0.11	0	0	0	0.61	0.15915	71.43	0.10286
0.12	0	0	0	0.62	0.16320	73.25	0.10548
0.13	0	0	0	0.63	0.16712	75.01	0.10801
0.14	0	0	0	0.64	0.17093	76.72	0.11047
0.15	0	0	0	0.65	0.17463	78.38	0.11287
0.16	0	0	0	0.66	0.17823	80.00	0.11520
0.17	0	0	0	0.67	0.18174	81.57	0.11746
0.18	0.00001	0.00	0.00001	0.68	0.18516	83.11	0.11967
0.19	0.00011	0.05	0.00007	0.69	0.18850	84.60	0.12183
0.20	0.00032	0.14	0.00021	0.70	0.19176	86.07	0.12394
0.21	0.00066	0.30	0.00043	0.71	0.19494	87.49	0.12599
0.22	0.00113	0.51	0.00073	0.72	0.19805	88.89	0.12800
0.23	0.00174	0.78	0.00112	0.73	0.20110	90.26	0.12997
0.24	0.00250	1.12	0.00161	0.74	0.20408	91.60	0.13190
0.25	0.00341	1.53	0.00220	0.75	0.20701	92.91	0.13379
0.26	0.00449	2.02	0.00290	0.76	0.20987	94.20	0.13564
0.27	0.00574	2.58	0.00371	0.77	0.21269	95.46	0.13746
0.28	0.00718	3.22	0.00464	0.78	0.21545	96.70	0.13925
0.29	0.00880	3.95	0.00569	0.79	0.21817	97.92	0.14100
0.30	0.01063	4.77	0.00687	0.80	0.22083	99.12	0.14273
0.31	0.01267	5.69	0.00819	0.81	0.22346	100.30	0.14443
0.32	0.01493	6.70	0.00965	0.82	0.22604	101.46	0.14610
0.33	0.01741	7.82	0.01125	0.83	0.22859	102.60	0.14774
0.34	0.02014	9.04	0.01302	0.84	0.23110	103.72	0.14936
0.35	0.02312	10.37	0.01494	0.85	0.23357	104.83	0.15096
0.36	0.02635	11.83	0.01703	0.86	0.23600	105.93	0.15253
0.37	0.02986	13.40	0.01930	0.87	0.23841	107.00	0.15409
0.38	0.03364	15.10	0.02174	0.88	0.24078	108.07	0.15562
0.39	0.03772	16.93	0.02438	0.89	0.24312	109.12	0.15714
0.40	0.04210	18.90	0.02721	0.90	0.24544	110.16	0.15863
0.41	0.04680	21.00	0.03024	0.91	0.24773	111.19	0.16011
0.42	0.05181	23.26	0.03349	0.92	0.24999	112.20	0.16157
0.43	0.05717	25.66	0.03695	0.93	0.25222	113.21	0.16302
0.44	0.06287	28.22	0.04063	0.94	0.25444	114.20	0.16445
0.45	0.06893	30.94	0.04455	0.95	0.25663	115.18	0.16586
0.46	0.07623	34.21	0.04927	0.96	0.25880	116.16	0.16726
0.47	0.08363	37.54	0.05405	0.97	0.26094	117.12	0.16865
0.48	0.09067	40.70	0.05860	0.98	0.26307	118.07	0.17003
0.49	0.09738	43.71	0.06294	0.99	0.26518	119.02	0.17139
0.50	0.10377	46.57	0.06707	1.00	0.26726	119.96	0.17274

18

Table 18-2 (Continued)					Table 18-2 (Continued)			
Head (feet)	CFS	GPM	MGD	Head (feet)	CFS	GPM	MGD
1.01	0.26934	120.89	0.17408	1.26	0.31688	142.22	0.20480
1.02	0.27139	121.81	0.17540	1.27	0.31866	143.02	0.20595
1.03	0.27343	122.72	0.17672	1.28	0.32043	143.82	0.20710
1.04	0.27545	123.63	0.17803	1.29	0.32219	144.61	0.20824
1.05	0.27745	124.53	0.17932	1.30	0.32395	145.40	0.20938
1.06	0.27945	125.42	0.18061	1.31	0.32570	146.19	0.21051
1.07	0.28142	126.31	0.18189	1.32	0.32745	146.97	0.21164
1.08	0.28339	127.19	0.18316	1.33	0.32919	147.75	0.21276
1.09	0.28534	128.07	0.18442	1.34	0.33093	148.53	0.21388
1.10	0.28728	128.94	0.18567	1.35	0.33266	149.31	0.21500
1.11	0.28920	129.80	0.18692	1.36	0.33438	150.08	0.21611
1.12	0.29111	130.66	0.18815	1.37	0.33610	150.85	0.21723
1.13	0.29302	131.52	0.18938	1.38	0.33781	151.62	0.21833
1.14	0.29491	132.36	0.19060	1.39	0.33952	152.39	0.21944
1.15	0.29679	133.21	0.19182	1.40	0.34122	153.15	0.22054
1.16	0.29866	134.05	0.19303	1.41	0.34292	153.91	0.22164
1.17	0.30052	134.88	0.19423	1.42	0.34462	154.68	0.22273
1.18	0.30237	135.71	0.19543	1.43	0.34631	155.43	0.22382
1.19	0.30422	136.54	0.19662	1.44	0.34799	156.19	0.22491
1.20	0.30605	137.36	0.19780	1.45	0.34968	156.95	0.22600
1.21	0.30787	138.18	0.19898	1.46	0.35135	157.70	0.22709
1.22	0.30969	139.00	0.20016	1.47	0.35303	158.45	0.22817
1.23	0.31150	139.81	0.20133	1.48	0.35470	159.20	0.22925
1.24	0.31330	140.62	0.20249	1.49	0.35636	159.95	0.23032
1.25	0.31509	141.42	0.20365	1.50	0.35803	160.69	0.23140

18

Table 18-3:
10 in. Isco Flow Metering Insert with V-notch Weir
Discharge Table with Head in Feet

Manufactured by Teledyne Isco, Inc. (Data from Teledyne Isco, Inc.)

Head (feet)	CFS	GPM	MGD	Head (feet)	CFS	GPM	MGD
0.01	0	0	0	0.51	0.07896	35.44	0.05103
0.02	0	0	0	0.52	0.08553	38.39	0.05528
0.03	0	0	0	0.53	0.09243	41.48	0.05974
0.04	0	0	0	0.54	0.09967	44.74	0.06442
0.05	0	0	0	0.55	0.10726	48.14	0.06933
0.06	0	0	0	0.56	0.11522	51.71	0.07447
0.07	0	0	0	0.57	0.12353	55.45	0.07984
0.08	0	0	0	0.58	0.13223	59.35	0.08546
0.09	0	0	0	0.59	0.13998	62.83	0.09047
0.10	0	0	0	0.60	0.14913	66.94	0.09639
0.11	0	0	0	0.61	0.15801	70.92	0.10212
0.12	0	0	0	0.62	0.16661	74.78	0.10768
0.13	0	0	0	0.63	0.17495	78.52	0.11307
0.14	0	0	0	0.64	0.18305	82.16	0.11831
0.15	0	0	0	0.65	0.19091	85.69	0.12339
0.16	0	0	0	0.66	0.19855	89.11	0.12832
0.17	0	0	0	0.67	0.20597	92.45	0.13312
0.18	0	0	0	0.68	0.21320	95.69	0.13779
0.19	0	0	0	0.69	0.22023	98.84	0.14234
0.20	0	0	0	0.70	0.22707	101.92	0.14676
0.21	0	0	0	0.71	0.23374	104.91	0.15107
0.22	0	0	0	0.72	0.24024	107.83	0.15527
0.23	0.00006	0.03	0.00004	0.73	0.24658	110.67	0.15937
0.24	0.00026	0.12	0.00017	0.74	0.25276	113.45	0.16336
0.25	0.00060	0.27	0.00039	0.75	0.25879	116.16	0.16726
0.26	0.00108	0.49	0.00070	0.76	0.26469	118.80	0.17107
0.27	0.00171	0.77	0.00111	0.77	0.27045	121.39	0.17480
0.28	0.00250	1.12	0.00162	0.78	0.27608	123.91	0.17843
0.29	0.00346	1.55	0.00223	0.79	0.28158	126.38	0.18199
0.30	0.00458	2.05	0.00296	0.80	0.28697	128.80	0.18547
0.31	0.00587	2.64	0.00380	0.81	0.29224	131.17	0.18888
0.32	0.00735	3.30	0.00475	0.82	0.29740	133.48	0.19222
0.33	0.00902	4.05	0.00583	0.83	0.30246	135.75	0.19548
0.34	0.01088	4.88	0.00703	0.84	0.30741	137.98	0.19869
0.35	0.01294	5.81	0.00836	0.85	0.31227	140.16	0.20183
0.36	0.01521	6.83	0.00983	0.86	0.31704	142.30	0.20491
0.37	0.01769	7.94	0.01143	0.87	0.32171	144.39	0.20793
0.38	0.02040	9.15	0.01318	0.88	0.32630	146.45	0.21089
0.39	0.02333	10.47	0.01508	0.89	0.33081	148.48	0.21381
0.40	0.02650	11.89	0.01713	0.90	0.33523	150.46	0.21667
0.41	0.02991	13.42	0.01933	0.91	0.33959	152.42	0.21948
0.42	0.03357	15.07	0.02170	0.92	0.34386	154.34	0.22224
0.43	0.03749	16.82	0.02423	0.93	0.34807	156.22	0.22496
0.44	0.04167	18.70	0.02693	0.94	0.35221	158.08	0.22764
0.45	0.04612	20.70	0.02981	0.95	0.35628	159.91	0.23027
0.46	0.05085	22.82	0.03287	0.96	0.36029	161.71	0.23286
0.47	0.05587	25.08	0.03611	0.97	0.36424	163.48	0.23542
0.48	0.06118	27.46	0.03954	0.98	0.36814	165.23	0.23793
0.49	0.06679	29.98	0.04317	0.99	0.37197	166.95	0.24041
0.50	0.07272	32.64	0.04700	1.00	0.37576	168.65	0.24286

18

Table 18-3 (Continued)			
Head (feet)	CFS	GPM	MGD
1.01	0.37949	170.33	0.24527
1.02	0.38317	171.98	0.24765
1.03	0.38681	173.61	0.25000
1.04	0.39039	175.22	0.25232
1.05	0.39394	176.81	0.25461
1.06	0.39744	178.38	0.25687
1.07	0.40090	179.94	0.25911
1.08	0.40432	181.47	0.26132
1.09	0.40771	182.99	0.26351
1.10	0.41106	184.50	0.26567
1.11	0.41437	185.98	0.26781
1.12	0.41765	187.45	0.26993
1.13	0.42090	188.91	0.27203
1.14	0.42412	190.36	0.27411
1.15	0.42731	191.79	0.27617
1.16	0.43047	193.21	0.27822
1.17	0.43360	194.61	0.28024
1.18	0.43671	196.01	0.28225
1.19	0.43979	197.39	0.28424
1.20	0.44285	198.76	0.28622
1.21	0.44589	200.13	0.28818
1.22	0.44890	201.48	0.29013
1.23	0.45190	202.83	0.29207
1.24	0.45487	204.16	0.29399
1.25	0.45783	205.49	0.29590

Table 18-3 (Continued)			
Head (feet)	CFS	GPM	MGD
1.26	0.46077	206.81	0.29780
1.27	0.46369	208.12	0.29969
1.28	0.46659	209.42	0.30157
1.29	0.46949	210.72	0.30344
1.30	0.47236	212.01	0.30530
1.31	0.47522	213.30	0.30715
1.32	0.47807	214.57	0.30899
1.33	0.48091	215.85	0.31082
1.34	0.48374	217.12	0.31265
1.35	0.48656	218.38	0.31447
1.36	0.48936	219.64	0.31628
1.37	0.49216	220.90	0.31809
1.38	0.49495	222.15	0.31989
1.39	0.49773	223.40	0.32169
1.40	0.50050	224.64	0.32348
1.41	0.50327	225.88	0.32527
1.42	0.50603	227.12	0.32706
1.43	0.50879	228.36	0.32884
1.44	0.51154	229.59	0.33061
1.45	0.51428	230.83	0.33239
1.46	0.51703	232.06	0.33416
1.47	0.51976	233.29	0.33593
1.48	0.52250	234.51	0.33770
1.49	0.52524	235.74	0.33947
1.50	0.52797	236.97	0.34124

18

Table 18-4:
12 in. Isco Flow Metering Insert with V-notch Weir
Discharge Table with Head in Feet

Manufactured by Teledyne Isco, Inc. (Data from Teledyne Isco, Inc.)

Table 18-4				Table 18-4 (Continued)			
Head (feet)	CFS	GPM	MGD	Head (feet)	CFS	GPM	MGD
0.01	0	0	0	0.51	0.05141	23.075	0.03323
0.02	0	0	0	0.52	0.05641	25.321	0.03646
0.03	0	0	0	0.53	0.06171	27.698	0.03989
0.04	0	0	0	0.54	0.06731	30.210	0.04350
0.05	0	0	0	0.55	0.07321	32.860	0.04732
0.06	0	0	0	0.56	0.07943	35.650	0.05134
0.07	0	0	0	0.57	0.08597	38.586	0.05556
0.08	0	0	0	0.58	0.09284	41.669	0.06000
0.09	0	0	0	0.59	0.10004	44.903	0.06466
0.10	0	0	0	0.60	0.10759	48.292	0.06954
0.11	0	0	0	0.61	0.11550	51.838	0.07465
0.12	0	0	0	0.62	0.12376	55.546	0.07999
0.13	0	0	0	0.63	0.13238	59.418	0.08556
0.14	0	0	0	0.64	0.14139	63.458	0.09138
0.15	0	0	0	0.65	0.15077	67.669	0.09744
0.16	0	0	0	0.66	0.16054	72.055	0.10376
0.17	0	0	0	0.67	0.17071	76.619	0.11033
0.18	0	0	0	0.68	0.18128	81.363	0.11716
0.19	0	0	0	0.69	0.19140	85.905	0.12370
0.20	0	0	0	0.70	0.20483	91.934	0.13238
0.21	0	0	0	0.71	0.21790	97.800	0.14083
0.22	0	0	0	0.72	0.23062	103.510	0.14905
0.23	0	0	0	0.73	0.24301	109.071	0.15706
0.24	0	0	0	0.74	0.25508	114.490	0.16486
0.25	0	0	0	0.75	0.26685	119.771	0.17247
0.26	0	0	0	0.76	0.27833	124.921	0.17989
0.27	0	0	0	0.77	0.28952	129.946	0.18712
0.28	0	0	0	0.78	0.30045	134.849	0.19418
0.29	0.00019	0.087	0.00013	0.79	0.31111	139.636	0.20108
0.30	0.00065	0.292	0.00042	0.80	0.32153	144.312	0.20781
0.31	0.00124	0.554	0.00080	0.81	0.33171	148.881	0.21439
0.32	0.00196	0.878	0.00126	0.82	0.34166	153.346	0.22082
0.33	0.00282	1.266	0.00182	0.83	0.35138	157.712	0.22711
0.34	0.00384	1.722	0.00248	0.84	0.36090	161.983	0.23326
0.35	0.00501	2.249	0.00324	0.85	0.37021	166.162	0.23927
0.36	0.00635	2.850	0.00410	0.86	0.37932	170.253	0.24516
0.37	0.00786	3.530	0.00508	0.87	0.38825	174.258	0.25093
0.38	0.00956	4.290	0.00618	0.88	0.39699	178.181	0.25658
0.39	0.01144	5.135	0.00739	0.89	0.40555	182.026	0.26212
0.40	0.01352	6.068	0.00874	0.9	0.41395	185.794	0.26754
0.41	0.01580	7.091	0.01021	0.91	0.42218	189.488	0.27286
0.42	0.01829	8.210	0.01182	0.92	0.43025	193.111	0.27808
0.43	0.02100	9.426	0.01357	0.93	0.43817	196.666	0.28320
0.44	0.02393	10.743	0.01547	0.94	0.44595	200.155	0.28822
0.45	0.02710	12.164	0.01752	0.95	0.45358	203.581	0.29316
0.46	0.03051	13.694	0.01972	0.96	0.46107	206.944	0.29800
0.47	0.03416	15.334	0.02208	0.97	0.46844	210.248	0.30276
0.48	0.03808	17.089	0.02461	0.98	0.47567	213.495	0.30743
0.49	0.04225	18.962	0.02731	0.99	0.48278	216.687	0.31203
0.50	0.04669	20.956	0.03018	1.00	0.48977	219.824	0.31655

18

Table 18-4 (Continued)				Table 18-4 (Continued)			
Head (feet)	CFS	GPM	MGD	Head (feet)	CFS	GPM	MGD
1.01	0.49665	222.910	0.32099	1.26	0.64019	287.339	0.41377
1.02	0.50341	225.946	0.32536	1.27	0.64509	289.537	0.41693
1.03	0.51007	228.933	0.32966	1.28	0.64994	291.714	0.42007
1.04	0.51662	231.874	0.33390	1.29	0.65475	293.871	0.42317
1.05	0.52307	234.769	0.33807	1.30	0.65951	296.008	0.42625
1.06	0.52942	237.620	0.34217	1.31	0.66423	298.126	0.42930
1.07	0.53568	240.429	0.34622	1.32	0.66890	300.225	0.43232
1.08	0.54185	243.197	0.35020	1.33	0.67354	302.306	0.43532
1.09	0.54793	245.926	0.35413	1.34	0.67814	304.370	0.43829
1.10	0.55392	248.616	0.35801	1.35	0.68270	306.417	0.44124
1.11	0.55983	251.269	0.36183	1.36	0.68722	308.448	0.44416
1.12	0.56566	253.886	0.36560	1.37	0.69171	310.463	0.44707
1.13	0.57141	256.468	0.36931	1.38	0.69617	312.463	0.44995
1.14	0.57709	259.017	0.37298	1.39	0.70060	314.449	0.45281
1.15	0.58270	261.533	0.37661	1.40	0.70499	316.421	0.45565
1.16	0.58823	264.018	0.38019	1.41	0.70935	318.380	0.45847
1.17	0.59370	266.472	0.38372	1.42	0.71369	320.325	0.46127
1.18	0.59910	268.896	0.38721	1.43	0.71799	322.258	0.46405
1.19	0.60444	271.292	0.39066	1.44	0.72227	324.179	0.46682
1.20	0.60972	273.661	0.39407	1.45	0.72653	326.088	0.46957
1.21	0.61494	276.003	0.39744	1.46	0.73076	327.986	0.47230
1.22	0.62010	278.318	0.40078	1.47	0.73496	329.873	0.47502
1.23	0.62520	280.609	0.40408	1.48	0.73914	331.750	0.47772
1.24	0.63025	282.876	0.40734	1.49	0.74330	333.617	0.48041
1.25	0.63525	285.119	0.41057	1.50	0.74744	335.475	0.48308

18

Table 18-5:
0.152 m Isco Flow Metering Insert with V-notch Weir
Discharge Table with Head in Meters

Manufactured by Teledyne Isco, Inc. (Data from Teledyne Isco, Inc.)

Table 18-5			Table 18-5 (Continued)		
Head (meters)	l/s	m³/hr	Head (meters)	l/s	m³/hr
0.005	0	0	0.235	3.7037	13.333
0.010	0	0	0.240	3.7604	13.538
0.015	0	0	0.245	3.8163	13.739
0.020	0	0	0.250	3.8712	13.936
0.025	0	0	0.255	3.9254	14.132
0.030	0	0	0.260	3.9789	14.324
0.035	0	0	0.265	4.0317	14.514
0.040	0.0005	0.002	0.270	4.0839	14.702
0.045	0.0071	0.026	0.275	4.1355	14.888
0.050	0.0221	0.080	0.280	4.1866	15.072
0.055	0.0466	0.168	0.285	4.2372	15.254
0.060	0.0818	0.295	0.290	4.2873	15.434
0.065	0.1289	0.464	0.295	4.3370	15.613
0.070	0.1891	0.681	0.300	4.3863	15.791
0.075	0.2637	0.949	0.305	4.4352	15.967
0.080	0.3540	1.275	0.310	4.4837	16.141
0.085	0.4615	1.662	0.315	4.5319	16.315
0.090	0.5876	2.115	0.320	4.5799	16.487
0.095	0.7338	2.642	0.325	4.6275	16.659
0.100	0.9122	3.284	0.330	4.6748	16.829
0.105	1.1433	4.116	0.335	4.7219	16.999
0.110	1.3492	4.857	0.340	4.7687	17.167
0.115	1.5341	5.523	0.345	4.8153	17.335
0.120	1.7015	6.125	0.350	4.8617	17.502
0.125	1.8540	6.675	0.355	4.9079	17.669
0.130	1.9940	7.179	0.360	4.9539	17.834
0.135	2.1233	7.644	0.365	4.9997	17.999
0.140	2.2433	8.076	0.370	5.0454	18.163
0.145	2.3554	8.479	0.375	5.0909	18.327
0.150	2.4605	8.858	0.380	5.1362	18.490
0.155	2.5596	9.2140	0.385	5.1814	18.653
0.160	2.6533	9.5520	0.390	5.2264	18.815
0.165	2.7424	9.8730	0.395	5.2713	18.977
0.170	2.8273	10.178	0.400	5.3161	19.138
0.175	2.9086	10.471	0.405	5.3607	19.299
0.180	2.9866	10.752	0.410	5.4053	19.459
0.185	3.0617	11.022	0.415	5.4497	19.619
0.190	3.1342	11.283	0.420	5.4941	19.779
0.195	3.2044	11.536	0.425	5.5383	19.938
0.200	3.2724	11.781	0.430	5.5824	20.097
0.205	3.3385	12.018	0.435	5.6265	20.255
0.210	3.4028	12.250	0.440	5.6705	20.414
0.215	3.4656	12.476	0.445	5.7144	20.572
0.220	3.5270	12.697	0.450	5.7582	20.729
0.225	3.5870	12.913	0.455	5.8019	20.887
0.230	3.6459	13.125	0.460	5.8456	21.044

18

Table 18-6:
0.203 m Isco Flow Metering Insert with V-notch Weir
Discharge Table with Head in Meters

Manufactured by Teledyne Isco, Inc. (Data from Teledyne Isco, Inc.)

Table 18-6			Table 18-6 (Continued)		
Head (meters)	l/s	m³/hr	Head (meters)	l/s	m³/hr
0.005	0	0	0.235	6.0305	21.710
0.010	0	0	0.240	6.1579	22.169
0.015	0	0	0.245	6.2818	22.614
0.020	0	0	0.250	6.4024	23.049
0.025	0	0	0.255	6.5200	23.472
0.030	0	0	0.260	6.6348	23.885
0.035	0	0	0.265	6.7471	24.289
0.040	0	0	0.270	6.8569	24.685
0.045	0	0	0.275	6.9646	25.072
0.050	0	0	0.280	7.0702	25.453
0.055	0.0003	0.001	0.285	7.1739	25.826
0.060	0.0068	0.024	0.290	7.2758	26.193
0.065	0.0226	0.081	0.295	7.3760	26.554
0.070	0.0486	0.175	0.300	7.4747	26.909
0.075	0.0858	0.309	0.305	7.5720	27.259
0.080	0.1354	0.487	0.310	7.6678	27.604
0.085	0.1984	0.714	0.315	7.7625	27.945
0.090	0.2759	0.993	0.320	7.8559	28.281
0.095	0.3690	1.329	0.325	7.9482	28.613
0.100	0.4791	1.725	0.330	8.0394	28.942
0.105	0.6072	2.186	0.335	8.1297	29.267
0.110	0.7547	2.717	0.340	8.2190	29.589
0.115	0.9229	3.322	0.345	8.3075	29.907
0.120	1.1130	4.007	0.350	8.3951	30.222
0.125	1.3265	4.776	0.355	8.4819	30.535
0.130	1.5648	5.633	0.360	8.5680	30.845
0.135	1.8293	6.585	0.365	8.6534	31.152
0.140	2.1439	7.718	0.370	8.7382	31.457
0.145	2.4835	8.941	0.375	8.8223	31.760
0.150	2.7966	10.068	0.380	8.9058	32.061
0.155	3.0863	11.111	0.385	8.9887	32.359
0.160	3.3558	12.081	0.390	9.0712	32.656
0.165	3.6072	12.986	0.395	9.1531	32.951
0.170	3.8428	13.834	0.400	9.2345	33.244
0.175	4.0644	14.632	0.405	9.3155	33.536
0.180	4.2734	15.384	0.410	9.3960	33.826
0.185	4.4712	16.096	0.415	9.4761	34.114
0.190	4.6589	16.772	0.420	9.5558	34.401
0.195	4.8376	17.416	0.425	9.6352	34.687
0.200	5.0083	18.030	0.430	9.7142	34.971
0.205	5.1715	18.617	0.435	9.7928	35.254
0.210	5.3281	19.181	0.440	9.8711	35.536
0.215	5.4787	19.723	0.445	9.9491	35.817
0.220	5.6237	20.245	0.450	10.027	36.096
0.225	5.7638	20.750	0.455	10.104	36.375
0.230	5.8992	21.237	0.460	10.181	36.653

18

Table 18-7:
0.254 m Isco Flow Metering Insert with V-notch Weir Discharge Table with Head in Meters

Manufactured by Teledyne Isco, Inc. (Data from Teledyne Isco, Inc.)

Table 18-7			Table 18-7 (Continued)		
Head (meters)	l/s	m³/hr	Head (meters)	l/s	m³/hr
0.005	0	0	0.235	7.6743	27.628
0.010	0	0	0.240	7.9334	28.560
0.015	0	0	0.245	8.1832	29.460
0.020	0	0	0.250	8.4245	30.328
0.025	0	0	0.255	8.6578	31.168
0.030	0	0	0.260	8.8835	31.981
0.035	0	0	0.265	9.1023	32.768
0.040	0	0	0.270	9.3144	33.532
0.045	0	0	0.275	9.5204	34.274
0.050	0	0	0.280	9.7207	34.994
0.055	0	0	0.285	9.9155	35.696
0.060	0	0	0.290	10.105	36.379
0.065	0	0	0.295	10.290	37.045
0.070	0.0017	0.006	0.300	10.471	37.695
0.075	0.0128	0.046	0.305	10.647	38.330
0.080	0.0346	0.125	0.310	10.820	38.951
0.085	0.0681	0.245	0.315	10.989	39.558
0.090	0.1140	0.410	0.320	11.154	40.154
0.095	0.1730	0.623	0.325	11.316	40.737
0.100	0.2459	0.885	0.330	11.475	41.310
0.105	0.3335	1.201	0.335	11.631	41.872
0.110	0.4367	1.572	0.340	11.785	42.425
0.115	0.5562	2.002	0.345	11.936	42.969
0.120	0.6930	2.495	0.350	12.085	43.505
0.125	0.8480	3.053	0.355	12.231	44.032
0.130	1.0219	3.679	0.360	12.376	44.553
0.135	1.2158	4.377	0.365	12.519	45.067
0.140	1.4305	5.150	0.370	12.660	45.574
0.145	1.6671	6.001	0.375	12.799	46.076
0.150	1.9263	6.935	0.380	12.937	46.573
0.155	2.2094	7.954	0.385	13.073	47.064
0.160	2.5171	9.062	0.390	13.209	47.551
0.165	2.8506	10.262	0.395	13.343	48.034
0.170	3.2108	11.559	0.400	13.476	48.513
0.175	3.5989	12.956	0.405	13.608	48.988
0.180	3.9782	14.321	0.410	13.739	49.461
0.185	4.3986	15.835	0.415	13.870	49.930
0.190	4.7980	17.273	0.420	13.999	50.397
0.195	5.1780	18.641	0.425	14.128	50.862
0.200	5.5401	19.944	0.430	14.257	51.325
0.205	5.8856	21.188	0.435	14.385	51.786
0.210	6.2160	22.377	0.440	14.513	52.246
0.215	6.5321	23.516	0.445	14.640	52.705
0.220	6.8351	24.606	0.450	14.768	53.163
0.225	7.1259	25.653	0.455	14.895	53.620
0.230	7.4054	26.659	0.460	15.022	54.077

18

Table 18-8:
0.305 m Isco Flow Metering Insert with V-notch Weir
Discharge Table with Head in Meters

Manufactured by Teledyne Isco, Inc. (Data from Teledyne Isco, Inc.)

Head (meters)	l/s	m³/hr	Head (meters)	l/s	m³/hr
0.005	0	0	0.235	8.2295	29.626
0.010	0	0	0.240	8.7319	31.435
0.015	0	0	0.245	9.2152	33.175
0.020	0	0	0.250	9.6805	34.850
0.025	0	0	0.255	10.129	36.464
0.030	0	0	0.260	10.562	38.022
0.035	0	0	0.265	10.980	39.526
0.040	0	0	0.270	11.383	40.980
0.045	0	0	0.275	11.774	42.387
0.050	0	0	0.280	12.153	43.749
0.055	0	0	0.285	12.519	45.069
0.060	0	0	0.290	12.875	46.349
0.065	0	0	0.295	13.220	47.592
0.070	0	0	0.300	13.556	48.800
0.075	0	0	0.305	13.882	49.974
0.080	0	0	0.310	14.199	51.116
0.085	0	0	0.315	14.508	52.229
0.090	0.0119	0.043	0.320	14.809	53.313
0.095	0.0381	0.137	0.325	15.103	54.371
0.100	0.0749	0.269	0.330	15.390	55.403
0.105	0.1230	0.443	0.335	15.670	56.411
0.110	0.1835	0.660	0.340	15.944	57.396
0.115	0.2572	0.926	0.345	16.211	58.360
0.120	0.3451	1.242	0.350	16.473	59.304
0.125	0.4481	1.613	0.355	16.730	60.228
0.130	0.5672	2.042	0.360	16.982	61.133
0.135	0.7032	2.532	0.365	17.228	62.022
0.140	0.8571	3.086	0.370	17.470	62.893
0.145	1.0299	3.708	0.375	17.708	63.750
0.150	1.2224	4.401	0.380	17.942	64.591
0.155	1.4356	5.168	0.385	18.172	65.418
0.160	1.6705	6.014	0.390	18.398	66.232
0.165	1.9278	6.940	0.395	18.621	67.034
0.170	2.2087	7.951	0.400	18.840	67.823
0.175	2.5139	9.050	0.405	19.056	68.602
0.180	2.8445	10.24	0.410	19.269	69.370
0.185	3.2013	11.525	0.415	19.480	70.127
0.190	3.5853	12.907	0.420	19.688	70.875
0.195	3.9975	14.391	0.425	19.893	71.615
0.200	4.4386	15.979	0.430	20.096	72.346
0.205	4.9098	17.675	0.435	20.297	73.069
0.210	5.3802	19.369	0.440	20.496	73.784
0.215	6.0005	21.602	0.445	20.692	74.493
0.220	6.5938	23.738	0.450	20.887	75.194
0.225	7.1619	25.783	0.455	21.081	75.890
0.230	7.7066	27.744	0.460	21.272	76.580

18

Table 18-9:
6 in. Isco Flow Metering Insert with Round Orifice
Discharge Table with Head in Feet

Manufactured by Teledyne Isco, Inc. (Data from Teledyne Isco, Inc.)

Table 18-9				Table 18-9 (Continued)			
Head (feet)	CFS	GPM	MGD	Head (feet)	CFS	GPM	MGD
0.01	0	0	0	0.51	0.19003	85.29	0.12282
0.02	0	0	0	0.52	0.19401	87.08	0.12539
0.03	0	0	0	0.53	0.19790	88.82	0.12790
0.04	0	0	0	0.54	0.20169	90.52	0.13036
0.05	0	0	0	0.55	0.20540	92.19	0.13275
0.06	0	0	0	0.56	0.20902	93.82	0.13509
0.07	0	0	0	0.57	0.21257	95.41	0.13739
0.08	0	0	0	0.58	0.21605	96.97	0.13963
0.09	0.00001	0.01	0.00001	0.59	0.21945	98.50	0.14184
0.10	0.00034	0.15	0.00022	0.60	0.22279	100.00	0.14400
0.11	0.00110	0.50	0.00071	0.61	0.22607	101.47	0.14611
0.12	0.00229	1.03	0.00148	0.62	0.22929	102.91	0.14820
0.13	0.00387	1.74	0.00250	0.63	0.23245	104.33	0.15024
0.14	0.00584	2.62	0.00378	0.64	0.23556	105.73	0.15225
0.15	0.00818	3.67	0.00528	0.65	0.23862	107.10	0.15422
0.16	0.01086	4.87	0.00702	0.66	0.24163	108.45	0.15617
0.17	0.01387	6.22	0.00896	0.67	0.24459	109.78	0.15808
0.18	0.01719	7.71	0.01111	0.68	0.24750	111.09	0.15996
0.19	0.02080	9.34	0.01344	0.69	0.25037	112.38	0.16182
0.20	0.02469	11.08	0.01596	0.70	0.25321	113.65	0.16365
0.21	0.02885	12.95	0.01865	0.71	0.25600	114.90	0.16546
0.22	0.03325	14.92	0.02149	0.72	0.25875	116.14	0.16724
0.23	0.03788	17.00	0.02448	0.73	0.26147	117.36	0.16899
0.24	0.04272	19.17	0.02761	0.74	0.26415	118.56	0.17073
0.25	0.04776	21.44	0.03087	0.75	0.26680	119.75	0.17244
0.26	0.05299	23.78	0.03425	0.76	0.26942	120.92	0.17413
0.27	0.05838	26.20	0.03773	0.77	0.27201	122.09	0.17580
0.28	0.06392	28.69	0.04132	0.78	0.27456	123.23	0.17746
0.29	0.06961	31.24	0.04499	0.79	0.27709	124.37	0.17909
0.30	0.07542	33.85	0.04874	0.80	0.27959	125.49	0.18071
0.31	0.08134	36.51	0.05257	0.81	0.28207	126.60	0.18231
0.32	0.08736	39.21	0.05646	0.82	0.28452	127.70	0.18389
0.33	0.09346	41.95	0.06041	0.83	0.28694	128.79	0.18546
0.34	0.09964	44.72	0.06440	0.84	0.28935	129.87	0.18701
0.35	0.10587	47.52	0.06843	0.85	0.29173	130.94	0.18855
0.36	0.11216	50.34	0.07249	0.86	0.29408	131.99	0.19007
0.37	0.11847	53.17	0.07657	0.87	0.29642	133.04	0.19158
0.38	0.12481	56.02	0.08067	0.88	0.29873	134.08	0.19308
0.39	0.13116	58.87	0.08477	0.89	0.30103	135.11	0.19456
0.40	0.13751	61.72	0.08887	0.90	0.30330	136.13	0.19603
0.41	0.14385	64.56	0.09297	0.91	0.30556	137.15	0.19749
0.42	0.14876	66.77	0.09614	0.92	0.30780	138.15	0.19894
0.43	0.15393	69.09	0.09949	0.93	0.31002	139.15	0.20037
0.44	0.15893	71.33	0.10272	0.94	0.31223	140.14	0.20180
0.45	0.16378	73.51	0.10585	0.95	0.31442	141.12	0.20321
0.46	0.16847	75.62	0.10889	0.96	0.31659	142.10	0.20462
0.47	0.17303	77.66	0.11183	0.97	0.31875	143.06	0.20601
0.48	0.17746	79.65	0.11469	0.98	0.32089	144.03	0.20740
0.49	0.18176	81.58	0.11748	0.99	0.32302	144.98	0.20877
0.50	0.18595	83.46	0.12018	1.00	0.32514	145.93	0.21014

18

Table 18-9 (Continued)			
Head (feet)	CFS	GPM	MGD
1.01	0.32724	146.87	0.21150
1.02	0.32933	147.81	0.21285
1.03	0.33140	148.74	0.21419
1.04	0.33347	149.67	0.21552
1.05	0.33552	150.59	0.21685
1.06	0.33756	151.51	0.21817
1.07	0.33958	152.42	0.21948
1.08	0.34160	153.32	0.22078
1.09	0.34361	154.22	0.22208
1.10	0.34560	155.12	0.22337
1.11	0.34759	156.01	0.22465
1.12	0.34957	156.9	0.22593
1.13	0.35153	157.78	0.22720
1.14	0.35349	158.66	0.22847
1.15	0.35544	159.53	0.22973
1.16	0.35738	160.40	0.23098
1.17	0.35931	161.27	0.23223
1.18	0.36123	162.13	0.23347
1.19	0.36314	162.99	0.23471
1.20	0.36505	163.85	0.23594
1.21	0.36695	164.7	0.23716
1.22	0.36884	165.55	0.23839
1.23	0.37072	166.39	0.23960
1.24	0.37260	167.23	0.24081
1.25	0.37446	168.07	0.24202

Table 18-9 (Continued)			
Head (feet)	CFS	GPM	MGD
1.26	0.37633	168.91	0.24323
1.27	0.37818	169.74	0.24442
1.28	0.38003	170.57	0.24562
1.29	0.38187	171.40	0.24681
1.30	0.38371	172.22	0.24800
1.31	0.38553	173.04	0.24918
1.32	0.38736	173.86	0.25036
1.33	0.38918	174.67	0.25153
1.34	0.39099	175.49	0.25270
1.35	0.39279	176.30	0.25387
1.36	0.39459	177.11	0.25503
1.37	0.39639	177.91	0.25619
1.38	0.39818	178.72	0.25735
1.39	0.39996	179.52	0.25850
1.40	0.40174	180.32	0.25965
1.41	0.40352	181.11	0.26080
1.42	0.40529	181.91	0.26195
1.43	0.40705	182.70	0.26309
1.44	0.40882	183.49	0.26422
1.45	0.41057	184.28	0.26536
1.46	0.41232	185.06	0.26649
1.47	0.41407	185.85	0.26762
1.48	0.41581	186.63	0.26875
1.49	0.41755	187.41	0.26987
1.50	0.41929	188.19	0.27099

18

Table 18-10:
8 in. Isco Flow Metering Insert with Round Orifice
Discharge Table with Head in Feet

Manufactured by Teledyne Isco, Inc. (Data from Teledyne Isco, Inc.)

Table 18-10				Table 18-10 (Continued)			
Head (feet)	CFS	GPM	MGD	Head (feet)	CFS	GPM	MGD
0.01	0	0	0	0.51	0.25049	112.43	0.16189
0.02	0	0	0	0.52	0.26087	117.09	0.16861
0.03	0	0	0	0.53	0.27091	121.59	0.17509
0.04	0	0	0	0.54	0.28060	125.94	0.18136
0.05	0	0	0	0.55	0.28998	130.15	0.18742
0.06	0	0	0	0.56	0.29907	134.23	0.19329
0.07	0	0	0	0.57	0.30787	138.18	0.19898
0.08	0	0	0	0.58	0.31640	142.01	0.20449
0.09	0	0	0	0.59	0.32468	145.73	0.20985
0.10	0	0	0	0.60	0.33272	149.34	0.21504
0.11	0	0	0	0.61	0.34054	152.84	0.22010
0.12	0	0	0	0.62	0.34814	156.26	0.22501
0.13	0	0	0	0.63	0.35553	159.57	0.22979
0.14	0.00011	0.05	0.00007	0.64	0.36273	162.81	0.23444
0.15	0.00069	0.31	0.00044	0.65	0.36975	165.96	0.23898
0.16	0.00176	0.79	0.00113	0.66	0.37659	169.03	0.24340
0.17	0.00330	1.48	0.00213	0.67	0.38326	172.02	0.24771
0.18	0.00530	2.38	0.00343	0.68	0.38978	174.94	0.25192
0.19	0.00775	3.48	0.00501	0.69	0.39614	177.80	0.25603
0.20	0.01064	4.78	0.00688	0.70	0.40235	180.59	0.26005
0.21	0.01395	6.26	0.00901	0.71	0.40843	183.32	0.26398
0.22	0.01766	7.93	0.01142	0.72	0.41438	185.99	0.26782
0.23	0.02178	9.77	0.01407	0.73	0.42020	188.60	0.27158
0.24	0.02627	11.79	0.01698	0.74	0.42590	191.16	0.27526
0.25	0.03114	13.98	0.02013	0.75	0.43148	193.66	0.27887
0.26	0.03637	16.32	0.02350	0.76	0.43696	196.12	0.28241
0.27	0.04194	18.82	0.02711	0.77	0.44232	198.53	0.28588
0.28	0.04785	21.47	0.03092	0.78	0.44759	200.89	0.28929
0.29	0.05407	24.27	0.03495	0.79	0.45276	203.21	0.29263
0.30	0.06061	27.20	0.03917	0.80	0.45784	205.49	0.29591
0.31	0.06745	30.27	0.04359	0.81	0.46283	207.73	0.29914
0.32	0.07457	33.47	0.04820	0.82	0.46774	209.94	0.30231
0.33	0.08197	36.79	0.05298	0.83	0.47256	212.10	0.30543
0.34	0.08963	40.23	0.05793	0.84	0.47731	214.23	0.30849
0.35	0.09755	43.78	0.06305	0.85	0.48198	216.33	0.31151
0.36	0.10570	47.44	0.06832	0.86	0.48658	218.39	0.31449
0.37	0.11409	51.21	0.07374	0.87	0.49111	220.43	0.31741
0.38	0.12269	55.07	0.07930	0.88	0.49558	222.43	0.32030
0.39	0.13151	59.03	0.08500	0.89	0.49998	224.41	0.32314
0.40	0.14052	63.07	0.09082	0.90	0.50432	226.35	0.32595
0.41	0.14972	67.20	0.09677	0.91	0.50860	228.28	0.32872
0.42	0.15910	71.41	0.10283	0.92	0.51283	230.17	0.33145
0.43	0.16864	75.69	0.10899	0.93	0.51700	232.05	0.33415
0.44	0.17834	80.04	0.11526	0.94	0.52112	233.89	0.33681
0.45	0.18818	84.46	0.12163	0.95	0.52519	235.72	0.33944
0.46	0.19817	88.94	0.12808	0.96	0.52921	237.53	0.34204
0.47	0.20827	93.48	0.13461	0.97	0.53319	239.31	0.34461
0.48	0.21850	98.07	0.14122	0.98	0.53712	241.08	0.34715
0.49	0.22883	102.71	0.14790	0.99	0.54101	242.82	0.34966
0.50	0.23926	107.39	0.15464	1.00	0.54486	244.55	0.35215

18

Table 18-10 (Continued)				Table 18-10 (Continued)			
Head (feet)	CFS	GPM	MGD	Head (feet)	CFS	GPM	MGD
1.01	0.54867	246.26	0.35461	1.26	0.63476	284.90	0.41025
1.02	0.55244	247.95	0.35705	1.27	0.63795	286.33	0.41232
1.03	0.55618	249.63	0.35947	1.28	0.64112	287.76	0.41437
1.04	0.55988	251.29	0.36186	1.29	0.64429	289.18	0.41641
1.05	0.56355	252.94	0.36423	1.30	0.64744	290.59	0.41845
1.06	0.56718	254.57	0.36658	1.31	0.65058	292.00	0.42048
1.07	0.57079	256.19	0.36891	1.32	0.65371	293.41	0.42251
1.08	0.57436	257.79	0.37122	1.33	0.65683	294.81	0.42452
1.09	0.57791	259.38	0.37351	1.34	0.65995	296.20	0.42653
1.10	0.58142	260.96	0.37578	1.35	0.66305	297.60	0.42854
1.11	0.58492	262.53	0.37804	1.36	0.66614	298.99	0.43054
1.12	0.58838	264.08	0.38028	1.37	0.66923	300.37	0.43253
1.13	0.59183	265.63	0.38251	1.38	0.67231	301.75	0.43452
1.14	0.59524	267.16	0.38472	1.39	0.67538	303.13	0.43651
1.15	0.59864	268.69	0.38691	1.40	0.67844	304.51	0.43849
1.16	0.60202	270.20	0.38909	1.41	0.68150	305.88	0.44046
1.17	0.60537	271.71	0.39126	1.42	0.68455	307.25	0.44244
1.18	0.60870	273.21	0.39342	1.43	0.68760	308.61	0.44441
1.19	0.61202	274.69	0.39556	1.44	0.69064	309.98	0.44637
1.20	0.61532	276.17	0.39769	1.45	0.69367	311.34	0.44833
1.21	0.61860	277.65	0.39981	1.46	0.69671	312.70	0.45029
1.22	0.62186	279.11	0.40192	1.47	0.69973	314.06	0.45225
1.23	0.62511	280.57	0.40402	1.48	0.70276	315.42	0.45420
1.24	0.62834	282.02	0.40610	1.49	0.70578	316.77	0.45616
1.25	0.63155	283.46	0.40818	1.50	0.70879	318.13	0.45811

18

Table 18-11:
10 in. Isco Flow Metering Insert with Round Orifice
Discharge Table with Head in Feet

Manufactured by Teledyne Isco, Inc. (Data from Teledyne Isco, Inc.)

Head (feet)	CFS	GPM	MGD	Head (feet)	CFS	GPM	MGD
0.01	0	0	0	0.51	0.25223	113.21	0.16302
0.02	0	0	0	0.52	0.26492	118.91	0.17122
0.03	0	0	0	0.53	0.27780	124.69	0.17955
0.04	0	0	0	0.54	0.29086	130.55	0.18799
0.05	0	0	0	0.55	0.30408	136.48	0.19653
0.06	0	0	0	0.56	0.31746	142.49	0.20518
0.07	0	0	0	0.57	0.33100	148.56	0.21393
0.08	0	0	0	0.58	0.34467	154.70	0.22277
0.09	0	0	0	0.59	0.35847	160.89	0.23169
0.10	0	0	0	0.60	0.37241	167.15	0.24069
0.11	0	0	0	0.61	0.38645	173.45	0.24977
0.12	0	0	0	0.62	0.40061	179.80	0.25892
0.13	0	0	0	0.63	0.41486	186.20	0.26813
0.14	0	0	0	0.64	0.42921	192.64	0.27740
0.15	0	0	0	0.65	0.44364	199.12	0.28673
0.16	0	0	0	0.66	0.45791	205.52	0.29595
0.17	0.00004	0.02	0.00003	0.67	0.47133	211.55	0.30463
0.18	0.00052	0.23	0.00034	0.68	0.48437	217.40	0.31306
0.19	0.00155	0.69	0.00100	0.69	0.49704	223.09	0.32125
0.20	0.00310	1.39	0.00200	0.70	0.50937	228.62	0.32922
0.21	0.00516	2.32	0.00334	0.71	0.52138	234.01	0.33698
0.22	0.00773	3.47	0.00500	0.72	0.53308	239.26	0.34454
0.23	0.01080	4.85	0.00698	0.73	0.54449	244.38	0.35191
0.24	0.01434	6.44	0.00927	0.74	0.55562	249.38	0.35911
0.25	0.01835	8.24	0.01186	0.75	0.56649	254.26	0.36613
0.26	0.02283	10.24	0.01475	0.76	0.57712	259.03	0.37300
0.27	0.02775	12.45	0.01793	0.77	0.58751	263.69	0.37972
0.28	0.03310	14.86	0.02139	0.78	0.59768	268.26	0.38629
0.29	0.03888	17.45	0.02513	0.79	0.60764	272.73	0.39273
0.30	0.04508	20.23	0.02913	0.80	0.61740	277.11	0.39904
0.31	0.05167	23.19	0.03340	0.81	0.62697	281.41	0.40522
0.32	0.05866	26.33	0.03791	0.82	0.63636	285.62	0.41129
0.33	0.06603	29.64	0.04268	0.83	0.64558	289.76	0.41725
0.34	0.07378	33.11	0.04768	0.84	0.65463	293.82	0.42310
0.35	0.08188	36.75	0.05292	0.85	0.66353	297.81	0.42885
0.36	0.09033	40.54	0.05838	0.86	0.67227	301.74	0.43450
0.37	0.09912	44.49	0.06406	0.87	0.68088	305.60	0.44006
0.38	0.10824	48.58	0.06996	0.88	0.68934	309.40	0.44554
0.39	0.11768	52.82	0.07606	0.89	0.69768	313.14	0.45092
0.40	0.12743	57.19	0.08236	0.90	0.70590	316.83	0.45623
0.41	0.13748	61.70	0.08885	0.91	0.71399	320.46	0.46146
0.42	0.14781	66.34	0.09553	0.92	0.72197	324.04	0.46662
0.43	0.15843	71.11	0.10239	0.93	0.72984	327.58	0.47171
0.44	0.16931	75.99	0.10943	0.94	0.73761	331.06	0.47673
0.45	0.18045	80.99	0.11663	0.95	0.74528	334.50	0.48169
0.46	0.19184	86.11	0.12399	0.96	0.75285	337.90	0.48658
0.47	0.20348	91.33	0.13151	0.97	0.76033	341.26	0.49141
0.48	0.21534	96.65	0.13918	0.98	0.76772	344.58	0.49619
0.49	0.22743	102.08	0.14699	0.99	0.77503	347.86	0.50091
0.50	0.23973	107.60	0.15494	1.00	0.78226	351.10	0.50558

18

Table 18-11 (Continued)				Table 18-11 (Continued)			
Head (feet)	CFS	GPM	MGD	Head (feet)	CFS	GPM	MGD
1.01	0.78940	354.31	0.51020	1.26	0.94964	426.23	0.61377
1.02	0.79648	357.48	0.51478	1.27	0.95551	428.86	0.61756
1.03	0.80348	360.63	0.51930	1.28	0.96135	431.49	0.62134
1.04	0.81041	363.74	0.52378	1.29	0.96717	434.09	0.62510
1.05	0.81728	366.82	0.52822	1.30	0.97295	436.69	0.62883
1.06	0.82408	369.87	0.53262	1.31	0.97871	439.28	0.63256
1.07	0.83082	372.90	0.53697	1.32	0.98444	441.85	0.63626
1.08	0.83750	375.89	0.54129	1.33	0.99015	444.41	0.63995
1.09	0.84412	378.87	0.54557	1.34	0.99583	446.96	0.64362
1.10	0.85069	381.82	0.54981	1.35	1.00150	449.50	0.64727
1.11	0.85720	384.74	0.55402	1.36	1.00710	452.02	0.65092
1.12	0.86366	387.64	0.55820	1.37	1.01270	454.54	0.65454
1.13	0.87008	390.52	0.56235	1.38	1.01830	457.05	0.65815
1.14	0.87644	393.38	0.56646	1.39	1.02390	459.55	0.66175
1.15	0.88276	396.21	0.57054	1.40	1.02940	462.04	0.66533
1.16	0.88904	399.03	0.57460	1.41	1.03500	464.52	0.66891
1.17	0.89527	401.83	0.57863	1.42	1.04050	466.99	0.67246
1.18	0.90146	404.60	0.58263	1.43	1.04590	469.45	0.67601
1.19	0.90761	407.36	0.58660	1.44	1.05140	471.91	0.67954
1.20	0.91372	410.11	0.59055	1.45	1.05690	474.35	0.68307
1.21	0.91979	412.83	0.59448	1.46	1.06230	476.79	0.68658
1.22	0.92583	415.54	0.59838	1.47	1.06770	479.22	0.69008
1.23	0.93183	418.24	0.60226	1.48	1.07310	481.64	0.69357
1.24	0.93780	420.91	0.60612	1.49	1.07850	484.06	0.69704
1.25	0.94374	423.58	0.60995	1.50	1.08390	486.47	0.70051

18

Table 18-12:
12 in. Isco Flow Metering Insert with Round Orifice Discharge Table with Head in Feet

Manufactured by Teledyne Isco, Inc. (Data from Teledyne Isco, Inc.)

Table 18-12				Table 18-12 (Continued)			
Head (feet)	CFS	GPM	MGD	Head (feet)	CFS	GPM	MGD
0.01	0	0	0	0.51	0.21867	98.15	0.14133
0.02	0	0	0	0.52	0.23257	104.38	0.15031
0.03	0	0	0	0.53	0.24681	110.77	0.15951
0.04	0	0	0	0.54	0.26138	117.32	0.16894
0.05	0	0	0	0.55	0.27629	124.01	0.17857
0.06	0	0	0	0.56	0.29152	130.84	0.18841
0.07	0	0	0	0.57	0.30706	137.82	0.19846
0.08	0	0	0	0.58	0.32291	144.93	0.20870
0.09	0	0	0	0.59	0.33906	152.18	0.21914
0.10	0	0	0	0.60	0.35551	159.57	0.22977
0.11	0	0	0	0.61	0.37225	167.08	0.24059
0.12	0	0	0	0.62	0.38926	174.71	0.25159
0.13	0	0	0	0.63	0.40655	182.47	0.26276
0.14	0	0	0	0.64	0.42411	190.35	0.27411
0.15	0	0	0	0.65	0.44192	198.35	0.28562
0.16	0	0	0	0.66	0.45999	206.46	0.29730
0.17	0	0	0	0.67	0.47830	214.68	0.30913
0.18	0	0	0	0.68	0.49685	223.00	0.32112
0.19	0	0	0	0.69	0.51564	231.43	0.33327
0.20	0	0	0	0.70	0.53465	239.97	0.34555
0.21	0	0	0	0.71	0.55388	248.60	0.35798
0.22	0.00005	0.02	0.00003	0.72	0.57332	257.32	0.37055
0.23	0.00058	0.26	0.00037	0.73	0.59297	266.14	0.38325
0.24	0.00168	0.75	0.00109	0.74	0.61282	275.05	0.39608
0.25	0.00335	1.50	0.00217	0.75	0.63286	284.05	0.40903
0.26	0.00558	2.50	0.00361	0.76	0.65309	293.13	0.42210
0.27	0.00836	3.75	0.00540	0.77	0.67350	302.29	0.43530
0.28	0.01168	5.24	0.00755	0.78	0.69409	311.53	0.44860
0.29	0.01553	6.97	0.01004	0.79	0.71484	320.84	0.46201
0.30	0.01991	8.93	0.01287	0.80	0.73575	330.23	0.47553
0.31	0.02480	11.13	0.01603	0.81	0.75281	337.89	0.48656
0.32	0.03020	13.55	0.01952	0.82	0.76899	345.15	0.49701
0.33	0.03610	16.20	0.02333	0.83	0.78485	352.26	0.50726
0.34	0.04249	19.07	0.02746	0.84	0.80039	359.24	0.51731
0.35	0.04937	22.16	0.03191	0.85	0.81563	366.08	0.52716
0.36	0.05672	25.46	0.03666	0.86	0.83058	372.79	0.53682
0.37	0.06454	28.97	0.04171	0.87	0.84526	379.38	0.54630
0.38	0.07282	32.68	0.04706	0.88	0.85966	385.84	0.55561
0.39	0.08155	36.60	0.05270	0.89	0.87380	392.19	0.56475
0.40	0.09072	40.72	0.05863	0.90	0.88770	398.43	0.57373
0.41	0.10033	45.03	0.06484	0.91	0.90135	404.55	0.58256
0.42	0.11036	49.53	0.07133	0.92	0.91477	410.58	0.59123
0.43	0.12082	54.23	0.07809	0.93	0.92797	416.50	0.59976
0.44	0.13169	59.11	0.08511	0.94	0.94095	422.33	0.60815
0.45	0.14296	64.17	0.09240	0.95	0.95372	428.06	0.61641
0.46	0.15463	69.40	0.09994	0.96	0.96629	433.70	0.62453
0.47	0.16669	74.82	0.10774	0.97	0.97867	439.26	0.63253
0.48	0.17913	80.40	0.11578	0.98	0.99085	444.73	0.64040
0.49	0.19195	86.15	0.12406	0.99	1.00290	450.11	0.64816
0.50	0.20513	92.07	0.13258	1.00	1.01470	455.42	0.65581

18

Table 18-12 (Continued)			
Head (feet)	CFS	GPM	MGD
1.01	1.0264	460.66	0.66335
1.02	1.0379	465.82	0.67078
1.03	1.0492	470.91	0.67811
1.04	1.0604	475.93	0.68533
1.05	1.0714	480.88	0.69247
1.06	1.0823	485.77	0.69951
1.07	1.0931	490.59	0.70646
1.08	1.1037	495.36	0.71332
1.09	1.1142	500.07	0.72010
1.10	1.1245	504.70	0.72680
1.11	1.1348	509.32	0.73341
1.12	1.1449	513.86	0.73996
1.13	1.1549	518.35	0.74842
1.14	1.1648	522.79	0.75282
1.15	1.1746	527.19	0.75915
1.16	1.1843	531.53	0.76541
1.17	1.1938	535.83	0.77160
1.18	1.2033	540.09	0.77773
1.19	1.2127	544.31	0.78380
1.20	1.2220	548.48	0.78981
1.21	1.2312	552.62	0.79577
1.22	1.2404	556.71	0.80166
1.23	1.2494	560.77	0.80751
1.24	1.2584	564.79	0.81330
1.25	1.2672	568.78	0.81904

Table 18-12 (Continued)			
Head (feet)	CFS	GPM	MGD
1.26	1.2760	572.73	0.82473
1.27	1.2848	576.65	0.83037
1.28	1.2934	580.53	0.83597
1.29	1.3020	584.39	0.84152
1.30	1.3105	588.21	0.84703
1.31	1.3190	592.01	0.85249
1.32	1.3274	595.78	0.85792
1.33	1.3357	599.52	0.86330
1.34	1.3440	603.23	0.86865
1.35	1.3522	606.92	0.87396
1.36	1.3604	610.58	0.87923
1.37	1.3685	614.21	0.88447
1.38	1.3765	617.83	0.88967
1.39	1.3845	621.42	0.89484
1.40	1.3925	624.99	0.89998
1.41	1.4004	628.53	0.90509
1.42	1.4082	632.06	0.91017
1.43	1.4161	635.57	0.91521
1.44	1.4238	639.05	0.92023
1.45	1.4315	642.52	0.92523
1.46	1.4392	645.97	0.93019
1.47	1.4469	649.40	0.93513
1.48	1.4545	652.81	0.94005
1.49	1.4620	656.21	0.94494
1.50	1.4696	659.59	0.94981

18

Table 18-13:
0.152 m Isco Flow Metering Insert with Round Orifice
Discharge Table with Head in Meters

Manufactured by Teledyne Isco, Inc. (Data from Teledyne Isco, Inc.)

Table 18-13			Table 18-13 (Continued)		
Head (meters)	l/s	m³/hr	Head (meters)	l/s	m³/hr
0.005	0	0	0.235	7.7096	27.755
0.010	0	0	0.240	7.8279	28.180
0.015	0	0	0.245	7.9440	28.598
0.020	0	0	0.250	8.0581	29.009
0.025	0	0	0.255	8.1704	29.414
0.030	0.0073	0.026	0.260	8.2809	29.811
0.035	0.0460	0.166	0.265	8.3898	30.203
0.040	0.1160	0.418	0.270	8.4971	30.590
0.045	0.2150	0.774	0.275	8.6029	30.970
0.050	0.3408	1.227	0.280	8.7073	31.346
0.055	0.4910	1.768	0.285	8.8104	31.717
0.060	0.6637	2.389	0.290	8.9122	32.084
0.065	0.8567	3.084	0.295	9.0128	32.446
0.070	1.0680	3.845	0.300	9.1123	32.804
0.075	1.2956	4.664	0.305	9.2108	33.159
0.080	1.5376	5.536	0.310	9.3081	33.509
0.085	1.7922	6.452	0.315	9.4045	33.856
0.090	2.0575	7.407	0.320	9.5000	34.200
0.095	2.3317	8.394	0.325	9.5946	34.541
0.100	2.6133	9.408	0.330	9.6883	34.878
0.105	2.9005	10.442	0.335	9.7812	35.212
0.110	3.1918	11.491	0.340	9.8734	35.544
0.115	3.4856	12.548	0.345	9.9648	35.873
0.120	3.7806	13.610	0.350	10.056	36.200
0.125	4.0751	14.670	0.355	10.146	36.524
0.130	4.3082	15.510	0.360	10.235	36.845
0.135	4.5409	16.347	0.365	10.324	37.165
0.140	4.7617	17.142	0.370	10.412	37.482
0.145	4.9718	17.899	0.375	10.499	37.797
0.150	5.1724	18.621	0.380	10.586	38.111
0.155	5.3643	19.312	0.385	10.673	38.422
0.160	5.5484	19.974	0.390	10.759	38.731
0.165	5.7254	20.611	0.395	10.844	39.039
0.170	5.8959	21.225	0.400	10.929	39.345
0.175	6.0604	21.817	0.405	11.014	39.650
0.180	6.2195	22.390	0.410	11.098	39.952
0.185	6.3736	22.945	0.415	11.182	40.254
0.190	6.5231	23.483	0.420	11.265	40.553
0.195	6.6683	24.006	0.425	11.348	40.852
0.200	6.8096	24.515	0.430	11.430	41.149
0.205	6.9473	25.010	0.435	11.512	41.444
0.210	7.0815	25.494	0.440	11.594	41.739
0.215	7.2126	25.966	0.445	11.676	42.032
0.220	7.3408	26.427	0.450	11.757	42.324
0.225	7.4663	26.879	0.455	11.838	42.615
0.230	7.5892	27.321	0.460	11.918	42.905

Table 18-14:
0.203 m Isco Flow Metering Insert with Round Orifice
Discharge Table with Head in Meters

Manufactured by Teledyne Isco, Inc. (Data from Teledyne Isco, Inc.)

Table 18-14			Table 18-14 (Continued)		
Head (meters)	l/s	m³/hr	Head (meters)	l/s	m³/hr
0.005	0	0	0.235	12.540	45.145
0.010	0	0	0.240	12.783	46.019
0.015	0	0	0.245	13.019	46.867
0.020	0	0	0.250	13.248	47.692
0.025	0	0	0.255	13.471	48.494
0.030	0	0	0.260	13.688	49.276
0.035	0	0	0.265	13.899	50.038
0.040	0	0	0.270	14.106	50.782
0.045	0.0143	0.052	0.275	14.308	51.509
0.050	0.0658	0.237	0.280	14.505	52.219
0.055	0.1530	0.551	0.285	14.699	52.916
0.060	0.2742	0.987	0.290	14.888	53.598
0.065	0.4279	1.541	0.295	15.074	54.267
0.070	0.6125	2.205	0.300	15.257	54.924
0.075	0.8263	2.975	0.305	15.436	55.569
0.080	1.0678	3.844	0.310	15.612	56.204
0.085	1.3355	4.808	0.315	15.786	56.828
0.090	1.6278	5.860	0.320	15.957	57.443
0.095	1.9432	6.996	0.325	16.125	58.050
0.100	2.2804	8.209	0.330	16.291	58.648
0.105	2.6378	9.496	0.335	16.455	59.238
0.110	3.0141	10.851	0.340	16.617	59.821
0.115	3.4079	12.268	0.345	16.777	60.397
0.120	3.8177	13.744	0.350	16.935	60.967
0.125	4.2424	15.273	0.355	17.092	61.531
0.130	4.6805	16.850	0.360	17.247	62.089
0.135	5.1308	18.471	0.365	17.401	62.642
0.140	5.5920	20.131	0.370	17.553	63.190
0.145	6.0630	21.827	0.375	17.704	63.734
0.150	6.5424	23.553	0.380	17.854	64.274
0.155	7.0489	25.376	0.385	18.003	64.809
0.160	7.5285	27.103	0.390	18.150	65.341
0.165	7.9818	28.735	0.395	18.297	65.870
0.170	8.4113	30.281	0.400	18.443	66.395
0.175	8.8189	31.748	0.405	18.588	66.918
0.180	9.2067	33.144	0.410	18.733	67.438
0.185	9.5763	34.475	0.415	18.877	67.956
0.190	9.9292	35.745	0.420	19.020	68.471
0.195	10.267	36.960	0.425	19.162	68.985
0.200	10.590	38.125	0.430	19.305	69.496
0.205	10.901	39.242	0.435	19.446	70.006
0.210	11.199	40.317	0.440	19.587	70.515
0.215	11.487	41.351	0.445	19.728	71.022
0.220	11.764	42.349	0.450	19.869	71.528
0.225	12.031	43.312	0.455	20.009	72.033
0.230	12.290	44.243	0.460	20.149	72.537

18

Table 18-15:
0.254 m Isco Flow Metering Insert with Round Orifice
Discharge Table with Head in Meters

Manufactured by Teledyne Isco, Inc. (Data from Teledyne Isco, Inc.)

Table 18-15			Table 18-15 (Continued)		
Head (meters)	l/s	m³/hr	Head (meters)	l/s	m³/hr
0.005	0	0	0.235	16.666	59.996
0.010	0	0	0.240	17.134	61.682
0.015	0	0	0.245	17.587	63.312
0.020	0	0	0.250	18.025	64.891
0.025	0	0	0.255	18.451	66.423
0.030	0	0	0.260	18.864	67.911
0.035	0	0	0.265	19.266	69.359
0.040	0	0	0.270	19.658	70.769
0.045	0	0	0.275	20.040	72.145
0.050	0	0	0.280	20.413	73.488
0.055	0.0158	0.057	0.285	20.778	74.801
0.060	0.0722	0.260	0.290	21.135	76.086
0.065	0.1683	0.606	0.295	21.485	77.345
0.070	0.3025	1.089	0.300	21.828	78.580
0.075	0.4734	1.704	0.305	22.164	79.792
0.080	0.6796	2.446	0.310	22.495	80.982
0.085	0.9196	3.311	0.315	22.820	82.153
0.090	1.1921	4.292	0.320	23.140	83.305
0.095	1.4957	5.384	0.325	23.455	84.439
0.100	1.8290	6.585	0.330	23.766	85.556
0.105	2.1908	7.887	0.335	24.072	86.658
0.110	2.5797	9.287	0.340	24.374	87.746
0.115	2.9943	10.780	0.345	24.672	88.819
0.120	3.4335	12.361	0.350	24.967	89.880
0.125	3.8959	14.025	0.355	25.258	90.928
0.130	4.3803	15.769	0.360	25.546	91.965
0.135	4.8855	17.588	0.365	25.831	92.990
0.140	5.4102	19.477	0.370	26.113	94.006
0.145	5.9533	21.432	0.375	26.392	95.011
0.150	6.5136	23.449	0.380	26.669	96.007
0.155	7.0899	25.524	0.385	26.943	96.994
0.160	7.6811	27.652	0.390	27.215	97.973
0.165	8.2860	29.830	0.395	27.484	98.944
0.170	8.9037	32.053	0.400	27.752	99.907
0.175	9.5328	34.318	0.405	28.018	100.86
0.180	10.173	36.621	0.410	28.281	101.81
0.185	10.822	38.958	0.415	28.543	102.76
0.190	11.479	41.325	0.420	28.803	103.69
0.195	12.144	43.719	0.425	29.062	104.62
0.200	12.818	46.144	0.430	29.318	105.55
0.205	13.443	48.393	0.435	29.574	106.47
0.210	14.038	50.538	0.440	29.828	107.38
0.215	14.608	52.588	0.445	30.080	108.29
0.220	15.153	54.552	0.450	30.332	109.19
0.225	15.677	56.437	0.455	30.582	110.09
0.230	16.180	58.249	0.460	30.831	110.99

18

Table 18-16:
0.305 m Isco Flow Metering Insert with Round Orifice
Discharge Table with Head in Meters

Manufactured by Teledyne Isco, Inc. (Data from Teledyne Isco, Inc.)

Table 18-16			Table 18-16 (Continued)		
Head (meters)	l/s	m³/hr	Head (meters)	l/s	m³/hr
0.005	0	0	0.235	19.129	68.866
0.010	0	0	0.240	20.089	72.320
0.015	0	0	0.245	21.029	75.703
0.020	0	0	0.250	21.785	78.426
0.025	0	0	0.255	22.517	81.060
0.030	0	0	0.260	23.225	83.609
0.035	0	0	0.265	23.911	86.080
0.040	0	0	0.270	24.577	88.477
0.045	0	0	0.275	25.224	90.805
0.050	0	0	0.280	25.852	93.067
0.055	0	0	0.285	26.463	95.267
0.060	0	0	0.290	27.058	97.409
0.065	0	0	0.295	27.638	99.496
0.070	0.0156	0.056	0.300	28.203	101.53
0.075	0.0744	0.268	0.305	28.755	103.52
0.080	0.1760	0.634	0.310	29.293	105.46
0.085	0.3193	1.149	0.315	29.820	107.35
0.090	0.5033	1.812	0.320	30.335	109.21
0.095	0.7269	2.617	0.325	30.839	111.02
0.100	0.9892	3.561	0.330	31.332	112.80
0.105	1.2890	4.640	0.335	31.816	114.54
0.110	1.6253	5.851	0.340	32.291	116.25
0.115	1.9973	7.190	0.345	32.756	117.92
0.120	2.4038	8.654	0.350	33.213	119.57
0.125	2.8439	10.238	0.355	33.662	121.19
0.130	3.3165	11.940	0.360	34.104	122.77
0.135	3.8208	13.755	0.365	34.538	124.34
0.140	4.3558	15.681	0.370	34.966	125.88
0.145	4.9205	17.714	0.375	35.387	127.39
0.150	5.5139	19.850	0.380	35.802	128.89
0.155	6.1352	22.087	0.385	36.211	130.36
0.160	6.7833	24.420	0.390	36.614	131.81
0.165	7.4575	26.847	0.395	37.013	133.25
0.170	8.1567	29.364	0.400	37.406	134.66
0.175	8.8801	31.968	0.405	37.794	136.06
0.180	9.6267	34.656	0.410	38.178	137.44
0.185	10.396	37.425	0.415	38.557	138.81
0.190	11.186	40.271	0.420	38.932	140.16
0.195	11.998	43.191	0.425	39.304	141.49
0.200	12.829	46.183	0.430	39.671	142.82
0.205	13.679	49.242	0.435	40.035	144.13
0.210	14.547	52.367	0.440	40.396	145.43
0.215	15.432	55.555	0.445	40.754	146.71
0.220	16.334	58.801	0.450	41.108	147.99
0.225	17.251	62.103	0.455	41.460	149.26
0.230	18.183	65.459	0.460	41.809	150.51

18

18

CHAPTER
19
Conversion Tables

Overview

This chapter contains conversion tables useful in flow measurement work. The tables contain volumetric, flow rate, and length conversions.

Conversion tables

Table 19-1:
Volumetric Conversion Factors

Note: Gallons are U.S. Gallons

Table 19-1		
To convert	Into	Multiply by
Acre Feet	Cubic Feet	4.356×10^4
	Cubic Meters	1233
	Gallons	3.259×10^5
	Liters	1.233×10^6
	Million Gallons	0.3259
Cubic Feet	Acre Feet	2.296×10^{-5}
	Cubic Meters	0.02832
	Gallons	7.481
	Liters	28.32
	Million Gallons	7.481×10^{-6}
Cubic Meters	Acre Feet	8.107×10^{-4}
	Cubic Feet	35.31
	Gallons	264.2
	Liters	1000
	Million Gallons	2.642×10^{-4}
Gallons	Acre Feet	3.069×10^{-6}
	Cubic Feet	0.1337
	Cubic Meters	3.785×10^{-3}
	Liters	3.785
	Million Gallons	1.000×10^{-6}
Liters	Acre Feet	8.107×10^{-7}
	Cubic Feet	0.03531
	Cubic Meters	1.000×10^{-3}
	Gallons	0.2642
	Million Gallons	2.642×10^{-7}
Million Gallons	Acre Feet	3.069
	Cubic Feet	1.337×10^5
	Cubic Meters	3785
	Gallons	1.000×10^6
	Liters	3.785×10^6

19

Table 19-2:
Flow Rate Conversion Factors

Note: Gallons are U.S. Gallons

Table 19-2		
To convert	Into	Multiply by
Acre Feet per Day	Cubic Feet per Day	4.356×10^4
	Cubic Feet per Hour	1815
	Cubic Feet per Minute	30.25
	Cubic Feet per Second	0.5042
	Cubic Meters per Day	1233
	Cubic Meters per Hour	51.40
	Cubic Meters per Minute	0.8566
	Cubic Meters per Second	0.01428
	Gallons per Hour	1.358×10^4
	Gallons per Minute	226.3
	Gallons per Second	3.771
	Liters per Second	14.28
	Million Gallons per Day	0.3259
Cubic Feet per Day	Acre Feet per Day	2.296×10^{-5}
	Cubic Feet per Hour	0.04167
	Cubic Feet per Minute	6.944×10^{-4}
	Cubic Feet per Second	1.157×10^{-5}
	Cubic Meters per Day	0.02832
	Cubic Meters per Hour	1.180×10^{-3}
	Cubic Meters per Minute	1.966×10^{-5}
	Cubic Meters per Second	3.277×10^{-7}
	Gallons per Hour	0.3117
	Gallons per Minute	5.195×10^{-3}
	Gallons per Second	8.658×10^{-5}
	Liters per Second	3.277×10^{-4}
	Million Gallons per Day	7.481×10^{-6}
Cubic Feet per Hour	Acre Feet per Day	5.510×10^{-4}
	Cubic Feet per Day	24.00
	Cubic Feet per Minute	0.01667
	Cubic Feet per Second	2.778×10^{-4}
	Cubic Meters per Day	0.6796
	Cubic Meters per Hour	0.02832
	Cubic Meters per Minute	4.719×10^{-4}
	Cubic Meters per Second	7.866×10^{-6}
	Gallons per Hour	7.481
	Gallons per Minute	0.1247
	Gallons per Second	2.078×10^{-3}
	Liters per Second	7.866×10^{-3}
	Million Gallons per Day	1.795×10^{-4}

19

Table 19-2 (Continued)		
To convert	Into	Multiply by
Cubic Feet per Minute	Acre Feet per Day	0.03306
	Cubic Feet per Day	1440
	Cubic Feet per Hour	60.00
	Cubic Feet per Second	0.01667
	Cubic Meters per Day	40.78
	Cubic Meters per Hour	1.699
	Cubic Meters per Minute	0.02832
	Cubic Meters per Second	4.719×10^{-4}
	Gallons per Hour	448.8
	Gallons per Minute	7.481
	Gallons per Second	0.1247
	Liters per Second	0.4719
	Million Gallons per Day	0.01077
Cubic Feet per Second	Acre Feet per Day	1.983
	Cubic Feet per Day	8.640×10^{4}
	Cubic Feet per Hour	3600
	Cubic Feet per Minute	60.00
	Cubic Meters per Day	2447
	Cubic Meters per Hour	101.9
	Cubic Meters per Minute	1.699
	Cubic Meters per Second	0.02832
	Gallons per Hour	2.693×10^{4}
	Gallons per Minute	448.8
	Gallons per Second	7.481
	Liters per Second	28.32
	Million Gallons per Day	0.6463
Cubic Meters per Day	Acre Feet per Day	8.107×10^{-4}
	Cubic Feet per Day	35.31
	Cubic Feet per Hour	1.471
	Cubic Feet per Minute	0.02452
	Cubic Feet per Second	4.087×10^{-4}
	Cubic Meters per Hour	0.04167
	Cubic Meters per Minute	6.944×10^{-4}
	Cubic Meters per Second	1.157×10^{-5}
	Gallons per Hour	11.01
	Gallons per Minute	0.1835
	Gallons per Second	3.058×10^{-3}
	Liters per Second	0.01157
	Million Gallons per Day	2.642×10^{-4}

19

Table 19-2 (Continued)

To convert	Into	Multiply by
Cubic Meters per Hour	Acre Feet per Day	0.01946
	Cubic Feet per Day	847.6
	Cubic Feet per Hour	35.31
	Cubic Feet per Minute	0.5886
	Cubic Feet per Second	9.810×10^{-3}
	Cubic Meters per Day	24.00
	Cubic Meters per Minute	0.01667
	Cubic Meters per Second	2.778×10^{-4}
	Gallons per Hour	264.2
	Gallons per Minute	4.403
	Gallons per Second	0.07338
	Liters per Second	0.2778
	Million Gallons per Day	6.340×10^{-3}
Cubic Meters per Minute	Acre Feet per Day	1.167
	Cubic Feet per Day	5.085×10^{4}
	Cubic Feet per Hour	2119
	Cubic Feet per Minute	35.31
	Cubic Feet per Second	0.5886
	Cubic Meters per Day	1440
	Cubic Meters per Hour	60.00
	Cubic Meters per Second	0.01667
	Gallons per Hour	1.585×10^{4}
	Gallons per Minute	264.2
	Gallons per Second	4.403
	Liters per Second	16.67
	Million Gallons per Day	0.3804
Cubic Meters per Second	Acre Feet per Day	70.05
	Cubic Feet per Day	3.051×10^{6}
	Cubic Feet per Hour	1.271×10^{5}
	Cubic Feet per Minute	2119
	Cubic Feet per Second	35.31
	Cubic Meters per Day	8.640×10^{4}
	Cubic Meters per Hour	3600
	Cubic Meters per Minute	60.00
	Gallons per Hour	9.510×10^{5}
	Gallons per Minute	1.585×10^{4}
	Gallons per Second	264.2
	Liters per Second	1000
	Million Gallons per Day	22.82

19

Table 19-2 (Continued)		
To convert	Into	Multiply by
Gallons per Hour	Acre Feet per Day	7.365×10^{-5}
	Cubic Feet per Day	3.208
	Cubic Feet per Hour	0.1337
	Cubic Feet per Minute	2.228×10^{-3}
	Cubic Feet per Second	3.713×10^{-5}
	Cubic Meters per Day	0.09085
	Cubic Meters per Hour	3.785×10^{-3}
	Cubic Meters per Minute	6.309×10^{-5}
	Cubic Meters per Second	1.052×10^{-6}
	Gallons per Minute	0.01667
	Gallons per Second	2.778×10^{-4}
	Liters per Second	1.052×10^{-3}
	Million Gallons per Day	2.400×10^{-5}
Gallons per Minute	Acre Feet per Day	4.419×10^{-3}
	Cubic Feet per Day	192.5
	Cubic Feet per Hour	8.021
	Cubic Feet per Minute	0.1337
	Cubic Feet per Second	2.228×10^{-3}
	Cubic Meters per Day	5.451
	Cubic Meters per Hour	0.2271
	Cubic Meters per Minute	3.785×10^{-3}
	Cubic Meters per Second	6.309×10^{-5}
	Gallons per Hour	60.00
	Gallons per Second	0.01667
	Liters per Second	0.06309
	Million Gallons per Day	1.440×10^{-3}
Gallons per Second	Acre Feet per Day	0.2652
	Cubic Feet per Day	1.155×10^{4}
	Cubic Feet per Hour	481.3
	Cubic Feet per Minute	8.021
	Cubic Feet per Second	0.1337
	Cubic Meters per Day	327.1
	Cubic Meters per Hour	13.63
	Cubic Meters per Minute	0.2271
	Cubic Meters per Second	3.785×10^{-3}
	Gallons per Hour	3600
	Gallons per Minute	60.00
	Liters per Second	3.785
	Million Gallons per Day	0.08640

19

Table 19-2 (Continued)		
To convert	Into	Multiply by
Liters per Second	Acre Feet per Day	0.07005
	Cubic Feet per Day	3051
	Cubic Feet per Hour	127.1
	Cubic Feet per Minute	2.119
	Cubic Feet per Second	0.03531
	Cubic Meters per Day	86.40
	Cubic Meters per Hour	3.600
	Cubic Meters per Minute	0.06000
	Cubic Meters per Second	1.000×10^{-3}
	Gallons per Hour	951.0
	Gallons per Minute	15.85
	Gallons per Second	0.2642
	Million Gallons per Day	0.02282
Million Gallons per Day	Acre Feet per Day	3.069
	Cubic Feet per Day	1.337×10^{5}
	Cubic Feet per Hour	5570
	Cubic Feet per Minute	92.83
	Cubic Feet per Second	1.547
	Cubic Meters per Day	3785
	Cubic Meters per Hour	157.7
	Cubic Meters per Minute	2.629
	Cubic Meters per Second	0.04381
	Gallons per Hour	4.167×10^{4}
	Gallons per Minute	694.4
	Gallons per Second	11.57
	Liters per Second	43.81

19

Table 19-3:
Length Conversion Factors

Table 19-3			Table 19-3 (Continued)		
Fractions in inches	Decimals of a foot	Millimeters	Fractions in inches	Decimals of a foot	Millimeters
$1/16$	0.0052	1.585	$2\ 9/16$	0.2135	65.075
$1/8$	0.0104	3.175	$2\ 5/8$	0.2188	66.690
$3/16$	0.0156	4.755	$2\ 11/16$	0.2240	68.275
$1/4$	0.0208	6.340	$2\ 3/4$	0.2292	69.860
$5/16$	0.0260	7.925	$2\ 13/16$	0.2344	71.445
$3/8$	0.0313	9.540	$2\ 7/8$	0.2396	73.030
$7/16$	0.0365	11.125	$2\ 15/16$	0.2448	74.615
$1/2$	0.0417	12.710	3	0.2500	76.200
$9/16$	0.0469	14.295	$3\ 1/16$	0.2552	77.785
$5/8$	0.0521	15.880	$3\ 1/8$	0.2604	79.370
$11/16$	0.0573	17.465	$3\ 3/16$	0.2656	80.955
$3/4$	0.0625	19.050	$3\ 1/4$	0.2708	82.540
$13/16$	0.0677	20.635	$3\ 5/16$	0.2760	84.125
$7/8$	0.0729	22.220	$3\ 3/8$	0.2813	85.740
$15/16$	0.0781	23.805	$3\ 7/16$	0.2865	87.325
1	0.0833	25.390	$3\ 1/2$	0.2917	88.910
$1\ 1/16$	0.0885	26.975	$3\ 9/16$	0.2969	90.495
$1\ 1/8$	0.0938	28.590	$3\ 5/8$	0.3021	92.080
$1\ 3/16$	0.0990	30.175	$3\ 11/16$	0.3073	93.665
$1\ 1/4$	0.1042	31.760	$3\ 3/4$	0.3125	95.250
$1\ 5/16$	0.1094	33.345	$3\ 13/16$	0.3177	96.835
$1\ 3/8$	0.1146	34.930	$3\ 7/8$	0.3229	98.420
$1\ 7/16$	0.1198	36.515	$3\ 15/16$	0.3281	100.005
$1\ 1/2$	0.1250	38.100	4	0.3333	101.590
$1\ 9/16$	0.1302	39.685	$4\ 1/16$	0.3385	103.175
$1\ 5/8$	0.1354	41.270	$4\ 1/8$	0.3438	104.790
$1\ 11/16$	0.1406	42.855	$4\ 3/16$	0.3490	106.375
$1\ 3/4$	0.1458	44.440	$4\ 1/4$	0.3542	107.960
$1\ 13/16$	0.1510	46.025	$4\ 5/16$	0.3594	109.545
$1\ 7/8$	0.1563	47.640	$4\ 3/8$	0.3646	111.130
$1\ 15/16$	0.1615	49.225	$4\ 7/16$	0.3698	112.715
2	0.1667	50.810	$4\ 1/2$	0.3750	114.300
$2\ 1/16$	0.1719	52.395	$4\ 9/16$	0.3802	115.885
$2\ 1/8$	0.1771	53.980	$4\ 5/8$	0.3854	117.470
$2\ 3/16$	0.1823	55.565	$4\ 11/16$	0.3906	119.055
$2\ 1/4$	0.1875	57.150	$4\ 3/4$	0.3958	120.640
$2\ 5/16$	0.1927	58.735	$4\ 13/16$	0.4010	122.225
$2\ 3/8$	0.1979	60.320	$4\ 7/8$	0.4063	123.840
$2\ 7/16$	0.2031	61.905	$4\ 15/16$	0.4115	125.425
$2\ 1/2$	0.2083	63.490	5	0.4167	127.010

19

Table 19-3 (Continued)			Table 19-3 (Continued)		
Fractions in inches	Decimals of a foot	Millimeters	Fractions in inches	Decimals of a foot	Millimeters
5 1/16	0.4219	128.595	7 9/16	0.6302	192.085
5 1/8	0.4271	130.180	7 5/8	0.6354	193.670
5 3/16	0.4323	131.765	7 11/16	0.6406	195.255
5 1/4	0.4375	133.350	7 3/4	0.6458	196.840
5 5/16	0.4427	134.935	7 13/16	0.6510	198.425
5 3/8	0.4479	136.520	7 7/8	0.6563	200.040
5 7/16	0.4531	138.105	7 15/16	0.6615	201.625
5 1/2	0.4583	139.690	8	0.6667	203.210
5 9/16	0.4635	141.275	8 1/16	0.6719	204.795
5 5/8	0.4688	142.890	8 1/8	0.6771	206.380
5 11/16	0.4740	144.475	8 3/16	0.6823	207.965
5 3/4	0.4792	146.060	8 1/4	0.6875	209.550
5 13/16	0.4844	147.645	8 5/16	0.6927	211.135
5 7/8	0.4896	149.230	8 3/8	0.6979	212.720
5 15/16	0.4948	150.815	8 7/16	0.7031	214.305
6	0.5000	152.400	8 1/2	0.7083	215.890
6 1/16	0.5052	153.985	8 9/16	0.7135	217.475
6 1/8	0.5104	155.570	8 5/8	0.7188	219.090
6 3/16	0.5156	157.155	8 11/16	0.7240	220.675
6 1/4	0.5208	158.740	8 3/4	0.7292	222.260
6 5/16	0.5260	160.325	8 13/16	0.7344	223.845
6 3/8	0.5313	161.940	8 7/8	0.7396	225.430
6 7/16	0.5365	163.525	8 15/16	0.7448	227.015
6 1/2	0.5417	165.110	9	0.7500	228.600
6 9/16	0.5469	166.695	9 1/16	0.7552	230.185
6 5/8	0.5521	168.280	9 1/8	0.7604	231.770
6 11/16	0.5573	169.865	9 3/16	0.7656	233.355
6 3/4	0.5625	171.450	9 1/4	0.7708	234.940
6 13/16	0.5677	173.035	9 5/16	0.7760	236.525
6 7/8	0.5729	174.620	9 3/8	0.7813	238.140
6 15/16	0.5781	176.205	9 7/16	0.7865	239.725
7	0.5833	177.790	9 1/2	0.7917	241.310
7 1/16	0.5885	179.375	9 9/16	0.7969	242.895
7 1/8	0.5938	180.990	9 5/8	0.8021	244.480
7 3/16	0.5990	182.575	9 11/16	0.8073	246.065
7 1/4	0.6042	184.160	9 3/4	0.8125	247.650
7 5/16	0.6094	185.745	9 13/16	0.8177	249.235
7 3/8	0.6146	187.330	9 7/8	0.8229	250.820
7 7/16	0.6198	188.915	9 15/16	0.8281	252.405
7 1/2	0.6250	190.500	10	0.8333	253.990

19

Table 19-3 (Continued)		
Fractions in inches	Decimals of a foot	Millimeters
10 1/16	0.8385	255.575
10 1/8	0.8438	257.190
10 3/16	0.8490	258.775
10 1/4	0.8542	260.360
10 5/16	0.8594	261.945
10 3/8	0.8646	263.530
10 7/16	0.8698	265.115
10 1/2	0.8750	266.700
10 9/16	0.8802	268.285
10 5/8	0.8854	269.870
10 11/16	0.8906	271.455
10 3/4	0.8958	273.040
10 13/16	0.9010	274.625
10 7/8	0.9063	276.240
10 15/16	0.9115	277.825
11	0.9167	279.410

Table 19-3 (Continued)		
Fractions in inches	Decimals of a foot	Millimeters
11 1/16	0.9219	280.995
11 1/8	0.9271	282.580
11 3/16	0.9323	284.165
11 1/4	0.9375	285.750
11 5/16	0.9427	287.335
11 3/8	0.9479	288.920
11 7/16	0.9531	290.505
11 1/2	0.9583	292.090
11 9/16	0.9635	293.675
11 5/8	0.9688	295.290
11 11/16	0.9740	296.875
11 3/4	0.9792	298.460
11 13/16	0.9844	300.045
11 7/8	0.9896	301.630
11 15/16	0.9948	303.215
12	1.0000	304.800

19

REFERENCES

1. Kirkpatrick, George A., and Shelley, Philip E. *Sewer Flow Measurement – A State-of-the-Art Assessment.* EPA Environmental Protection Technology Series, EPA-600/2-75-027, 1975.

2. Spitzer, David W., Editor. *Flow Measurement: Practical Guides for Measurement and Control.* 2nd ed. Instrument Society of America, Research Triangle Park, NC, 2001.

3. *Water Measurement Manual.* 3rd ed. revised. United States Department of the Interior, Bureau of Reclamation, Denver, CO, 2001.

4. Wilson, James F.; Cobb, Ernest D.; and Kilpatrick, Frederick A. "Flourometric Procedures for Dye Tracing." *Techniques of Water-Resources Investigations* Book 3, Chapter A12, U.S. Geological Survey, United States Department of the Interior, Washington, DC, 1986.

5. ISO 9555-1:1994, *Measurement of liquid flow in open channels – Tracer dilution methods for measurement of steady flow.* Part 1: General, International Organization for Standardization, Geneva, Switzerland, 1994.

6. Pratt, E.A. *"Another Proportional-Flow Weir: Sutro Weir."* Engineering News, 72, No. 9 (August 27, 1914): 462-463.

7. Mavis, F.T.; Soucek, E.; and Howe, H.E. *"Sutro Weir Investigations Furnish Discharge Coefficients."* Engineering News Record, 117, No. 20 (November 12, 1936): 679-680.

8. Kulin, Gershon, and Compton, Philip R. *A Guide to Methods and Standards for the Measurement of Water Flow.* National Technical Information Service, Springfield, VA, 1975.

9. Vanleer, B.R. *"The California Pipe Method of Water Measurement."* Engineering News Record (August 3, 1922, August 21, 1924).

10. Kilpatrick, F.A., and Schneider, V.R., "Use of Flumes in Measuring Discharges" *Techniques of Water-Resources Investigations*, Book 3, Chapter A14, U.S.

Geological Survey, United States Department of the Interior, Washington, DC, 1983.

11. Parshall, R.L. "Measuring Water in Irrigation Channels with Parshall Flumes and Small Weirs." U.S. Soil Conservation Service, Circular 843 (May 1950).

12. Skogerboe, Gaylord V.; Hyatt, M. Leon; England, Joe D.; and Johnson, J. Raymond. "Design and Calibration of Submerged Open Channel Flow Measurement Structures - Part 2: Parshall Flumes." Utah Water Research Laboratory, Utah State University, 1967.

13. Palmer, Harold K., and Bowlus, Fred D. "Adaptation of Venturi Flumes to Flow Measurements in Conduits." *Transactions, American Society of Civil Engineers*, Vol. 101, (1936): 1195-1216.

14. Wells, Edwin A., Jr., and Gotaas, Harold B. "Design of Venturi Flumes in Circular Conduits." *Transactions, American Society of Civil Engineers*, Vol. 123 (1958): 749-771.

15. Gwinn, E. R., and Parson, D.A. "Discharge Equations for HS, H, and HL Flumes." *Journal of the Hydraulics Division, ASCE*, Vol. 102 (January 1976), No. HY1, Proc. Paper 11874: 73-88. 11.

16. *Field Manual for Research in Agricultural Hydrology*, Agricultural Handbook No. 224, Agricultural Research Service, Soil and Water Conservation Research Division, U.S. Department of Agriculture, Washington, DC, 1962.

17. Robinson, A.R. "Trapezoidal Flumes for Measuring Flow in Irrigation Channels." ARS 41-140, Agricultural Research Service, U.S. Department of Agriculture (March 1968).

18. Robinson, A.R., and Chamberlain, A.R. "Trapezoidal Flumes for Open-Channel Flow Measurement." *Transactions of The American Society of Agricultural Engineers*, Vol. 3, No. 2 (1960): 120-128.

19. ISO 4359:1983, *Liquid flow measurement in open channels -Rectangular, trapezoidal and U-shaped flumes*. International Organization for Standardization, Geneva, Switzerland, 1983.

20. Skogerboe, Gaylord V.; Bennett, Ray S.; and Walker, Wynne R. "Generalized Discharge Relations For Cutthroat Flumes." *Journal of the Irrigation and Drainage Division, ASCE*, Vol. 98, No. IR4 (December 1972): 569-583.

21. Skogerboe, Gaylord V.; Hyatt, M. Leon; Anderson, Ross Kay; and Eggleston, Keith O. "Design and Calibration of Submerged Open Channel Flow Measurement Structures - Part 3: Cutthroat Flumes." Utah Water Research Laboratory, Utah State University, 1967.

22. Mougenot, G. "Measuring Sewage Flow Using Weirs and Flumes." *Water & Sewage Works* (July 1974): 78-81.

23. Manning, Robert. "On the Flow of Water in Open Channels and Pipes." *Transactions of Civil Engineers of Ireland*, Vol. 20 (1891): 161-207; Supplement, Vol. 24 (1895): 179-207.

24. Chow, V.T. *Open-Channel Hydraulics*. McGraw-Hill Book Company, New York, NY, 1959.

25. Camp, Thomas R. "Design of Sewers to Facilitate Flow." *Sewage Works Journal*, Vol. 18 (January-December, 1946): 1-16.

26. Maynes, John S. "Flow Data Collection for Infiltration-Inflow Analysis." *Journal, Water Pollution Control Federation*, Vol. 28, No. 8 (August 1974): 2055-2061.

27. Lanfear, Kenneth J., and Coll, John J. "Modifying Manning's Equation for Flow Rate Estimates." *Water & Sewage Works* (March 1978): 68-69.

28. Cuthbert, Daniel, and Wood, Fred S. *Fitting Equations to Data: Computer Analysis of Multifactor Data*. 2nd edition. John Wiley & Sons, Hoboken, NJ, 1999.

29. ISO 748:1997, *Measurement of liquid flow in open channels – velocity-area methods*. International Organization for Standardization, Geneva, Switzerland, 1997.

30. Trivedi, Kaushal, and Walkowiak, Diane K. "Flow Measurement Technology for Collection System Studies." *Pollution Engineering* (April 2005): 12-16.

31. Mort, S.F. "The Practical Gauging of Dirty Water and Its Applications to Sewer Design." *Journal of the Irrigation and Drainage Division*, ASCE, Part 3, No. 1 (1955): 81-113.

32. Thomas, C.W. "Errors in Measurement of Irrigation Water." *Proceedings, American Society of Civil Engineers*, 83, IR3, Proc. Paper 1362 (September 1957): 14.

INDEX